▭ TEACHER'S EDITION ▭▬▬▬ 5 ▭

Joseph Abruscato   Joan Wade Fossaceca   Jack Hassard   Donald Peck

HOLT SCIENCE

Holt, Rinehart and Winston, Publishers
New York · Toronto · Mexico City · London · Sydney · Tokyo

THE AUTHORS

Joseph Abruscato
Associate Dean
College of Education and Social Services
University of Vermont
Burlington, Vermont

Joan Wade Fossaceca
Teacher
Pointview Elementary School
Westerville City Schools
Westerville, Ohio

Jack Hassard
Professor
College of Education
Georgia State University
Atlanta, Georgia

Donald Peck
Supervisor of Science
Woodbridge Township School District
Woodbridge, New Jersey

Cover photos, front: Fred Bavendam/Peter Arnold, Inc.; back: Chesher/
Photo Researchers, Inc.
The diversity of marine invertebrate life is typified by the hard and soft corals of
the Bahamas shown on the front cover and the blue vase sponge on the back cover.

In the sections of Holt Science *dealing with evolution, scientific
data have been used to present this material as theory rather than fact. The
information presented allows for the widest possible interpretation that can
be applied to any set of values, either religious or scientific. Every
effort has been made to present this material in a nondogmatic manner.*

Photo and Art credits on page 359

ACKNOWLEDGEMENTS

Teacher Consultants

Armand Alvarez
District Science Curriculum Specialist
San Antonio Independent School District
San Antonio, Texas

Sister de Montfort Babb, I.H.M.
Earth Science Teacher
Maria Regina High School
Uniondale, New York
Instructor
Hofstra University
Hempstead, New York

Ernest Bibby
Science Consultant
Granville County Board of Education
Oxford, North Carolina

Linda C. Cardwell
Teacher
Dickinson Elementary School
Grand Prairie, Texas

Betty Eagle
Teacher
Englewood Cliffs Upper School
Englewood Cliffs, New Jersey

James A. Harris
Principal
Rothschild Elementary School
Rothschild, Wisconsin

Rachel P. Keziah
Instructional Supervisor
New Hanover County Schools
Wilmington, North Carolina

J. Peter O'Neil
Science Teacher
Waunakee Junior High School
Waunakee, Wisconsin

Raymond E. Sanders, Jr.
Assistant Science Supervisor
Calcasieu Parish Schools
Lake Charles, Louisiana

Content Consultants

John B. Jenkins
Professor of Biology
Swarthmore College
Swarthmore, Pennsylvania

Mark M. Payne, O.S.B.
Physics Teacher
St. Benedict's Preparatory School
Newark, New Jersey

Robert W. Ridky, Ph.D.
Professor of Geology
University of Maryland
College Park, Maryland

Safety Consultant

Franklin D. Kizer
Executive Secretary
Council of State Science Supervisors, Inc.
Lancaster, Virginia

Readability Consultant

Jane Kita Cooke
Assistant Professor of Education
College of New Rochelle
New Rochelle, New York

Curriculum Consultant

Lowell J. Bethel
Associate Professor, Science Education
Director, Office of Student Field Experiences
The University of Texas at Austin
Austin, Texas

Special Education Consultant

Joan Baltman
Special Education Program Coordinator
P.S. 188 Elementary School
Bronx, New York

TABLE OF CONTENTS

UNIT 5 LIVING ORGANISMS

UNIT 6 EXPLORING THE UNIVERSE

Why the HOLT SCIENCE Program?

The name *Holt* has meant excellence in science education for over sixty years. *Holt Science* is the result of careful research and evaluation and continues the tradition of quality texts that meet the needs of students and teachers.

Flexibility — Organization of the text chapters into short sections makes it easy for teachers to use with students of varying abilities.

Reading Level/Readability — Every pupil edition has been carefully monitored to be at grade reading level. Writing style, illustrations, and overall design make the text enjoyable to read.

deer eating grass

bird eating worm

squirrel eating acorns

Content — The ideal balance of life, earth, and physical science exposes students to all the major disciplines of science. Concepts appropriate to each grade level are taught using examples from everyday life.

Activities — Students are given opportunities for hands-on experiences that enable them to master concepts and practice science skills.

Science Words — Vocabulary is carefully developed. All new science words appear in bold type.

Illustrations — Diagrams and graphs were developed hand in hand with the text to explain concepts and give students a chance to practice interpreting skills.

Evaluation — Questions in the pupil's text, as well as extra work sheets and tests in the Teacher's Edition, help make the evaluation program for *Holt Science* one of the most comprehensive to be found.

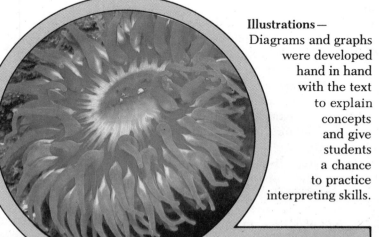

Affordable — The program for each grade level is complete with just the pupil text and Teacher's Edition. Worksheet masters and test masters are provided in the Teacher's Edition and can be easily reproduced. Activity materials are inexpensive and easy to find.

SCOPE AND SEQUENCE

Development of the scope and sequence for *Holt Science* called for careful attention to the selection of concepts and skills for each grade level. As children develop intellectually, it is important they be taught concepts and skills generally appropriate to their age group. At the same time, the curriculum must be flexible because of the variations in intellectual development among students within the same age group. The science program should continuously reinforce skills which are taught and provide opportunities for students to apply these newly acquired skills to many different areas of science. Toward this end, the scope and sequence for *Holt Science* has been carefully planned to include a balanced coverage of all the major science areas. The program spirals so that concepts taught in grades K–3 are reviewed and covered in greater detail in grades 4–6. Although this spiraling of topics increases the depth of study as students progress toward higher grades, understanding the content of one grade does not depend on having learned any previous grade's material. Thus, a student can enter the program at any grade level and anticipate success. The goal of the program is to expose students to all the major science disciplines and provide them with the fundamental science skills.

GRADE	LIFE SCIENCE
K	1. The Senses: Touch, Smell, Taste 2. The Senses: See and Hear 11. Plants 12. Animals
1	1. Use Your Senses 2. Living Things 4. Staying Alive 8. People Grow and Change
2	1. Animals are Different 2. More Animal Groups 11. Parts of Plants 12. Plants and Living Things

3	Unit 1 The Living World
	  1. What Is a Living Thing?
	  2. How Living Things Grow
	  3. Simple Living Things
	Unit 6 Where Plants and Animals Live
	  16. The Forest and the Grassland
	  17. The Desert and the Tundra
	  18. Water Habitats

4	Unit 5 Animal and Plant Populations
	  14. Living Things
	  15. The Cycles of Populations
	  16. Survival and Change
	Unit 6 Animal and Plant Communities
	  17. Energy for Living
	  18. The Food Cycle
	  19. The Web of Life

5	Unit 3 Sensing and Moving
	  6. Your Senses
	  7. Bones and Muscles
	Unit 5 Living Organisms
	  11. Cells and Simple Organisms
	  12. Plants
	  13. Animals without Backbones
	  14. Animals with Backbones

6	Unit 4 Human Body Systems
	  10. Food and Nutrition
	  11. Digestion and Circulation
	  12. Respiration and Excretion
	  13. Taking Care of Yourself
	Unit 6 Heredity
	  17. Reproduction
	  18. The Passing of Traits
	  19. Heredity, Environment, and Learning

EARTH SCIENCE

PHYSICAL SCIENCE

EASY TO FOLLOW

All chapters are divided into short, titled sections to give the teacher maximum flexibility in planning lessons and assignments for students of varying abilities.

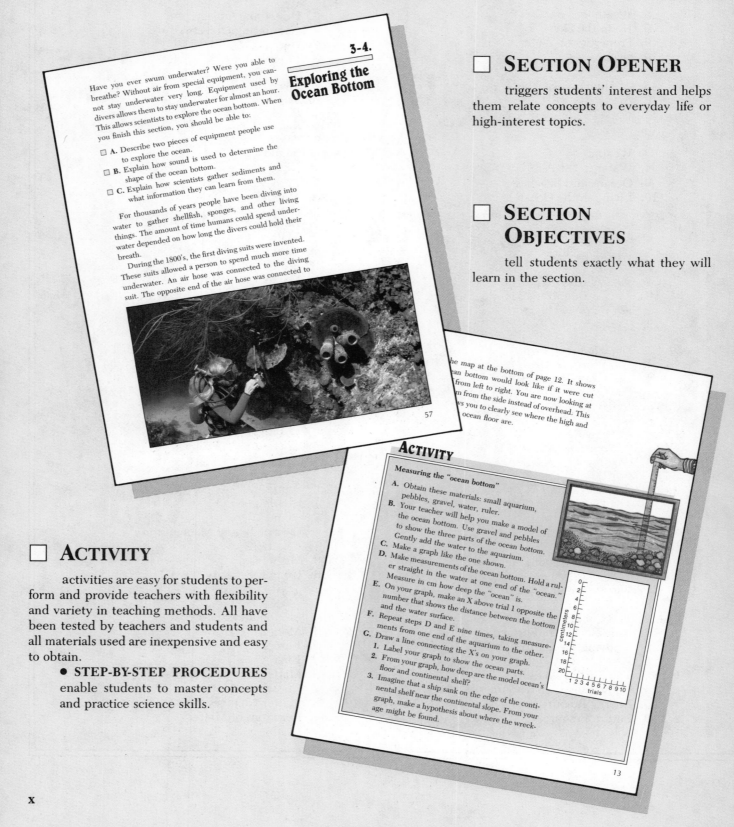

☐ SECTION OPENER

triggers students' interest and helps them relate concepts to everyday life or high-interest topics.

☐ SECTION OBJECTIVES

tell students exactly what they will learn in the section.

☐ ACTIVITY

activities are easy for students to perform and provide teachers with flexibility and variety in teaching methods. All have been tested by teachers and students and all materials used are inexpensive and easy to obtain.

● **STEP-BY-STEP PROCEDURES** enable students to master concepts and practice science skills.

PUPIL'S EDITION

☐ DEVELOPMENT

of concepts is always logical and written at grade reading level.

• **ILLUSTRATIONS** work with text to explain concepts and reinforce science skills.

• **MARGIN VOCABULARY** points out new words in each section.

are eaten by herring. If one species is harmed by chemicals, so are all the others.

The eastern brown pelican is a species that was in danger from pesticide pollution. This bird is also part of an ocean food chain. Through the food chain, pesticides entered the bodies of these birds. As a result, the pelicans laid eggs with very thin shells. The eggs would crack and the unhatched pelican chicks would die. This situation received the attention of concerned scientists. Laws were passed against the use of certain pesticides. Now there are more brown pelicans than before.

Some animals are in danger for a reason other than pollution. Blue whales are in danger of becoming **extinct** (ek-**stinkt**). An animal is *extinct* when there aren't any left. Blue whales have been hunted for many years. They are hunted for their meat, bones, and teeth.

Extinct: Does not exist anymore.

55

Sometimes earth passes between the moon and the sun. Earth blocks the sun's light that would light up the moon. A shadow of earth is cast on the moon. The moon loses its light. It may appear to have a red color. This is a **lunar eclipse** (loo-ner ee-**klips**), shown above. The bottom diagram on page 303 shows the positions of the moon, earth, and sun during a *lunar eclipse*.

Lunar eclipse: Occurs when the earth passes between the moon and the sun.

Section Review

Main Ideas: The moon is earth's satellite. Its surface has craters, mountains, and marias. The moon seems to change in shape. At certain times, solar and lunar eclipses can occur.

Questions: Answer in complete sentences.
1. What is a satellite? What is the earth's satellite called?
2. Name and describe two features that are found on the moon's surface.
3. Why does the moon seem to change shape?
4. Name six phases of the moon. In which phase is the moon invisible?
5. What is the difference between a solar eclipse and a lunar eclipse?

304

☐ SECTION REVIEW

provides reinforcement and evaluation of concepts developed in the section.

• **MAIN IDEAS** give students a summary of key concepts in the section.

• **QUESTIONS** of recall, interpretation, and application are keyed to student objectives at the beginning of each section and provide a self-test and immediate reinforcement.

SPECIAL FEATURES

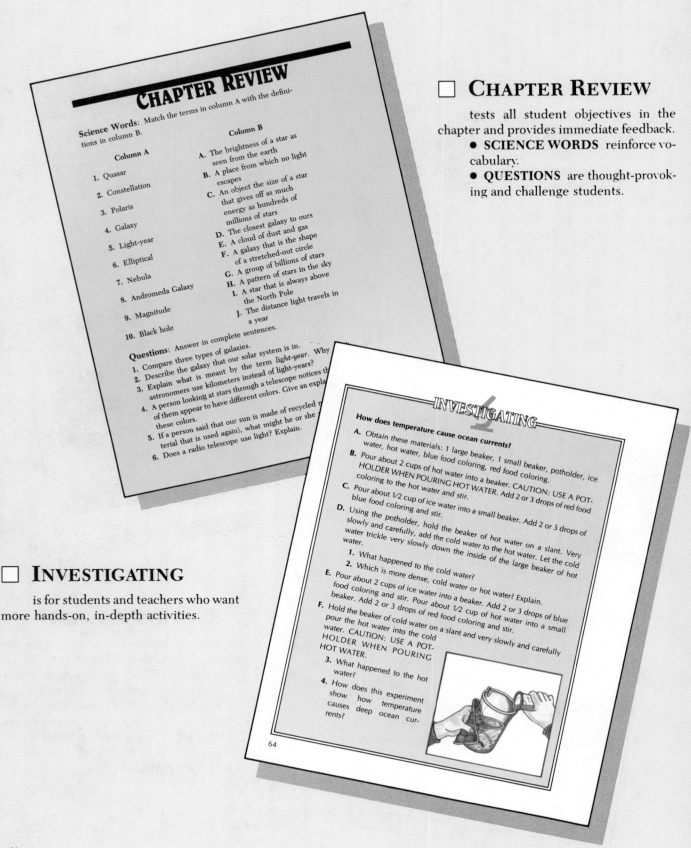

CHAPTER REVIEW

Science Words: Match the terms in column A with the definitions in column B.

Column A

1. Quasar
2. Constellation
3. Polaris
4. Galaxy
5. Light-year
6. Elliptical
7. Nebula
8. Andromeda Galaxy
9. Magnitude
10. Black hole

Column B

A. The brightness of a star as seen from the earth
B. A place from which no light escapes
C. An object the size of a star that gives off as much energy as hundreds of millions of stars
D. The closest galaxy to ours
E. A cloud of dust and gas
F. A galaxy that is the shape of a stretched-out circle
G. A group of billions of stars
H. A pattern of stars in the sky
I. A star that is always above the North Pole
J. The distance light travels in a year

Questions: Answer in complete sentences.

1. Compare three types of galaxies.
2. Describe the galaxy that our solar system is in.
3. Explain what is meant by the term *light-year*. Why astronomers use kilometers instead of light-years?
4. A person looking at stars through a telescope notices th of them appear to have different colors. Give an expla these colors.
5. If a person said that our sun is made of recycled terial that is used again), what might he or she
6. Does a radio telescope use light? Explain.

☐ CHAPTER REVIEW

tests all student objectives in the chapter and provides immediate feedback.

• **SCIENCE WORDS** reinforce vocabulary.
• **QUESTIONS** are thought-provoking and challenge students.

☐ INVESTIGATING

is for students and teachers who want more hands-on, in-depth activities.

INVESTIGATING

How does temperature cause ocean currents?

A. Obtain these materials: 1 large beaker, 1 small beaker, potholder, ice water, hot water, blue food coloring, red food coloring.
B. Pour about 2 cups of hot water into a beaker. CAUTION: USE A POTHOLDER WHEN POURING HOT WATER. Add 2 or 3 drops of red food coloring to the hot water and stir.
C. Pour about ½ cup of ice water into a small beaker. Add 2 or 3 drops of blue food coloring and stir.
D. Using the potholder, hold the beaker of hot water on a slant. Very slowly and carefully, add the cold water to the hot water. Let the cold water trickle very slowly down the inside of the large beaker of hot water.
   1. What happened to the cold water?
   2. Which is more dense, cold water or hot water? Explain.
E. Pour about 2 cups of ice water into a beaker. Add 2 or 3 drops of blue food coloring and stir. Pour about ½ cup of hot water into a small beaker. Add 2 or 3 drops of red food coloring and stir.
F. Hold the beaker of cold water on a slant and very slowly and carefully pour the hot water into the cold water. CAUTION: USE A POTHOLDER WHEN POURING HOT WATER.
   3. What happened to the hot water?
   4. How does this experiment show how temperature causes deep ocean currents?

64

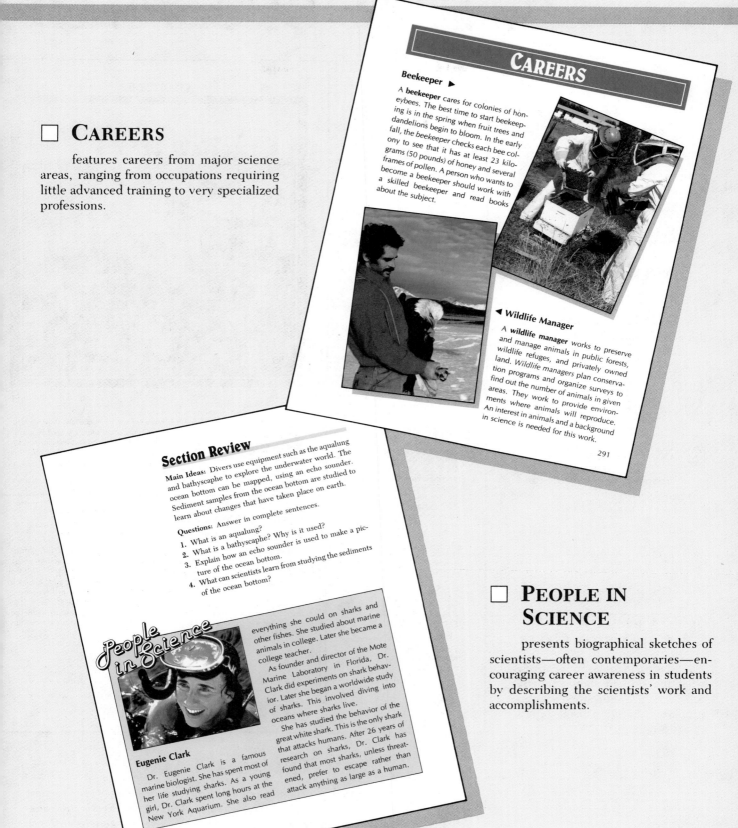

☐ CAREERS

features careers from major science areas, ranging from occupations requiring little advanced training to very specialized professions.

CAREERS

Beekeeper ▶

A **beekeeper** cares for colonies of honeybees. The best time to start beekeeping is in the spring when fruit trees and dandelions begin to bloom. In the early fall, the beekeeper checks each bee colony to see that it has at least 23 kilograms (50 pounds) of honey and several frames of pollen. A person who wants to become a beekeeper should work with a skilled beekeeper and read books about the subject.

◀ Wildlife Manager

A **wildlife manager** works to preserve and manage animals in public forests, wildlife refuges, and privately owned land. Wildlife managers plan conservation programs and organize surveys to find out the number of animals in given areas. They work to provide environments where animals will reproduce. An interest in animals and a background in science is needed for this work.

291

Section Review

Main Ideas: Divers use equipment such as the aqualung and bathyscaphe to explore the underwater world. The ocean bottom can be mapped, using an echo sounder. Sediment samples from the ocean bottom are studied to learn about changes that have taken place on earth.

Questions: Answer in complete sentences.
1. What is an aqualung?
2. What is a bathyscaphe? Why is it used?
3. Explain how an echo sounder is used to make a picture of the ocean bottom.
4. What can scientists learn from studying the sediments of the ocean bottom?

People in Science

Eugenie Clark

Dr. Eugenie Clark is a famous marine biologist. She has spent most of her life studying sharks. As a young girl, Dr. Clark spent long hours at the New York Aquarium. She also read everything she could on sharks and other fishes. She studied about marine animals in college. Later she became a college teacher.

As founder and director of the Mote Marine Laboratory in Florida, Dr. Clark did experiments on shark behavior. Later she began a worldwide study of sharks. This involved diving into oceans where sharks live.

She has studied the behavior of the great white shark. This is the only shark that attacks humans. After 26 years of research on sharks, Dr. Clark has found that most sharks, unless threatened, prefer to escape rather than attack anything as large as a human.

62

☐ PEOPLE IN SCIENCE

presents biographical sketches of scientists—often contemporaries—encouraging career awareness in students by describing the scientists' work and accomplishments.

CLEARLY ORGANIZED

☐ **CHAPTER OBJECTIVES**

consolidate all student objectives for each section into broad chapter objectives for the teacher.

☐ **SECTION BACKGROUND**

supplies information about the science content of the section.

☐ **MATERIALS**

lists items needed to carry out the Activity.

☐ **EXCEPTIONAL STUDENT IEP CHAPTER GOAL**

states in measurable terms what the student should be able to do. It aids educators who are preparing individualized educational programs.

CHAPTER OBJECTIVES

1. Describe the parts of an individual cell and how cells are organized into tissues, organs, and organ systems.
2. Describe the parts and functions of the nervous system, and how the sense of smell functions.
3. Identify the taste areas of the tongue, and how smell and taste are related.
4. Describe the parts and functions of the ears and the eyes.
5. Identify the parts of the nervous system that provide the sense of touch.

SECTION BACKGROUND

The human nervous system consists of the central nervous system (the brain and the spinal cord) and the peripheral nervous system (all the nerves in the body outside the brain and the spinal cord). The brain receives stimuli that have been carried by nerve cells (neurons) from the sense organs. The brain interprets the information and reacts by sending commands to various parts of the body. Humans have five senses: sight, smell, hearing, taste, and touch. The nose is the sense organ of smell. Small nerve endings in the mucous membrane that lines the nose receive stimuli and transmit the smell message to the olfactory nerve. The olfactory nerve sends the smell message to the brain, where it is interpreted as "smell."

MATERIALS

graph paper, pencil

Exceptional Student IEP Chapter Goal

At the end of this chapter have the student name the main nerve in each of the five sense organs.

T–114

CHAPTER 6

YOUR SENSES

6-1.

Sense Organs

114

Being good at a sport takes a lot of effort. Whether leaping, throwing, passing, or catching, you must be able to control the movements of your body. Knowing how your body works will help you to control it. When you finish this section, you should be able to:

BASIC TEACHING PLAN
MOTIVATION

You may want to introduce this lesson by displaying magazine photographs of various athletes who are using their bodies in active ways. Engage the class in a discussion of what seems to make some athletes better than others. Try to focus the discussion on the necessity for such qualities as strength, agility, and the ability to recognize a threatening situation and to react quickly and properly. Indicate to the students that they will begin learning how the brain picks up information from the outside world, and how the body reacts to the information it receives from the brain.

☐ **BASIC TEACHING PLAN**

Provides everything needed to plan the teaching of each section —including *Motivation, Development, Activity,* and *Section Review.*
 ● *Motivation* gives information to develop student interest further. It contains suggestions for a teacher demonstration or discussion questions for the class.
 ● *Development* is a unique feature that uses a numbered square to key teaching suggestions to the pupil page.

☐ **A.** Describe some parts of a cell.
☐ **B.** Describe how cells, tissues, and organs work together in body systems.
☐ **C.** Describe what the nervous system does.
☐ **D.** Trace the path that messages of odors take from the nose to the brain.

Every living thing is made of one or more **cells** (**selz**). The *cell* is a tiny living part of a plant or animal. Most cells are smaller than the period that ends this sentence. Your body is made of almost 3 trillion (3,000,000,000,000) cells.

Each of your cells has an outside covering called a **cell membrane** (**mem**-brayn). Inside the cell is a **nucleus** (**nyoo**-klee-us), which is round in shape. The *nucleus* controls all the activities of a cell.

Each cell is able to produce more cells that are just like it. Food and oxygen are carried to the cells through the blood. Cells are able to use the food and oxygen to produce energy for your body.The blood also carries waste products away from the cells.

Using microscopes, scientists have found that cells have different shapes and sizes. They have also found that cells doing the same job are usually found together. **Nerve cells** have the job of carrying information, or messages, from parts of the body to the brain. The picture below shows a *nerve cell* as seen under a microscope.

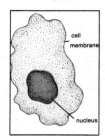

Cell: Tiny living part of the body.

Cell membrane: Outside covering of a cell.

Nucleus: The part of the cell that controls its activities.

Nerve cell: Cell that carries information.

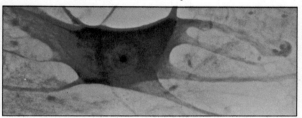

115

EXTENSIONS

Enrichment
Research — Library
Students could do a comparative study of organisms with different types of nervous systems and how they react. Suggested organisms are: protozoa, hydra, starfish, grasshoppers, and fish. The students will be surprised to learn that even organisms that have no specialized sense organs are able to respond to their environments.
   Students could also do research on tropism, or the tendency of an organism or one of its parts to turn or grow in response to an outside stimulus. An example is how certain plants turn toward the sun.

☐ **EXTENSIONS**

provide for three ways to extend the lesson:
Reinforcement– for all students to clarify a difficult topic. This can also be used with slower learners.
Enrichment– for students to learn more about the topic.
Application– for all students to show how science directly affects our lives.

Each type of Extension focuses on one of the three subcategories:
a. Science Skill
b. Activity
c. Research

This feature can be correlated with other disciplines for use in an interdisciplinary curriculum. Extensions give students the opportunity to practice and develop reading, math, writing, library, and research skills.

DEVELOPMENT

1 **Teaching Tips** — If the students have never seen a cell and if you happen to have a small microscope available, you may want to make a slide of tissue from an onion. Use a small amount of iodine to stain the cells.
2 **Skill Development** — Have the students practice *reading illustrations* by locating the various parts of a cell on the diagram.
3 **Teaching Tips** — Tell the students that their bodies are made of cells and that different parts of the body are composed of different types of cells. Be sure that they understand that the photograph at the bottom of the page is of just one type of cell.

Exceptional Student
Visually Impaired
The teacher should make a three-dimensional diagram of a cell to help the visually impaired students understand the components of a cell.

T–115

☐ **EXCEPTIONAL STUDENT**

provides specific suggestions to teachers who have a handicapped student mainstreamed into the regular classroom.

1 *Skill Development:* Each time a science skill appears it is identified, enabling the teacher to present concepts to students through the teaching of a science skill.
2 *Teaching Tips:* When students have difficulty understanding a topic, this offers the teacher suggestions to help get the concept across.
3 *Text Questions:* Pupil text questions are printed again for the teacher. Answers printed in *italics* follow immediately.

EXTENSIONS

Enrichment
Research — Library

Ask the students to find the following:

A. The meaning of the words *soprano, alto, tenor,* and *bass.* They will find that soprano is the highest singing voice of women and young boys; that alto is the lowest range of the female singing voice; that tenor is the highest range of the male singing voice; and that bass is the lowest range of the male singing voice.

B. Which of these singing voices produces sound waves of the highest frequency? the lowest frequency?

C. How can singers make their voices sound very loud? very soft? Does the loudness of the sound affect the frequency or pitch of the sound produced?

ACTIVITY

Changing pitch and intensity

A. Obtain these materials: 6 bottles of the same size, water, grease pencil, a ruler or wooden stick.

B. Number the bottles 1 through 6 and line them up in a straight row.

C. Add water to the bottles, putting the least in bottle 1 and the most in bottle 6.

D. Tap each bottle gently with the stick to create a different pitch. Adjust the amount of water in each to create the notes of a musical scale.

  1. Which bottle had the most air?
  2. Which bottle produced the highest pitch?
  3. Write a conclusion that explains the relationship between the amount of air in the bottles and pitch.
  4. What can you do to change the intensity of the sounds you create?

94

ACTIVITY

Skill Development — *Comparing and Contrasting, Finding Cause and Effect, Concluding and Generalizing*

Safety Tips — If the students work in groups, allow enough space for each group to ensure that the bottles can be safely tapped.

Answers to Questions — 1. *The bottle with the least amount of water.* 2. *The bottle with the shortest air column or the most water.* 3. *As the amount of air within the bottle increases, the pitch becomes lower.* 4. *The bottles could be tapped with more force.*

6 **Teaching Tips** — To demonstrate that it is the column of air that is vibrating and not the glass, ask several students to wrap their hands around a bottle and blow across the top. Ask the class to notice that the sound is produced even though the bottle is not vibrating.

T–94

☐ ACTIVITY

commentary includes three types of aid for teachers.

1) *Helpful Tips:* Ways for the teacher to help students execute the Activity.

2) *Safety Tips:* Notes to teacher and students to insure proper procedure and care in using materials.

3) *Answers to Questions:* Answers are printed in *italics*.

CHAPTER REVIEW

Science Words: Match the terms in column A with the definition in column B.

Column A	Column B
1. Sound wave	A. Bounced
2. Medium	B. Vibrations per second
3. Vacuum	C. Loudness or softness
4. Intensity	D. A vibration that moves through matter
5. Pitch	E. Space without matter
6. Frequency	F. A reflected sound
7. Decibel	G. Matter through which sound can travel
8. Echo	H. The part of the telephone you speak into
9. Reflected	I. Unit of sound intensity
10. Transmitter	J. Highness or lowness

Questions: Answer in complete sentences.

1. What are two things that can happen when sound waves strike an object?
2. How is a sound wave like a coiled spring?
3. Robert Boyle did an experiment using a bell placed in a vacuum. What was the hypothesis that he was testing? What were his results?
4. The moon does not have any air. If one of two astronauts on the moon's surface struck a rock with a hammer, would the other astronaut hear it? Explain.
5. A person at a baseball game sees the bat hit the ball before hearing the sound. Explain why this is so.
6. Lazzaro Spallanzani experimented with the night flight of bats. What were his results?
7. Can a sound get louder without changing its pitch? Explain.

109

EXTENSIONS

Enrichment
Research — Library

This section of the chapter gives you an excellent opportunity to have students learn more about three exceptional American inventors: Samuel Morse, Alexander Graham Bell, and Thomas Edison. Ask the students to do library research to find out about their lives and accomplishments. Focus their research with these questions:
1. When did each of these inventors live?
2. What kind of childhood did each of these men have?
3. What were some of their other accomplishments? (These need not be inventions only. Samuel Morse, for example, was a talented artist.)
4. For each of these men, name the invention that is considered to be his most important.
5. How did the major inventions of these men change the lives of people?

CHAPTER REVIEW

Science Words
1. D   2. G   3. E   4. C   5. J   6. B   7. I   8. F   9. A
10. H

Answers to Questions
1. The sound can be reflected or absorbed.
2. Sound energy causes the air molecules to bunch up and spread out as the vibrations move out from the source of the sound. A coil that is pushed and pulled moves in a similar manner.
3. Boyle's hypothesis was that sound does not travel in a vacuum. A bell could not be heard when rung in a jar without air.
4. No. Sound cannot travel in a vacuum.
5. Light travels faster than sound.
6. He found that bats produce ultrasonic sounds that reflect off objects. The bats listen for echoes to tell where the objects are.
7. Yes. Pitch depends on the frequency of the sound wave. Intensity depends upon how much energy produced the sound.

SUGGESTED TEST MASTERS
p. T–65f, g, h

T–109

☐ **CHAPTER REVIEW**

provide answers to all questions.

UNIT PLANNING CHART

UNIT 2 SOUND

	SECTION	BASIC SCIENCE SKILLS	ACTIVITY MATERIALS STUDENT/GROUP	EXTENSIONS		EXTRA ACTIVITIES/ DEMONSTRATIONS	WORKSHEET MASTERS	EVALUATIONS	BOOKS FOR STUDENTS
CHAPTER 4 HEARING SOUND	4-1 p.T-68 How Sounds Are Made	*Reading the illustration to* locate vibration sources *Finding the cause and effect* between vibration and sound p.T-70	wooden or plastic ruler	• Reinforcement pp.T-70, T-71 • Application p.T-72		• Hidden sound makers p.T-68 • Sound hike p.T-69	Sound Waves (SK) p.T-65i	Section Review p.T-72	Bailey, Bernadine. *Bells, Bells, Bells,* New York: Dodd, 1978 Berger, Melvin. *The Clarinet & The Saxophone,* New York: Lothrop, Lee & Shepard, 1975 Darwin, Len. *What Makes a Telephone Work?,* Boston: Little, 1970 Gilmore, Lee, illus. by George Overlie. *Folk Instruments,* Minneapolis: Lerner, 1962
	4-2 p.T-73 Instruments of Sound	*Reading the illustration to* locate clarinet valves p.T-75 *Observing* the kettle drum pedal p.T-78	4 plastic straws, scissors, small cup of water	• Enrichment pp.T-74, T-75, T-77 • Application p.T-76, T-78		• Musical Instruments p.T-73	Seeing Sound (AC) p.T-65j	Section Review p.T-78	Heuer, Kenneth. *Thunder, Singing Sounds & Other Wonders: Sound in the Atmosphere,* New York: Dodd, 1981 Jacobs, Francine, illus. by Jean P. Zallinger. *Sounds in the Sea,* New York: Morrow, 1977
	4-3 p.T-79 Sound Travels	*Comparing and contrasting* the speed of light and sound p.T-81		• Reinforcement pp.T-80, T-82, T-83 • Enrichment p.T-81		• Whistle blowing p.T-80 • Light and distance p.T-81	Hearing Sound (SK) p.T-65k Crossword (SK) p.T-65l	Section Review p.T-82 Chapter Review p.T-83 Test Masters pp.T-65d,e	Kettlekamp, Larry. *The Magic of Sound,* New York: Morrow, 1982 Knight, David. *Silent Sound: The World of Ultrasonics,* New York: Morrow, 1980 Kuferberg, Herbert. *Rainbow of Sound: The Instruments of the Orchestra and Their Music,* New York: Scribner, 1973
CHAPTER 5 SOUND WAVES	5-1 p.T-84 Sound and Matter	*Observing a wave in a spring* p.T-85 *Reading the illustration to* study a stethoscope p.T-88 *Finding the effect* of a vacuum on sound p.T-89	ticking watch, meter stick	• Enrichment pp.T-85, T-86, T-89, T-90 • Application pp.T-87, T-88		• Waves p.T-85	Riddles (SK) p.T-65m Vacuum (AH) p.T-65n	Section Review p.T-90	O'Connor, Jerome J. *The Telephone, How It Works,* East Rutherford, NJ: Putnams, 1971 Wade, Harlan. *A Book About Sound,* Milwaukee: Raintree, 1977
	5-2 p.T-91 Different Sounds	*Observing the effect of a* vibrating tuning fork p.T-92 *Comparing the pitch of* sounds p.T-93	8 bottles (same size) water, grease pencil, ruler or wooden stick	• Reinforcement p.T-92 • Enrichment pp.T-93, T-94, T-95, T-96		• Sound effect records p.T-91 • Tuning fork p.T-92 • Guitar p.T-93	Different Sounds (AC) p.T-65o	Section Review p.T-96	**FILMS** *Ears: Have You Heard the Latest,* 10½ min, Centron *Listen! Hear!,* 15 min, National Geographic *Vibrations,* 14 min, Britannica
	5-3 p.T-97 Sound Waves Reflect	*Reading the illustration to* find the animals that can hear ultrasonic sound p.T-99 *Comparing and contrasting* how materials react to sound p.T-101		• Reinforcement pp.T-98, T-101 • Enrichment p.T-99 • Application p.T-100		• Ball reflection p.T-97 • Echo survey p.T-98 • Ceiling tile p.T-100	Pitch and Frequency (SK) p.T-65p	Section Review p.T-101	**FILMSTRIPS** *Introducing Sound, Light and Color,* 2 filmstrips, 2 cassettes, 15 min each, National Geographic *Your Senses and How They Help You,* 2 filmstrips, 2 cassettes, 12–15 min each, National Geographic Educational
	5-4 p.T-102 Sound Messages	*Sequencing the steps by* which a telephone works p.T-104 *Comparing and contrasting* old and new phonographs p.T-106		• Reinforcement p.T-107 • Enrichment pp.T-104, T-105, T-106, T-108, T-109, T-110 • Application pp.T-103, T-111		• Telegraph p.T-103 • Old Telephone p.T-104 • Investigating p.T-105	Morse Code (AC) p.T-65q	Section Review p.T-108	Pet, 16k BASIC, rams

T-65a

T-65b

SECTION	BASIC SCIENCE SKILLS	
4-1 p.T-68 How Sounds Are Made	*Reading the illustration to* locate vibration sources *Finding the cause and effect* between vibration and sound p.T-70	
4-2 p.T-73 Instruments of Sound	*Reading the illustration to* locate clarinet valves p.T-75 *Observing* the kettle drum pedal p.T-78	4 sc w
4-3 p.T-79 Sound Travels	*Comparing and contrasting* the speed of light and sound p.T-81	

for your convenience ...

One for each of the six units in the text. Organizes all the necessary information needed to plan lessons efficiently. All chapters, sections, and Activities are listed for the teacher. References to all evaluation material, including reproducible worksheet and test masters, are listed for each chapter.

BLACKLINE MASTERS

Every Teacher's Edition contains a complete set of worksheet and test masters.* They are located after each Unit Planning Chart and address a variety of needs.

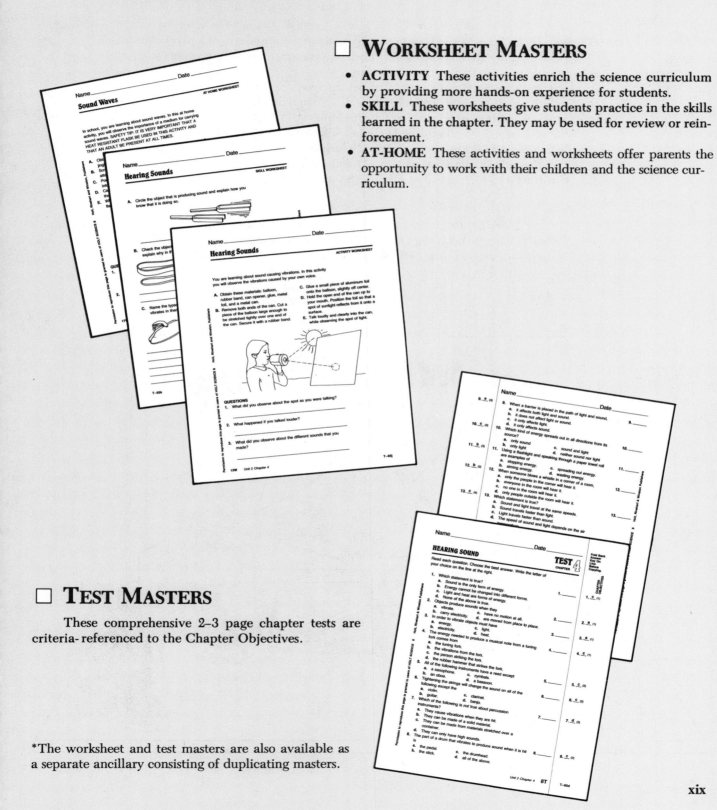

☐ WORKSHEET MASTERS

- **ACTIVITY** These activities enrich the science curriculum by providing more hands-on experience for students.
- **SKILL** These worksheets give students practice in the skills learned in the chapter. They may be used for review or reinforcement.
- **AT-HOME** These activities and worksheets offer parents the opportunity to work with their children and the science curriculum.

☐ TEST MASTERS

These comprehensive 2–3 page chapter tests are criteria-referenced to the Chapter Objectives.

*The worksheet and test masters are also available as a separate ancillary consisting of duplicating masters.

LEARNING CENTERS

A Learning Center consisting of additional activities and research topics is a good way for teachers to expand the science curriculum. Students can work at the Learning Center by themselves or in small groups. The selection of work to be done at the Center should match the ability level of a particular class. Because students are encouraged to work independently, teachers will be able to meet their individual needs.

The Learning Center should be set up away from the rest of the class, preferably in a corner that receives indirect sunlight. If this is not possible, artificial lights may be needed for green plants. A large, low table is best, but several small tables pushed together will also work well. The table should be positioned next to a bulletin board which displays drawings, photographs, and the title of the Center. If no bulletin board is available, it is easy to construct a tri-fold backdrop using tagboard, cardboard, and duct tape. Shoe boxes and other containers can be used as files for activities and research topics, as well as for the materials needed to complete them. The Center is an ideal place for an aquarium or terrarium, if one is kept in the classroom.

Suggestions for Learning Center titles and displays appear at the beginning of each unit. Activities and worksheets that are found in the Teacher's Edition are also listed for the unit.

BASIC SCIENCE SKILLS

The term *basic science skills* is used in the *Holt Science* program to refer to a range of skills. These include reading and math skills, which are critical-thinking skills. They are fundamental to all learning processes. Hence, the teaching of basic science skills involves the teaching of those same skills taught in reading and math. The only difference is the application of these skills in the science content area.

Science is the ideal setting for students to practice and reinforce the reading and math skills they have learned. Students are naturally curious about the world around them. The science skills they acquire become tools which they can use to find answers to their questions. They will in time discover, as often happens in science, that answers to questions often trigger new questions. This questioning approach, which requires a logical use of science skills, is the basis of the scientific method. Science is within the reach of all students once they understand that it includes the practice of the same skills that they have already been taught.

The rationale of the *Holt Science* program is to teach these basic science skills to students. This is done in a number of ways. First of all, specific skills are used to develop concepts. Through concrete experiences in which students can manipulate objects and materials, more skills are learned. The skills of observing, measuring, recording, and predicting take on meaning for students as they perform each Activity. And finally, thought-provoking questions encourage students to develop the ability to compare and contrast, classify, identify, form sequences, infer, hypothesize, and generalize.

For the teacher, the close parallel between science skills and reading and math skills is pointed out in the Basic Teaching Plan of each section. The applicable skills are identified for the teacher and additional teaching tips are suggested to help the teacher explain particularly difficult concepts. The teaching of reading and math skills and the teaching of science skills become one: the teaching of those critical thinking skills needed for all branches of learning.

The ability to communicate in written and oral form is one of the basic science skills strengthened by the *Holt Science* program. Students learn how to discuss and write about what they have learned. The Teacher's Edition contains suggestions for discussion questions. Research topics are often suggested in the Extensions. Activities are worded in a way that requires students to write their own conclusions and results.

Care has been taken to develop skills which are appropriate for each age group. In the lower grades, the concentration is on the more fundamental skills, such as *observing* and *comparing*. As students progress, more advanced skills are introduced at each grade level. Provision has been made for the fact that students within any age group progress at different rates. Extensions to each section have reinforcement of skills for slower learners and enrichment and application of skills for students of higher ability.

The chart on pages xxii and xxiii lists the basic science skills which have been stressed in the *Holt Science* program.

BASIC SCIENCE SKILLS

volcano erupts

FOLLOWING DIRECTIONS

requires that students be able to follow both written and verbal instructions. The ability to follow directions in sequence will determine the successful outcome of an Activity or experiment.

READING ILLUSTRATIONS

requires that students be able to extract information from photographs, drawings, diagrams, charts, and graphs. Illustrations are especially important in the lower grades where children are just beginning to read.

BUILDING SCIENCE VOCABULARY

requires that students use word-attack skills as they are introduced to new science words. In science, the understanding of prefixes, suffixes, and root words is especially important.

FINDING THE MAIN IDEA

requires that students be able to pick out the main idea after reading a passage in the text. The ability to do this shows that students have comprehended what they have read. It is a skill that older students use when they prepare outlines and take notes in class.

OBSERVING

requires that students be able to use one or more senses to note and then describe the properties of objects or events.

COMPARING AND CONTRASTING

requires that students be able to identify common and distinguishing characteristics among items or events. In the lower grades, students are asked to tell how things are the same or different.

CLASSIFYING

requires that students be able to organize information into logical categories. The students should be able to arrange items, places, or events into groups by identifying a common characteristic. Hence the ability to compare and contrast is necessary before classifying can be done.

SEQUENCING

requires that students be able to arrange items or events according to a characteristic. This skill depends on the ability to observe, compare, and contrast. With younger children, the words "put things in order" can be used.

FINDING CAUSE AND EFFECT RELATIONSHIPS

requires that students be able to recognize the relationship of cause and effect. Younger children will learn to relate the two while older children may be asked to infer or predict the outcome of an event.

MEASURING

requires that students be able quantitatively to describe the length, area, volume, mass, and temperature of objects. The ability to use units of measure and read measuring equipment is part of this skill. This skill is important in increasing the accuracy of observations.

RECORDING DATA

requires that students be able to organize data in a logical way so that results can be interpreted and reviewed.

PREDICTING

requires that students be able to anticipate the consequences of a new or changed situation. Students must use their past experiences and the skill of recognizing cause and effect in making predictions.

HYPOTHESIZING

requires that students be able to suggest answers to questions or problems that can be tested.

INFERRING

requires that students be able to propose an explanation based on observations and data.

CONCLUDING AND GENERALIZING

requires that students be able to use and synthesize several skills so that results of an experiment and other observations can be explained.

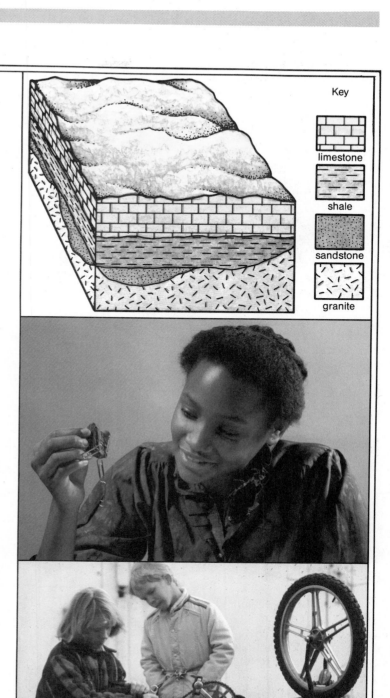

Key

limestone

shale

sandstone

granite

BACKGROUND

Scientists investigate and interpret the events of the natural and physical world. They conduct their investigations in a particular way, using a process called the scientific method. This usually involves making observations, recognizing a problem (i.e., asking a question), formulating hypotheses, and testing these hypotheses through observation and/or experimentation in order to arrive at certain conclusions. Scientists, however, are not the only ones who use these skills.

This section acquaints students with some of the skills scientists use to study the world around them. The text, activities, and extensions are concerned with these skills. In this section, the subject matter is secondary. Learning about the skills and how to use them is more important. Thus, stress the skills rather than the subject.

These skills can help students answer questions that puzzle them. But it is a myth that using the scientific method always leads to the right answer. Make it clear to the students that using these skills and following the procedures do not guarantee success. Emphasize, however, that any information obtained may be useful.

This section is meant to dispel the idea that the processes of science are too difficult for the average person. Its intent is to make the student feel at ease about science and to demonstrate that, to some extent, everyone can be a scientist. A person just needs curiosity, a bit of knowledge, and a few skills.

MATERIALS

paper, pencil, 3 empty coffee cans, 6 plastic lids, can opener, scissors, wire, heavy string, bird seed, spoon, baby powder

SKILLS OF SCIENCE

For Charles, the cold winter day began at 3 A.M. He turned off the alarm and slipped into warm clothes and boots. He grabbed his notebook, then headed down the road. It was still dark when he met up with the bird-counting party at the edge of town.

"Glad you could come," said Alice, the group leader. "Since this is your first bird count, just stick with me. Keep watching. Write down the name of every bird you see. If you can't identify a bird, I'll help."

Charles was one of thousands of people taking part in the Christmas Bird Count. In 1,400 different places, people spend a day each December counting the kinds of birds they see. Some of the counters are scientists. Most counters are only interested bird-watchers. The only requirement is that they be good observers. They must be able to identify different kinds or **species** of birds. Some counters go out into the field. Others stay at bird feeders. At the end of the day, the number of birds of each *species* seen in each area is added up.

Species: All of the same kind of living thing.

BASIC TEACHING PLAN

MOTIVATION

Tell the students that everyone is a scientist to some extent. Tell them that every time they wonder or ask a question about something in the world around them, they are acting like scientists. Explain that the difference between a scientist and themselves lies in the method they use to answer their questions. Ask: What are some of the things in your environment that you are curious about? How might you go about answering your question? Guide students into a discussion of observing, experimenting, and making conclusions. Tell the students that by the end of this section they will have learned about the method scientists use to solve problems and that it is a method they can also use.

From a bird count, scientists can learn about the health of a bird **population**. A *population* is a group of the same kind of plant or animal living in the same place. A healthy population is one that is growing in number or staying the same. A population in trouble is one that is going down in number.

Population: A group of the same kind of plant or animal living in the same place.

SKILL BUILDING ACTIVITY

Can you identify different bird species?

A. Obtain these materials: paper, pencil.

B. Read the descriptions below. Then match each description to the correct bird.

    1. What are the correct names of birds A, B, and C?

    2. Which bird can grow to be the longest? Which bird is the smallest?

    3. Which two birds do you think are most closely related? How can you tell? (Hint: look for an important feature that they share.)

Descriptions:

Finch: Small, brown bird, from 14 to 16 centimeters long. Red forehead and underside. Sides are streaked. Short, light bill.

House wren: Small, brown bird, from 10.5 to 13.5 centimeters long. Carries tail almost straight up and down. White underside. Long, thornlike bill.

Chipping sparrow: Small, brown bird, from 12.5 to 14 centimeters long. Reddish cap. White line over eye and a black line through eye. White underside. Short, black bill.

1

EXTENSIONS

Application
Activity

A bird count is a type of census, or survey. Have students do a human population survey by profiling members of their own families.

A. Before beginning, have the students decide what constitutes a family; they may choose to include stepparents or grandparents, or only the people living with them.

B. Have the students list the ages of all their family members on a piece of paper and indicate whether each individual is male or female.

C. Use a horizontal histogram to illustrate and analyze the data. Depending on time and skill, either you or the students could plot the information on the graph.

D. Once the graph is drawn, ask:

    1. What is the most numerous age group? (probably the student's own)
    2. What is the smallest? (depends on the graph)
    3. Why is there a large number of people in the age range of 31 to 45? (parents' age group)
    4. From this graph, can you tell whether more students in this class have an older sibling or a younger sibling? (depends on graph)

DEVELOPMENT

ACTIVITY

Skill Development—*Observing, Comparing and Contrasting, Concluding, Classifying*

Teaching Tips—Tell the students that identifying and classifying different species depends on carefully observing the traits, or characteristics, of individuals. It also depends on determining the relative importance of various traits. Some traits distinguish individuals within the same species; others distinguish between species. Tell the students to use these guidelines when answering the questions.

Answers to Questions—1. A—sparrow, B—wren, C—finch. 2. Finch; wren. 3. Sparrow and finch, on the basis of the structure of their bills.

EXTENSIONS

Reinforcement
Science Skills —
Observing, Classifying

To demonstrate that not all observing is accomplished visually, have students identify objects using their senses of smell and touch.

A. Collect a variety of objects that have a distinct odor. Include such things as perfumed soap, an orange, basil, onion powder, a piece of peppermint candy or gum, a ball of clay. (Avoid pungent odors such as ammonia, which may burn the nostrils.) Keep objects hidden in a box until students put on blindfolds.

B. Ask the students to identify each object, using only their sense of smell. Students can also sort, or classify, the substances according to criteria such as whether the odor is pleasant or nasty, strong or weak.

C. Collect a variety of objects with different textures, such as pieces of sandpaper, corduroy, wool, aluminum foil, carpet, tile, and wood.

D. Ask blindfolded students to identify the object, using touch alone. Have them verbally describe the texture and classify it as rough or smooth, hard or soft, etc. Texture is a characteristic that is observed through the sense of touch.

Investigate: To study carefully.

Observe: To watch closely.

Record: To write down information.

Bird counts taken during the late 1930s brought scientists some bad news about *whooping cranes*, the birds shown in the photograph. Whooping cranes are tall, white birds that live near water. The birds were down to a population of about 20. Scientists feared that illness or a bad storm could wipe out the rest.

One flock of these birds spent the winter along the Texas coast. A second flock lived year-round in Louisiana. But no one knew where the Texas birds lived in the summer. And no one knew why the whooping crane population was so low. Wildlife scientists wanted to find out why.

In 1946 Robert Allen, the scientist shown at left, was asked to study or **investigate** the "whoopers." He began his *investigation* by watching closely or **observing** a wild flock of whoopers. He *observed* the birds that wintered at Aransas National Wildlife Refuge in Texas. From sunup to sundown Allen watched the birds. He knew when they slept and what they ate. He watched them care for their young. Like all good scientists, he carefully **recorded** his observations. *Recording* information is an important step in investigating.

Next, Allen investigated where the whoopers spend their summers. Each spring the whoopers leave Texas.

2

1 **Teaching Tips** — When scientists observe a subject, such as a bird, they do more than just look at it. They use other senses as well. Ask: What sense besides sight might Allen use to observe and understand the whoopers? *Hearing.* In fact, depending on the subject being studied, scientists may use all their senses to make observations. Ask: Why is the sense of smell needed to study the behavior of skunks? How might the sense of touch help in studying rocks? Warn students that smelling, touching, and tasting unknown substances indiscriminately is dangerous and should not be done without proper supervision.

2 **Teaching Tips** — Ask: Why is it important to record everything you observe during an experiment and not just what seems to be important or useful? *Answers will vary, but should include a discussion of honesty in research and a discussion about how you don't know ahead of time which bits of information are going to be the most important.* Stress that all information is useful and that a person should remain open-minded while carrying out scientific investigations.

They head north to breed. They return to Texas in the fall. Allen found out where the whoopers had been spotted over the years. He was able to guess where the cranes went to, or *migrated*. Making a guess, or **hypothesis,** is part of how scientists solve a problem. Allen's *hypothesis* was that the cranes migrated to Canada. In 1952 Allen found the summer home of the whoopers: Wood Buffalo National Park. The map shows the route the cranes took to get there.

Allen learned many things at the birds' summer home. Whooping cranes lay two eggs each season. Although they are good parents, adult birds raise only one young bird a year. The whoopers also need to be alone. They must have a lot of space around them. Allen's observations led him to make these final statements or **conclusions:** The whooping cranes were dying out because they did not produce enough young cranes each year to make up for the ones that were hunted by people. Also, they were being crowded out of their living space by the growing human population.

Allen's *conclusions* helped scientists to think of *ideas* that would help the whoopers. Each idea was carefully studied and *tested*. One idea was to give the birds more food and protection from outsiders at their winter home. The idea worked. The flock of Aransas whoopers went up from 20 to 70 birds.

Hypothesis: A scientific guess.

Conclusion: A final statement based on observations.

3

EXTENSIONS

Enrichment
Research — Library

Have students go to the library to research the types of clouds.

A. Instruct them to make a chart, listing the various kinds of clouds (cirrus, cirrocumulus, nimbus, etc.), describing what each kind looks like, how high it is in the sky, and what kind of weather each cloud type brings. For example, cumulonimbus — dense, white, gray, black; full and fluffy; range from 500 feet to 50,000 feet; thunderstorms. The students should also try to obtain a good picture illustrating the types of clouds.

B. Using their charts and pictures, have the students observe the clouds for one week each morning as they come into school. They should record their observations right away by identifying the clouds they see, how much cloud cover there is in the sky, and whether the clouds are blowing toward or away from them. They should try to make predictions about the weather. Later in the day, by actually observing the weather, they can check (test) their predictions.

3 **Teaching Tips** — The entire scientific method is discussed on this page, so this is a good place to emphasize the sequence in the process: **a.** observing a subject, event, or phenomenon; **b.** asking a question (recognizing a problem); **c.** making an hypothesis; **d.** testing the hypothesis through more observation or experimentation; **e.** answering some questions, but raising new ones; **f.** making new hypotheses, and so on. Stress that science is a continuing endeavor. Scientists may answer one question, only to discover many more questions. For example, Allen answered where the cranes' summer home was, but then he had to ask, and answer, what did the cranes do there?

EXTENSIONS

Application
Science Skills — Measuring

Accurate measurements are necessary in science, yet it is impossible to measure anything accurately with absolute certainty. Scientists overcome this problem by making many measurements of the same thing and using statistics to calculate mean values and standard deviations. The arithmetic average is an acceptable alternative. To demonstrate how difficult it is to measure the same thing with the same result more than once, divide the class into teams of 5 or 6 students.

A. Have them choose four things in the classroom to measure. They should choose something very short (paper clip), something short (pencil or book), something medium (desk or person), and something long (length of blackboard or classroom). Each team member should measure each item independently and record the date (in cm or mm) separately.

B. When all team members are finished, have each team construct a chart to summarize the team's results. Students will see that the measurements vary from student to student.

C. Each team should calculate the average length of each item, and compare it to the separate measurements. To confirm their results, the teams could exchange items and then repeat the measurements and calculations as before.

1. Which item's measurement varies the most? the least?
2. Is there a relationship between the length of an item and the range of measurements?
3. If one team member's measurement is way off, should it be discarded when calculating the average? (Yes)

SKILL BUILDING ACTIVITY

Keeping records of bird migrations

A. Obtain these materials: pencil, paper.
B. Study the chart below. It shows the number of whooping cranes observed during their spring and fall migrations.

WHOOPING CRANES OBSERVED

Year	Season	Number of birds
1976	spring	14
	fall	15
1978	spring	28
	fall	29
1980	spring	31
	fall	35

1. How many cranes were observed in the fall of 1976? How many were seen in the fall of 1980? In which year were more cranes observed?
2. Draw a conclusion about what happened to the crane population between 1976 and 1980.
3. Predict what the number of birds seen in 1982 might have been.
4. What information would you need to see if your prediction is right?
5. Why do you think the number of cranes increased?

C. Draw a bar graph similar to the one shown. Draw in bars to show the number of cranes seen in the spring and fall of each year. One year has been done for you.

6. During which migration were more birds seen, spring or fall? Can you explain why?

4

ACTIVITY

Skill Development—*Recording Data, Predicting, Concluding and Generalizing, Cause and Effect*

Teaching Tips—Instruct students to read the chart carefully in order to understand the information it contains and to answer the questions.

Answers to Questions—1. 15, 35, 1980. 2. The population more than doubled. 3. 38–40. 4. The bird count for 1982. 5. Perhaps scientists provided the cranes with more food and space, so few died. 6. Fall. Cranes reproduce over the summer.

4 **Teaching Tips** — This is a good place to discuss the role of creativity in science. Ask: Is creativity something you associate only with music and the arts? How are scientists creative? *During the discussion, students should come to realize that scientists act creatively when they come up with possible solutions to problems and when they design experiments. For example, it was a creative idea to try to hatch a crane egg in captivity.*

Scientists had another idea for increasing the number of whooping cranes. They took eggs from the wild flock to raise in captivity. Later, the captive birds could be released in the wild. Allen had already shown that whoopers raise only one young bird a year. Scientists predicted that taking one egg from a nest would cause no harm. This was tested and proved true. Since 1967, many eggs have been taken from whooper nests in Canada. These eggs have been flown to a research center in Maryland. There, many of the eggs have hatched. Now a captive flock of 25 birds lives there. Scientists have made a good home for the birds. They hope the birds will soon produce eggs on their own.

Scientists had still another idea. They would give whooper eggs to *sandhill cranes* to raise. Sandhill cranes are small relatives of the whoopers. Sandhill cranes live in the Rocky Mountains. Could the sandhill cranes serve as foster parents for the whoopers?

In 1975, the first whooping crane egg was placed in a sandhill nest. The sandhills accepted the egg as their own egg. Now about 17 whoopers live in the Rocky Mountains with sandhill cranes. They migrate with the sandhills and even eat the same food as the sandhills. Can you find the whooper in the photograph below?

5

EXTENSIONS

Application
Science Skills — Hypothesizing, Measuring, Recording Data, Concluding

Have students study their pulse rates in order to test the following hypotheses:

1. All fifth-graders have the same pulse.
2. There is a difference in the pulse rate between boys and girls in the fifth grade.
3. Exercise makes our hearts pump faster.

A. Instruct the students to sit quietly for two minutes and then take their pulses by placing their index and middle fingers lightly on the underside of their wrists. After locating the pulse and practicing counting it, have the students count the number of beats in 15 seconds. To get beats per minute, multiply these numbers by 4. Record this number. This is the resting pulse rate.

B. Next have students jog in place for two minutes, sit down, and immediately take their pulses as before.

C. Gather the data from each child and organize it into a table with separate columns for boys and girls, and for before and after exercise. Ask students to conclude whether the three hypotheses are wrong or right. (**1.** false; **2.** may be true or false depending on the relative activity level of the two sexes; **3.** true)

5 **Teaching Tips** — After reading this account, ask: Why can't scientists say that their experiment is a success as yet? *Because the sandhill-raised cranes have not reproduced yet, which is the ultimate goal of the experiment.* Tell the students that scientists break their problems down into steps and that they can have successes along the way without obtaining the end result. For example, scientists first had to show that removing crane eggs did not harm the parent cranes. They succeeded in showing that. Ask: What other successes did these scientists have? *Sandhills would hatch the crane eggs; sandhills would raise the cranes.*

EXTENSIONS

Reinforcement

Science Skills — Predicting, Comparing and Contrasting, Measuring

To determine how much water different kinds of soil can hold, have students obtain several samples of different kinds of soil. Have students guess, or predict, which soil type will hold the most and least water. Record these predictions.

A. Punch small holes into the bottom of milk cartons (all same size) and set the cartons over beakers. Add equal amounts of each soil type to the cartons and label the carton according to the type of soil it contains. (If the cartons leak at this point, cover the bottoms of the cartons with cloth fastened with rubber bands.) Next add the same volume of water to each soil sample. The volume of water added is equal to the volume of soil in the carton. Record this volume.

B. Allow the water to seep down through the soil and drip out. Collect the leaking water in the beakers. When no more water drips out, measure the amount of water in each beaker. Calculate how much water each soil sample holds by subtracting the volume of water that passed through the soil into the beaker from the amount of water that was added.

C. Sort the soil samples according to how much water they hold. Use the data to test the predictions made at the beginning of the experiment.

SKILL BUILDING ACTIVITY

What foods do birds prefer?

A. Obtain these materials: 3 empty coffee cans, 6 plastic lids that fit the cans, can opener, scissors, wire, heavy string, mixed birdseed, sunflower seeds, baby powder.

B. Carefully remove the metal lids from both ends of the coffee cans. CAUTION: MAKE SURE THERE ARE NO ROUGH METAL EDGES. Use the scissors to cut a small hole shaped like a half moon in each of the plastic lids. CAUTION: USE SCISSORS CAREFULLY.

C. Place the cans on their sides. In the center of the first can, place some mixed birdseed. In the second can, place sunflower seeds. Inside the third can, sprinkle a thin film of baby powder. This will help you to tell if birds have visited this can.

D. Put the lids on each can. Place the "feeders" outdoors where birds are seen often. Use the string and wire to hand the feeders on low tree branches or on buildings. Hang all the cans in the same location.
  1. Predict which feeder will attract the greatest number of birds.

E. For a few days observe the birds that visit the feeders. Record your observations onto a chart.
  2. From which feeder did the birds take the most food?
  3. Was your prediction correct?
  4. Did the same kinds of birds visit each feeder? Why or why not?
  5. Did any birds visit the feeder that has no food? That feeder was the *control* in this experiment. The results from the control are used to compare what happened at the other feeders.

6

ACTIVITY

Skill Development—*Predicting, Comparing and Contrasting, Recording Data, Concluding*

Teaching Tips—Students may wish to attach the feeders to the side of a building near a window. Be sure that the feeders are checked periodically to ensure that a constant supply of food is available.

Answers to Questions—1. Allow students to make their predictions and give their reasons. **2.** Probably, the mixed seed. **3.** Answers will vary. **4.** Some species of birds have a more specific taste preference. Birds such as finches, cardinals, crossbills, blue jays, and evening grosbeaks will be attracted to the sunflower seeds. **5.** Yes, if tracks were seen in the powder.

Scientists now keep a close watch on the whooping cranes. Some birds have been fitted with radio transmitters. From the radio signals, scientists are able to track the cranes' every move.

Thanks to the efforts of many scientists, there is more hope now for the whooping cranes than there was in the late 1930s. The work scientists have done with the cranes shows some of the ways scientific investigations are carried out. You have seen how a scientist asks questions and keeps careful records of observations. By observing the same subject over and over again, a scientist notices when changes take place. The observations lead to experiments. But experiments don't always show the results a scientist predicts. The scientist must then ask some new questions!

A scientist studies the world and the way things work. When scientists get involved in solving problems, they follow the steps you see outlined below. You can follow the same steps in your own investigations.

Ask Questions / Make Observations → Come Up With Ideas

Answer Question and Then Ask Another Question

Test the Idea or Hypothesis

Record Results / Make Conclusions ← Carry Out an Experiment

7

6 **Teaching Tips** — Point out to the students that doing research requires technology in the form of instruments and equipment. Ask: What instruments and equipment did scientists use to study cranes? *Binoculars, plane, radio transmitters.*

7 **Teaching Tips** — Review and discuss the flow chart showing the steps scientists take when doing research.

Enrichment
Activity

Fill a jar with jelly beans and ask students to guess how many jelly beans are in the jar. Tell the students that they can approach the problem in two ways. They can make a wild guess or they can use scientific skills to estimate the number.

A. First, have the students write down a "wild guess" (to do this, don't let the students too near the jar).

B. Then ask them to write down a way they could use to estimate the number. For example, they could count the number of beans on the bottom layer and multiply it by the number of layers.

C. Next, ask the students to write down whether they think the guess or the estimate will prove to be more accurate.

D. Have students individually carry out whatever estimation scheme they have decided upon, make their calculations, and record that number. Finally count the beans.

1. Was the guess or the estimate more accurate?
2. Did they predict correctly?
3. Why is the estimate more accurate? (Estimation reduces the range of possible answers.)
4. Sometimes the guess might be more accurate. Why might this be the case? (Luck or chance)
5. Does luck play a role in science? (Yes)

UNIT 1 OCEAN FRONTIERS

	SECTION	BASIC SCIENCE SKILLS	ACTIVITY MATERIALS STUDENT/GROUP	EXTENSIONS	
CHAPTER 1 THE OCEAN	**1-1** p. T-10 The Ocean Bottom	*Reading illustration* of relief map of ocean bottom p. T-12	clear plastic container or small aquarium, pebbles, gravel, water, ruler	• Reinforcement p. T-13 • Enrichment pp. T-11, T-12 • Application p. T-14	
	1-2 p. T-15 Salts and Sediments	*Sequencing* salinity p. T-16 and desalination p. T-17 *Finding the cause and effect* of submarine canyon p. T-18	2 plastic bowls, water	• Enrichment pp. T-16, T-17, T-18, T-19	
	1-3 p. T-20 Changes in the Ocean Floor	*Reading illustrations* of formation of mid-ocean ridge p. T-21 *Reading illustration* and *finding the cause and effect* of formation of ocean trench p. T-22		• Reinforcement pp. T-21, T-24, T-25 • Enrichment p. T-22 • Application p. T-23	
CHAPTER 2 OCEAN MOVEMENTS	**2-1** p. T-26 Currents	*Finding the cause and effect* of currents p. T-27 *Reading illustrations* of circling currents p. T-28 *Sequencing* the formation of currents p. T-29		• Reinforcement p. T-29 • Enrichment pp. T-27, T-28 • Application p. T-30	
	2-2 p. T-31 Waves	*Finding cause and effect* in wave formation p. T-32 *Comparing and contrasting* waves p. T-36	2 blocks of wood, long tray, milk container, sand, pebbles, water	• Enrichment pp. T-32, T-35, T-36 • Application pp. T-33, T-34	
	2-3 p. T-37 Tides	*Predicting* high and low tides p. T-40 *Comparing and contrasting* spring tides and neap tides p. T-40	graph paper	• Reinforcement p. T-42 • Enrichment pp. T-38, T-40, T-41 • Application p. T-39	
CHAPTER 3 OCEAN EXPLORATION	**3-1** p. T-43 Ocean Resources	*Predicting* problems with desalination p. T-47 *Comparing and contrasting* desalination steps p. T-47		• Enrichment pp. T-44, T-46, T-47 • Application pp. T-45, T-48	
	3-2 p. T-49 Ocean Life	*Sequencing* food chain p. T-49 *Sequencing* food pyramid p. T-51		• Reinforcement p. T-50 • Application p. T-51	
	3-3 p. T-52 The Ocean in Danger	*Predicting* effects p. T-53 *Finding the cause and effect* of pollution on herring population p. T-55	cotton, motor oil, pan, paper, spoon, water	• Enrichment pp. T-55, T-56 • Application pp. T-53, T-54	
	3-4 p. T-57 Exploring the Ocean Bottom	*Building science vocabulary* by making a dictionary p. T-58 *Reading illustration* and *generalizing* concept of sonar p. T-59		• Reinforcement pp. T-59, T-63 • Enrichment pp. T-61, T-62, T-64, T-65 • Application pp. T-58, T-60	

EXTRA ACTIVITIES/ DEMONSTRATIONS	WORKSHEET MASTERS	EVALUATIONS
	• The Ocean Bottom (AC) p. T-7k • The Ocean Floor (AC) p. T-7l	Section Review p. T-14
• Instant Ocean p. T-15	• Rivers (AC) p. T-7m	Section Review p. T-19
• Using a globe p. T-23	• The Ocean (SK) p. T-7n • Vocabulary Word Puzzle (SK) p. T-7o	Section Review p. T-24 Chapter Review p. T-25 Test Masters pp. T-7d, e
• Winds and currents p. T-28		Section Review p. T-30
• Wave motion p. T-31 • Wave structure p. T-32	• Ocean Currents (AC) p. T-7p	Section Review p. T-36
• Tidal effects model p. T-38 • Tidal positions of sun, moon, and earth p. T-40	• Tides, Waves, (SK) p. T-7q • Crossword Puzzle (SK) p. T-7r	Section Review p. T-41 Chapter Review p. T-42 Test Masters pp. T-7f, g, h
• Seaweed p. T-43	• Food From the Ocean (AH) p. T-7s	Section Review p. T-48
• Ocean specimens p. T-49	• Food Pyramids (SK) p. T-7t	Section Review p. T-51
• Petroleum products p. T-52		Section Review p. T-56
• Aqualung p. T-57 • Investigating p. T-64	• Cartesian Diver (AC) p. T-7u	Section Review p. T-62 Chapter Review p. T-63 Test Masters p. T-7i, j

BOOKS FOR STUDENTS

Bendick, Jeanne. *Exploring an Ocean Tide Pool*, Champaign, Ill.: Garrad Pub. Co., 1976
Cook, Jan Leslie. *The Mysterious Undersea World*, illus., New York: National Geographic Society, 1980
Hargreaves, Pat, ed. *The Sea & Science Series*, illus., Morristown, N.J.: Silver Burdett, 1981 (*The Arctic, The Pacific*)
Iverson, Genie. *Jacques Cousteau*, New York: G. P. Putnam's Sons, 1976
Lambert, David. *The Oceans*, illus., New York: Warwick, 1980
Myers, Arthur. *Sea Creatures Do Amazing Things*, illus. by Jean Day Zallinger, New York: Step Up Books, Random House, 1981
Scheffer, Victor B. *The Amazing Sea Otter*, illus. by Gretchen Daiber, New York: Scribner's, 1981
Soule, Gardner. *Mysterious Monsters of the Deep*, illus., New York: Franklin Watts, 1981
Zim, Herbert S. and Krantz, Lucretia. *Sea Stars and Their Kin*, New York: Morrow Junior Books, 1976

FILMS

Antarctica: Desert of Ice, Sea of Life, 29 min, CRM/McGraw-Hill
Beach and Tidepool Life, 17 min, International
Coral Reef, 23 min, National Geographic
The Beach: A River of Sand, 21 min, Britannica
Waves on Water, 16 min, Britannica
The Earth: Its Oceans, 21 min, Coronet
Our Round Earth: Its Waters, 10½ min, Coronet
We Explore the Beach, 11½ min, Coronet
We Explore Ocean Life, 10½ min, Coronet
Adaptations to Ocean Environments, 11 min, Captioned Films for the Deaf

FILMSTRIPS

Oceanography: Understanding Our Deep Frontier, sound, Britannica
Oceanography, color, Coronet
The Science of Oceanography, cassette, 17 min, National Geographic

---

KEY (AC)—Activity   (AH)—At Home   (SK)—Skill

BULLETIN BOARD IDEAS

The purpose of this bulletin board is to make the students more aware of the variety of materials that we obtain from the ocean. Early in the unit, students could participate by sketching various underwater plants and animals. Sandpaper could be used to depict the ocean bottom. Students could do research into selected ocean resources. The information should include the form in which the material is found, the place where it is located, the uses of the material, and any human or chemical threat to its supply. The cards could be placed under the name of each resource.

FIELD TRIP IDEAS

To a Local Body of Running Water

On a suitable day, plan to visit a local stream or river. Ask your students to observe the area around the water. Have them describe the kind of run-off water that enters the stream or river. They should classify the run-off as industrial, agricultural, or natural. Obtain a sample of water to be studied for its sedimentation and microscopic life. On a map, trace the path of the water to the next larger body of water and finally to the ocean. Discuss whether the water in your community contributes to the pollution of the ocean.

To Make Core Samples

Core samples of sediment are used to study the ocean bottom. Core samples can also be done on land. Take the students outdoors to an area covered with soil. Give each student an empty tin can that has both ends removed and that has been greased on the inside with cooking oil. The students should pound the cans lengthwise into the soil so that about 2.5 cm (1 in) of the cans stick out of the soil. Then they should pull the cans out of the soil and remove the soil samples by gently easing the samples out of the cans. Have the students observe the layers of sediment.

Fold Back
Answer
Key On
Line
Before
Copying.

THE OCEAN

TEST 1
CHAPTER

CHAPTER OBJECTIVES

Read each question. Choose the best answer from those listed.
Write the letter of your choice on the line at the right.

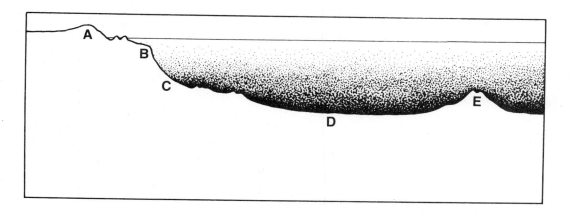

1. Look at the map above. Which letter shows the continental slope?
   a. A   **b.** B   **c.** C   **d.** D

   1._____   1. <u>c</u> (1)

2. Look at the map above. What does letter E show?
   a. the continental shelf   **c.** the mid-ocean ridge
   b. the continental slope   **d.** the abyssal plain

   2._____   2. <u>c</u> (1)

3. The part of the ocean bottom that starts where the land ends is
   a. the mid-ocean ridge.   **c.** the continental slope.
   b. the abyssal plain.   **d.** the continental shelf.

   3._____   3. <u>d</u> (1)

4. Two parts that form the ocean floor are the
   a. abyssal plain and mid-ocean ridge.
   b. continental slope and continental shelf.
   c. mid-ocean ridge and continental slope.
   d. continental shelf and abyssal plain.

   4._____   4. <u>a</u> (1)

5. How does sodium chloride get into the ocean?
   a. It was always there.
   b. It comes from ocean plants.
   c. Rivers carry it over the land to the ocean.
   d. Boats bring it from the land.

   5._____   5. <u>c</u> (2)

6. Salt is left behind in the ocean when
   a. currents are very fast.   **c.** it rains heavily.
   b. the weather is cloudy.   **d.** the water evaporates.

   6._____   6. <u>d</u> (2)

7. Much of the water that evaporates from the ocean forms
   a. ice.   **b.** fog.   **c.** salt.   **d.** clouds.

   7._____   7. <u>d</u> (2)

8. __c__ (2)

8. The water at the equator is less salty than in some other parts of the ocean because

8. _____

    a. there is a lot of melting ice.

    b. there is less rainfall over the equator.

    c. there is more rainfall over the equator.

    d. there is less water.

9. __a__ (3)

9. Which sentence is *not* true?

9. _____

    a. Sediments build up quickly on the ocean floor.

    b. Sand, mud, clay, and rocks are sediments.

    c. Some sediments are brought to the ocean by wind.

    d. Animal and plant remains can form sediment.

10. __b__ (3)

10. Sediments that settle close to the shore form

10. _____

    a. lakes.   **c.** plains.

    b. beaches.   **d.** mountains.

11. __b__ (3)

11. A submarine canyon is

11. _____

    a. a groove formed by a submarine.

    b. a groove formed by sliding sediment.

    c. a mountain formed by sediment.

    d. the bottom layer of sediment.

12. __b__ (3)

12. After an underwater landslide, sediment settles

12. _____

    a. on the continental shelf.   **c.** on the coast.

    b. on the abyssal plain.   **d.** on the mid-ocean ridge.

13. __b__ (4)

13. What happens when the new ocean floor pushes against sections of the old floor?

13. _____

    a. The ocean floor moves closer to the crack.

    b. The ocean floor spreads away from the crack.

    c. The crack closes up.

    d. There are no changes.

14. __a__ (4)

14. Europe and North America are moving apart as the Atlantic Ocean becomes

14. _____

    a. wider.   **c.** deeper.

    b. narrower.   **d.** shallower.

15. __c__ (4)

15. What forms when the ocean floor moves down under the land bordering the ocean?

15. _____

    a. salt   **c.** ocean trench

    b. continental shelf   **d.** an island

16. __d__ (4)

16. The mid-ocean ridge is a place where there is

16. _____

    a. volcanic activity.

    b. new rock being formed.

    c. spreading of the ocean floor.

    d. all of the above.

Name_____Date_____

OCEAN MOVEMENTS

TEST 2
CHAPTER

Read each question. Choose the best answer from those listed.
Write the letter of your choice on the line at the right.

1. Currents on the surface of the ocean are caused by
   a. boats.   **c.** wind.
   b. sun.   **d.** salt.

   1._____   1._**c**_ (1)

2. Trade winds blow
   a. away from the equator. **c.** from north to south.
   b. toward the equator.   **d.** faster over salt water.

   2._____   2._**b**_ (1)

3. Which of the following does *not* cause a deep ocean current?
   a. warm water replacing sinking cold water
   b. less salty water moving over more salty water
   c. uneven heating of ocean water by the sun
   d. the blowing of the westerlies

   3._____   3._**d**_ (1)

4. How does the sun affect deep ocean currents?
   a. It causes trade winds.
   b. It causes the water to be saltier in some places.
   c. It causes the water to be deep in some parts and shallow
          in others.
   d. It has no effect.

   4._____   4._**b**_ (1)

5. Which of the following does *not* cause waves?
   a. underwater earthquakes **c.** ships
   b. wind   **d.** sand

   5._____   5._**d**_ (2)

6. Breakers change the shape of a shoreline by
   a. depositing sand on the shore.
   b. carrying sand away from the beach.
   c. breaking down rocks on the shore.
   d. all of the above.

   6._____   6._**d**_ (2)

7. What changes the shape of cliffs along the shoreline?
   a. waves mixed with small pieces of rocks
   b. neap tides
   c. very salty water
   d. deep ocean currents

   7._____   7._**a**_ (2)

8. Tsunamis are waves caused by
   a. large boats.
   b. strong currents.
   c. underwater earthquakes.
   d. high winds.

   8._____   8._**c**_ (2)

9. **b** (3)

9. The crest of a wave is
   a. the lowest point.   c. the midpoint.
   b. the highest point.   d. the width.

9. _____

10. **a** (3)

10. What would you measure to find the length of a wave?
    a. from the crest of one wave to the crest of the next
    b. from the crest of a wave to its trough
    c. from the crest of one wave to the trough of the next
    d. how far up on the beach it went

10. _____

11. **b** (3)

11. The height of a wave is determined by the
    a. sun.   c. surface current.
    b. strength of the wind. d. air temperature.

11. _____

12. **c** (3)

12. Which of the following sentences is true?
    a. The trough is the highest point of the wave.
    b. Waves move against the wind.
    c. Waves move in the same direction as the wind.
    d. The waves get smaller as the wind gets stronger.

12. _____

Look at the diagram below. Then answer questions 13 and 14.

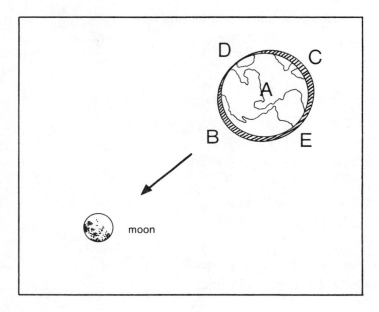

13. **a** (4)

13. What happens when the moon pulls the ocean water at point B and the earth at point A?

13. _____

    a. There is a high tide at points B and C.
    b. There is a high tide at points D and E.
    c. There is a low tide at points B and C.
    d. There is a low tide at points B, C, D, and E.

4T   *Unit 1 Chapter 2*

14. The tides at points B, C, D, and E on the earth will change

14. _____

    a. as the earth spins.   c. once a year.

    b. as the moon spins.   d. never.

15. A tide is

15. _____

    a. the pull of the earth.

    b. regular rise and fall of ocean water.

    c. the pull of the moon.

    d. a dangerously high wave.

16. Tell if the sentence below is true or false. If it is false, tell which time can be used in place of the underlined time to make the sentence true.

16. _____

    If a low tide occurs at 4:00 A.M., the next high tide would occur at <u>8:00 A.M.</u>

    a. The sentence is true.   c. 10:00 A.M.

    b. 6:00 P.M.   d. 10:00 P.M.

17. What type of tide occurs when the sun, the earth, and the moon are at right angles to each other?

17. _____

    a. spring tide   c. high tide

    b. neap tide   d. very low tide

18. When the sun, the earth, and the moon are in a straight line in space,

18. _____

    a. low tides are very low, but high tides are not high.

    b. low tides are very low, and high tides are very high.

    c. low tides are not very low, and high tides are not very high.

    d. low tides are not very low, and high tides are very high.

19. Tides that can cause flooding are called

19. _____

    a. neap tides.   c. spring tides.

    b. everyday high tides.   d. low tides.

20. What decreases the effect of the moon's pull on the earth during neap tides?

20. _____

    a. the pull of the sun   c. a flattening of the ocean.

    b. bulges in the earth   d. the sun's going behind the moon

OCEAN EXPLORATION

Read each question. Choose the best answer from those listed. Write the letter of your choice on the line at the right.

1. <u>d</u> (1)

1. What material is not dissolved in the ocean?
   a. gold
   c. iodine
   b. iron
   d. sugar

1._____

2. <u>d</u> (1)

2. The ocean can provide us with
   a. agar.
   b. diatoms.
   c. food.
   d. all these things.

2._____

3. <u>a</u> (1)

3. Fossil fuels were formed under the ocean floor when
   a. dead plants and animals were covered with sediment.
   b. waves carried oil from the land.
   c. sand was put under a lot of pressure.
   d. the ocean became salty.

3._____

4. <u>d</u> (2)

4. The last step in desalination is
   a. water forms steam and leaves salt behind.
   b. ocean water is heated.
   c. ocean water is pumped into large tanks.
   d. steam is cooled and forms fresh water.

4._____

5. <u>a</u> (2)

5. To get pure water, the desalination plant in Key West, Florida, uses
   a. high pressure.
   b. energy from the sun.
   c. oil from wells under the ocean.
   d. natural gas.

5._____

6. <u>d</u> (2)

6. Which of the following is not a use of desalinated water?
   a. growing crops
   c. building industries
   b. drinking water
   d. saltwater aquariums

6._____

7. <u>a</u> (3)

7. A food chain is
   a. an eating pattern that tells who eats whom.
   b. fish food.
   c. a chain of plankton.
   d. food that is not healthy.

7._____

8. <u>d</u> (3)

8. At the bottom of many food chains in the ocean are
   a. herring.
   c. anemones.
   b. copepods.
   d. all kinds of plankton.

8._____

9. Many fish are the same colors as their surroundings. This helps

    a. to protect them from plants.
    b. to protect them from each other.
    c. to keep the ocean looking clean.
    d. to find plankton.

9. _____   9. _b_ (3)

10. Pesticides that are carried to the ocean

    a. enter all the plants but none of the fish.
    b. turn into sodium chloride.
    c. enter the bodies of living things.
    d. become harmless in the water.

10. _____   10. _c_ (4)

11. Pollution of the ocean by the dumping of sewage can be prevented

    a. by spraying insects that fly around sewage.
    b. by building sewage treatment plants.
    c. by using hay to absorb the sewage.
    d. by dumping only small amounts of sewage.

11. _____   11. _b_ (4)

12. Which of the following sentences is true?

    a. Pollution can cause the extinction of a species.
    b. Pollution cannot cause serious harm to the environment.
    c. Pollution caused by oil spills is harmful only to human beings.
    d. Pollution does not affect the food chain.

12. _____   12. _a_ (4)

13. A piece of equipment that helps people to explore very deep areas of the ocean without being crushed is

    a. a bathyscaphe.   **c.** a diving suit.
    b. an aqualung.   **d.** an air hose.

13. _____   13. _a_ (5)

14. By using an echo sounder, scientists can learn

    a. how far they are from shore.
    b. how far down the bottom is.
    c. how fast the wind is blowing.
    d. the height of the waves.

14. _____   14. _b_ (5)

15. From a core of sediment from the ocean, scientists can learn

    a. about the earth's past.
    b. what animals inhabited the earth a long time ago.
    c. when volcanoes erupted in the past.
    d. all of the above.

15. _____   15. _d_ (5)

The Ocean Bottom

Identify the following on the graph below: the two continental slopes, the three deepest sections, the mid-ocean ridge, and the Azores.

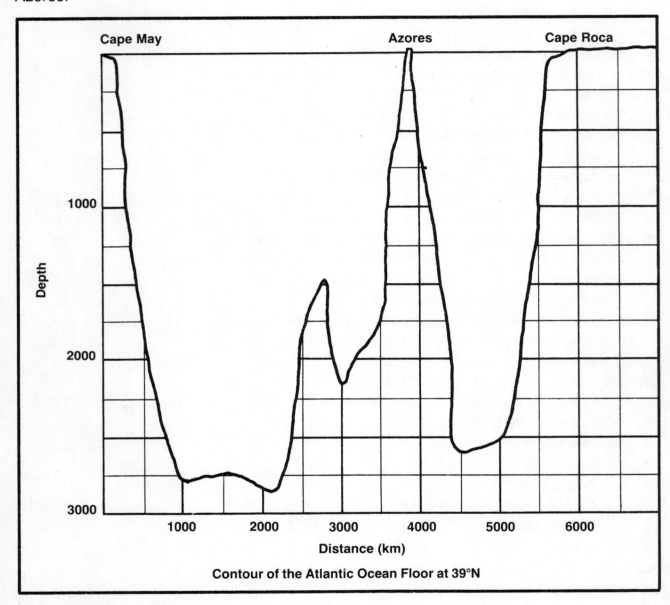

Contour of the Atlantic Ocean Floor at 39°N

List the distances of the three deepest areas in the Atlantic Ocean.

_____

Refer to the EXTENSIONS on page T-11

Name _____ Date _____

The Ocean Bottom

Identify the following structures on the map: continental shelf, continental slope, mid-ocean ridge, and abyssal plain.

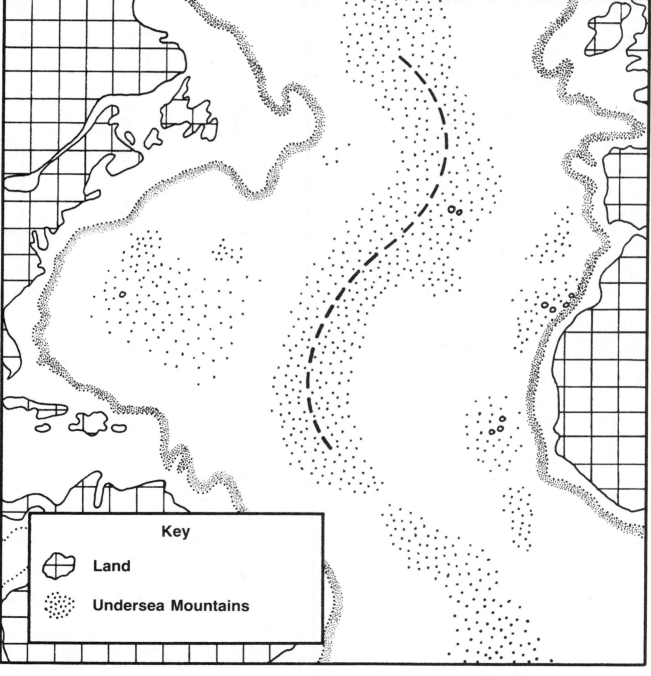

Key

⊕ **Land**

⠿ **Undersea Mountains**

Refer to the EXTENSIONS on page T-11

Salts and Sediments

Choose one of the rivers shown on the map below. Find where it begins and where it flows into the ocean. Use reference books to discover its age, flow, delta, and any erosion or flooding problems it may have. Write a brief description of the river on the lines provided.

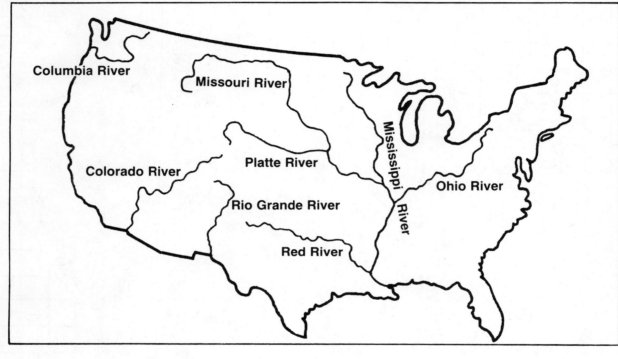

_____

_____

_____

_____

_____

_____

_____

Refer to the EXTENSIONS on page T-18

Name ______________________ Date ______________

The Ocean

SKILL WORKSHEET

Using the information given in the chapter, explain why the following things are found where they are.

1. The mid-ocean ridge

____

____

2. Submarine canyons in the continental slope

____

____

____

3. Thick layers of sediments on the abyssal plain

____

____

____

4. The sodium chloride in ocean water

____

____

5. Deep Pacific Ocean trenches near the coasts of continents

____

6. The remains of ocean animals and plants found on land

____

____

7. Islands such as the Azores

____

____

The Ocean Bottom

Find the science words below. Look across, up, down, and diagonally. Then use those words to complete the sentences below.

```
S O D I U M C H L O R I D E E Z
E U I S P L F M P J T R B Y V S
D F B T M P T F D S N F S N K H
I Z C M I D O C E A N R I D G E
M Y F O A M A L D Q F C S E B L
E A G L G R T N R V R I B V T F
N P T T F Y I D L N R C V E L R
T E N E T O H N T R E N C H E S
S F P N M Y T A E G V X A N A D
L S U U B D G P W C D P B I B J
M E W T J U O R T G A T L B Y P
O R Z P O L I W H G U N O D H E
T O A D S F M N R S O B Y F B S
A Z K Y T O C E A N F L O O R L
C A T A B Y S S A L P L A I N T
```

1. The part of the ocean bottom that is near land is the continental _____.

2. The part of the ocean bottom that plunges downward sharply is the continental _____.

3. The part of the ocean bottom that lies at the bottom of #2 is the _____.

4. The flat part of the ocean floor is the _____.

5. The mountain chain on the ocean floor is the _____.

6. _____ is a salt.

7. Sand, clay, and other materials that settle in water are called _____.

8. A groove cut in the continental slope and shelf is a _____.

9. Something melted by heat is _____.

10. Deep ocean valleys are _____.

11. The _____ are islands in the North Atlantic.

Name_____ Date_____

Ocean Movements

Using reference works, place these currents in their proper locations and indicate if each is a hot or a cold current: Gulf Stream, North Atlantic Drift, Labrador Current, North Equatorial Current, California Current, Japan Current, Antarctic Current.

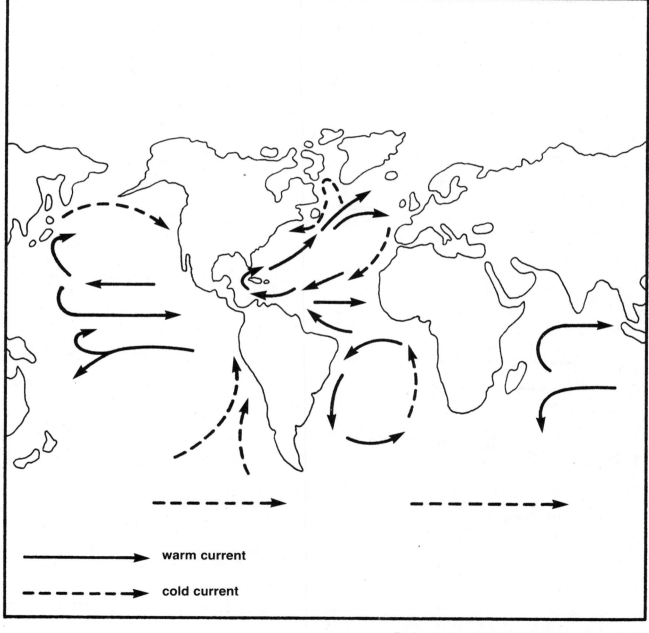

warm current

cold current

Refer to the EXTENSIONS on page T-27

Name ______________________ Date ______________

Ocean Movements

SKILL WORKSHEET

The diagrams below show situations that cause something to happen. In the spaces at the right, draw what happens. Then write a short explanation of why it happens. Name each of the events from this list: spring tide, neap tide, waves, deep current, deep current.

CAUSE | EFFECT | NAME AND EXPLANATION

1.
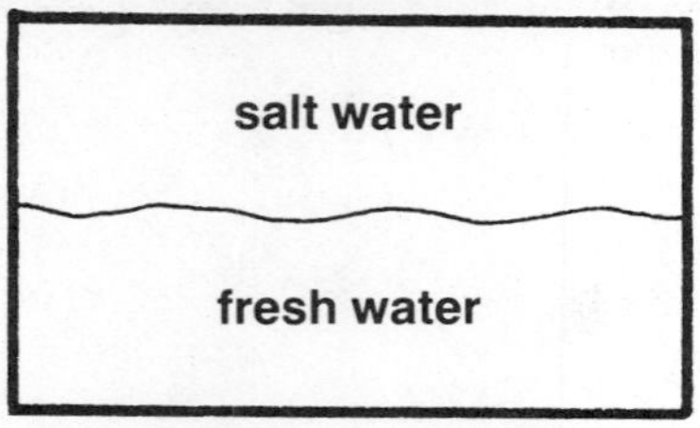
salt water
fresh water

2.
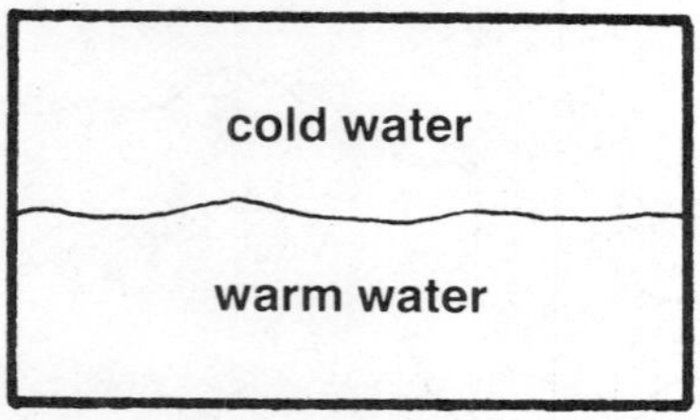
cold water
warm water

3.
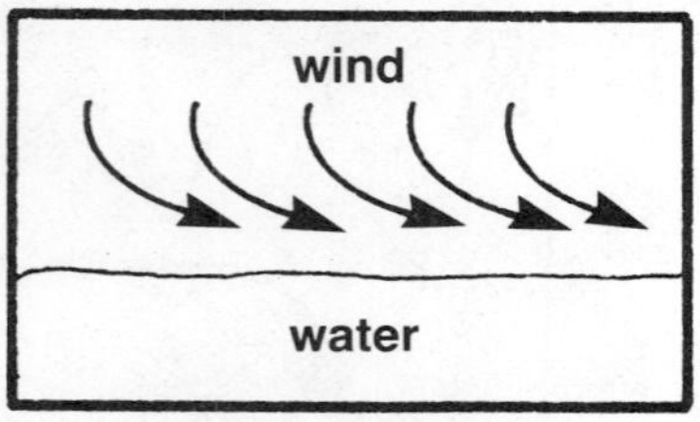
wind
water

4.
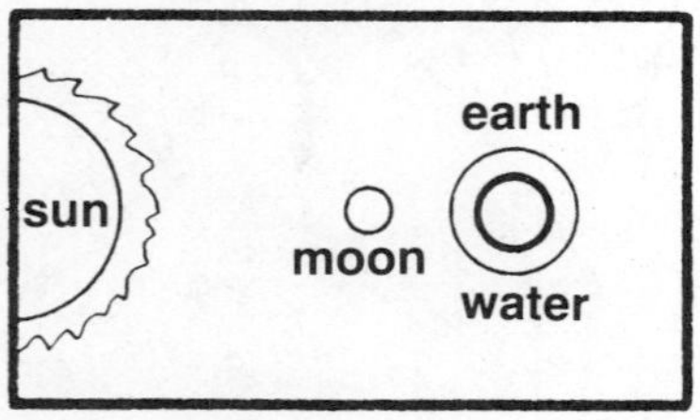
sun
moon
earth
water

5.
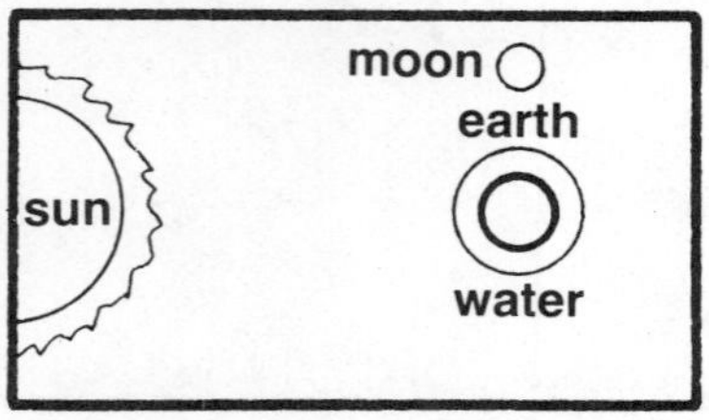
sun
moon
earth
water

Ocean Movements

Use the clues below to solve the puzzle.

ACROSS

1. Water that moves in a certain direction
2. Tides when the highs are not very high
3. Winds blowing away from the equator from west to east

DOWN

1. The highest point of a wave
4. Tide with the highest high tide
5. Giant waves caused by earthquakes
6. A wave whose crest has tumbled over
7. The rise and fall of water
8. The lowest part of a wave
9. Winds that blow toward the equator from east to west

Name _____ Date _____

Ocean Resources

You are learning how the ocean's resources are used. In this
at home activity, you will see how they can be used as food. THIS
ACTIVITY MUST BE SUPERVISED BY AN ADULT.

A. Obtain these materials: measuring
cups and spoons, mixing bowl, cookie
sheet, Chlorella (algae, available from
natural food stores), 2 cups flour, 1/2
tsp salt, 4 tbs shortening, 3/4 cup
milk, and 3 tbs baking powder.

B. Combine all the dry ingredients and
mix them together thoroughly.

C. Slowly add the milk and stir it into the
dry ingredients until you form a batter.

D. Place teaspoon-sized drops of this
mixture on a greased cookie sheet
until all the batter is used up.

E. Bake at 175°C, or 350°F, for 10 to 15
minutes.

F. Remove the cookies and allow them
to cool before tasting them.

QUESTIONS

1. How do the cookies taste?

   _____

2. Do you think algae make a good source of food?

   _____

   _____

3. Can you name other foods we obtain from the sea?

   _____

Refer to the EXTENSIONS on page T-44

Name_____ Date _____

Ocean Life

A. Place each of these sea creatures in its proper place in the pyramid of life below: herring, shark, codfish, plankton, copepod.

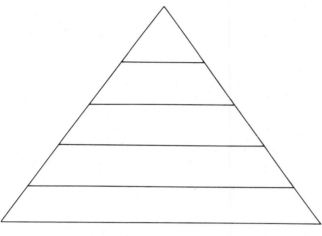

B. Using what you had for your last meal, create a pyramid of life for yourself.

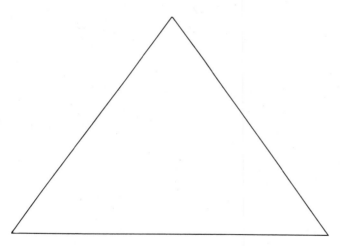

C. Describe what would happen to the other creatures in the first pyramid if all the plankton were to die.

_____

_____

_____

Name _____ Date _____

Exploring the Ocean Bottom

You are learning about the devices used to explore the ocean bottom. By building a Cartesian diver, you will observe how some of them work.

A. Obtain these materials: balloon, glass jar, medicine dropper, rubber band, scissors, and water.

B. Pour water into the glass jar until it is 3/4 full.

C. Fill the medicine dropper with water and place it, tube end down, into the water. If the dropper sinks, remove it and adjust the water level in it until it floats.

D. Cut a piece of the balloon and stretch it over the mouth of the jar. Use a rubber band to hold it in place.

E. Press down on the stretched balloon. Watch what happens to the medicine dropper.

F. Take your hand off the balloon. Watch what happens to the dropper.

 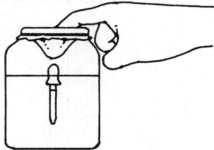

QUESTIONS

1. What happened to the dropper when you pressed down on

   the balloon? _____

2. Why did the dropper sink? _____

   _____

   _____

3. How do you think this is similar to what a bathyscaphe does

   to sink into the ocean? _____

   _____

Permission to reproduce this page is granted to users of HOLT SCIENCE 5   Holt, Rinehart and Winston, Publishers

Top-left worksheet

Name_____ Date_____

The Ocean Bottom

Identify the following on the graph below: the two continental slopes, the three deepest sections, the mid-ocean ridge, and the Azores.

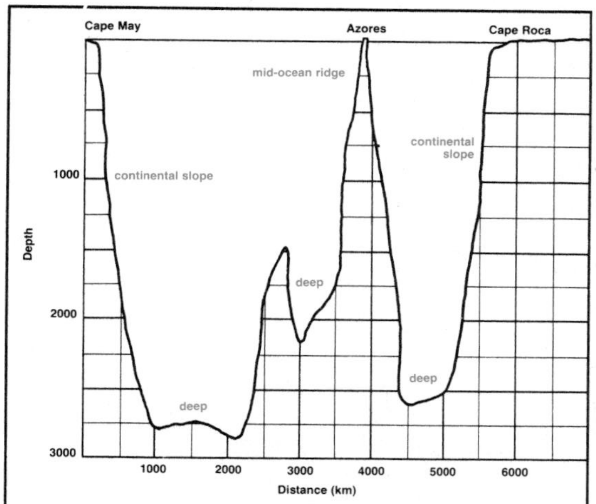

Cape May   Azores   Cape Roca

mid-ocean ridge

continental slope

continental slope

1000

Depth

deep

2000

deep

deep

3000

1000   2000   3000   4000   5000   6000

Distance (km)

Contour of the Atlantic Ocean Floor at 39°N

List the distances of the three deepest areas in the Atlantic Ocean.

They are located at about 1,500 km, 3,000 km, and 4,750 km.

Refer to the EXTENSIONS on page T-11

T–7k   Unit 1 Chapter 1   1W

Top-right worksheet

Name_____ Date_____

The Ocean Bottom

Identify the following structures on the map: continental shelf, continental slope, mid-ocean ridge, and abyssal plain.

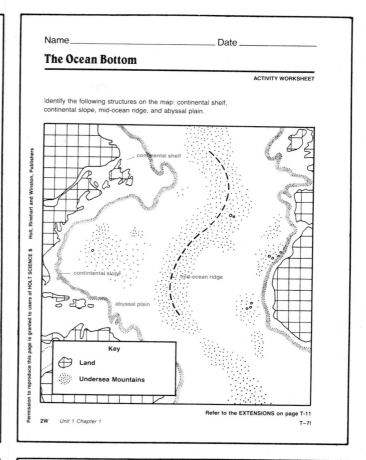

continental shelf

continental slope

mid-ocean ridge

abyssal plain

Key

Land

Undersea Mountains

Refer to the EXTENSIONS on page T-11

2W   Unit 1 Chapter 1   T–7l

Bottom-left worksheet

Name_____ Date_____

Salts and Sediments

Choose one of the rivers shown on the map below. Find where it begins and where it flows into the ocean. Use reference books to discover its age, flow, delta, and any erosion or flooding problems it may have. Write a brief description of the river on the lines provided.

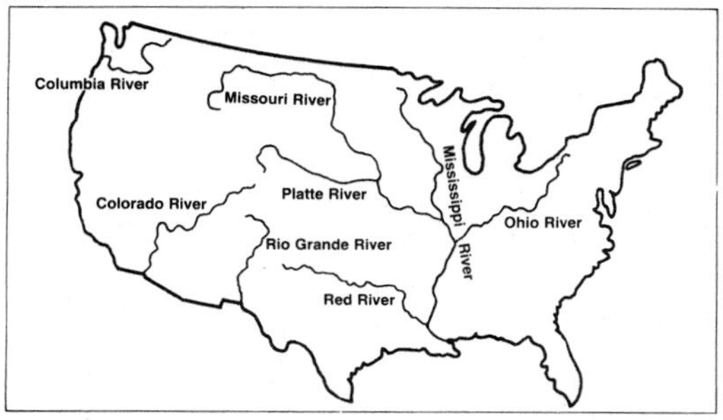

Columbia River

Missouri River

Colorado River   Platte River

Rio Grande River   Mississippi River   Ohio River

Red River

Answers will vary.

_____

_____

_____

_____

_____

_____

_____

Refer to the EXTENSIONS on page T-18

T–7m   Unit 1 Chapter 1   3W

Bottom-right worksheet

Name_____ Date_____

The Ocean

Using the information given in the chapter, explain why the following things are found where they are.

1. The mid-ocean ridge
   Large mountains are formed where molten rock breaks
   through large cracks in the earth's crust.

2. Submarine canyons in the continental slope
   Sediments on top of the continental slope sometimes slide
   down, cutting into the slope and eventually forming
   a canyon.

3. Thick layers of sediments on the abyssal plain
   These sediments have built up from the dead bodies of plants
   and animals, the rock particles blown out to sea, and
   sediments moving off the slopes.

4. The sodium chloride in ocean water
   As rivers flow over the ground, they pick up sodium chloride
   from the ground and deposit it in the oceans.

5. Deep Pacific Ocean trenches near the coasts of continents
   Trenches form when one crustal plate plunges under another.

6. The remains of ocean animals and plants found on land
   Parts of the world that are now dry land were at one time
   under water.

7. Islands such as the Azores
   These islands are the tops of mountains that are part of the
   mid-ocean ridge.

4W   Unit 1 Chapter 1   T–7n

Name_____ Date_____

The Ocean Bottom

SKILL WORKSHEET

Find the science words below. Look across, up, down, and diagonally. Then use those words to complete the sentences below.

```
S O D I U M C H L O R I D E E Z
E U I S P L F M P J T R B Y V S
D F B T M P T F D S N F S N K H
I Z C M I D O C E A N R I D G E
M Y F O A M A L D Q F C S E B L
E A G L G R T N R V R I B V T F
N P T T F Y I D L N R C V E L R
T E N E T O H N T R E N C H E S
S F P N M Y T A E G V X A N A D
L S U U B D G P W C D P B I B J
M E W T J U O R T G A T L B Y P
O R Z P O L I W H G U N O D H E
T O A D S F M N R S O B Y F B S
A Z K Y T O C E A N F L O O R L
C A T A B Y S S A L P L A I N T
```

1. The part of the ocean bottom that is near land is the continental _____.
2. The part of the ocean bottom that plunges downward sharply is the continental _____.
3. The part of the ocean bottom that lies at the bottom of #2 is the _____.
4. The flat part of the ocean floor is the _____.
5. The mountain chain on the ocean floor is the _____.
6. _____ is a salt.
7. Sand, clay, and other materials that settle in water are called _____.
8. A groove cut in the continental slope and shelf is a _____.
9. Something melted by heat is _____.
10. Deep ocean valleys are _____.
11. The _____ are islands in the North Atlantic.

T–7o   Unit 1 Chapter 1   5W

Name_____ Date_____

Ocean Movements

ACTIVITY WORKSHEET

Using reference works, place these currents in their proper locations and indicate if each is a hot or a cold current: Gulf Stream, North Atlantic Drift, Labrador Current, North Equatorial Current, California Current, Japan Current, Antarctic Current.

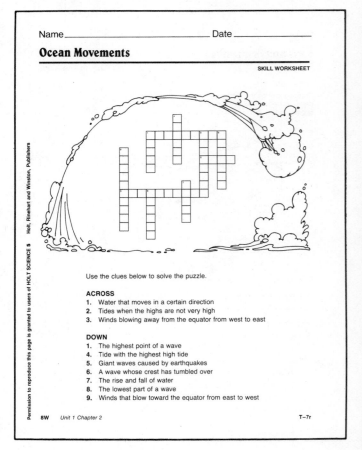

→ warm current

- - → cold current

Refer to the EXTENSIONS on page T-28

6W   Unit 1 Chapter 2   T–7p

Name_____ Date_____

Ocean Movements

SKILL WORKSHEET

The diagrams below show situations that cause something to happen. In the spaces at the right, draw what happens. Then write a short explanation why it happens. Name each of the events from this list: spring tide, neap tide, waves, deep current, deep current.

CAUSE	EFFECT	NAME AND EXPLANATION
1. salt water / fresh water		_____
2. cold water / warm water		_____
3. wind / water		_____
4. sun / moon / earth / water		_____
5. sun / moon / earth / water		_____

T–7q   Unit 1 Chapter 2   7W

Name_____ Date_____

Ocean Movements

SKILL WORKSHEET

Use the clues below to solve the puzzle.

ACROSS
1. Water that moves in a certain direction
2. Tides when the highs are not very high
3. Winds blowing away from the equator from west to east

DOWN
1. The highest point of a wave
4. Tide with the highest high tide
5. Giant waves caused by earthquakes
6. A wave whose crest has tumbled over
7. The rise and fall of water
8. The lowest part of a wave
9. Winds that blow toward the equator from east to west

8W   Unit 1 Chapter 2   T–7r

Ocean Resources

Name_____ Date_____

AT HOME WORKSHEET

You are learning how the ocean's resources are used. In this at-home activity, you will see how they can be used as food. THIS ACTIVITY MUST BE SUPERVISED BY AN ADULT.

A. Obtain these materials: measuring cups and spoons, mixing bowl, cookie sheet, Chlorella (algae, available from natural food stores), 2 cups flour, 1/2 tsp. salt, 4 tbsps. shortening, 3/4 cup milk, and 3 tbsps. baking powder.

B. Combine all the dry ingredients and mix them together thoroughly.

C. Slowly add the milk and stir it into the dry ingredients until you form a batter.

D. Place teaspoon-sized drops of this mixture on a greased cookie sheet until all the batter is used up.

E. Bake at 175°C, or 350°F, for 10 to 15 minutes.

F. Remove the cookies and allow them to cool before tasting them.

QUESTIONS

1. How do the cookies taste?
   Answers will vary.

2. Do you think algae make a good source of food?
   Students should point out that algae are full of
   vitamins and other nutrients.

3. Can you name other foods we obtain from the sea?
   Answers will vary, but they should include fish and seafood.

T–7s

Refer to the EXTENSIONS on page T–44

Unit 1 Chapter 3   9W

Ocean Life

Name_____ Date_____

SEQUENCING, CLASSIFYING, FINDING CAUSE AND EFFECT   SKILL WORKSHEET

A. Place each of these sea creatures in its proper place in the pyramid of life below: herring, shark, codfish, plankton, copepod.

shark
codfish
herring
copepod
plankton

B. Using what you had for your last meal, create a pyramid of life for yourself.

Answers
will
vary.

C. Describe what would happen to the other creatures in the first pyramid if all the plankton were to die.
   Since the copepods would lose their food source, they would
   quickly die. This process would continue up the pyramid until
   the top organism, the shark, would die.

10W   Unit 1 Chapter 3

T–7t

Exploring the Ocean Bottom

Name_____ Date_____

ACTIVITY WORKSHEET

You are learning about the devices used to explore the ocean bottom. By building a Cartesian diver, you will observe how some of them work.

A. Obtain these materials: balloon, glass jar, medicine dropper, rubber band, scissors, and water.

B. Pour water into the glass jar until it is 3/4 full.

C. Fill the medicine dropper with water and place it, tube end down, into the water. If the dropper sinks, remove it and adjust the water level in it until it floats.

D. Cut a piece of the balloon and stretch it over the mouth of the jar. Use a rubber band to hold it in place.

E. Press down on the stretched balloon. Watch what happens to the medicine dropper.

F. Take your hand off the balloon. Watch what happens to the dropper.

QUESTIONS

1. What happened to the dropper when you pressed down on the balloon?   The dropper sank to the bottom.

2. Why did the dropper sink?   It sank because water
   from the jar went into it, making it heavier than
   the upward force of the water.

3. How do you think this is similar to what a bathyscaphe does to sink into the ocean?   The bathyscaphe fills special
   compartments with water in order to sink.

T–7u

Unit 1 Chapter 3   11W

Permission to reproduce this page is granted to users of HOLT SCIENCE 5   Holt, Rinehart and Winston, Publishers

UNIT OVERVIEW

This is an earth science unit on oceanography. The ocean bottom is made of mountain chains, valleys, and plains similar to those found on land. Salts and sediments found on land are continuously being carried to the ocean by rivers and by water runoff. It is thought that molten rock from inside the earth seeps out through cracks in the mid-ocean ridge. This causes the ocean floor to spread apart slowly.

Surface ocean currents caused by wind move in wide circling directions in both the Northern and Southern hemispheres. Slower moving deep ocean currents circle from the upper reaches of the ocean to the ocean bottom. These are caused by differences in temperature of the ocean water.

Waves striking against the shorelines of continents change the appearance of the land. Tides are caused by the pull of the moon's and sun's gravity.

The ocean is a treasure of natural resources that humans are only beginning to tap. Meanwhile, pollution from human activities threatens ocean life and its resources. Through the use of special equipment, humans are studying the ocean and its resources.

**Exceptional Student
IEP Unit Goal**

At the end of this unit the student will verbally define: continental slope, currents, food chain, and pollution.

OCEAN FRONTIERS

UNIT OPENER

This is a photo of a Jim suit, built by Joseph Peuss in 1921, and the Star II submarine, its carrier. They are being used in a 30 m (100 ft) practice dive to gather red coral off the coast of Hawaii. The Star II submarine has carried the Jim suit to depths of up to 380 m (1,250 ft). The claws and legs of the Jim suit are operated by the diver inside the suit, providing great maneuverability and dexterity. Ask students these questions: What kind of conditions exist on the ocean floor that would make this kind of equipment necessary? *High pressure, cold temperature, etc.* What similarities can you see to the space suit worn by astronauts on the moon? *Answers may include need for oxygen supply, protection from extreme temperatures, etc.* Why is the ocean considered a frontier? *Because it is largely unexplored, just like the United States was before settlers moved west.* Tell students that in this unit they will be learning more about the structure of the ocean floor as well as the ocean waters.

UNIT 1

LEARNING CENTER

A suggested title for a Learning Center could be "Exploring the Earth's Oceans." Photos showing humans exploring the oceans and their discoveries can be displayed.

Copies of the blackline masters should be made available to the students. You may wish to create a file of Extensions that students can work on independently. The materials for these activities should be available in the learning center. The following Extensions are suitable for the Learning Center: making models of the ocean floor, p. T-13 (plaster, papier-mâché, or clay); graphing the content of ocean water, p. T-16 (graph paper); electrical conductivity of salt water, p. T-17 (salt, water, glasses, batteries, wire, flashlight bulb in socket); graphing tides, p. T-39 (graph paper, tide tables); desalination, p. T-47 (pie pan, glass dish, bowl, salt, water). Create another file of research topics, using these Extensions: exploring shipwrecks, p. T-12; major U.S. rivers, p. T-18; continental drift, p. T-24; tsunami waves, p. T-36; offshore drilling, p. T-45; whales, p. T-55.

CHAPTER 1

CHAPTER OBJECTIVES

1. Describe the structure of the ocean bottom.
2. Describe the sequence of events that causes the ocean to become salty.
3. Explain the process by which sediments are deposited on the ocean bottom.
4. Explain the causes for and the effects of the ocean floor spreading at the mid-ocean ridge.

SECTION BACKGROUND

Over 70 percent of the earth's surface is covered by ocean water. The shape of the ocean bottom is somewhat different from that of the land. The mountains are higher, the canyons are deeper, and the plains are flatter. The ocean bottom has three parts: the continental shelf, the continental slope, and the ocean floor. The continental shelf slants gently from the shoreline to a region that has a steep incline. The ocean floor begins at the bottom of the continental slope. The flat part of the ocean floor is the abyssal plain. Large mountain ranges on the ocean floor are called ocean ridges.

MATERIALS

clear plastic container or small aquarium, pebbles, gravel, water, ruler

**Exceptional Student
IEP Chapter Goal**

When directed by the teacher, the student will make an illustration of the ocean floor, including the following components: land, continental shelf, continental slope, abyssal plain, and mid-ocean ridge. The visually impaired student will label each part of a three-dimensional representation of the ocean floor.

THE OCEAN

1-1.

The Ocean Bottom

10

In 1622, the *Santa Margarita* sank off the coast of Florida during a storm. Today, divers have recovered gold and jewels from the shipwreck. In order to locate the ship, they studied the ocean bottom. When you finish this section you should be able to:

BASIC TEACHING PLAN

MOTIVATION

The source for this account is *National Geographic*, February 1982. Have the children discuss the challenges involved in journeys across the ocean during the time of this shipwreck. You may wish to mention pirates, the problems of having fresh food and water available for the crew, boredom, and so on.

You may be able to locate drawings of Spanish galleons to show the students what the *Santa Margarita* may have looked like. Point out to the students that these vessels typically had three masts and three or four decks. They should be able to tell from the rather squared-off shape of the vessel that they were clumsy and slow. Treasure hunters are particularly interested in the galleons because they were designed to haul cargo, and were quite vulnerable to storms and to the attacks of quicker pirate ships.

☐ **A.** Describe and compare the three main parts of the ocean bottom.

☐ **B.** Describe the structure of the ocean floor.

Many people think that the ocean bottom is completely flat. Some areas are flat like plains on land. However, the ocean bottom has high and low places. These are similar to the mountains and valleys found on land.

The ocean bottom is divided into three main parts. The first part is called the **continental** (kahn-tih-**nen**-tul) **shelf**. The *continental shelf* starts where the part of the land we live on ends. It is part of the continent, but it is covered with water. The continental shelf is the shallowest part of the ocean. Its average depth is about 60
2 meters (200 feet).

At the end of the continental shelf, the land plunges downward sharply. This part of the ocean bottom is called the **continental slope**. The ocean may be 3,050 m (10,100 ft) deep at the bottom of the *continental slope*.
3 Why do you think the word *slope* is used to describe what occurs?

The third part of the ocean bottom, called the **ocean floor**, begins where the continental slope ends. The *ocean floor* covers most of the ocean bottom. Where the ocean floor is flat it is called the **abyssal** (uh-**bis**-ul) **plain**.

At one time, scientists thought the whole ocean bottom was smooth and flat. Today we know there is a huge chain of mountains on the ocean bottom. This mountain chain is called the **mid-ocean ridge**. The *mid-ocean ridge* is about 65,000 kilometers (40,000 miles) long and runs through every ocean on the earth.

Look at the map on top of page 12. It shows what the Atlantic Ocean would look like with all the water removed. Find the *abyssal plain* and the mid-ocean
4 ridge. Can you find the crack in the center of the mid-ocean ridge? It is 13 to 48 km (8 to 30 mi) wide and more than 1.6 km (1 mi) deep in some places.

Continental shelf: **1**
Part of the ocean bottom near land.

Continental slope:
Part of the ocean bottom where the continental shelf plunges downward sharply.

Ocean floor:
Part of the ocean bottom that lies at the bottom of the continental slope.

Abyssal plain:
Flat part of the ocean floor.

Mid-ocean ridge:
Mountain chain on the ocean floor.

11

EXTENSIONS

Enrichment
Science Skills —
Reading Illustrations

Ask the students to interpret the graph in the interunit pages (Contour of the Atlantic Ocean Floor at 39° N). Using this graph and the map of the Atlantic Ocean on page T-7l, have the class:

A. Identify on the graph the continental shelf and slope on both shorelines.

B. Notice the variations in depth and the occurrence of the Azores along the mid-Atlantic ridge.

C. List the depths of the three deepest areas in the Atlantic Ocean.

This Extension serves as an excellent introduction to this chapter.

DEVELOPMENT

1 **Teaching Tips** — Write the vocabulary terms on the chalkboard in the order that they appear in the text. When students look at the map, they can then refer to the chalkboard for guidance as to what to locate.

2 **Teaching Tips** — If the students are unfamiliar with the metric system, this would be an excellent opportunity to familiarize them with its linear measurement units.

3 **Text Questions** — Why do you think the word *slope* is used to describe what occurs? *Slope is land that is on a slant or incline; it is not flat.* The continental slope is a steep slope.

4 **Text Questions** — Find the abyssal plain and the mid-ocean ridge. Can you find the crack in the center of the mid-ocean ridge? *Students should be able to locate both plain and ridge easily on the map.*

EXTENSIONS

Enrichment
Research — Library

Have students do research to locate an article describing the exploration of the remains of a shipwreck. Ask them to use the information they find in the article as the basis for the creation of a one-page excerpt from the diary of a captain or a passenger on board the ship during its last day afloat. Excellent articles that you may wish to refer students to are: "Treasure from the Ghost Galleon," *National Geographic*, February 1982, pp. 228-243; "Graveyard of the Quicksilver Galleons," *National Geographic*, December 1979, pp. 850-876; "Reach for the New World," *National Geographic*, December 1977, pp. 724-767.

Exceptional Student
Visually Impaired

Using string and oaktag, the teacher should make a three-dimensional map as shown, and let the student feel the chain of mountains on the ocean floor.

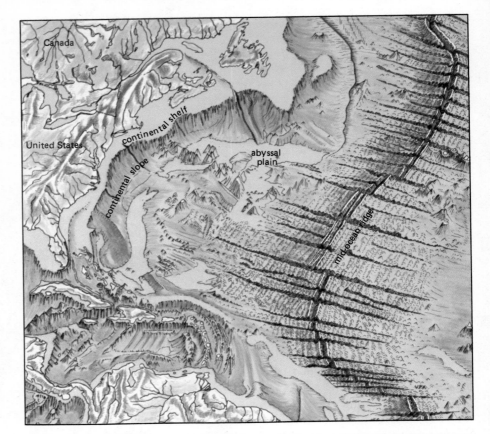

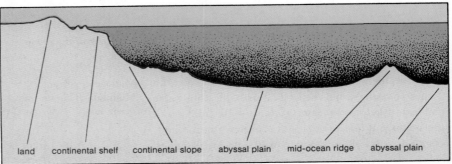

land   continental shelf   continental slope   abyssal plain   mid-ocean ridge   abyssal plain

12

5 **Skill Development** — The students will be learning to *read illustrations* as they study the relief map of the ocean bottom. Help them develop a sense of the ocean bottom as a place with many diverse features.

6 **Teaching Tips** — You can have students do dictionary work as they study the features on the map. Among other things, they can check the meaning of the word *plain* and the prefix *mid-* against their scientific usages on the map.

Look at the map at the bottom of page 12. It shows what the ocean bottom would look like if it were cut exactly in half from left to right. You are now looking at the ocean bottom from the side instead of overhead. This type of map allows you to clearly see where the high and low places on the ocean floor are.

ACTIVITY

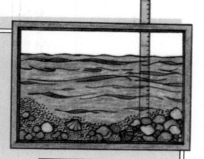

Measuring the "ocean bottom"

A. Obtain these materials: small aquarium, pebbles, gravel, water, ruler.

B. Your teacher will help you make a model of the ocean bottom. Use gravel and pebbles to show the three parts of the ocean bottom. Gently add the water to the aquarium.

C. Make a graph like the one shown.

D. Make measurements of the ocean bottom. Hold a ruler straight in the water at one end of the "ocean." Measure in cm how deep the "ocean" is.

E. On your graph, make an X above trial 1 opposite the number that shows the distance between the bottom and the water surface.

F. Repeat steps D and E nine times, taking measurements from one end of the aquarium to the other.

G. Draw a line connecting the X's on your graph.

1. Label your graph to show the ocean parts.
2. From your graph, how deep are the model ocean's floor and continental shelf?
3. Imagine that a ship sank on the edge of the continental shelf near the continental slope. From your graph, make a hypothesis about where the wreckage might be found.

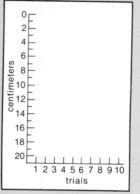

13

EXTENSIONS

Reinforcement
Activity

Scientists often construct models to represent things that they are studying. Models allow us to view things from vantage points that might be difficult to obtain during direct observations.

A. Have students construct a plaster, papier-mâché, or clay model of the ocean bottom. The map of the ocean bottom in the text may be used as a reference. The students should include the continental shelf, continental slope, abyssal plain, and mid-ocean ridge.

B. Students could explain their models to the class or other classes. If possible, they could construct their model to scale.

ACTIVITY

Skill Development — *Measuring and Recording Data*

Teaching Tips — The depth of the container should be about 25 cm (10 in.).

If you do this activity as a demonstration, build the model ocean bottom in a location of the room that will be easily visible and accessible to students. Have various students come forward to carry out each step of the activity. Students should prepare their charts for the recording of the measurements that will be made.

If space and materials are available, you may wish to construct a few model oceans with varying ocean bottoms. Students can then make graphs using data from each model.

Answers to Questions — **1.** Each student should prepare an appropriately labeled graph.   **2.** Answers will vary depending on the model used.   **3.** On the abyssal plain, near the bottom of the continental slope.

Exceptional Student
Visually Impaired

When doing this activity, allow the visually impaired student to put his/her hand in the aquarium and feel the shape of the bottom.

T–13

EXTENSIONS

Application
Research

You may wish to increase student awareness related to an oceanography career. Oceanographers study ocean movements, the properties of the water, and ocean plant and animal life.

A. Students can do library research to become familiar with the training and qualifications needed for this profession. They can find out about different types of oceanographers such as biological oceanographers, physical oceanographers, chemical oceanographers, and geological oceanographers.

B. Students may wish to employ their letter-writing skills to obtain information about oceanography. They can write to the following places to request information: Woods Hole Oceanographic Institute, Woods Hole, MA 02543; Bedford Institute, Halifax, Nova Scotia; and the Scripps Institution of Oceanography, La Jolla, CA 92037.

The structure of the ocean bottom is always changing. But it is hard to see these changes over a short period of time. Most changes take place over millions of years. Forces within the earth can push parts of the ocean bottom upward to form land. Some areas of land were once part of the ocean bottom. Ocean plant and animal remains have been found on land. This shows that this land was once part of the ocean bottom.

Section Review

Main Ideas: The continental shelf begins at the point where the land meets the ocean. At the end of the continental shelf, the ocean bottom plunges downward, forming the continental slope. At the bottom of the continental slope, the ocean floor begins. The abyssal plain and mid-ocean ridge form the ocean floor.

Questions: Answer in complete sentences.

1. Describe three parts of the ocean bottom.
2. Below is a cross section of the ocean bottom. It shows the area between the Hawaiian Islands and the California coast. Identify parts A–D.
3. On the diagram below, which letter is best described by each of the following definitions?
   (1) the part of the continent covered by water
   (2) a mountain chain on the ocean floor
   (3) the flat part of the ocean floor

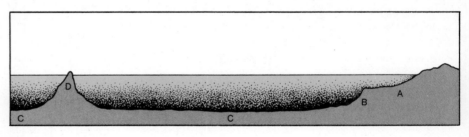

14

SECTION REVIEW

Answers to Questions
1. Continental shelf — part of the continent that is covered with water. Continental slope — the sloping part of the ocean bottom. Ocean floor — the part of the ocean bottom that begins where the continental slope ends.
2. a) continental shelf; b) continental slope; c) abyssal plain; d) mid-ocean ridge.
3. 1) a; 2) d; 3) c

Do you know how to do any magic tricks? This student is doing one that you may wish to try. The egg placed in one container sinks. The egg placed in the magic container floats. What do you think is so special about the water in the magic container?

Before the trick was performed, salt was dissolved in the water of the magic container. Adding salt made the water like ocean water. When you finish this section you should be able to:

☐ **A.** Explain what causes ocean water to be salty.
☐ **B.** Describe how materials are carried to the ocean bottom.
☐ **C.** Describe what causes submarine canyons.

Ocean water is very different from ordinary drinking water. One difference is that ocean water contains salt. You might wonder how much salt ocean water contains. One kilogram (about 35 ounces) of ocean water contains about 27 grams (less than an ounce) of table salt. The rest is water and other materials. The amount of salt varies slightly in different parts of the ocean. It is the amount of salt in water that determines how well objects float. The floating egg trick works because a lot of salt was dissolved in the water.

Besides salt, ocean water contains other materials. You may wonder how these materials got into ocean water. These materials actually came from the land and are called *minerals*. First rain falls onto the land. Some of this rainwater eventually flows into streams and rivers.

15

SECTION BACKGROUND

The oceans contain about 97 percent of all of the earth's water. Ocean water is a mixture of gases and solids dissolved in pure water. The salt in ocean water has accumulated over millions of years, due to the earth's water cycle. Rivers carry dissolved salts to the ocean.

Rivers also carry sand, mud, clay, and rocks. These materials are called sediments, and eventually settle on the ocean bottom. Sediments that settle near the shore can form beaches. Some sediments are carried farther out and settle on the continental shelf. Sometimes the sediments on the shelf slide. As they slide, grooves are cut in the continental shelf and slope. These grooves are called submarine canyons. Another type of sediment forms from the remains of plants and animals that settle to the ocean bottom.

MATERIALS

2 plastic bowls, salt, water

BASIC TEACHING PLAN

MOTIVATION

You may wish to acquire a material called Instant Ocean. This is available at pet stores that sell aquarium supplies. The product is the residue left when sea water is evaporated and is sold as an additive to water that is going to be used in marine (salt water) aquariums.

Using Instant Ocean, or ordinary table salt dissolved in water, you could do the egg trick as a demonstration to heighten motivation. Explain that adding salt changes the density of the water and that this change enables the egg to float.

DEVELOPMENT

1 **Teaching Tips** — If you have a set of metric masses available, you may wish to show the students the relationship between 27 g of sodium chloride and 1,000 g of ocean water.

EXTENSIONS

Enrichment
Science Skills — Recording Data

Sodium chloride accounts for about 75% of the total salt content of ocean water. The following table lists the 7 most abundant sea water salts:

Salt	Grams/Liter
Sodium chloride	27.213
Magnesium chloride	3.807
Magnesium sulfate	1.658
Calcium sulfate	1.260
Potassium sulfate	0.863
Calcium carbonate	0.123
Magnesium bromide	0.076
Total	35.000 grams

Therefore, in every 1,000 grams of ocean water, there are about 35 grams of salts.

A. Using this information, students could make circle or bar graphs to illustrate the above information.

B. Students could also do research to discover some of the commercial uses of the salts in sea water.

Exceptional Student
Visually Impaired

If time permits, the teacher should make a collage illustrating the water cycle.

T–16

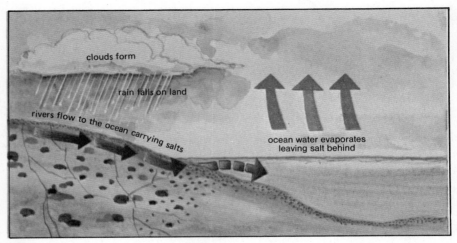

clouds form

rain falls on land

rivers flow to the ocean carrying salts

ocean water evaporates leaving salt behind

3

Sodium chloride: A salt.

Rivers flow from mountain lakes to the oceans. As the rivers flow over the land, they carry materials from the land. Some of these materials are salts. The salts are dissolved in the water. One kind of salt that rivers carry is **sodium chloride** (so-dee-um **klor**-ide). The salt you use on food is *sodium chloride*. When a river empties into an ocean, the salt mixes with the ocean water. The picture shows salt from a river mixing with ocean water.

Ocean water is heated by the sun. As ocean water is heated, it evaporates. This means that the water changes **2** from a liquid to a gas. What happens to the salt in this evaporating water?

Study the above picture. Notice the order of events. Start by looking at the clouds. First rain falls on the land. Water then flows toward the ocean. Along the way it picks up salts that are found in the earth. Water containing salts eventually reaches the ocean. Arrows in the diagram show water evaporating from the ocean. Salts are left behind in the ocean. Evaporated water from the ocean can form clouds, which may pass over land. Rain falling from the clouds begins the sequence again.

16

2 **Text Questions** — What happens to the salt in this evaporating water? *Use this as a motivational question. The text that follows explains that it is left behind.*

3 **Skill Development** — The text and illustration provide an excellent opportunity to reinforce the skill of placing events in proper *sequence.*

Each time this sequence of events takes place, salts from the land are brought to the ocean. This process has been taking place for millions of years. This explains why the ocean is salty. Ocean water at the equator is less salty than some other parts of the ocean. This is because there **4** is more rainfall over the equator. Ocean water at the poles is even less salty than at the equator. This is because the melting ice at the poles is mostly fresh water. As the ice melts, fresh water mixes with the salty ocean water, making it less salty.

Salts are not the only materials carried to the oceans by rivers. Rivers also carry sand, mud, clay, and rocks. These materials are called **sediments** (sed-uh-ments). *Sediments* settle to the bottom in still water. Most sediments settle close to the shore and form beaches. Other

Sediments: Sand, clay, and other materials that settle in water.

ACTIVITY

What happens when salt water evaporates?

A. Obtain these materials: 2 small, clean plastic bowls labeled A and B, 2 containers, water, salt.

B. In one container, dissolve 30 g of salt in 200 ml of water.

C. In bowl A, pour the salt water to a depth of 4 or 5 cm. This is the experiment.

D. Pour the same amount of plain, unsalted water into bowl B. This is the control.

   1. Why is a control necessary?

E. Place both bowls in the same warm place.

   2. Predict what both bowls will look like in two days.

F. Observe the bowls for the next two days.

   3. How do your results compare with your predictions?

17

4 **Skill Development** — *Sequencing* of the events leading to the desalination of ocean water.

ACTIVITY

Skill Development — *Comparing and Contrasting*

Teaching Tips — You may wish to create one sample of saltwater that has a very high concentration of salt. Do this by adding salt to a glass of water to a point where no more salt will dissolve. Students may wish to use a drop from this sample as well as the one used in the activity.

Answers to Questions — **1.** A control is used so that a comparison can be made between ordinary tap water and salt water. **2.** Prediction should be that there will be solids left behind in the bowl containing saltwater as the water evaporates. **3.** Results should correspond to predictions.

EXTENSIONS

Enrichment
Activity

The following activity will test the electrical conductivity of salt water.

A. Obtain a 1.5-volt dry cell, three pieces of copper-insulated wire, and a flashlight bulb in a socket.

B. Strip about 2.5 cm (1 in.) of insulation off the wire ends.

C. If the dry cell being used has terminals, attach a wire to each battery terminal. Attach the end of one wire to the screw on the socket. Attach the third wire to the other screw. Two wire ends should be free.

If the students are using ordinary flashlight batteries they can tape one wire to the top and one to the bottom of the battery.

D. Place tap water in one glass and salted water in a second glass. Dip the ends of the two free wires into the fresh water.

E. The students will observe that the bulb lights when the wires are dipped in the salted water. They can then experiment with different concentrations of salt, as the brightness of the bulb varies by changing the concentration of salt in the water.

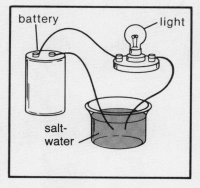

Exceptional Student
Visually Impaired

Assign a partner to the student if he/she cannot observe and record unassisted.

T–17

Students could work in small groups to do research about major rivers in the United States.

A. As a starting point, they could use the map in the inter-unit pages to find out into which ocean each river empties.

B. Further research could include topics such as the continental divide, the age of the river, the rate of flow, delta formation, problems with erosion, and flooding conditions that exist.

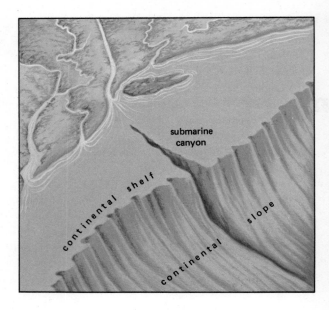

**Submarine canyon:
A groove cut in the
continental shelf and
slope.**

sediments are carried farther out. They settle on the continental shelf. Sometimes the sediments on the shelf move or slide. They slide down the continental slope.

5 This movement makes deep cuts in the shelf and slope. These cuts are called **submarine canyons** (sub-muh-reen **kan**-yunz). Look at the diagram. Can you find the *submarine canyon*? Some of this sediment stays at the bottom of the slope. Some of the sediment moves farther out and settles on the abyssal plain.

6 Another type of sediment on the ocean bottom comes from plants and animals. When animals and plants die, their remains settle to the ocean bottom. They become part of the layers of sediment on the ocean bottom.

Some sediments are brought to the ocean floor by wind. Rock particles that are blown out to sea settle on the ocean surface and eventually sink to the bottom of the ocean.

18

5 **Skill Development** — Following the reading of the text and discussion of the drawing, you will be able to help the students relate the *effect* they observe (the submarine canyon) to a *cause* (the sliding of sediments down the slope).

6 **Teaching Tips** — You may wish to mention that the fossil remains of sea animals and plants are sometimes found in mountainous areas on earth. Solicit their ideas for a possible cause. Two explanations are that the mountains were once under water and then pushed upward, or that they were once under water and the ocean bottom around them sank.

SECTION REVIEW

Main Ideas — You may wish to encourage students to make a sketch of the sedimentation process as a review of this section.

Sediments are deposited very slowly on the ocean bottom. In fact, sediments carried to the ocean cause an increase of only 10 to 20 centimeters (4 to 8 inches) every thousand years! Plant and animal remains and other sediments account for another 2 to 3 cm (about 1 in.) every thousand years. In spite of this slow buildup of sediments, some parts of the ocean have thick layers of sediment. Sediments slide down the continental slope during underwater landslides. Millions of tons of sediments can be dumped over large areas of the abyssal plain. In this way, thick layers of sediments build up on the ocean floor.

Section Review

Main Ideas: Salts and sediments are carried from land to the ocean by streams and rivers. This is why ocean water is salty. This sequence of events has taken place for millions of years. Sediments carried to the ocean can slide over the continental shelf. This causes submarine canyons to form on the ocean floor.

Questions: Answer in complete sentences.

1. What causes submarine canyons to form?
2. Explain the sequence of events that causes the ocean to become salty.
3. Explain why some parts of the ocean are saltier than others.
4. How do each of the following get to the ocean floor?
    a. mud and clay from rivers
    b. animal remains
    c. plant remains
    d. rock particles
5. Is the buildup of sediment on the ocean floor a fast or slow process? Explain.

19

Answers to Questions
1. Sliding of sediments down the continental slope may cause them.
2. Rainwater dissolves salts on land. This water enters rivers. The rivers carry dissolved salts into oceans. Ocean water evaporates, leaving salts. Water in the air may form clouds that pass over land. Rain from these clouds reaches land. The cycle begins again.
3. Saltier parts of the ocean have less rainfall (away from the equator) and less dilution of the salt water due to the melting of ice (away from the poles).
4. a. Most of the clay and mud carried to oceans by rivers settles near shore. But some of it is carried farther out, settling eventually at the bottom.   b. & c. When plants and animals die in the ocean, their remains settle at the bottom.   d. Rock particles that are blown out to sea settle on the surface and eventually sink.
5. A slow process; sediments carried to the ocean increase by only 10–20 cm (4–8 in) every 1,000 years. Plant and animal remains and other sediment account for another 2–3 cm (about 1 in) every 1,000 years.

SUGGESTED WORKSHEET MASTERS
p. T-7m

Scientists believe that the mid-ocean ridges were formed at areas where the earth's crust split apart. This concept is in agreement with the theory of continental drift, which holds that the continents were once joined together as a supercontinent, that this supercontinent broke up, and that the continents slowly drifted apart.

The phenomenon of drifting continents is still taking place. Molten rock from the mantle is being pushed up continuously through cracks in the ridges. This molten rock forms new ocean floor on both sides of the crack. The new floor pushes against sections of the old floor, causing the old floor to move in opposite directions, away from the crack.

This pushing outward of the ocean floor has resulted in older ocean floor rocks being pushed into the earth, under the continents that border the ocean. Deep ocean trenches have formed at such locations.

MATERIALS

1-3.

Changes in the Ocean Floor

These students are using a special globe to figure out the answer to a riddle. The riddle is: "Mt. Everest is about 8,851 m (29,040 ft) high. It is the tallest mountain on land, but not the tallest mountain in the world. What is the tallest mountain in the world?"

The globe they are using is different from most globes. It has a surface that shows the bumps, ridges, and smooth spots on the ocean's bottom. Looking at the earth's surface under the ocean may provide them with the answer. When you finish this section, you should be able to:

☐ **A.** Explain the major cause of changes in the ocean floor.

☐ **B.** Describe three effects of the spreading out of the ocean floor.

☐ **C.** Explain what causes ocean valleys to form.

1 The students noticed that parts of the mid-ocean ridge extended above sea level. One part of a ridge in the Pacific Ocean was higher than any other. Using the library, they were able to discover the name of the tallest mountain in the world. It is Mauna Kea, the highest peak in the state of Hawaii. Measured from its underwater base, the mountain is 10,200 m (33,500 ft) high. How do such tall mountains form from the ocean floor? The answer can be explained by the changes that take place on the ocean floor.

20

BASIC TEACHING PLAN

MOTIVATION

You may wish to motivate this section by first finding the approximate elevation above sea level for your community. Make a rough scale diagram on the chalkboard showing both sea level and the elevation of your community. After the students have read the motivation paragraph, indicate the elevation of Mt. Everest on your diagram. Reserve space on your scale drawing for the name of the mountain that is used as the answer to the posed riddle.

Exceptional Student
Visually Impaired
A topographic globe could be borrowed for use by the visually impaired.

Scientists think it is very hot inside the earth. It is believed to be so hot there that rock within the earth can melt, or become **molten** (**mol**-ten). This hot, *molten* rock in the earth can move up toward the earth's surface under the giant crack in the mid-ocean ridge. When the molten rock breaks through the surface, it forms new ocean floor on both sides of the crack. The new ocean floor pushes against sections of the old floor. Many scientists think that the old floor on both sides of the crack moves. Therefore, scientists say the ocean floor is spreading away from the crack.

Molten: Melted by heat.

2

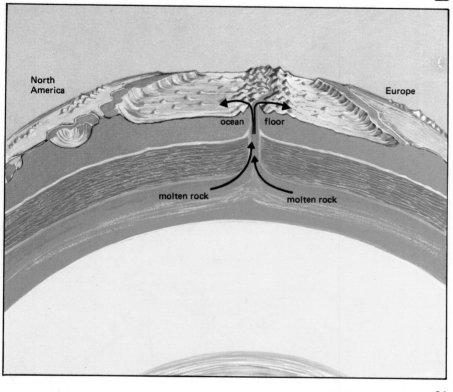

North America

Europe

ocean   floor

molten rock   molten rock

21

Reinforcement
Science Skills — Following Directions

To illustrate what happens to the old rock as new rock is being forced to the surface at the mid-ocean ridge, students could do this activity.

A. Have students work in groups of two. Provide each group with two sheets of paper and tape.

B. Tape the two sheets of paper together. If desired, cutouts of the continents could be taped on.

C. Fold the paper along the taped edges. Hang the folded paper between two tables.

D. Place a hand on each piece of paper. Spread your hands apart very slowly.

E. Compare the action at the taped edges to the activity at the mid-ocean ridge.

DEVELOPMENT

1 **Teaching Tips** — Ask the students if they think the area along the mid-ocean ridge would be a very safe place for people to explore. Since there is so much volcanic and earthquake activity due to the molten rock moving upward, underwater explorers along the ridge have to be extremely careful. Scientists are interested in the ridge areas for a number of reasons. One that may be interesting to your students has been the discovery of places along the ridge where hot water is pouring out. These warm-water sea floor springs are called hydrothermal vents. Animal life that appears nowhere else on the planet has been discovered at these vents.

2 **Skill Development** — To reinforce the students' ability to *interpret an illustration*, ask them to trace the steps described in the paragraph by placing a finger on the molten rock shown in the drawing and then moving their finger as they follow the path described.

Exceptional Student
Visually Impaired

Using collage materials, the teacher or interested students can make three-dimensional maps that the visually impaired student can feel.

Enrichment
Science Skills — Recording Data

Have students develop a bar graph to represent the depths of the following major ocean trenches. Some students may be interested in doing library work that will enable them to make scale drawings that contrast the depth of these underwater trenches with major land features such as Mt. Everest and the Grand Canyon.

Trench	Depth (meters)
Pacific Ocean	
Aleutian	8,100
Kurile	10,542
Japan	8,412
Mariana	11,033
Philippine	10,500
Tonga	10,882
Kermadec	10,003
Peru-Chile	8,055
Atlantic Ocean	
Puerto Rico	8,648
South Sandwich	8,400
Indian Ocean	
Java	7,725

Scientists believe that the idea of sea-floor spreading explains changes in the earth's surface. They believe that the Atlantic Ocean is getting wider by 3 cm (about 1 in.) each year. Thus, the continents of Europe and North America are moving apart.

As the Atlantic Ocean floor spreads and the land moves apart, what do you think is happening to the Pacific Ocean? The Pacific Ocean is getting narrower. As the Pacific narrows, its ocean floor moves downward under the land that borders the ocean. Deep ocean valleys called **trenches** are formed. *Trenches* are some of the deepest places in the oceans. The drawing below shows how trenches are formed.

Look at the world map on page 23. The red lines show where most ocean trenches are located. In which ocean **4** do you see most of the ocean trenches?

Trenches: Deep ocean valleys.

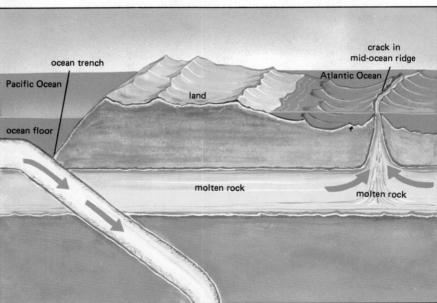

22

3 **Skill Development** — Using the *illustration*, note that the pushing upward of molten rock at the mid-ocean ridge in the Atlantic *results* in ocean floor being pushed under the land that borders the Pacific. An additional *effect* is the formation of ocean trenches at the location where the ocean floor is pushed downward.

4 **Text Question** — In which ocean do you see most of the ocean trenches? *The Pacific.*

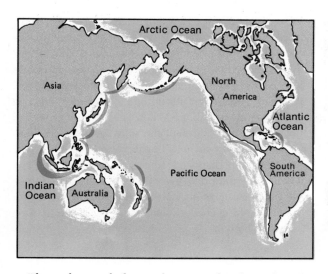

The molten rock that pushes up under the mid-ocean ridge causes the ocean floor to spread. However, it also forms mountains as it cools and hardens. Sometimes these mountains are so high they stick out of the water. We call them islands. The Azores (**ay**-zorz) are a group of islands in the North Atlantic Ocean. The Azores are really the tops of mountains that are part of the mid-ocean ridge.

EXTENSIONS

Application
Activity

Convection currents occur whenever something is heated unevenly. As hot spots form beneath the mid-ocean ridges, convection currents are set up to transport new rock to the surface. The following is a good demonstration of these currents.

A. Obtain these materials: a small amount of paint; turpentine; a small glass bottle with a lid, or a test tube with a cork.

B. Fill bottle or test tube with turpentine. Add a few drops of the paint. Seal the bottle or test tube. Shake the mixture.

C. Wrap your hand around the bottom of the container and observe what happens to the mixture after 30 seconds of your heat application.

D. Ask the class to describe the direction and rate of movement of the mixture. Compare the demonstration to the movement of rock within the earth at the mid-ocean ridge.

5 **Teaching Tips** — If you have a world map or globe available in your room, you may wish to have students come to the front of the room and make guesses as to the location of the Azores. You can make a game out of this by telling successive volunteers whether they were "hotter" (closer) or "colder" (farther away) than previous students. Other hints that you may wish to give are: they are 1,300 km (800 mi) off the west coast of Portugal, 30 degrees west longitude, 38 degrees north latitude. After the Azores have been located, use the map or globe to indicate that the mid-ocean ridge goes from Iceland to Antarctica with the Azores being some of the peaks of the ridge.

Did you know that Hawaii is also part of a ridge in the ocean? Like the Azores, Hawaii consists of many islands that are the tops of underwater mountains.

This photograph shows the Kilauea volcano in Hawaii erupting in 1959. Molten rock is pouring down its slope. Scientists believe that this liquid rock comes from a vast underground chamber. When the liquid is forced upward, it bursts through the tops and sides of volcanoes. This action changes the surface of the earth. The very same thing happens at many places along the parts of the mid-ocean ridge. Scientists study the changes that occur on volcanoes on land. In this way, they can get some idea of the changes that may occur at locations on the ocean bottom.

Section Review

Main Ideas: Changes in the ocean floor are caused by molten rock. This liquid rock pushes upward through the mid-ocean ridge, cools, and forms a new part of the ocean floor. Mountains are gradually built up along the ridge. The ocean floor spreads apart and deep ocean trenches form as the ocean floor moves.

Questions: Answer in complete sentences.

1. What causes the major changes in the ocean floor?
2. What are three effects of changes in the ocean floor?
3. Where are deep ocean valleys located? What causes them?
4. Look at the world map at the top of page 23. What is meant by the red lines along the west coast of South America?
5. Study the photograph of one of the Azores Islands on page 23. What evidence is there that the mid-ocean ridge is a place that undergoes change?

24

6 **Text Questions** — Did you know that Hawaii is also part of a ridge in the ocean? *Hawaii is part of the East Pacific Ridge.*

SECTION REVIEW

Answers to Questions
1. The upward movement of molten rock at the mid-ocean ridges.
2. Any 3 of these responses would be acceptable: Europe and North America are moving apart. Deep ocean valleys are being formed near the land that borders the oceans. The Pacific Ocean is getting narrower. Old ocean floor is being pushed under the edges of the continents.
3. The borders of the continents; most of them are in the Pacific Ocean. They are caused by the spreading of the sea floor.
4. The red lines on the drawing are deep ocean valleys.
5. You can see the remains of old volcanoes. Molten rock from the volcanoes has spread out and cooled to form the sloping land.

CHAPTER REVIEW

Science Words

Select the definition from column B that goes best with each word in column A.

Column A	Column B
1. continental shelf	a. sand, clay, and other materials that settle in water
2. trenches	b. a salt
3. sediments	c. deep ocean valleys
4. continental slope	d. flat part of the ocean floor
5. mid-ocean ridge	e. part of the ocean bottom near land
6. sodium chloride	f. groove cut in continental shelf and slope
7. ocean floor	g. mountain chain on the ocean bottom
8. submarine canyon	h. sloping part of the ocean bottom
9. abyssal plain	i. part of the ocean bottom that begins where the continental slope ends

Questions: Answer in complete sentences.

1. How do sediments from the land reach the ocean floor?
2. Scientists predict that the mid-ocean ridges will be the location of many earth movements and volcanoes in the future. What have you learned that would support that prediction?
3. Where is the most likely place on the ocean bottom to find a mountain? Where would you find a submarine canyon?
4. Explain how the movement of water from land to ocean causes ocean water to become salty.
5. How do scientists know that the ocean bottom is changing?
6. How are the mountains and plains of the United States like the ocean floor?

25

EXTENSIONS

Reinforcement
*Science Skills —
Building Science Vocabulary*

In preparation for reviewing the chapter materials with the class, ask one group to serve as assistants. Give this group construction paper and felt-tip markers so that they will be able to prepare some vocabulary review materials for use with the entire class.

A. The group members should place each vocabulary term on a separate sheet of paper.

B. Also on separate sheets of paper, they should make a drawing or diagram that conveys the meaning of each vocabulary term.

C. When you are reviewing the chapter, have this group come forward to display their sheets in random order across the front of the room. Now have a volunteer from the group lead the class in trying to match vocabulary terms with diagrams.

CHAPTER REVIEW

Science Words
1. e, **2.** c, **3.** a, **4.** h, **5.** g, **6.** b, **7.** i, **8.** f, **9.** d

Answers to Questions
1. Rain that falls on the land picks up sediments. Water containing sediments enters rivers and streams. Water from the rivers and streams reaches the oceans. The sediments settle on the ocean bottom.
2. Mid-ocean ridges are places where molten rock is pushed upward. The push causes earth movements. Sometimes volcanoes are made.
3. a. mid-ocean ridge; **b.** continental slope.
4. Minute amounts of dissolved salt are carried to oceans by rivers. As water evaporates, it leaves ocean salt. The water falls as rain to begin the cycle again.
5. Evidence includes: activity at the mid-ocean ridge, the formation of new islands, earthquakes, volcanoes.
6. They resemble the structure of the ocean floor and have similar areas of high earthquake and volcanic activity.

SUGGESTED WORKSHEET MASTER
p. T-7o

SUGGESTED TEST MASTERS
p. T-7d, e

CHAPTER 2

CHAPTER OBJECTIVES

1. Explain the causes for surface and deep ocean currents.
2. Explain the cause of waves and their effects on the shoreline.
3. Describe the structure of waves.
4. Relate the pull of the moon to the occurrence of high and low tides.
5. Describe the causes and effects of spring and neap tides.

SECTION BACKGROUND

Water moves within the ocean in streams referred to as currents. Surface currents are caused by the winds. In the Northern Hemisphere, large circular currents move in a clockwise direction while in the Southern Hemisphere they move in a counterclockwise di-

Deep currents are caused by the uneven heating of ocean water by the sun. Cold water at the poles sinks and moves toward the equator. Water warmed at the equator moves toward the poles. Thus, deep sea currents circle below the ocean's surface.

This uneven heating of the ocean also forms deep-water currents as a result of its effect on the salinity of water. In areas where there is a high rate of evaporation the salt concentration increases. More salty water sinks and comes into contact with less salty water, which is less dense and rises. The result is a circling underwater current.

MATERIALS

**Exceptional Student
IEP Chapter Goal**

The student will state the cause of each of the following: currents, waves, and tides.

OCEAN MOVEMENTS

2-1.
Currents

26

How does throwing bottles into the ocean help scientists learn about the ocean? A few years ago, students dropped 2,000 bottles into the ocean west of San Diego, California. Each bottle contained a brightly colored postcard. It asked the finder to let scientists know when and

BASIC TEACHING PLAN
MOTIVATION

Text Questions — How does throwing bottles into the ocean help scientists learn about the ocean? *The path of the bottles would show the various directions of currents within the ocean.*

You may be able to build interest in this lesson by displaying and reading from books by Thor Heyerdahl, a modern-day explorer who has investigated the ways in which early peoples were able to traverse the oceans. The books describe the experiences of Heyerdahl and his crew as they build rafts or boats out of primitive materials and seek out ocean winds and currents to carry them long distances. Widely available books are: *Kon-Tiki*. Chicago: Rand McNally, 1966; *The Ra Expeditions*. Garden City, N. Y.: Doubleday, 1971; and *The Tigris Expedition*. Garden City: Doubleday, 1981.

You can stimulate discussion by asking students if any of them have visited the ocean and observed objects deposited by the waves.

where the bottle came ashore. In this way, scientists could learn more about ocean currents. When you finish this section, you should be able to:

☐ **A.** Explain how wind causes currents.
☐ **B.** Describe the location and direction of major currents.
☐ **C.** Explain what causes deep ocean currents.

Five days after the bottles were dumped into the ocean, the first bottle was found. A boy found a bottle while fishing in Bahia de Todos Santos, a bay in Mexico. Other bottles have since been found in the United States, Mexico, and the Philippines. This shows that the ocean can carry objects over great distances. Objects may be carried by ocean **currents**. A *current* is water that moves in a certain direction.

Right now, as you are reading your book, the earth is spinning. You don't feel the spinning because the movement is slow. However, the spinning causes the air around the earth to move. Moving air creates wind. The wind moves over the ocean surface and pushes against the water. The water moves with the wind.

Current: Water that moves in a certain direction.

1

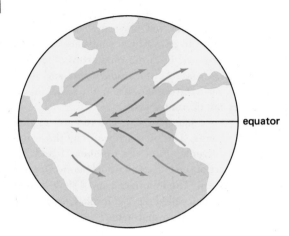

equator

27

EXTENSIONS

Enrichment
Research — Library

Ask the students to find out the names of the major surface currents and where they are located. The major currents are: the Gulf Stream, North Atlantic Drift, Labrador Current, North Equatorial Current, California Current, Alaska Drift, Kuroshio Current, and North Pacific Current. Using the map on page T-7p, students should indicate the locations of these currents.

DEVELOPMENT

1 **Skill Development** — The text material and illustrations on this page and the following pages emphasize the *causes* of surface and deep currents.

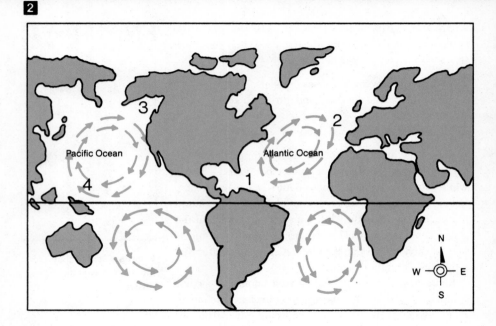

EXTENSIONS

Enrichment
Research — Library

The students can find out about the early history of ocean exploration. The Phoenicians were thought to be the first to sail the oceans. The students can also find out about the Vikings, Chinese, Greeks, Romans, and Polynesians. Possible guiding questions for the students' research can be:

1. What type of vessels were used by each group?
2. Where did these groups sail?
3. What discoveries about the ocean were made by these groups?

Trade winds: Winds that blow from east to west toward the equator.

Westerlies: Winds that blow from west to east away from the equator.

As they blow toward the equator, the winds move from east to the west. These winds are called **trade winds**. Look at the diagram at the bottom of page 27. Find the equator. Find the red arrows that show the blowing *trade winds*. Winds that blow away from the equator move from west to east. These winds are called **westerlies** (**west**-ter-leez). Find the blue arrows that show the blowing *westerlies*. As the trade winds and westerlies blow, they push the ocean water in the same direction. A giant, circling current results.

Look at the diagram above. The red arrows show the circling currents. The blue arrows show the winds that cause the currents. Find the numbers *1* and *2*. They show the part of the current in the Atlantic Ocean called the Gulf Stream. The numbers *3* and *4* show a current in the Pacific Ocean called the California Current. Why do you think it was given that name?

28

---

2   **Skill Development** — Have the students study the *illustration* carefully. Be sure that they understand that the circling current in the Atlantic Ocean is the Gulf Stream and that the current in the Pacific is the California Current. An important point for them to understand is that the blue arrows represent the winds, and that it is these winds that produce the currents.

3   **Teaching Tips** — Using a globe or copies of the map in the interunit pages, review the location and direction of the various winds and currents discussed so far.

4   **Text Questions** — Why do you think it was given that name? *The current moves along the coast of California.*

The currents you just read about are on the ocean surface. Other currents are below the surface. They are caused by the sun. The heat from the sun warms the ocean water. The sun does not evenly heat all the ocean **5** water. At the equator, ocean water is warm. Where do **6** you think ocean water is cold?

Cold water moves to the bottom of the ocean. You can think of it as slowly sinking to the bottom. The cold water at the North and South Poles sinks to the ocean bottom. The cold water slowly moves toward the equator. Warm water near the equator moves toward the poles to replace the sinking cold water. The movement of the cold and warm waters causes deep currents. The currents circle between the poles and the equator.

7 You know the amount of salt in ocean water is not the same all over. How does the sun's heat cause the water in some places to be saltier? The more salt in the water, the heavier the water is. Heavy water sinks to the ocean bottom. When it meets less salty water, the less salty water moves over it. A circling current forms. For example, the water of the Mediterranean Sea is saltier than the Atlantic Ocean. Where these two bodies of water meet there is a deep current. The saltier, heavy water moves along the ocean bottom. The less salty water moves over the heavier water into the Mediterranean Sea.

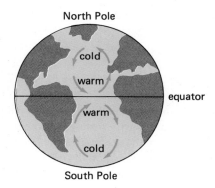

29

5 **Text Questions** — Where do you think ocean water is cold? *At or near the poles.*

6 **Skill Development** — The information contained in this paragraph helps students develop an understanding of the *sequence* of events leading to a circling underwater current. Be sure that the students relate each sentence to the illustration.

7 **Text Questions** — How does the sun's heat cause the water in some places to be saltier? *Heat from the sun causes the evaporation of water. As more water evaporates, salt is left behind. The water that remains is saltier.*

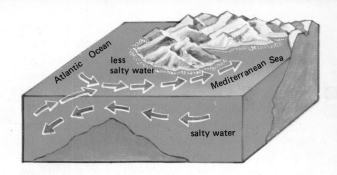

EXTENSIONS

Application

Science Skills — Comparing and Contrasting

Some students may have noticed that the term *current* used in the discussion of ocean water movement is also used when people are talking about the movement of air.

A. Have students do a little research into the meaning of the term *convection* (the movement of gases or liquids due to differing temperatures).

B. Ask the students to make classroom observations of temperature differences from floor to ceiling to see if colder, denser air is at the floor or at the ceiling. The ceiling measurement can be made with a thermometer taped to a broom handle.

C. The students will find that the ceiling air (unless it is near a heating or cooling vent) will be warmer. Have them compare this to what is discussed in this section regarding the movement of cold and warm water when they are in contact with one another.

Currents at the ocean's surface and deep ocean currents are different in another way. Usually the deep ocean currents move more slowly than currents at the surface. It takes about 30 years before they circle up to the equator. It takes the same amount of water in the Gulf Stream only a few years to complete a circle of the ocean.

Section Review

Main Ideas: Currents are caused by the movement of wind at the ocean's surface. Deep ocean currents can be caused by the uneven heating of ocean water by the sun. The different amounts of salt in different parts of the ocean also cause deep ocean currents.

Questions: Answer in complete sentences.

1. Explain what causes a current at the ocean's surface.
2. Describe the location and the direction of movement of: **a.** the Gulf Stream **b.** the California Current.
3. The oceans of the earth are unevenly heated by the sun. Explain how this causes deep ocean currents.
4. Some parts of the ocean are saltier than other parts of the ocean. Explain how this can cause deep ocean currents.

30

SECTION REVIEW

Answers to Questions

1. Winds cause surface currents by pushing against the surface of the water. The wind causes the water to move in the same direction.
2. **a.** The Gulf Stream is in the Atlantic Ocean. It moves in a clockwise direction. **b.** The California Current is in the Pacific Ocean. It moves in a clockwise direction.
3. Cold water at the poles sinks and moves toward the equator. Warm water at the equator moves toward the poles. A deep ocean current is caused by these differences in temperature.
4. Saltier water is heavy and sinks. Less salty water moves over it. When salty water meets less salty water, a current is formed.

As a wave moves toward land, it undergoes many changes. The wave rises up and water breaks and tumbles into the shore. Surfers make use of the force of this moving water and ride the waves as they move toward the shore. In this section, you will learn about waves and their effects. When you finish this section, you should be able to:

☐ **A.** Explain how wind causes waves.
☐ **B.** Identify the parts of a wave.
☐ **C.** Explain how waves can affect shorelines.

Surfers can tell something about the speed and direction of a wave as it moves toward the shore. They try to choose waves that will give them a long, smooth ride. What is it that makes the water move and form waves?

31

SECTION BACKGROUND

Waves in the ocean are produced by winds, by earth movements such as earthquakes, and by the gravitational pull of the moon and sun. A wave is a disturbance that travels through a medium. Ocean water moves up and down as a wave moves through the water. A concrete example of this is the manner by which a floating cork moves as a wave moves through the water in which it is floating. The cork moves up and down as the wave moves ahead.

Waves are described as having two parts: the crest (highest point) and the trough (lowest point). The distance between two successive crests is termed a wavelength.

When a wave reaches shallow water, its crest may lean over and tumble forward, forming a white foam called a breaker. Shorelines are changed as a result of the action of breakers, as rocks are abraded and sand is redeposited.

MATERIALS

2 blocks of wood, long tray (30 cm × 40 cm), milk container, sand, pebbles, water

BASIC TEACHING PLAN

MOTIVATION

Demonstrate wave motion by having a student come forward to blow across the surface of a pan of water. Ask volunteers to make observations. They will see waves being formed.

Text Questions — What is it that makes the water move and form waves? *Causes include the wind, movements within the earth, and the pull of the moon.*

Exceptional Student
Visually Impaired
Learning Disabled
Using a basin and water, have the students feel the waves with their hands. This would be a concrete experience for the students that would enable them to learn about waves.

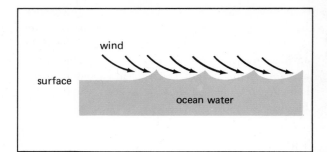

EXTENSIONS

Enrichment
Science Skills — Following Directions

The following instructions will enable students to prepare a visual model that represents the movement of a wave.

A. Give each student 10 index cards or slips of paper.

B. Tell the students to make small, vertical lines, 1.2 cm (1/2 in.) apart, along the bottom of each card. The lines will be used as a reference for drawing on each card.

C. On the first card, the students should draw a beach at one side of the card, water across the card, and a wave on the water's surface at the other side of the card.

D. Each successive card is drawn the same way except the wave is closer to the beach each time.

E. Once the wave is drawn breaking on the beach, the drawings that follow should show the wave moving away and carrying sand from the beach.

F. When the drawings are complete and in proper sequence, they can be stacked and stapled together.

G. Have the students quickly flip the pages and look at the drawings. The wave will look as though it is in continuous motion.

Exceptional Student
Visually Impaired
Learning Disabled

Using a basin and water, have the students blow on the water to create waves. Have them place their hands in the basin to feel the waves.

T–32

---

1   Waves form because of forces that act on the ocean water. You can experiment with the forces that cause waves by using a basin of water. You can use your hand to push the water and make waves. By dropping an object into the water, small waves can also be made. You can gently push the basin of water back and forth to create waves. Without forces acting on the water, the surface of the water would be almost as smooth as a mirror.

Like the basin of water, the ocean also has forces acting on it. Ships that travel across it push against water and make waves. The forces of earthquakes under the ocean also create waves.

In the last section, you learned how wind causes currents. Wind also causes waves. As wind moves over the water, it pushes against the surface. This movement causes part of the water to rise. The wind then pushes on the raised water and a wave is created. As the wind continues to blow, more waves are made.

Crest: The highest point of a wave.

Trough: The lowest point of a wave.

2   What does a wave look like? A wave has two parts. The highest point of the wave is called the **crest**. The lowest
3 point is called the **trough** (**trof**). The height of a wave is the distance from its *crest* to its *trough*. The length of a wave is the distance from its crest to the crest of the next wave. Waves move in the same direction as the wind. The size of a wave depends on the strength of the wind.

32

DEVELOPMENT

1   **Skill Development** — As you begin discussion of this material, ask the students whether a wave is a *cause* or an *effect* relative to wind. You may wish to point out that waves, which are effects in this context, may themselves be causes for other effects such as the changing of a shoreline.

2   **Text Questions** — What does a wave look like? *Answers could be: As mild as a ripple in lake water or as forceful as storm waves.*

3   **Teaching Tips** — To show wave structure, gather a long rope (5 m, or 17 ft) and a piece of string (64 cm, or 25 in.). Have a volunteer come forward to hold one end of the rope. Hold the other end and stand apart from the student so that the rope does not sag. Gently raise and lower your end of the rope to produce waves. Point out to the students that it is the wave that moves across their field of view and not the rope. The rope moves up and down as the wave moves across. Demonstrate this by tying a short piece of string around the middle of the rope. Have the students observe the movement of the string as the wave moves by. They will see that the string moves up and down.

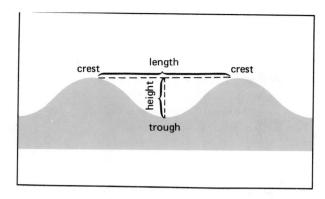

As a wave moves into shallow water near the shore, its trough rubs against the ocean bottom. The rubbing causes the trough to slow down. However, the crest still moves quickly. It gets higher and leans forward. The crest may lean so far forward that it tumbles over, form- **4** ing a white foam. The wave is then called a **breaker**. After a wave breaks against the beach, the wave moves back into the ocean. It moves under the waves coming in. As the wave moves back into the ocean, it carries sand from the beach. The force of waves striking the shore over a long period of time can reshape a beach area.

Breaker: A wave in which the crest has tumbled forward.

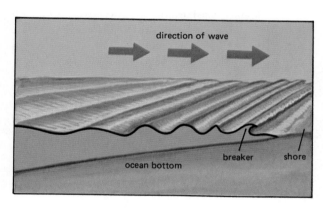

33

EXTENSIONS

Application
Science Skills — Comparing and Contrasting

The content and related activi- ties in this section introduce students to the analysis of the nature of a water wave. Have students extend their knowl- edge to other types of waves that occur in nature. This can be accomplished by having stu- dents relate what they have learned to sound waves or radio waves. They can do library re- search into other wave forms and summarize what they have learned using diagrams.

4 **Teaching Tips** — If students have played in breakers along a shore- line, ask them to describe their experiences. They probably will mention the force of the breakers. Based on their discussion, ask them to imagine how humans might be able to harness the energy of waves.

EXTENSIONS

Application
Research — Library

In this section students learn that waves can affect and re-shape the beaches and rocks along a shoreline. You may wish to have some students make a more detailed study of particularly interesting features. They should be able to locate descriptions and photographs of sea cliffs (steep rock faces), sea terraces (flat platforms at the bases of cliffs), sea stacks (columns of rocks that have resisted wave action), and sea caves (hollowed out parts of sea cliffs). Some students may be able to make models of these features to show to the rest of the class.

What are the effects of waves on the beach?

A. Obtain these materials: 2 blocks of wood, long tray (30 cm x 40 cm), milk container, sand, pebbles, water.

B. Place one block of wood under one end of the tray so that the tray is on a slope.

C. Fill that end of the tray with sand. Add some pebbles to the sand. Shape the sand and pebbles into a sloping "beach."

D. Fill your milk container with water. Gently pour the water into the tray at the other end. Stop pouring when the level of the water meets the beach.

E. Very slowly move the other block of wood toward the beach and then back 10 times. Wait a few seconds between each time.

F. Increase the force of your waves by pushing harder. Do 10 times. This represents storm waves.

1. How did the beach change?
2. What caused the waves in this activity?
3. What causes surface waves in nature?
4. Carefully observe the beach. Where was some of the sand moved? Were any pebbles moved?
5. A real sandy beach can be destroyed by a storm. Powerful waves can move sand back into the ocean. Make a hypothesis that explains why destroyed beaches are sometimes rebuilt by nature. Test your hypothesis using your equipment.

beach

push gently

34

ACTIVITY

Skill Development — *Finding Cause and Effect Relationships* and *Hypothesizing*

Teaching Tips — You may wish to do this activity as a demonstration.

Answers to Questions — 1. Some sand was carried away from the beach. 2. The force of my hand pushing the block back and forth. 3. Most surface waves are caused by the wind. 4. Some of the sand was moved into the water. The smaller pebbles were moved. 5. Sand that is moved into the ocean settles near the shoreline. Waves that move on shore rub across the sand and bring it into the breakers. The breakers deposit the sand back on the beach. The students can test out their hypothesis in this question by placing some sand off shore and observing the effect of waves' action upon it.

Exceptional Student
Visually Impaired
Have the student feel the altered "beach."

Some students may be encouraged to do research into the characteristics of two shoreline features that result from the action of waves on sandy beaches: sandbars and spits. They will learn that the sandbar is an underwater pile of sand and the spit is a sandbar that is connected to a curving shoreline. Students should also try to locate photographs of these features and, if possible, make models of these features.

Even shores of rocks and mountain cliffs are changed by the action of waves. The pounding of the waves breaks rocks into small pieces. Water then pushes these pieces against even larger rocks. The mixture of water and small rocks crashing against a rocky shoreline eventually causes a change in the shoreline.

5 Can you explain how these unusual features were formed? Once these were part of the shoreline. Wave action wore away the cliff unevenly. Some rocks formed arches, while other rocks stuck up through the water.

35

5 Text Questions — Can you explain how these unusual features were formed? *The force of the waves broke the rock into smaller pieces. Then other waves smashed the rock surfaces with water containing the smaller pieces of rock. This helped to wear away the larger rocks.*

EXTENSIONS

Enrichment
Research — Library

Have the students use reference books to find out about tsunami waves. Tsunamis are very high waves caused by earthquakes, volcanic eruptions, and landslides that take place underwater. They are sometimes over 100 feet high and travel over 470 miles an hour. They can cause a great deal of damage. Have the students find out what tsunamis are, what causes them, how high they are, and how fast they travel. Also have them report on the damage caused by tsunami waves in the past, such as the one that occurred in Hilo, Hawaii, in 1946.

Tsunami: Giant wave caused by movements at the ocean floor.

6 Can you imagine a wave as high, or even higher than, your school building? The largest wave ever recorded was 64 m (210 ft) high. The wave was seen off the coast of Siberia on October 6, 1737.

7 Giant waves called **tsunamis** (tsoo-**nah**-meez) are caused by earthquakes or other movements of the ocean floor. These waves travel at speeds of several hundred kilometers per hour. The force of a *tsunami* can be so great that buildings near the shoreline can be destroyed. Scientists can track tsunamis. Warnings are sent to people to go to a safe place before these waves strike. These pictures show the damage caused by a tsunami.

Section Review

Main Ideas: Wind causes waves by pushing against the surface of the water. When the crest of a wave tumbles into foam, a breaker forms. Breakers carry sand away from the beach. Over a long period of time, the force of waves can change the shape of a shoreline.

Questions: Answer in complete sentences.

1. Using the diagram on page 32, explain how wind causes waves.
2. Draw a labeled diagram that shows these wave parts: crest, trough, height, length.
3. Using the diagram on page 33, explain how waves can reshape the shoreline.

36

6 **Text Questions** — Can you imagine a wave as high, or even higher than, your school building? *The question is motivational and sets the stage for the discussion that follows.*

7 **Skill Development** — The discussion of the tsunami provides an excellent opportunity to have students *compare* it with an ordinary wave.

SECTION REVIEW
Answers to Questions
1. Winds push against the water's surface. Part of the water rises and then falls. This creates a wave.
2. The drawing should look like the one at the top of page 33.
3. Waves striking the shoreline bring sand back into the ocean when the water carried on shore flows back to the ocean.

SUGGESTED WORKSHEET MASTER
p. T-7p

Both of these pictures were taken at the same place and on the same day. What is the major difference? As you can see, the water's edge might not be the best spot for a picnic. If you stayed long enough, your family and your picnic would float out to sea! The rise in water level is due to the *tide* coming in. When you finish this section, you should be able to:

☐ **A.** Explain what is meant by the word *tide*.
☐ **B.** Explain how the moon causes *tides*.
☐ **C.** Explain the effects of both the sun and the moon on *tides*.

These pictures show the shoreline of the Bay of Fundy in Canada. Twice in a 24-hour period water rises to the height you see in the bottom picture. In fact, these changes in water level occur all over the world at every shoreline.

37

SECTION BACKGROUND

A person observing the ocean from the shore over a period of time would notice the following. For approximately six hours the water slowly rises. After reaching a maximum height of 2 or 3 m (about 7 to 9 ft), it returns over the next six hours to its previous low level. These rise and fall patterns are called the tides. The effect of the tides is most pronounced in long narrow bays.

Tides are caused by the gravitational pull of the moon and sun. When the moon pulls on the side of the earth facing it, the earth's waters bulge out toward the moon and a high tide occurs on that side of the earth. At the same time, the moon pulls the solid part of the earth away from the water on the opposite side, causing the water to bulge there. This results in a high tide. Other areas of water are flattened out and low tides are created there. Because of the earth's rotation, the tides move around the earth.

MATERIALS

graph paper

BASIC TEACHING PLAN

MOTIVATION

Text Question — What is the major difference? *The water levels along the shoreline.*

If you have access to any major newspaper published near a coastal area, locate the tide tables for a given day. (If you are far from a coastline, your school or community library may subscribe to a major newspaper published on the east or west coast.) The tide table will show the time and heights of the tides projected for a given day. Ask the students why they think the newspapers publish such information. *The fishing and shipping industries require such information to plan for the arrival and departure of ships so that they can take advantage of outgoing and incoming tides.*

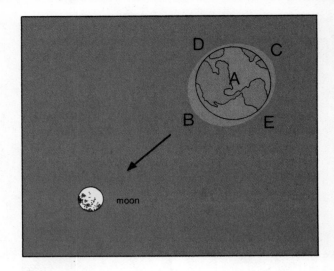

**Tides: The rise and fall
of ocean water.**

The rise and fall of ocean water are called **tides**. When
the water is at its highest level, we say there is a high
1 *tide.* Which picture on page 37 shows the Bay of Fundy
at high tide? When the water is at its lowest level, there
is a low tide. Which picture shows the Bay of Fundy at
low tide?

2 Tides occur along every ocean coast. The heights of the
tides differ from one place to another. Tides are caused
by the pull of the moon on the earth. Look at the diagram. The letter *A* represents the earth. The letters *B*,
C, *D*, and *E* represent the oceans on the earth. The
moon pulls on the ocean water at *B*, causing the water to
bulge. The bulge creates a high tide on that side of the
earth. The moon also pulls on the solid earth, shown as
A. The moon pulls more on *A* than on *C*, causing another
bulge. This bulge creates a high tide on the opposite side
of the earth. The water at *D* and *E* flattens and low tides
occur there. Because of the earth's spinning, the tides at
B, *C*, *D*, and *E* will change. When the tides become high
at *D* and *E*, there will be low tides at *B* and *C*.

38

DEVELOPMENT

1 **Text Questions** — Which picture on page 37 shows the Bay of
Fundy at high tide? *The bottom one.* Which picture shows the Bay of
Fundy at low tide? *The top one.*

2 **Teaching Tips** — If you have access to a globe and a small ball, you
can use them to model the tidal effects described in the student text.

ACTIVITY

How do tides affect water level?

A. Obtain some graph paper.

B. Scientists recorded the height of water in Boston Harbor for January 1.

Height of Water in Boston Harbor on January 1

time	1 A.M.	2 A.M.	3 A.M.	4 A.M.	5 A.M.	6 A.M.	7 A.M.	8 A.M.	9 A.M.	10 A.M.	11 A.M.	12 noon
height of water (meters)	2.0	1.7	1.6	1.9	2.4	2.9	3.4	3.8	4.0	3.7	3.3	2.7

time	1 P.M.	2 P.M.	3 P.M.	4 P.M.	5 P.M.	6 P.M.	7 P.M.	8 P.M.	9 P.M.	10 P.M.	11 P.M.	12 mid-night
height of water (meters)	2.2	1.6	1.2	1.3	1.6	2.1	2.6	4.6	3.4	3.5	3.2	2.8

C. Make a graph like the one below that shows how the height of water changed over 24 hours.

1. At what time did the first low tide occur? The first high tide?

2. How many hours passed between the first low tide and the first high tide?

3. At what time did the second low tide occur? The second high tide?

4. How many hours passed between the first and the second high tides? Between the low tides?

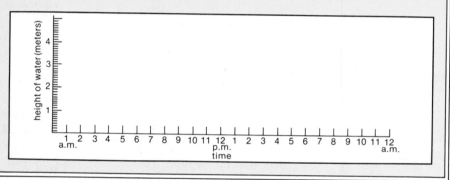

39

EXTENSIONS

Application
Science Skills — Recording Data

If the students have access to newspapers from major coastal cities saved in the periodical section of a school, community, or college library, they will be able to locate published tide tables. The students can make graphs representing this data for different times of the year. You may wish to display their graphs.

ACTIVITY

Skill Development — Recording Data

Teaching Tips — Although this is intended as an in-class activity, you could have students do it as a home assignment.

Answers to Questions — 1. The first low tide was at 3:00 A.M. The first high tide was at 9:00 A.M.   2. Six hours passed between the high and low tide.   3. The second low tide was at 3:00 P.M. The second high tide was at 8:00 P.M.   4. Eleven hours passed between the high tides. Twelve hours passed between the low tides.

EXTENSIONS

Enrichment
Science Skills — Building Science Vocabulary

Ask some students to do research to find the meanings of the following terms associated with the observation of tides: flood (the period of time in which water from a tide moves toward shore); ebb (the period when water moves away from the shore); slack water (the instant when the tidal current is changing direction — the water is moving neither in nor out); set (the direction of current flow); drift (the speed of water movement).

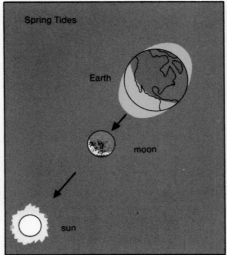

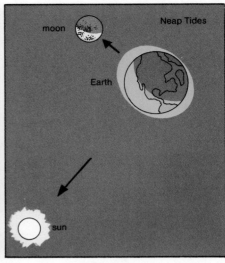

Spring tides: Very high and very low tides.

Neap tides: Low tides that are not very low; high tides that are not very high.

40

Tides change from high to low every six hours. Within a 24-hour period a sequence would be high tide, low tide, high tide, and finally low tide. If you know when

3 the last high tide occurred, you can predict when the next one will occur. For example, if a high tide occurred

4 at 2 P.M., when would you expect the next high tide to occur?

There are certain times when the tides are very high and very low. These tides occur when the sun, earth, and

5 moon form a straight line in space. At this time, both the sun and the moon pull on the earth. As a result, high tides are higher than usual, and low tides are lower than usual. This only occurs twice a month. These very high and very low tides are called **spring tides.**

When the earth, moon, and sun are at right angles to each other, low tides are not very low. High tides are not very high. The tides are not as great because the pull of the sun decreases the moon's pull on the earth. These are called **neap (neep) tides.** The diagrams show the posi-

---

3 **Skill Development** — The students are asked to make a *prediction* based on the information found in this paragraph.

4 **Text Questions** — When would you expect the next high tide to occur? *2:00 A.M.*

5 **Skill Development** — Have the students *compare* the position of the sun, moon, and earth during spring tides with their positions for neap tides. The information in the paragraphs and on the illustrations should assist them in this comparison.

6 **Teaching Tips** — You may wish to have three student volunteers come to the front of the room and work together to show the class the positions of the sun, moon, and earth for spring and neap tides.

6 tions of the earth, moon, and sun when *spring tides* and *neap tides* occur. Look at the positions of the earth, moon, and sun in each diagram. The arrows show the direction of the moon's pull and the sun's pull.

In some coastal areas of the world, spring tides can cause problems. Flooding may take place, especially if the weather is stormy. In the United States, flooding usually happens during the spring season.

Section Review

Main Ideas: This chart summarizes the types of tides.

Tide	Cause	Effect
every day tide	the pull of the moon on the oceans	high and low tides every 24 hours
spring tide	sun and moon in line with the earth	very high tides and very low tides
neap tide	sun and moon at right angles to the earth	high tides that are not as high; low tides that are not as low

Questions: Answer in complete sentences.

1. Explain what tides are.
2. Using a diagram, explain how the moon affects the rise and fall of ocean water.
3. Using a diagram, explain how the moon and sun together affect the tides.
4. What do you think would happen to the tides if the earth had no moon?
5. Use the diagrams on page 40 to answer this question: Why are neap tides not as large as spring tides?

41

EXTENSIONS

Enrichment
Activity

Find or make a recording of ocean sounds: waves breaking, birds squawking, people swimming, children playing. A local record store may carry a sound effects record. Play the recording for your class. Have the students sit quietly with their eyes closed as they listen. Tell them to let the sounds take them on a fantasy trip. Let the sounds foster images about the beach and ocean. After the students have listened to the recording, they can do one of the following: write a few paragraphs about their fantasy trip; write a poem about ocean sounds; or create an art piece that depicts an ocean scene.

SECTION REVIEW

Main Ideas — You may wish to point out to students that they may want to consider making charts of their own as a technique to assist them when they are reviewing material.

Answers to Questions
1. Tides are the rise and fall of ocean water.
2. Students should prepare a diagram similar to the one on page 38.
3. Students should create a diagram that shows both the moon and the sun pulling on the earth and oceans. Their explanation should include reference to the combined effect produced when both the sun and moon are lined up.
4. The tides would be of lesser intensity. There would only be the pull of the sun.
5. Neap tides happen when the sun and moon are at right angles to the earth. The effect of the pull of the moon is lessened because the sun is pulling in a different direction. During spring tides the sun and moon are lined up and their pull is combined.

Do this activity as part of your review of the chapter. Ask a group of students to prepare the needed materials in advance.

A. The group should study the illustrations in the chapter. For each illustration they should prepare three sheets of construction paper. Each sheet should contain one phrase (hint) that identifies the illustration. The first hint should be vague, the second more specific, and the third quite specific. For example, the hints for the drawing on page 30 (saltwater currents in the Mediterranean) might be:

1. It shows water, 2. It shows a current, and 3. Mediterranean Sea is shown.

B. When the group is ready, they should show the vague phrase first and ask the class to identify what pictures would "fit." The class should have their books open for this. With the showing of each of the three phrases, the class will eventually reach a conclusion about which picture is being described. This should be done with each set of three phrases.

SUGGESTED WORKSHEET MASTERS
p. T-7q, r

SUGGESTED TEST MASTERS
pp. T-7f, g, h

CHAPTER REVIEW

Science Words

A. What term best fits each definition given?
 1. Winds that blow from east to west toward the equator.
 2. Winds that blow from west to east away from the equator.
 3. Water that moves in a certain direction.
 4. The highest point of a wave.
 5. The lowest point of a wave.
B. Unscramble the letters to find the correct terms.
 6. The D I E T is the rise and fall of ocean water.
 7. The S I S M A N U T are giant waves caused by underwater earthquakes.
 8. A R E R A K B E is a wave in which the crest has tumbled forward.
 9. Very high and very low tides are called G N I P S R tides.
 10. P N E A tides are low tides that are not very low and high tides that are not very high.

Questions: Answer in complete sentences.

1. Compare the direction and location of the trade winds and westerlies.
2. How do trade winds and westerlies cause ocean currents?
3. Describe the movement of deep ocean currents as they move from the polar regions to the equator.
4. The tides rise and fall in a regular pattern every 24 hours.
 a. How much time will pass between two high tides?
 b. How much time will pass between a high tide and a low tide?
 c. How many high tides will occur in a 24-hour period?
 d. How many low tides will occur in a 24-hour period?
5. When are high tides very high and low tides very low? Draw the positions of the earth, sun, and moon.

42

CHAPTER REVIEW

Science Words
1. trade winds, 2. westerlies, 3. current, 4. crest, 5. trough, 6. tide, 7. tsunamis, 8. breaker, 9. spring, 10. neap

Answers to Questions
1. Trade winds blow from east to west toward the equator. Westerlies blow from west to east away from the equator.
2. Trade winds and westerlies push on the ocean's surface and cause the water to move in the same direction as the winds.
3. Deep ocean currents occur as cold water at the poles sinks and moves to the equator and warmer water rises and moves to replace the cold water.
4. a. About 12 hours   b. About 6 hours   c. 2   d. 2
5. When the earth, the moon, and the sun form a straight line in space. Drawing should look like the one at the left on the top of page 40 in the student text.

CHAPTER 3

OCEAN EXPLORATION

Do you eat a kind of food that is made from seaweed? Do you brush your teeth with sea plants? The answer is probably yes! These are just two examples of products the ocean can provide us with. When you finish this section, you should be able to:

3-1.
Ocean Resources

43

CHAPTER OBJECTIVES

1. Describe the resources that we get from the ocean.
2. Explain the process of desalination.
3. Understand the role of the food chain as a link between ocean plants and animals.
4. Relate sources of pollution and their effects.
5. Describe techniques being used to explore the ocean bottom.

SECTION BACKGROUND

For thousands of years, humans have gathered foods such as clams, mussels, and seaweed along the shoreline. The invention of fishing devices and boats enabled early humans to travel farther from the shoreline to gather food.

In modern times, the ocean's bounty has expanded to include nonfood resources. Every mineral found on dry land is also found dissolved in sea water. Gold, silver, iron, and many other minerals are all potential ocean resources, but the cost of removing them from sea water is still excessively high. Fossil fuels are now being removed from deposits under the ocean floor. Offshore drilling platforms are used to acquire such fuels.

The ocean is also a source of fresh water. Through a process called desalination, salt can be removed from ocean water.

MATERIALS

Exceptional Student
IEP Chapter Goal

At the end of this chapter, the student will describe the food chain of the ocean.

BASIC TEACHING PLAN

MOTIVATION

You can obtain samples of food products from the sea from a natural food store. Some cooked samples of seaweed that might be of particular interest to volunteers who are willing to taste them are: wakame, nori, and kombul. You may also be able to locate some kelp seasoning that could be used as a spice for the cooked seaweed.

Enrichment
Activity

Your class should enjoy baking algae cookies as an in-class project or an at-home assignment. The recipe can be found on page T-7s. The type of algae used is chlorella and can be obtained in natural food stores. If you do this as a class project, a toaster oven could be used.

Agar: A tasteless, odorless material made from seaweed.

Diatoms: Tiny ocean plants.

☐ **A.** Give examples of four kinds of resources that we get from the ocean and explain their uses.

☐ **B.** Explain how fresh water can be made from salt water.

Commercial ice cream and toothpaste are made from substances that come from sea plants. Ice cream is thickened with a material called **agar** (**ah**-gar). *Agar* is a tasteless, colorless material made from seaweed. Toothpaste also contains an ocean product. It has gritty material in it that rubs food particles from your teeth. This gritty material consists of the remains of tiny ocean plants called **diatoms** (**dy**-uh-tahmz). In the ocean, *diatoms* are a main food source for ocean animals. When diatoms die, their remains settle to the ocean bottom. The diatom material in your toothpaste is millions of years old. It is obtained by mining land that was once an ocean bottom. Agar and diatoms are only two of the many products that the ocean provides for us.

The ocean is also a rich source of food. However, only **1** ten percent of our food supply comes from the ocean.

44

DEVELOPMENT

1 **Teaching Tips** — Since the oceans cover more than twice the surface area of the earth than land does, students may wonder why the ocean is not used as a food resource more often. Fish constitute only a small percentage of food available from the sea. Difficulties in ocean "farming" include: the small size of ocean plants and the need for fencing-off and fertilizing ocean-farming areas.

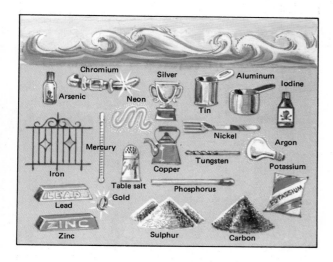

On land, people have learned to farm to supply the food they need. New crops are grown each year and new animals raised to replace what has been used. People hunt for food in the ocean. They take food from the ocean but do not replace it. Scientists believe we can learn to farm in the ocean. We can grow new ocean plants or crops each year and raise ocean animals. Ocean farming would increase the amount of food we get from the ocean. Also, we would be able to replace the food we take from the ocean. Ocean farming has been tried in different countries in order to feed hungry people. It is not an easy job. What problems would it cause?

Ocean water contains many materials also found on land. These materials are dissolved in the water. You have learned about a dissolved salt. Can you name it? Look at the drawing. The words you see are names of other materials dissolved in ocean water. The drawing also shows how the materials may be used. It is very expensive to get some of these materials out of the water. However, as we use up the supplies of these materials from the land, the ocean will be our only source.

45

2 **Teaching Tips** — Some current human activities within the ocean more or less constitute "farming." Examples include: the production of cultured pearls resulting from underwater divers inserting bits of shell in pearl oysters; sponges cultivated by placing small sections of sponges at specific locations; and the selection of specific locations for the preparation of oyster beds for harvesting oysters as food.

If you or a school librarian could secure photographs of any of the above activities, they could provide an interesting stimulus for further discussions of ocean farming.

3 **Text Questions** — What problems would it cause? *Some problems would include the fencing-in of ocean areas, fertilization of plants, and the need for specialized equipment.*

4 **Text Questions** — Can you name it? *Sodium chloride.*

T–45

Enrichment
Research — Library

Some of the Middle East countries, African countries, and countries of Central and South America have an abundance of oil. Students could investigate the extent to which the United States and Europe are dependent upon these countries as suppliers of fuel to meet their energy needs. If possible, students could prepare graphs showing the countries to which these oil-rich nations export their fuel products.

Fossil fuels: Fuels formed from remains of plants and animals.

Petroleum: A fossil fuel in liquid form.

Natural gas: A fossil fuel in gas form.

5 The largest supply of **fossil fuels** (fah-sil fyoo-ellz) on earth may lie under the ocean bottom. *Fossil fuels* are formed from the remains of plants and animals that lived very long ago. These remains settled on the ocean bottom and were covered with layers of other sediment. The layers of sediment pushed down on the remains. After millions of years the remains changed to a liquid called **petroleum** (peh-**troh**-lee-um). *Petroleum* is a fossil fuel found under the ocean bottom. It is used to make gasoline and heating oil. Another fossil fuel is **natural gas.** *Natural gas* also is used to heat homes. Natural gas and petroleum are usually found together. Find the gas in the **6** picture below. Between which layers is it found?

The picture on the right shows what is used to drill under the ocean bottom for fossil fuels. Scientists decide where to drill. Drilling is difficult and expensive. Some-**7** times there are accidents and oil gets into the ocean water. However, when the supply from the land is used up, the ocean may be the only source of fossil fuels. There is a limited amount of fuels in the ocean as well. We will soon have to find other sources of fuels.

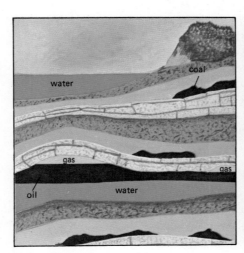

46

5 Teaching Tips — Most people are unaware of the vast amounts of fossil fuels that lie under the continental shelf and nearby ocean floor areas. Geologists estimate that there exists an amount of fossil fuel offshore that equals at least half of the petroleum reserves that are on land. Recent estimates put the amount under the ocean floor at 2,000,000,000,000 barrels. You may want to write this figure on the chalkboard.

6 Text Questions — Between which layers is it found? *Between the oil and the rock layers just above the oil.*

7 Teaching Tips — Since the ecological consequences of oil exploration are discussed so widely in the media, you may wish to encourage some students to do library research to gather information that will assist the class in thinking through the economic and human consequences of increasing or decreasing offshore drilling. Students should try to discover the types of machinery required for undersea oil exploration, the numbers of workers likely to be employed at drilling platforms, the time required to develop an offshore oil well, and the costs involved.

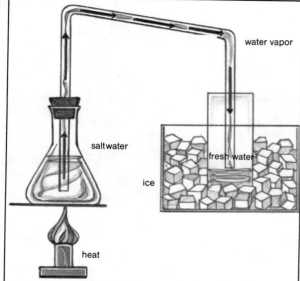

8

water vapor

saltwater

ice

fresh water

heat

The ocean can also provide us with water that we can drink. Scientists have found several ways to remove salt and other materials from sea water.

Salt can be removed from saltwater by **desalination** (dee-sal-ih-**nay**-shun). The diagram shows how *desalination* works. It is something that can be done in a class-**9** **room.** Saltwater is heated. The steam it produces goes through a tube. The steam is then cooled. It forms fresh water. The salt stays behind.

This idea is used in many desalination plants. They are large buildings near the ocean. Ocean water is pumped into large tanks. The water is heated until it becomes steam. The steam is cooled into fresh water.

This process is necessary in areas where fresh water is scarce. Fresh water is needed for drinking, farming, and industry. A place like Key West, Florida, is such an area. It has a new type of desalination plant as shown in the

Desalination: The process of removing salt from ocean water.

47

Enrichment
Science Skills —
Following Directions

Students could build a function-ing model desalination plant that operates using solar energy. Directions are as follows.

A. Obtain a pie pan, a glass dish smaller than the pan, a clear plastic mixing bowl (to fit over the pie pan when in-verted), and saltwater.

B. Place the glass dish in the pie pan.

C. Pour some salt water into the dish.

D. Cover with the mixing bowl and place in sunlight. The salt-water will evaporate and collect on the inside of the mixing bowl. Eventually the water will drip down the sides into the pie pan. This water will be fresh. The salt will be left in the dish.

8 **Skill Development** — Have the students *observe* the diagram show-ing desalination. Ask them to *predict* what some of the problems related to the operation of a large-scale desalination plant would be using this process. Their predictions may include: the high energy cost associated with heating the water unless solar energy is used; the high energy cost for cooling equipment to cause the evaporated water to condense; and the cost of transporting the water from the shoreline to the agricultural regions or cities that require the fresh water.

9 **Skill Development** — Ask the students to *compare* the steps of the desalination process, detailed in the paragraphs, to the diagram of the process.

EXTENSIONS

Application
Research

Have the students go to the supermarket and look for food items that come from the ocean. They could make a list of all the ocean products that they find. They could also note how each product was processed and where it was processed. Tell them to check the frozen foods section, the canned foods section, the fresh fish department, the pet foods section, and the ethnic foods section. They should also check the ingredients on ice-cream containers and packages of marshmallows. Algin is a product made from algae that is added to ice cream and marshmallows to make them smooth and creamy.

photograph. It uses very powerful filters to get salt out of the ocean water. This plant can produce up to 12 million liters (3 million gallons) of fresh water a day. Filtering does not cost as much as heating the water does. It also uses less energy.

Section Review

Main Ideas: In the future, we will be more dependent on the ocean for its many resources. It is a source of food, fossil fuels, minerals, and fresh water.

Questions: Answer in complete sentences.

1. Name four resources we get from the ocean.
2. Providing food for all the people in the world is a difficult problem. Explain how ocean farming would help.
3. What is desalination?
4. Explain the sequence of steps that occurs during desalination.
5. What is the main idea shown in the picture at the top of page 45?

48

SECTION REVIEW

Main Ideas — One way to review this section is to have the students make an outline of the major topics discussed. This would be a good opportunity for students to see how outlining can be used as a reviewing technique when they study.

Answers to Questions
1. Food, fossil fuels, fresh water, and minerals dissolved in sea water.
2. Ocean farming would give us more food from the ocean and allow us to replace what we remove.
3. Desalination is the process of removing salt from ocean water.
4. Salt water is heated. Water evaporates, leaving salt behind. The evaporated water cools and changes to liquid water.
5. The main idea in the drawing is that ocean water contains many materials that are useful to humans.

SUGGESTED WORKSHEET MASTER
p. T-7s

T–48

One of the most feared ocean animals is the great white shark. This animal can grow to a length of 9 m (about 30 ft). Fortunately, the great white shark spends most of its time far away from people. Great white sharks feed on fish by attacking them with powerful jaws. The shark's jaw contains rows of razor-sharp teeth. The great white shark is only one of the many forms of ocean life that usually remain hidden in the ocean's waters. When you finish this section, you should be able to:

☐ **A.** Describe the forms of life found at three ocean locations.

☐ **B.** Explain how sea animals depend on one another and on plants for food.

☐ **C.** Explain the sequence of events that occurs in an ocean food chain.

Some living things in the ocean are much larger than the great white shark. The whale shark, for example, can grow to over 15 m (about 50 ft) in length.

Did you know that the largest animal in the world lives in the ocean? The blue whale can grow to a length of 30 m (about 100 ft). The ocean is also the home for some plants and animals that are so tiny that they can be seen only with a powerful microscope. Although life in the ocean comes in many shapes and sizes, most living things seem to be concentrated in three ocean areas. These areas are the surface, just below the surface, and the bottom of the ocean near the shore.

1 Thousands of tiny plants and animals float on the surface of the ocean. They are called **plankton** (plank-tun). *Plankton* are so tiny they cannot be seen with the naked eye. Plankton live on the ocean surface, where there is sunlight, rather than on the ocean bottom. Tiny shrimp-like animals called **copepods** (koh-peh-podz) eat plankton. A *copepod* is as small as the head of a pin. Even big animals, such as some whales, eat plankton, too.

On the ocean bottom near the shore, there are many

3-2.

Ocean Life

Plankton: Tiny plants and animals on the ocean surface.

Copepods: Tiny shrimplike animals.

49

SECTION BACKGROUND

All life in the sea directly or indirectly depends upon sunlight. Sunlight is converted into food by plantlike floating organisms (phytoplankton). The phytoplankton is eaten by animallike plankton (zooplankton).

Ocean feeding relationships, just as feeding relationships in other ecosystems, are thought of as consisting of a series of food chains with energy being transmitted along the chain as one organism feeds upon another. Since many organisms may feed upon a particular type of organism, food chains can be thought of as being interconnected to form a food web. A pyramid is often used as a way of representing the interconnection of food chains and webs. Chief ocean predators are at the top of the pyramid and plankton are at its bottom.

MATERIALS

BASIC TEACHING PLAN

MOTIVATION

As the ocean is a complex environment containing many diverse organisms, it would be helpful to display a collection of as many ocean life photographs and specimens as you can acquire. The inclusion of shells, natural sponges, and possibly a clam or shrimp acquired at a fish store will assist you in stressing the range of creatures that inhabit the ocean.

DEVELOPMENT

1 **Skill Development** — Be sure that students understand the first step in the *sequence* — tiny floating plants make food from sunlight. This conversion of the sun's energy to food is the beginning of the ocean's first food chain. This, of course, is an example of photosynthesis, the starting point for food chains on land.

Reinforcement
Activity

Ask students to select a food chain described within the text and to prepare posters showing the chosen food chains. Additional information about the living things that are part of the food chain should be included. This information might relate to the size of the organisms, the typical physical location (e.g., near the shore, in deep water), and the methods by which the organisms obtain their food. If desired, the Extension could be expanded to include other life functions of the organisms within the food chain.

plants and animals. Here, sunlight reaches the bottom
2 and many plants are able to grow. Why do you think there is little plant growth in the deeper parts of the ocean?

A great variety of animals live in the water near the shore. Crabs, lobsters, and shrimps move along the ocean bottom looking for food. Some fish swim along the
3 bottom, too. They all eat plankton that fall from the surface. They also eat parts of other ocean animals. The starfish uses its long arms to pry open clams and scallops. The **sea anemone** (uh-**nem**-uh-nee) sits on the ocean bottom waiting for a fish to touch its poisonous arms. The *sea anemone*, shown in the picture on the right, looks more like a plant than an animal.

Most fish live in the deeper water, just below the ocean surface. Fish eat other fish to stay alive. Large fish eat smaller ones, which eat smaller ones, which eat still smaller ones. The small fish eat copepods and plankton. For example, sharks may eat codfish, which eat herring, which eat copepods, which eat plankton. This eating pattern is called a **food chain**. A *food chain* can be described as who-eats-whom.

Sea anemone: An ocean animal.

Food chain: A pattern of who-eats-whom.

50

2 Text Questions — Why do you think there is little plant growth in the deeper parts of the ocean? *Sunlight does not penetrate to the bottom. Plants cannot live without sunlight.*

3 Teaching Tips — Students may be interested to learn that there are some extremely large animals in the ocean that feed directly on plankton. Among these plankton feeders are those members of the whale family that have no teeth — baleen whales. These whales have hundreds of thin strips of material, called baleen, that hang from their upper jawbone. The baleen serves as a strainer that separates plankton from ocean water. Baleen whales include gray whales, humpback whales, and the largest creature that has ever lived on earth — the blue whale.

4 Life in the ocean is like a pyramid. On the bottom of the pyramid are plankton. Each animal feeds on the plants and animals below it on the pyramid. At the top of the pyramid is the largest ocean animal, the whale.

In the ocean there are few places for fish to hide. Therefore, many fish have coloring to protect them. From above, ocean water looks blue. Many fish are blue on top. From below, the water looks white, and many fish have white bellies. The stingray is a fish whose color matches the ocean bottom, where it lives. Look at the picture below. Can you find the stingray buried in the sand?

5

Section Review

Main Ideas: Most ocean plants and animals are found in three main areas. They depend on one another for food. The picture shows an ocean food chain.

Questions: Answer in complete sentences.

1. Give three examples of living things found on the ocean bottom near the shore.
2. What types of living things would you expect to find floating on the ocean's surface?
3. What types of living things would you expect to find in deep water?
4. What is meant by the term "food chain"?
5. Place these animals in the correct sequence for a food chain: copepods, plankton, shark, codfish.

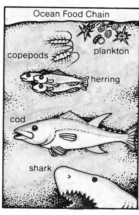

Ocean Food Chain

51

EXTENSIONS

Application
Research

Some of the animals discussed in this lesson are food for humans. Seafood has a high nutritive value. Using food calorie charts and health-diet books, students can find out the amount of calories, protein, carbohydrates, fats, and minerals in seafoods. To illustrate what they have learned, they could prepare charts comparing the nutritional values of various seafoods.

4 **Skill Development** — After the students have read the first paragraph on this page, refer them to the drawing of the pyramid. Ask them to identify the *sequence* of who-eats-whom.

5 **Teaching Tips** — The students may be interested to learn that the animals at the top of the food pyramid shown on this page (the killer whale, the walrus, and the seal) are all mammals. They differ from fish in that they are warm-blooded, breathe air, and feed their young with milk.

SECTION REVIEW

Answers to Questions

1. Three of the following: crabs, lobsters, shrimps, starfish, clams, sea anemones, some fish.
2. Plankton are found floating on the ocean's surface.
3. Sharks, codfish, whales.
4. A food chain is a pattern of who-eats-whom.
5. Plankton, copepods, codfish, shark.

SUGGESTED WORKSHEET MASTER
p. T-7t

The oceans on earth have become vast dumping grounds. Sewage is the most obvious of civilization's waste products that are transferred to the oceans. Other materials are: radioactive waste materials, oil from oil spills, and pesticides brought into the ocean by streams and rivers. Even heat, resulting from the use of ocean water to cool power plant condensers, has been a problem. Lead, a highly toxic substance that is part of the exhaust of internal combustion engines, precipitates from the air and reaches ocean food chains. Mercury, a residue from a variety of industrial processes, has been detected in the bodies of some fish.

The use of the ocean as a dumping ground initially affects ocean life. With the passage of time, the pollutants produced by humans on the land and discharged into the ocean may eventually return to affect human life.

MATERIALS

cotton, motor oil, pan, paper, spoon, water

3-3.

The Ocean in Danger

Pollution: The adding of harmful materials to the environment.

Sewage: Waste materials carried by sewers and drains.

52

One morning in March, 1980, the *Amoco Cadiz*, a giant tanker carrying crude oil, was sailing off the northern coast of France. At 10:45 A.M. the ship's steering equipment broke down. The giant tanker became impossible to control. Within only 12 hours the ship was torn apart by powerful waves. The tanker broke apart, pouring out 69 million gallons of crude oil. Can you guess how this affected the ocean? When you finish this section, you should be able to:

☐ **A.** Explain what pollution is.
☐ **B.** Describe how human activity affects the ocean and living things in it.

The spreading oil slick from the sinking tanker eventually reached and covered 160 km (about 100 mi) of the French coastline. Animals and plants in the area were coated with a thick layer of oil. Even sea birds floating on the water were affected. Hundreds of people worked hard to clean the oil from the birds' feathers. Unfortunately, very few of the birds survived.

There are many substances other than crude oil that are accidentally dumped into the ocean. Some substances are deliberately added to the ocean. These substances, whether harmful or harmless, are not normally found in the sea.

The cause for the addition of these substances is human activity. In some places along the shoreline, the ocean has become a place to dump garbage. Some industries produce wastes that eventually reach the ocean. Many people are careless and do not think about the effect that these substances will have on the ocean. The addition of harmful materials to the environment is called **pollution** (poh-**loo**-shun).

Pollution of the ocean is often caused by the dumping of **sewage** (**soo**-ij) into the water. *Sewage* is waste material carried by sewers and drains. Sewage contains germs that cause disease in ocean plants and animals. To pre-

BASIC TEACHING PLAN
MOTIVATION

Text Questions — Can you guess how this affected the ocean? *The oil caused harm to marine plants and animals, and because the oil spread over a large area it was difficult to clean up.*

You could start the class discussion by displaying a chart that lists a wide range of commonly used petroleum products derived from petrochemicals (chemicals made from petroleum or natural gas). Include products such as detergents, fertilizers, medicines, plastics, and synthetic fibers. The students will be surprised to see that we have developed a large dependence on petroleum products. Our desire for such products coupled with our use of petroleum for fuel has resulted in a dependence on petroleum that must be considered in light of the ecological risks of danger to the ocean. Tell the students that this section will focus on the risks to the environment and that they will need to keep in mind why societies seem to be willing to take the risks of offshore exploration.

vent pollution, many cities have sewage-treatment plants like the one shown above. At these plants, the harmful materials are removed from the sewage.

Pollution can also be caused by chemicals in the water. Some chemicals are carried to the ocean by rivers. For example, **pesticides** (**pes-tih-sydz**), chemicals sprayed on crops, run off the land into rivers. The *pesticides* are carried to the ocean. They are harmful to the living things there. What do you think happens to the plants and animals as a result?

Some plants and animals will die. For those living things that survive, chemicals enter their bodies. If humans and other animals eat food from the ocean, these harmful substances affect them, too. To prevent this type of pollution, laws have been passed to limit the amount and kinds of chemicals used for spraying crops.

Since early times, people have depended on the ocean for food. Today, people in many parts of the world still depend almost totally on fish and shellfish. At the same

Pesticides: Chemicals sprayed on crops.

53

DEVELOPMENT

1 Skill Development — Ask the students to make a *prediction* about what the effect of not using pesticides would be (e.g., decreased food production, fruits and vegetables that would show the effects of insect activity, farms having difficulty operating because of low crop yields). Emphasize the tension that exists between societal needs and expectations and the risks involved in responding to these needs and expectations.

Application

*Science Skills — Finding
Cause and Effect Relationships*

Ask some students to investigate the causes and the effects of thermal pollution (the release of heated water into streams, lakes, or oceans). They will find that electric utility companies use water to cool steam condensers needed in the process of producing electricity. Water that is used for this purpose leaves the steam condenser about 15 degrees hotter than the body of water from which it came. Among the effects of thermal pollution are the reduction in the amount of oxygen in the water (less oxygen is available to fish), and the increased temperature of the water, which causes more algae to grow. This upsets the population balance among the members of food chains that depend on algae, further reduces the available oxygen, and reduces the depth to which sunlight can penetrate the water as a result of the shielding out of the sunlight by the larger algae population.

ACTIVITY

Can you remove oil from water?

A. Obtain these materials: cotton, motor oil, pan, paper, spoon, water.

B. Fill the pan with water.

C. Pour some oil into the water.

   1. Did the oil mix with the water?

D. Try to remove the oil from the water with a spoon, the cotton, and the paper.

   2. Were you able to get the oil out of the water?

   3. As a result of what you have learned in this activity, how would animals be affected by an oil spill?

   4. Using what you have learned in this activity, suggest a way to clear up an oil spill.

Species: All of the same kind of living thing.

time that food is being removed from the ocean, harmful materials are being added to it. We add garbage, sewage, oil, and chemicals to the very same waters that provide us with food. Ocean pollution is a threat to fish, to birds that feed on fish, and to humans.

2   Ocean pollution not only affects individual animals and plants. It can affect entire **species**. *Species* is the name for all of the same kind of living thing. Entire species could disappear because one of their major food sources dies from pollution.

Here is an example that will help you understand why. Imagine that chemicals dumped into a river are carried to the ocean. If the chemicals kill the plankton, the copepods that feed on the plankton will lose their food supply. Many copepods will die. Since copepods are an important part of the herring's diet, the herring could also die. In the food chain, plankton is eaten by copepods, which

54

ACTIVITY

Skill Development — *Inferring*

Teaching Tips — If your students have not had much laboratory experience, you may wish to place all the material for each activity group on a plastic tray. Then have a representative from each group come forward to receive the tray of materials.

Answers to Questions — **1.** The oil did not mix with water.
2. Most students will experience some difficulty.   **3.** The animals would be covered with oil during an oil spill. Birds trying to clean their feathers would eat the oil and be poisoned. The oil on the water would reduce the amount of sunlight that reached the plankton. Anything that affects the plankton will affect all food chains.   **4.** You need to use something to soak up the oil. In the activity, we were able to soak up the oil with the paper and the cotton.

are eaten by herring. If one species is harmed by chemicals, so are all the others.

3 The eastern brown pelican is a species that was in danger from pesticide pollution. This bird is also part of an ocean food chain. Through the food chain, pesticides entered the bodies of these birds. As a result, the pelicans laid eggs with very thin shells. The eggs would crack and the unhatched pelican chicks would die. This situation received the attention of concerned scientists. Laws were passed against the use of certain pesticides. Now there are more brown pelicans than before.

Some animals are in danger for a reason other than pollution. Blue whales are in danger of becoming **extinct** (ek-**stinkt**). An animal is *extinct* when there aren't any left. Blue whales have been hunted for many years. They are hunted for their meat, bones, and teeth.

Extinct: Does not exist anymore.

55

EXTENSIONS

Enrichment
Research — Library

Using basic research books and current periodicals, your class could further examine whales. Perhaps some students could interview someone at a local marine aquarium or an environmental-oceanographic society to obtain current information. Their research should include: a description of the different types of whales; the locations of whales throughout the world; and the human uses of the meat, bones, and body parts of the whale.

2 **Skill Development** — Use the information in this section as a stimulus for discussing the *cause and effect* relationship between pesticide pollution and the herring population.

3 **Teaching Tips** — The discussion of the diminishing number of eastern brown pelicans can be tied to a somewhat similar effect on the bald eagle population in the United States. The eagles also started producing eggs whose shells were so thin that they could not provide an appropriate covering for developing chicks. This was the result of the entry of the pesticide DDT into the bald eagle's food chain.

Enrichment
Research — Library

In order to replace the large numbers of fish removed from the ocean waters through commercial fishing, the government has created fish hatcheries. Students may wish to investigate how these hatcheries operate and the types of saltwater fish that are raised. Their investigation will lead them to information about salmon hatcheries on the Pacific Coast and cod, flounder, mackerel, and lobster hatcheries on the Atlantic Coast. They may even be able to acquire figures that indicate the number of fish and fish eggs that are produced by hatcheries and that are placed in fresh and salt water. It is now estimated that over 6,000,000,000 fish and fish eggs are produced each year.

The graph below shows the number of blue whales killed since 1930. How many were killed in 1930? How many were killed in 1980? The number of whales killed each year has decreased. There are two reasons for this. **4** Because so many were killed between 1930 and 1940, there were fewer left to be killed later. Also, it is now against the law for Americans and Europeans to hunt blue whales.

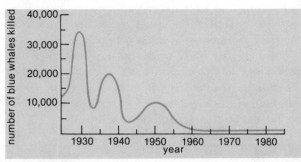

Section Review

Main Ideas: Human activity has resulted in ocean pollution. Pollutants such as sewage, oil, and chemical pesticides affect ocean food chains. This may cause some species to become extinct. Overhunting by humans has also threatened many species.

Questions: Answer in complete sentences.
1. How are pollutants added to the ocean?
2. Explain how these pollutants are harmful to ocean water: **a.** sewage **b.** chemical pesticides **c.** oil.
3. Explain how pollutants affect food chains.
4. What threatened the population of the blue whale? What was the effect of laws that were passed?
5. How are sewage and pesticide pollution reduced?
6. Study the graph above. How many blue whales were killed in 1930, 1950, and 1980? What conclusions can you make from these numbers?

56

4 **Text Questions** — How many were killed in 1930? *Over 30,000.* In 1980? *Relatively few — less than 1,000.*

SECTION REVIEW
Answers to Questions
1. Sewage; pesticides carried by rivers; oil spills from tankers.
2. **a.** Sewage contains things that can cause disease in ocean plants and animals. **b.** They are poisons and can cause damage to the living things in the ocean. **c.** Oil adheres to plants and animals.
3. When pollutants enter the cells of one member of a food chain, they affect all animals that consume the affected animal or plant.
4. Too many whales were killed by hunters; fewer were killed.
5. Sewage can go through a treatment plant before it reaches streams, rivers, and the ocean. Pesticide pollution can be slowed by limiting the amount and kind of chemicals used to spray crops.
6. 1930, over 30,000; 1950, 10,000; 1980, less than 1,000. Two conclusions: so many were killed that the available population declined and laws were passed to limit the hunting.

Have you ever swum underwater? Were you able to breathe? Without air from special equipment, you cannot stay underwater very long. Equipment used by divers allows them to stay underwater for almost an hour. This allows scientists to explore the ocean bottom. When you finish this section, you should be able to:

☐ **A.** Describe two pieces of equipment people use to explore the ocean.
☐ **B.** Explain how sound is used to determine the shape of the ocean bottom.
☐ **C.** Explain how scientists gather sediments and what information they can learn from them.

For thousands of years people have been diving into water to gather shellfish, sponges, and other living things. The amount of time humans could spend underwater depended on how long the divers could hold their breath.

During the 1800's, the first diving suits were invented. These suits allowed a person to spend much more time underwater. An air hose was connected to the diving suit. The opposite end of the air hose was connected to

3-4.
Exploring the Ocean Bottom

57

SECTION BACKGROUND

In early times, the extent to which underwater life and land formations could be explored was limited by the amount of time the breath could be held and by the depth to which a diver could reach without being harmed by the water pressure. Diving suits, invented in the early 1800s, were rather complicated and dangerous, since the diver's air supply came through a fragile hose descending from a ship at the surface. The invention in 1943 of the aqualung by Jacques Yves Cousteau and Emile Gagnan provided much more freedom of movement.

The bathyscaphe, an underwater deep-sea ship, was invented to enable scientists to reach great ocean depths. Two bathyscaphes and the depths they have reached are: *Alvin*, 3,750 m (about 12,000 ft) and *Trieste*, 10,940 m (about 35,000 ft).

Undersea exploration has also been improved through the use of the echosounder, a device to measure the depth of the ocean, and through the use of core sampling techniques to analyze ocean sediment.

MATERIALS

BASIC TEACHING PLAN

MOTIVATION

Text Questions — Have you ever swum under water? *Allow students to describe their experiences.* Were you able to breathe? *No (unless they had special equipment).*

Since the aqualung is widely used for recreational and salvage purposes in fresh water as well as in the oceans, there is a good possibility that someone in your locale has access to aqualung equipment and might be willing to bring it to your class. You may be able to make contact with such individuals by calling suppliers for recreational diving (check your phone book Yellow Pages under "Divers" and "Divers' Equipment and Supplies"). Another way is to call your nearest state police installation to make contact with officers who specialize in underwater rescue and evidence acquisition. They may be willing to visit your classroom and display their specialized underwater equipment.

EXTENSIONS

Application
Activity

If you are able to locate a diver who is willing to come to your class, you can capitalize on the career awareness opportunity by asking students to develop a list of questions to ask of the guest. Students can also prepare a list of answers that they think the diver might give, and in a post-visit class discussion, compare their predictions with the actual responses that were given. Possible questions might include: Why did you become a diver? What training is needed? What are the dangers involved? What are some interesting and dangerous things that have happened to you underwater?

an air supply on board a ship. However, there was danger in using this equipment. The hoses would often tangle and break, cutting off the diver's air supply. People risked using these diving suits to search shipwrecks for treasure. The first person to use diving gear for scientific study was the nineteenth-century French scientist Henri Milne-Edwards.

In 1943, the **aqualung** (ak-wuh-lung) was invented. The *aqualung* is an air tank worn on the diver's back with a hose from the tank to the diver's mouth. The aqualung allows divers to explore underwater for long periods of time. Look at the picture of the diver on page 57. Can you locate the parts of the aqualung? What do divers wear to open their eyes safely and see underwater?

Even with an aqualung and a face mask, a diver can only swim to a certain depth. After a depth of more than 133 m (439 ft), the water presses against the diver so

Aqualung: An air tank worn on a diver's back.

58

DEVELOPMENT

1 **Text Questions** — Can you locate the parts of the aqualung? *The students should be able to point to the tank and hose.* What do divers wear to open their eyes safely and see under water? *A face mask.*

2 **Skill Development** — Have the students begin a list of the *vocabulary* words in this section. They should include the definitions. You may wish to consider the possibility of having students begin their own *science vocabulary* dictionary that would contain all terms introduced in science class.

Exceptional Student
Visually Impaired

If possible, bring in a face mask that a diver uses. Have the student put it on. Discuss the purpose of the mask and other diving equipment.

much that it can crush the diver. In order to explore greater depths, **bathyscaphes** (bath-ih-scafs) were invented. A *bathyscaphe* is an underwater ship. It can carry people and equipment to a depth of 3,600 m (about 12,000 ft). The bathyscaphe in the picture is called *Alvin*.

Finding out what the ocean floor looks like is difficult. To map the surface of the ocean bottom, an **echo sounder** is used. This instrument uses sound, which travels through water. When sound hits the bottom of the ocean, it bounces back to the ship. The time it takes for the sound to hit the ocean bottom and return to the ship is measured. Scientists can figure out how far the sound traveled if they know how long it took to return. Therefore, they know how far down the bottom is. They can map the high and low places on the ocean bottom.

Look at the boats pictured below. Each boat is using an echo sounder. With your finger, follow the sound waves sent out from the boat on the left. Continue to the place where the sounds hit the ocean bottom. Now follow the path of the sound bouncing back. Now look at the boat in deeper water, as shown on the right. Would it take more or less time for the sound to bounce back to that boat?

Bathyscaphe: An **2** **underwater ship.**

Echo sounder: An instrument that sends out sounds that hit the ocean bottom.

sound sent out

sound bouncing back

59

Reinforcement
Science Skills — Vocabulary

Ask some of your students to do dictionary research to find the derivation of bathyscaphe and aqualung. Have them share the information. They will discover that bathyscaphe comes from *bathy* based on a Greek word meaning "of the sea," and *skaphe*, a Greek word meaning "bowl." Aqualung comes from the Latin *aqua* meaning "water," and *lungen*, an Old English word meaning "an organ for breathing."

3   **Teaching Tips** — You may wish to do a little work at the chalkboard to help your students understand that, if we know the speed of something and the time elapsed during its journey, we are able to calculate how far it traveled. Use the example of an automobile traveling at a constant speed. For example, a car traveling 50 km/h (30 mi/h) for 2 hours travels a total of 100 km (60 mi). We multiply the speed by the time to find the distance covered.

4   **Skill Development** — If you carry out Teaching Tip 3 above, you can help students *generalize* their understanding of the *illustration*. Since the sound makes a trip down and returns, the elapsed time needs to be halved before scientists calculate the distance from the ship to the ocean bottom.

5   **Teaching Tips** — Sound travels about 1,450 m/sec (4,780 ft/sec) in water.

6   **Text Questions** — Would it take more or less time for the sound to bounce back to that boat? *More time (the sound has to travel over a longer distance).*

Application

Science Skills — Measuring

Sound travels at 1,450 m/sec (4,780 ft/sec) in water. Pose the following problem to your students: A ship sends out a sound that returns to the ship in four seconds.

1. How long did it take the sound to hit bottom? Two seconds.
2. If it took the sound two seconds, how many meters (feet) did it travel? 2 x 1,450 m (2 x 4,780 ft) = 2,900 m (9,560 ft).
3. How deep is the ocean bottom at that place? 2,900 m (9,560 ft).

You can repeat these computations and vary the number of seconds the sound took to travel.

ACTIVITY

Making observations from an echo sounder chart

A. Study the chart below and answer these questions:
   1. At what depth is the underwater mountain?
   2. How high is the mountain?
   3. How deep is the deepest part of the ocean shown on the chart?

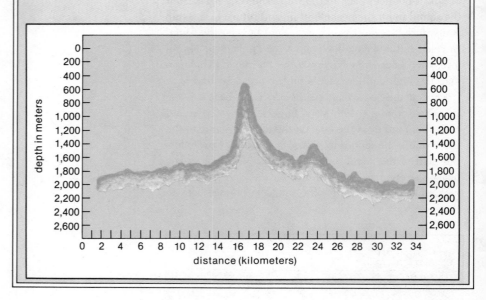

The layers of sediments on the ocean bottom built up over a very long period of time. Studying them can provide information about the history of the earth. They contain the remains of plants and animals that lived in the ocean long ago. When they died, they sank to the bottom and became covered with sediment. Even changes that take place on land are recorded in the ocean

60

ACTIVITY

Skill Development — Reading Illustrations

Teaching Tips — Underwater depth is often measured using the fathom as the unit for distance. The relationship between fathoms, meters, and feet is as follows: 1 fathom = 1.83 meters = 6 feet.

Due to the irregularities of the ocean's surface, the echosounder display of distance will provide students with a less sharp picture of the ocean's bottom than they may have expected. Consequently, their readings will show some variation from student to student.

Answers to Questions — 1. The underwater mountain is about 641 meters (350 fathoms) below the surface.   2. The mountain is 1,190 meters (650 fathoms) high, if you consider its base to be at 1,830 meters (1,000 fathoms) under the water.   3. The deepest part of the ocean shown is about 2,013 meters (1,100 fathoms).

sediments. Dust from volcanoes sometimes reaches the oceans and filters through the water. Eventually some of it is added to the sediment. Sediments carried to the ocean from streams and rivers on land also tell us what the soil on the earth's surface was like in the past.

Scientists get samples of sediment by drilling a long hollow tube into the ocean bottom. The tube is then brought to the surface of the water. The hollow part contains a sample of sediment from the ocean bottom. Scientists remove the core of ocean sediment from the tube. They do this just like you would remove the core of an apple. The core is carefully sliced in half lengthwise.

The layers of sediment in a core are like clues for a detective. Here is a diagram of sediment layers in a core. Which layer do you think formed first? If you think it is the bottom layer, you are right. The only way for it to be where it is is that it reached the ocean floor first. Everything that fell on it had to have settled from the ocean at a later time. Which layer formed last?

7 Imagine that the C and F layers in the core sample are sediments from the dust of two different volcanoes. Which volcano was the first to burst? Which of the vol-
8 canoes probably erupted for the longer time?

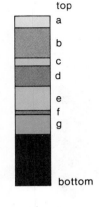

top
a
b
c
d
e
f
g

bottom

61

Enrichment
Activity

Some students may enjoy creating a mock public service television message about pollution of the ocean. They should take a position on the issue and discuss their views. Suggest that they use a song, poem, or skit to portray their message. Allow the students to present their messages to other classes. They can find out if their messages were effective by discussing the issue with other classes.

7 **Text Questions** — Which layer formed last? *A*.
8 **Text Questions** — Which volcano was the first to burst? *The one that caused the sediment layer F.* Which of the volcanoes probably erupted for the longer time? *The one that caused sediment in layer C.*

EXTENSIONS

Enrichment
Science Skills — Building Science Vocabulary

Here are additional vocabulary words related to this unit. The students can use their dictionary and research skills to identify the meaning of these words and their relation to the unit's concepts.

Guyot: A volcano rising from the ocean floor. Its top has been flattened by erosion.

Coral: A small animal that lives in the warm shallow waters of the ocean.

Ooze: Sea floor sediments formed from the remains of living things.

Nodule: A lump of sediment found on the ocean floor that contains valuable minerals.

Swell: Long and regular waves moving great distances across the oceans.

Section Review

Main Ideas: Divers use equipment such as the aqualung and bathyscaphe to explore the underwater world. The ocean bottom can be mapped, using an echo sounder. Sediment samples from the ocean bottom are studied to learn about changes that have taken place on earth.

Questions: Answer in complete sentences.

1. What is an aqualung?
2. What is a bathyscaphe? Why is it used?
3. Explain how an echo sounder is used to make a picture of the ocean bottom.
4. What can scientists learn from studying the sediments of the ocean bottom?

People in Science

Eugenie Clark

Dr. Eugenie Clark is a famous marine biologist. She has spent most of her life studying sharks. As a young girl, Dr. Clark spent long hours at the New York Aquarium. She also read everything she could on sharks and other fishes. She studied about marine animals in college. Later she became a college teacher.

As founder and director of the Mote Marine Laboratory in Florida, Dr. Clark did experiments on shark behavior. Later she began a worldwide study of sharks. This involved diving into oceans where sharks live.

She has studied the behavior of the great white shark. This is one shark that attacks humans. After 26 years of research on sharks, Dr. Clark has found that most sharks, unless threatened, prefer to escape rather than attack anything as large as a human.

62

SECTION REVIEW

Answers to Questions
1. An aqualung is an air tank with a hose to the diver's mouth.
2. An underwater ship, the bathyscaphe is used to carry people and equipment to great depths.
3. Sound is sent to the ocean bottom from a ship. When the sound hits the bottom, it bounces back to the ship. The time it takes for the echo to return to the ship is an indication of the depth of the water.
4. They can learn about the history of the earth.

CHAPTER REVIEW

Science Words
1. Chemicals sprayed on crops to kill pests.   2. An instrument that sends out sounds that hit the ocean bottom.   3. Patterns of who-eats-whom.   4. Waste materials carried by sewers and drains.
5. The adding of harmful materials to the ocean.   6. Plants and animals.   7. Petroleum and natural gas.   8. Salt.   9. Plankton.
10. Copepods.

SUGGESTED WORKSHEET MASTER
p. T-7u

CHAPTER REVIEW

Science Words Define each of these words:

1. pesticides
2. echo sounder
3. food chains
4. sewage
5. pollution

What word best fits each of the blanks?

6. A fossil fuel is formed from the remains of _____ and _____.
7. Two fossil fuels are _____ and _____.
8. Desalination is the process for removing _____ from ocean water.
9. _____ are tiny plants and animals on the ocean surface.
10. Tiny shrimplike animals are called _____.

Questions: Answer in complete sentences.

1. What are the four important resources that the ocean provides?
2. Describe the causes of ocean pollution.
3. This is an example of an ocean food chain: plankton → copepods → cod → seal → shark. How would the copepods and seals be affected if the cod became extinct? Explain your answer.
4. How is an echo sounder used to map the ocean bottom?
5. Which living things in each pair would be the highest in the ocean's pyramid of life? Give a reason for each of your choices.
   a. pelican, fish **b.** plankton, fish **c.** seaweed, fish **d.** seaweed, pelican **e.** seal, fish.
6. How can ocean water be changed into fresh drinking water?
7. What devices help scientists explore the ocean?

63

EXTENSIONS

Reinforcement
Activity

The following class activity will serve to illustrate the interdependence among organisms in the oceans.

A. Have each student select an ocean plant or animal to study. They should focus their efforts on three tasks related to their organism: 1. The construction of a papier-mâché model or full-color drawing. 2. The preparation of a brief report on the characteristics of the organism. 3. A description of two or three members of its food chain.

B. On a given day, the class should arrange the models or drawings so that organisms with a close feeding relationship are near one another. For example, plankton and the baleen whale would be organized so that the baleen whale is "feeding" on the plankton. As individual organisms may be part of many food chains, assist the students in rearranging the models so that the classroom shows the food chains in relations to one another — for example, plankton is fed on by the baleen whale and copepods.

Answers to Questions
1. Food, fossil fuels, fresh water, and valuable minerals.
2. Chemicals, sewage, and oil spills.
3. If the fish became extinct, the seals would have no food. They might also become extinct. There would be an increase in the number of copepods because the fish would not be there to eat them.
4. The echosounder sends out sound waves. They bounce off the ocean bottom and return to the ship. By knowing how long it took for the sound to travel down and back, scientists can find how far the ocean bottom is from the ship.
5. **a.** Pelican — Pelicans eat fish.   **b.** Fish — Fish eat plankton.
c. Fish — Fish eat living things that eat seaweed.   **d.** Pelican — Pelicans eat fish that eat other living things that eat seaweed.
e. Seal — Seals eat fish.
6. Ocean water is heated until it becomes steam. The steam cools and then liquifies. The salt is left behind, so the water is now fresh.
7. Diving suits, aqualungs, and the bathyscaphe.

SUGGESTED TEST MASTERS
p. T-7i, j

EXTENSIONS

Enrichment
Activity

Are icebergs salty? By doing this activity, students will learn that they are not.

A. Gather these materials: table salt, water, ice cubes, a quart jar, rock salt, a metal bowl, teaspoon, large plastic container (metal bowl must fit in it).

B. Make a salt solution by adding one teaspoon of salt to a quart jar of water. Place in a metal bowl. In a large plastic container make a mixture of rock salt and ice cubes.

C. Place the metal container in the plastic container on top of the ice. Stir the salt solution with the teaspoon. Have a student taste the solution. It should taste salty. After it freezes, have another student taste the ice that forms. It should not be salty, since the salt is left behind when the water freezes.

INVESTIGATING

How does temperature cause ocean currents?

A. Obtain these materials: 1 large beaker, 1 small beaker, potholder, ice water, hot water, blue food coloring, red food coloring.

B. Pour about 2 cups of hot water into a large beaker. CAUTION: USE A POTHOLDER WHEN POURING HOT WATER. Add 2 or 3 drops of red food coloring to the hot water and stir.

C. Pour about 1/2 cup of ice water into a small beaker. Add 2 or 3 drops of blue food coloring and stir.

D. Using the potholder, hold the beaker of hot water on a slant. Very slowly and carefully, add the cold water to the hot water. Let the cold water trickle very slowly down the inside of the large beaker of hot water.
   1. What happened to the cold water?
   2. Which is more dense, cold water or hot water? Explain.

E. Pour about 2 cups of ice water into a large beaker. Add 2 or 3 drops of blue food coloring and stir. Pour about 1/2 cup of hot water into a small beaker. Add 2 or 3 drops of red food coloring and stir.

F. Hold the beaker of cold water on a slant and very slowly and carefully pour the hot water into the cold water. CAUTION: USE A POT-HOLDER WHEN POURING HOT WATER.
   3. What happened to the hot water?
   4. How does this experiment show how temperature causes deep ocean currents?

64

INVESTIGATING

Skill Development — *Predicting, Cause and Effect*

Teaching Tips — The hot water should be boiling and the cold water should be ice water. The water should be poured together very carefully so that the layers will not be disrupted.

Safety Tips — Use a potholder when pouring hot water. Use beakers rather than regular jars so that the glass does not crack.

Answers to Questions — **1.** It sunk to the bottom.   **2.** Cold water is more dense since it sunk.   **3.** It stayed on top.   **4.** Colder ocean water sinks and warmer ocean water rises, which causes vertical ocean currents.

CAREERS

Marine Biologist ▶

A **marine** (muh-**reen**) **biologist** is a scientist who studies the ocean's living things. *Marine biologists* are especially interested in ocean food chains. Anything that harms a species in the ocean will probably affect many food chains. By studying ocean species, marine biologists can help to prevent species from becoming extinct. They study science for many years and are usually expert divers and swimmers.

◀ Salvage Diver

A **salvage diver** is a person who finds sunken ships and brings valuable objects to the surface. Much time is spent studying old records to locate shipwrecks. Once located, the area around the ship must be carefully studied. Water currents could cause the sunken ship to move while divers are working on or near it. Great skill and patience are needed for this dangerous work.

65

EXTENSIONS

Enrichment
Research — Library

Interested students could do research on careers in geological oceanography. Marine geologists study the ocean's underwater mountain ranges, rocks, and sediments, and investigate geological phenomena such as continental drift. They also look for minerals, oil, and gas beneath the ocean floor. Many of the jobs in marine geology require ocean expeditions and working underwater with scuba gear. The minimum requirement for a beginning professional job in oceanography is a bachelor's degree in a science-related field.

CAREERS

Teaching Tips — About 65 colleges and universities offer undergraduate degrees in marine sciences. For more information write to: Marine Technology Society, 1730 M Street N.W., Washington, D.C. 20036. Salvage divers learn their trade on the job. They must be excellent swimmers and know how to scuba-dive.

UNIT 2 SOUND

	SECTION	BASIC SCIENCE SKILLS	ACTIVITY MATERIALS STUDENT/GROUP	EXTENSIONS	
CHAPTER 4 HEARING SOUND	**4-1** p.T-68 How Sounds Are Made	*Reading the illustration* to locate vibration sources p.T-70 *Finding the cause and effect* between vibration and sound p.T-70	plastic ruler	• Reinforcement pp.T-69, T-70, T-71, T-72	
	4-2 p.T-73 Instruments of Sound	*Reading the illustration* to locate clarinet valves p.T-75 *Observing* the kettle drum pedal p.T-78	4 plastic straws, scissors, small glass of water	• Enrichment pp.T-74, T-75, T-77 • Application p.T-76, T-78	
	4-3 p.T-79 Sound Travels	*Comparing and contrasting* the speed of light and sound p.T-81		• Reinforcement pp.T-80, T-82, T-83 • Enrichment p.T-81	
CHAPTER 5 SOUND WAVES	**5-1** p.T-84 Sound and Matter	*Observing* a wave in a spring p.T-86 *Reading the illustration* to study a stethoscope p.T-88 *Finding the effect* of a vacuum on sound p.T-89	ticking watch, meter stick	• Reinforcement p.T-87 • Enrichment pp.T-85, T-86, T-89, T-90 • Application p.T-88	
	5-2 p.T-91 Different Sounds	*Observing the effect* of a vibrating tuning fork p.T-92 *Comparing* the pitch of sounds p.T-92	8 bottles (same size), water, grease pencil, ruler or wooden stick	• Reinforcement p.T-92 • Enrichment pp.T-93, T-94, T-95, T-96	
	5-3 p.T-97 Sound Waves Reflect	*Reading the illustration* to find the animals that can hear ultrasonic sound p.T-99 *Comparing and contrasting* how materials react to sound p.T-100		• Reinforcement pp.T-98, T-101 • Enrichment p.T-99 • Application p.T-100	
	5-4 p.T-102 Sound Messages	*Sequencing* the steps by which a telephone works p.T-104 *Comparing and contrasting* a telephone receiver with a phonograph speaker p.T-106 *Comparing and contrasting* old and new phonographs p.T-106		• Reinforcement p.T-107 • Enrichment pp.T-104, T-105, T-106, T-108, T-109, T-110 • Application pp.T-103, T-111	

EXTRA ACTIVITIES/ DEMONSTRATIONS	WORKSHEET MASTERS	EVALUATIONS
• Hidden sound makers p.T-68 • Sound hike p.T-69	Sound Waves (SK) p.T-65i	Section Review p.T-72
• Musical instruments p.T-73	Seeing Sound (AC) p.T-65j	Section Review p.T-78
• Whistle blowing p.T-80 • Light and distance p.T-81	Hearing Sound (SK) p.T-65k Crossword (SK) p.T-65l	Section Review p.T-82 Chapter Review p.T-83 Test Masters pp.T-65d,e
• Waves p.T-85	Riddles (SK) p.T-65m Vacuum (AH) p.T-65n	Section Review p.T-90
• Sound effect records p.T-91 • Tuning fork p.T-92 • Guitar p.T-93	Different Sounds (AC) p.T-65o	Section Review p.T-96
• Ball reflection p.T-97 • Echo survey p.T-98 • Ceiling tile p.T-100	Pitch and Frequency (SK) p.T-65p	Section Review p.T-101
• Telegraph p.T-103 • Old telephone p.T-104 • Investigating p.T-110	Morse Code (AC) p.T-65q	Section Review p.T-108 Chapter Review p.T-109 Test Masters pp.T-65f,g,h

BOOKS FOR STUDENTS

Bailey, Bernadine. *Bells, Bells, Bells*, New York: Dodd, 1978

Berger, Melvin. *The Clarinet & The Saxophone*, New York: Lothrop, Lee & Shepard, 1975

Darwin, Len. *What Makes a Telephone Work?*, Boston: Little, 1970

Gilmore, Lee, illus. by George Overlie. *Folk Instruments*, Minneapolis: Lerner, 1962

Heuer, Kenneth. *Thunder, Singing Sounds & Other Wonders: Sound in the Atmosphere*, New York: Dodd, 1981

Jacobs, Francine, illus. by Jean P. Zallinger. *Sounds in the Sea*, New York: Morrow, 1977

Kettlekamp, Larry. *The Magic of Sound*, New York: Morrow, 1982

Knight, David. *Silent Sound: The World of Ultrasonics*, New York: Morrow, 1980

Kuferberg, Herbert. *Rainbow of Sound: The Instruments of the Orchestra and Their Music*, New York: Scribner, 1973

O'Connor, Jerome J. *The Telephone, How It Works*, East Rutherford, NJ: Putnams, 1971

Wade, Harlan. *A Book About Sound*, Milwaukee: Raintree, 1977

FILMS

Ears: Have You Heard the Latest, 10½ min, Centron

Listen! Hear!, 15 min, National Geographic

Vibrations, 14 min, Britannica

FILMSTRIPS

Introducing Sound, Light and Color, 2 filmstrips, 2 cassettes, 15 min each, National Geographic

Your Senses and How They Help You, 2 filmstrips, 2 cassettes, 12–15 min each, color, National Geographic Educational Services

COMPUTER AIDS

Sound, Tutorial Apple, Pet, 16k BASIC, tape/disk Right On Programs

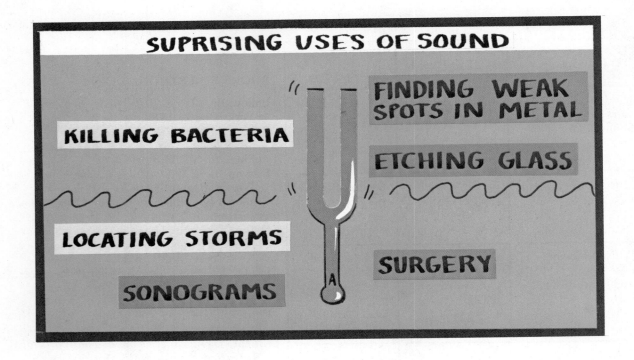

SUPRISING USES OF SOUND

KILLING BACTERIA

FINDING WEAK SPOTS IN METAL

ETCHING GLASS

LOCATING STORMS

SURGERY

SONOGRAMS

A

BULLETIN BOARD IDEAS

Students will be aware of using sounds to provide music. To stimulate them to investigate less common uses of sound energy, construct the following bulletin board. Show the tuning fork with sound waves being made around the fork. You may wish to use the illustration in the beginning of the unit to describe the effects of sound energy on particles of air. Among less obvious uses of sound are: applications in surgery, sunstorms, clouds, detecting weak places in metal, killing bacteria, and etching glass.

FIELD TRIP IDEAS

To an Audio Equipment Store

Students will probably have a high interest in visiting a store that specializes in sound systems. Ask the sales clerk to show your class the various components of a stereo system. The optimum time for this trip would be toward the end of the unit because terms such as *receiver, transmitter,* and *amplifier* will have more meaning to your students. Have the class notice the walls and floors of the room in which high-quality equipment is displayed.

To a Music Room

Take your class to visit the music room of your school or the band room of your local high school. If possible, make the visit during a practice session and ask several music students to play scales on various instruments to determine the range of pitch of specific instruments and to discuss how the pitch can be changed. Compare the sound intensity of various instruments.

HEARING SOUND

TEST 4
CHAPTER

CHAPTER OBJECTIVES

Read each question. Choose the best answer. Write the letter of your choice on the line at the right.

1. Which statement is true?
   a. Sound is the only form of energy.
   b. Energy cannot be changed into different forms.
   c. Light and heat are forms of energy.
   d. None of the above is true.

   1._____   1. **c** (1)

2. Objects produce sounds when they
   a. vibrate.   c. have no motion at all.
   b. carry electricity.   d. are moved from place to place.

   2._____   2. **a** (1)

3. In order to vibrate, objects must have
   a. energy.   c. light.
   b. electricity. d. heat.

   3._____   3. **a** (1)

4. The energy needed to produce a musical note from a tuning fork comes from
   a. the tuning fork.
   b. the vibrations from the fork.
   c. the person striking the fork.
   d. the rubber hammer that strikes the fork.

   4._____   4. **c** (1)

5. All of the following instruments have a reed except
   a. a saxophone.   c. cymbals.
   b. an oboe.   d. a bassoon.

   5._____   5. **c** (2)

6. Tightening the strings will change the sound on all of the following except the
   a. violin.   c. clarinet.
   b. guitar.   d. banjo.

   6._____   6. **c** (2)

7. Which of the following is *not* true about percussion instruments?
   a. They cause vibrations when they are hit.
   b. They can be made of a solid material.
   c. They can be made from materials stretched over a container.
   d. They can only have high sounds.

   7._____   7. **d** (2)

8. The part of a drum that vibrates to produce sound when it is hit is
   a. the pedal.   c. the drumhead.
   b. the stick.   d. all of the above.

   8._____   8. **c** (2)

9. __a__ (3)

9. When a barrier is placed in the path of light and sound,   9. _____
   a. it affects both light and sound.
   b. it does not affect light or sound.
   c. it only affects light.
   d. it only affects sound.

10. __c__ (3)

10. Which kind of energy spreads out in all directions from its   10. _____
    source?
    a. only sound   c. sound and light
    b. only light   d. neither sound nor light

11. __b__ (3)

11. Using a flashlight and speaking through a paper towel roll   11. _____
    are examples of
    a. stopping energy.   c. spreading out energy.
    b. aiming energy.   d. wasting energy.

12. __b__ (3)

12. When someone blows a whistle in a corner of a room,   12. _____
    a. only the people in the corner will hear it.
    b. everyone in the room will hear it.
    c. no one in the room will hear it.
    d. only people outside the room will hear it.

13. __c__ (4)

13. Which statement is true?   13. _____
    a. Sound and light travel at the same speeds.
    b. Sound travels faster than light.
    c. Light travels faster than sound.
    d. The speed of sound and light depends on the air
       temperature.

14. __a__ (4)

14. Sonic booms *cannot* cause   14. _____
    a. lightning.   c. loud sounds.
    b. buildings to vibrate.   d. glass and walls to crack.

15. __b__ (4)

15. A supersonic jet   15. _____
    a. flies at the same speed as sound.
    b. flies faster than sound.
    c. flies slower than sound.
    d. flies slower than an ordinary jet.

16. __a__ (4)

16. Which statement is true?   16. _____
    a. You see lightning before you hear thunder.
    b. You hear thunder before you see lightning.
    c. You see lightning and hear thunder at the same time.
    d. None of the above is true.

Fold Back
Answer
Key On
Line
Before
Copying.

SOUND WAVES

TEST 5
CHAPTER

Read each question. Choose the best answer. Write the letter of your choice on the line at the right.

CHAPTER OBJECTIVES

1. What forms when air particles bunch together and then spread out?
    - **a.** a sound wave
    - **b.** a vacuum
    - **c.** a medium
    - **d.** a coil

    1. _____   1. _a_ (1)

2. If the gases were removed from the tube of a stethoscope, the doctor would hear
    - **a.** a very loud heartbeat.
    - **b.** a very soft heartbeat.
    - **c.** a loud and soft heartbeat.
    - **d.** no difference.

    2. _____   2. _b_ (1)

3. Sound travels fastest through
    - **a.** water.
    - **b.** air.
    - **c.** wood.
    - **d.** steel.

    3. _____   3. _d_ (1)

4. Which of the following is *not* true about sound waves?
    - **a.** They have an up and down motion.
    - **b.** They are vibrations that move through matter.
    - **c.** They spread in all directions.
    - **d.** They start where the vibration is produced.

    4. _____   4. _a_ (1)

5. The loudness or softness of a sound is its
    - **a.** medium.
    - **b.** frequency.
    - **c.** intensity.
    - **d.** pitch.

    5. _____   5. _c_ (2)

6. As the vibrations of an object increase in strength,
    - **a.** the sound gets louder.
    - **b.** the sound waves get smaller.
    - **c.** the sound stops completely.
    - **d.** the intensity decreases.

    6. _____   6. _a_ (2)

7. Sound can change in
    - **a.** pitch.
    - **b.** intensity.
    - **c.** frequency.
    - **d.** all of the above.

    7. _____   7. _d_ (2)

8. Which sound would have the highest decibel reading?
    - **a.** a fire engine siren
    - **b.** a jet plane taking off
    - **c.** a piano
    - **d.** a whisper

    8. _____   8. _b_ (2)

9. A sound that is low pitched *cannot* be
    - **a.** loud.
    - **b.** soft.
    - **c.** low frequency.
    - **d.** high frequency.

    9. _____   9. _d_ (3)

10. <u>c</u> (3)   **10.** A flute has a high-pitched sound because the air column   **10.** _____
  a. does not vibrate   **c.** vibrates rapidly.
  b. vibrates slowly.   **d.** does none of the above.

11. <u>b</u> (3)   **11.** The number of vibrations per second gives a sound its   **11.** _____
  a. energy.   **c.** intensity.
  b. frequency.   **d.** decibel.

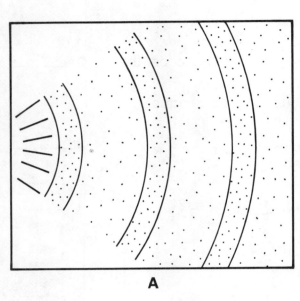 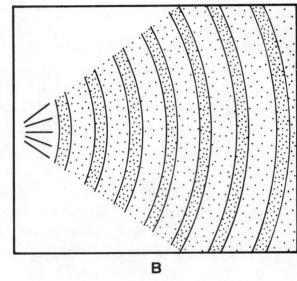

A   B

12. <u>b</u> (3)   **12.** Look at the pictures. Which statement is true?   **12.** _____
  a. The sound waves in picture A have a higher frequency than in picture B.
  b. The sound waves in picture B have a higher frequency than in picture A.
  c. The sound waves in pictures A and B have the same frequency.
  d. The sound waves in pictures A and B do not have any frequency.

13. <u>a</u> (4)   **13.** You can hear an echo when sound waves   **13.** _____
  a. bounce off an object.
  b. are absorbed by an object.
  c. disappear.
  d. are no more than 2 m from an object.

14. <u>d</u> (4)   **14.** Which of the following would *not* absorb sound waves?   **14.** _____
  a. a rug   **c.** a room full of people
  b. heavy drapes   **d.** a metal cabinet

15. All of the following will help stop noise pollution except   15._____   15. _c_ (4)
   a. stopping the noise at its source.
   b. putting up sound barriers.
   c. keeping a room as bare as possible.
   d. using materials that absorb sounds.

16. Tell if the sentence below is true or false. If it is false, tell which   16._____   16. _a_ (4)
   word can be used in place of the underlined word to make the
   sentence true.
   Bats can hear ultrasonic sounds.
   a. The sentence is true.   c. Robins
   b. Humans   d. Moths

17. When you listen to a record, the phonograph needle is   17._____   17. _c_ (5)
   a. erasing the grooves on the record.
   b. cutting a pattern in the record.
   c. picking up the vibration pattern of the original sounds.
   d. doing none of the above.

18. Which two parts produce sound waves?   18._____   18. _a_ (5)
   a. telephone receiver and phonograph speaker
   b. telephone transmitter and receiver
   c. telephone receiver and phonograph needle
   d. phonograph needle and speaker

19. A telephone changes   19._____   19. _c_ (5)
   a. sound waves into electrical energy.
   b. electrical energy into sound waves.
   c. both of the above.
   d. none of the above.

20. A message sent by telegraph is   20._____   20. _b_ (5)
   a. transmitted without wires.
   b. tapped out as clicks and pauses.
   c. sent by satellite.
   d. spoken.

Name _____ Date _____

How Sound Travels

A. Draw the sound waves as they spread out from the source.

B. How could the person in the next room lower the sound he hears without touching the radio? Explain why this method would work.

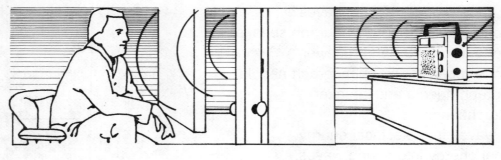

_____

_____

C. Circle the person to whom the sound would seem louder and explain why.

_____

_____

_____

Name _____ Date _____

Hearing Sounds

You are learning about sound causing vibrations. In this activity you will observe the vibrations caused by your own voice.

A. Obtain these materials: balloon, rubber band, can opener, glue, metal foil, and a metal can.

B. Remove both ends of the can. Cut a piece of the balloon large enough to be stretched tightly over one end of the can. Secure it with a rubber band.

C. Glue a small piece of aluminum foil onto the balloon, slightly off center.

D. Hold the open end of the can up to your mouth. Position the foil so that a spot of sunlight reflects from it onto a surface.

E. Talk loudly and clearly into the can, while observing the spot of light.

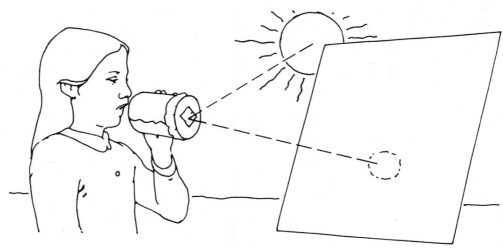

QUESTIONS

1. What did you observe about the spot as you were talking?

   _____

2. What happened if you talked louder?

   _____

3. What did you observe about the different sounds that you made?

   _____

Hearing Sounds

A. Circle the object that is producing sound and explain how you know that it is doing so.

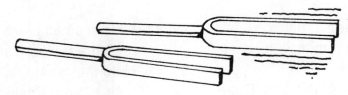

_____

_____

B. Check the object that would make the higher sound and explain why in the space provided.

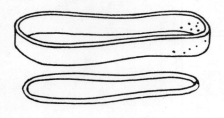  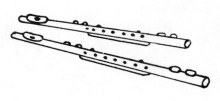

_____ _____ _____

_____ _____ _____

C. Name the types of instruments below and identify what vibrates in them to produce sound.

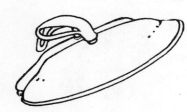  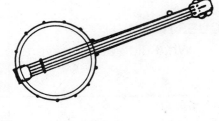

_____ _____ _____

_____ _____ _____

_____ _____ _____

_____ _____ _____

Name_____ Date _____

6

Hearing Sounds

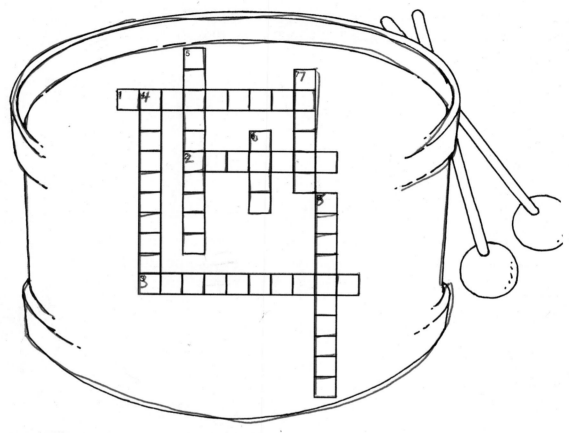

Use the clues below to complete the puzzle.

ACROSS

1. A fast back and forth motion
2. Certain instruments can tighten or loosen these to change the sounds they make
3. A device used to tune musical instruments

DOWN

4. A device for making music
5. This type of instrument produces a sound when struck
6. This type of instrument produces sound from a vibrating column of air
7. The ability to do work
8. Travelling faster than the speed of sound

Name_____ Date_____

Sound Waves

A. Look at the drawing below of air particles. In the space on the right, draw how they would look if a sound wave moved through them.

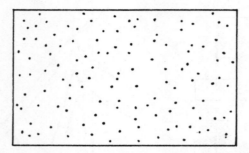
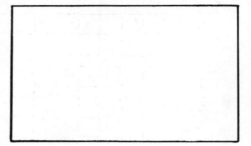

B. Number the drawings below in the order in which the person will hear the sound. Explain your answer in the space provided.

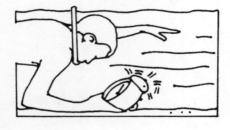

_____   _____   _____

_____

_____

C. Solve these riddles in the spaces provided.
1. A person sees a bell moving, but cannot hear it ring. Where is the bell? _____
2. The matter through which sound can travel is neither large nor a small. It is a _____.
3. If you are holding a disc in your hand and have tubes in your ears, and are listening to your heartbeat, you are using a _____.
4. Air particles first bunch up, then spread out. What just traveled through them? _____

Name_____ Date _____

Sound Waves

In school, you are learning about sound waves. In this at home activity, you will observe the importance of a medium for carrying sound waves. SAFETY TIP: IT IS VERY IMPORTANT THAT A HEAT RESISTANT FLASK BE USED IN THIS ACTIVITY AND THAT AN ADULT BE PRESENT AT ALL TIMES.

A. Obtain these materials: 2 cup hooks, 2 heat-resistant flasks, 2 jingle bells, 2 rubber stoppers, 2 pieces of string.

B. Screw the cup hooks into the bottom of the stoppers. Then attach the string to the bell, and to the hook.

C. Pour a small amount of water into the flask. Place the flask into a hot water bath. Heat it until it is filled with steam.

D. Carefully hold the top of the flask with a potholder and place the stopper tightly in the flask's opening as shown.

E. While this flask is cooling, place the stopper in the second flask. Shake both flasks. Listen for the bells' sound.

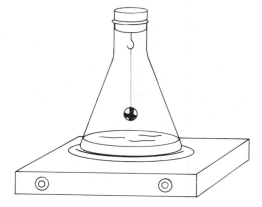

QUESTIONS

1. How did the bells sound to you? _____

_____

_____

2. How can you explain this? _____

_____

_____

Name _____ Date _____

Different Sounds

You are learning about how different types of sounds are made. In this activity, you will simulate how your vocal cords allow you to make different sounds.

A. Obtain these materials: funnel, rubber band, scissors, balloon or rubber sheet.

B. Stretch the rubber sheet or balloon over the funnel, as shown. Hold it in place with the rubber band.

C. Cut a narrow slit in the covering, as shown.

D. Blow into the narrow end of the funnel. Listen to the sound. Then blow into it again while looking at the slit with a mirror.

E. Tighten the sheet by stretching it tighter and repeat step **D.**

F. Place your fingers on your Adam's apple or thorax. Make a low and then a high sound. Think about what you feel.

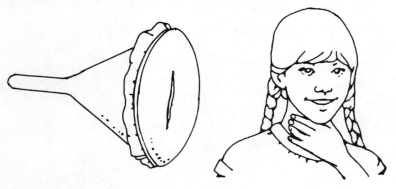

QUESTIONS

1. What happened the first time you blew into the funnel and air passed through the slit? _____

_____

2. How was the sound different the second time you blew into the funnel? _____

3. Your vocal cords are bands of tissue stretched over your voice box. What do you think happens to the vocal cords when you make a sound?

_____

_____

Name_____ Date_____

Sound Waves

A. Circle (○) the drawing with the higher intensity and place a square (□) around the drawing with the smaller sound waves.

B. **1.** Which bell would have the higher pitch? _____

_____

2. Which bell would have the lower frequency?

_____

3. Which bell would you ring and how would you ring it if you wanted a low-pitched sound with

high intensity? _____

_____

C. Choose which room would have more echoes and explain why you chose it.

_____

_____

_____

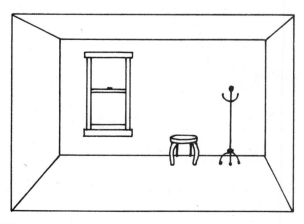 

Name_____ Date_____

Sound Messages

Use these Morse code signals to send messages to your friends.

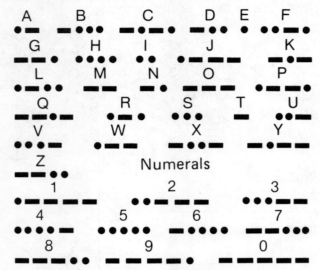

QUESTIONS

1. This code was used with a device called a _____.

2. Why did Samuel Morse need to invent this code for his device?

   _____

3. Translate this message into English:

   _____

Refer to EXTENSIONS on page T-104

Name_____ Date_____

How Sound Travels

HYPOTHESIZING, COMPARING AND CONTRASTING,   **SKILL WORKSHEET**
CONCLUDING AND GENERALIZING

A. Draw the sound waves as they spread out from the source.

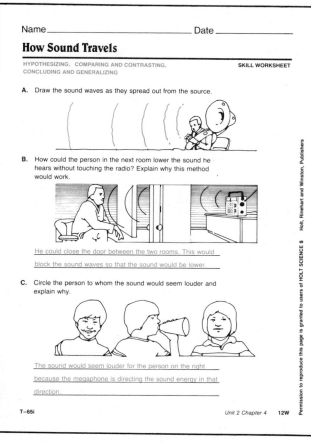

B. How could the person in the next room lower the sound he hears without touching the radio? Explain why this method would work.

He could close the door between the two rooms. This would
block the sound waves so that the sound would be lower.

C. Circle the person to whom the sound would seem louder and explain why.

The sound would seem louder for the person on the right
because the megaphone is directing the sound energy in that
direction.

T–65i   Unit 2 Chapter 4   12W

Name_____ Date_____

Hearing Sounds

ACTIVITY WORKSHEET

You are learning about sound causing vibrations. In this activity you will observe the vibrations caused by your own voice.

A. Obtain these materials: balloon, rubber band, can opener, glue, metal foil, and a metal can.

B. Remove both ends of the can. Cut a piece of the balloon large enough to be stretched tightly over one end of the can. Secure it with a rubber band.

C. Glue a small piece of aluminum foil onto the balloon, slightly off center.

D. Hold the open end of the can up to your mouth. Position the foil so that a spot of sunlight reflects from it onto a surface.

E. Talk loudly and clearly into the can, while observing the spot of light.

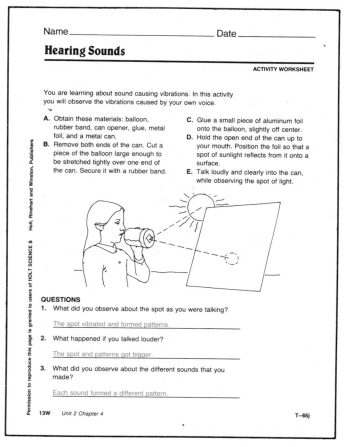

QUESTIONS

1. What did you observe about the spot as you were talking?

   The spot vibrated and formed patterns.

2. What happened if you talked louder?

   The spot and patterns got bigger.

3. What did you observe about the different sounds that you made?

   Each sound formed a different pattern.

13W   Unit 2 Chapter 4   T–65j

Name_____ Date_____

Hearing Sounds

CLASSIFYING, COMPARING AND CONTRASTING,   **SKILL WORKSHEET**
FINDING CAUSE AND EFFECT

A. Circle the object that is producing sound and explain how you know that it is doing so.

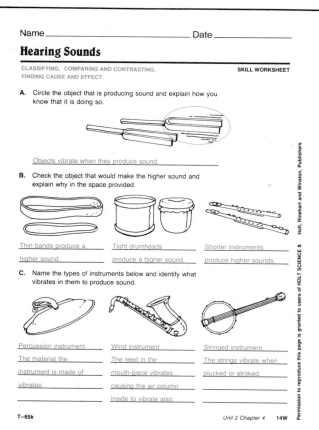

Objects vibrate when they produce sound.

B. Check the object that would make the higher sound and explain why in the space provided.

Thin bands produce a   _Tight drumheads_   _Shorter instruments_
higher sound.   _produce a higher sound._ _produce higher sounds._

C. Name the types of instruments below and identify what vibrates in them to produce sound.

Percussion instrument   _Wind instrument_   _Stringed instrument_
The material the   _The reed in the_   _The strings vibrate when_
instrument is made of   _mouth-piece vibrates_   _plucked or stroked._
vibrates.   _causing the air column_
                          inside to vibrate also.

T–65k   Unit 2 Chapter 4   14W

Name_____ Date_____

Hearing Sounds

BUILDING SCIENCE VOCABULARY   **SKILL WORKSHEET**

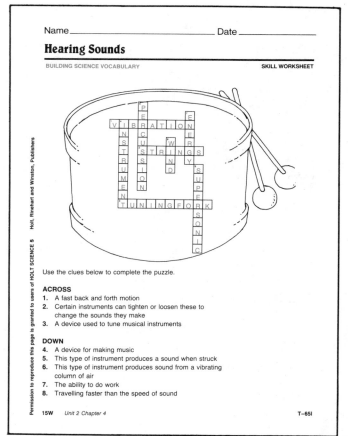

Use the clues below to complete the puzzle.

ACROSS

1. A fast back and forth motion
2. Certain instruments can tighten or loosen these to change the sounds they make
3. A device used to tune musical instruments

DOWN

4. A device for making music
5. This type of instrument produces a sound when struck
6. This type of instrument produces sound from a vibrating column of air
7. The ability to do work
8. Travelling faster than the speed of sound

15W   Unit 2 Chapter 4   T–65l

Worksheet 1 (top left)

Name_____ Date_____

Sound Waves

A. Look at the drawing below of air particles. In the space on the right, draw how they would look if a sound wave moved through them.

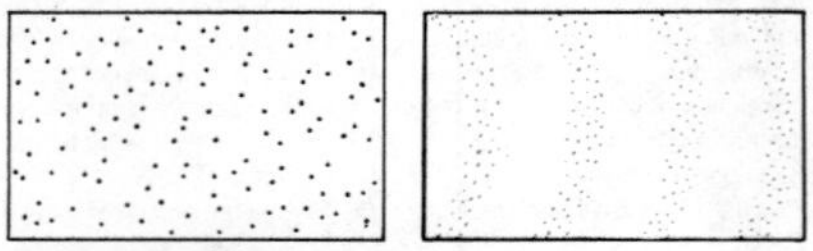

B. Number the drawings below in the order in which the person will hear the sound. Explain your answer in the space provided.

2   3   1

Sound travels through solids faster than through liquids and
through liquids faster than through gases.

C. Solve these riddles in the spaces provided.
1. A person sees a bell moving, but cannot hear it ring. Where is the bell? _In a vacuum_
2. The matter through which sound can travel is neither large nor a small. It is a _Medium_
3. If you are holding a disc in your hand and have tubes in your ears, and are listening to your heartbeat, you are using a _Stethoscope_
4. Air particles first bunch up, then spread out. What just traveled through them? _A sound wave_

Permission to reproduce this page is granted to users of HOLT SCIENCE 5   Holt, Rinehart and Winston, Publishers

---

Worksheet 2 (top right)

Name_____ Date_____

Sound Waves

In school, you are learning about sound waves. In this at home activity, you will observe the importance of a medium for carrying sound waves. SAFETY TIP: IT IS VERY IMPORTANT THAT A HEAT RESISTANT FLASK BE USED IN THIS ACTIVITY AND THAT AN ADULT BE PRESENT AT ALL TIMES.

A. Obtain these materials: 2 cup hooks, 2 heat-resistant flasks, 2 jingle bells, 2 rubber stoppers, 2 pieces of string.
B. Screw the cup hooks into the bottom of the stoppers. Then attach the string to the bell, and to the hook.
C. Pour a small amount of water into the flask. Place the flask into a hot water bath. Heat it until it is filled with steam.
D. Carefully hold the top of the flask with a potholder and place the stopper tightly in the flask's opening as shown.
E. While this flask is cooling, place the stopper in the second flask. Shake both flasks. Listen for the bells' sound.

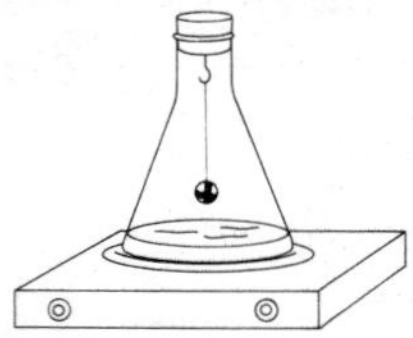

QUESTIONS
1. How did the bells sound to you? _The bell in the heated flask could not be heard at all. The second bell could be heard clearly._
2. How can you explain this? _The steam forced the air out of the first flask forming a vacuum. Since sound needs a medium to travel in, it cannot travel in a vacuum._

Permission to reproduce this page is granted to users of HOLT SCIENCE 5   Holt, Rinehart and Winston, Publishers

---

Worksheet 3 (bottom left)

Name_____ Date_____

Different Sounds

You are learning about how different types of sounds are made. In this activity, you will simulate how your vocal cords allow you to make different sounds.

A. Obtain these materials: funnel, rubber band, scissors, balloon or rubber sheet.
B. Stretch the rubber sheet or balloon over the funnel, as shown. Hold it in place with the rubber band.
C. Cut a narrow slit in the covering, as shown.
D. Blow into the narrow end of the funnel. Listen to the sound. Then blow into it again while looking at the slit with a mirror.
E. Tighten the sheet by stretching it tighter and repeat step **D.**
F. Place your fingers on your Adam's apple or thorax. Make a low and then a high sound. Think about what you feel.

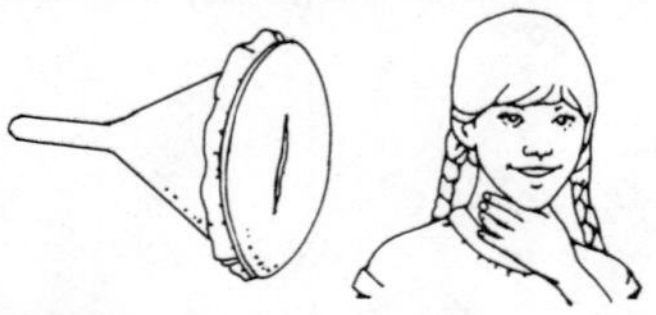

QUESTIONS
1. What happened the first time you blew into the funnel and air passed through the slit? _The sheet vibrated and a sound was made._
2. How was the sound different the second time you blew into the funnel? _The sound was higher._
3. Your vocal cords are bands of tissue stretched over your voice box. What do you think happens to the vocal cords when you make a sound? _The vocal cords vibrate when air moves over them. The sound is higher when the vocal cords are tightened._

Permission to reproduce this page is granted to users of HOLT SCIENCE 5   Holt, Rinehart and Winston, Publishers

---

Worksheet 4 (bottom right)

Name_____ Date_____

Sound Waves

A. Circle (○) the drawing with the higher intensity and place a square (□) around the drawing with the smaller sound waves.

B.
1. Which bell would have the higher pitch? _The smaller one_
2. Which bell would have the lower frequency? _The larger one_
3. Which bell would you ring and how would you ring it if you wanted a low-pitched sound with high intensity? _You would ring the larger bell very loudly._

C. Choose which room would have more echoes and explain why you chose it.
Room A would have more echoes because hard surfaces reflect sound waves and there are no sound-absorbing materials in the room.

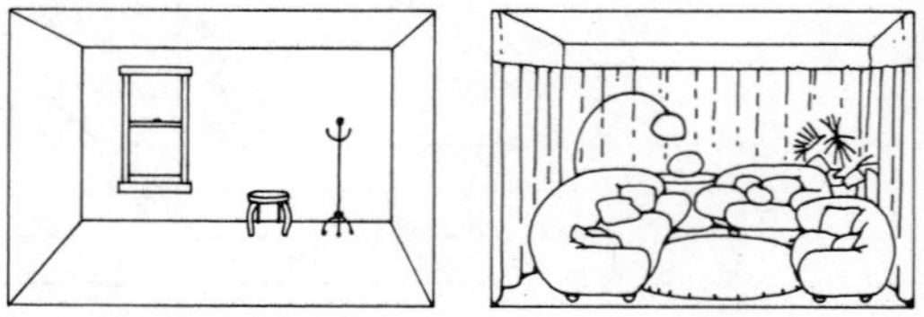

Permission to reproduce this page is granted to users of HOLT SCIENCE 5   Holt, Rinehart and Winston, Publishers

Name_____ Date_____

Sound Messages

Use these Morse code signals to send messages to your friends.

Numerals

Punctuation and other signs

Period   Comma   Interrogation

Colon   Semicolon   Quotation Marks

SOS   Start   Wait

End of Message   Understand   Error

S A M U E L   M O R S E

QUESTIONS

1. This code was used with a device called a ___telegraph___.

2. Why did Samuel Morse need to invent this code for his device?

   It could not send human speech over the wires.

3. Translate this message into English:

   Samuel Morse

Refer to EXTENSIONS on page T-104

T–65q

Unit 2 Chapter 5   **20W**

Unit Overview

This is a physical science unit on sound. Sound is a form of energy. In order for a sound to be produced, something must vibrate. Musical instruments produce sound when strings, columns of air, or solid objects are made to vibrate.

Sound travels in the form of a wave. The particles of the matter through which sound is traveling are alternately compressed and spread far apart. For this reason, sound cannot travel in a vacuum. Generally, it travels fastest through solids, slower through liquids, and slowest through gases.

Pitch depends upon the speed with which the sound-producing object is vibrating. High-speed vibrations produce wavelengths of high frequency and high pitch. The intensity, or loudness, of a sound depends upon how much energy was used in producing the sound. The intensity is measured in decibels.

Sound waves can be reflected off surfaces or can be absorbed by them. The study of *acoustics* deals with this property of sound. Energy can be changed from sound energy to electrical energy and back to sound energy. This has made possible many inventions, such as the telephone, the microphone, and the phonograph.

SOUND

Unit Opener

This is a photograph of a college band playing at a football game. You can ask the students the following questions as motivation: What kind of sound would this band make? *The students responses will vary*. Would it be loud? *Yes*. Would it be high or low? *It would depend on what they were playing*. Where would the sound be loudest? *Down on the field with the band*. How many different kinds of instruments are there in this band? *The three general kinds of instruments are brass, woodwind, or percussion*.

LEARNING CENTER

A suggested title for the Learning Center could be "Good Vibrations." Photos showing musical instruments and other sources of sound could be used as displays. You may wish to create a file for copies of the worksheet masters and Extensions that the students can work on independently.

The following Extensions are especially suitable for the Learning Center. The materials for these Extensions should be available in the learning center: sound map, p. T–70 (pencil, paper); sound collages, p. T–72 (magazines, scissors, paste, construction paper); spoon sounds, p. T–87 (spoon, string, pencil); old records, p. T–92, (records, hand lens); pipe signals, p. T–103 (worksheet); Morse code, p. T–104 (worksheet, tape recorder).

In addition, an index file of suggested research topics could be set up using the following Extensions: guitar and violin making (p. T–74), historical instruments (p. T–75), dolphins (p. T–85), radio (p. T–90), singing (p. T–94), noise (p. T–96), sonar (p. T–99), satellites (p. T–108), inventors (p. T–109), Slinky (p. T–110).

UNIT 2

**Exceptional Student
IEP Unit Goal**

At the end of Unit 2, the student will describe the following concepts in one sentence: how sound is made, how sound travels in a room, how sound travels through solids, and how sound travels across long distances.

CHAPTER 4

CHAPTER OBJECTIVES

1. Explain how energy, movement, and sound are related.
2. Classify musical instruments on the basis of their vibrating part or parts.
3. Describe the similarities between sound energy and light energy.
4. Identify the differences between sound and light. Describe the speed of jet planes.

SECTION BACKGROUND

The sounds of a human voice, a bird chirping, a plane flying overhead: all these sounds originate from vibrations.

Sound is a form of energy transmitted by vibrating objects. Energy is the capacity to cause an object that is not moving to move. Sound energy transmitted by a vibrating object causes the molecules of the medium surrounding the object to move, or vibrate. The molecules of gases in the air (or the molecules of a liquid or a solid) near the vibrating object are temporarily moved from their normal location. The vibrating object loses energy, and the medium surrounding it gains energy. When the vibrations stop, the sound stops. By adding energy to a vibrating object, we enable it to transmit more energy to its surroundings.

MATERIALS

A plastic ruler

**Exceptional Student
IEP Chapter Goal**

In a specific situation, such as when a teacher is speaking to the class, the student with no visual problem can illustrate how sound travels from its source. The visually impaired student will explain verbally how sound travels from its source.

HEARING SOUND

4-1.
How Sounds Are Made

68

The crowd has quieted down. The runners are down at the starting line. They strain to hear the voice of the starter. "Ready. On your mark. Get set." The sharp sound of the starter's whistle rings in their ears. They leap from the starting line. When you finish this section, you should be able to:

BASIC TEACHING PLAN
MOTIVATION

Assemble a collection of sound-producing objects that you keep hidden. Possibilities include party noisemakers and two small pans that can be struck together. Produce a sound from each object without the students seeing the objects. While you make these sounds, ask the students to keep their eyes closed and to guess what the source of each sound is. Display the objects after you make the sounds. Have the students discuss how they think the sounds got from the objects to their ears. Don't resolve the question at this point, as they will be discovering the answers in the chapters that follow in this unit.

You may wish to use the opening photograph as a stimulus to have students who participate in athletic activities describe the sounds that are important in their favorite sports—for example, umpires yelling "safe" or "out," or halftime buzzers sounding. Ask those students what things sometimes make it difficult for them to hear these sounds, for example, the roar of the crowd or protective headgear.

☐ **A.** Explain what causes sound.
☐ **B.** Describe the relationship between movement and sound.

The sound made by the whistle needs **energy** (eh-ner-jee). *Energy* is the ability to do work. Energy causes objects to move. When you pick up a book, you use energy to move it. The starter used energy to say,

Energy: The ability to do work.

ACTIVITY

Observing the cause of sound

A. Obtain a plastic ruler.

B. Take turns with a partner in this activity. One of you should put your ear against the desk top in order to listen. The other should place the ruler so that half of it extends over the edge of the desk.

C. With one hand, hold the ruler flat against the desk top. With the other hand, lightly hit the free end of the ruler.

D. The listener should describe the sound produced by the ruler.
  1. What did it sound like?
  2. What caused the sound?
  3. What do you notice when the ruler stops?
  4. Where did the energy to move the ruler come from?

E. Changing the length of the ruler that extends over the desk changes the sound.
  5. Make a hypothesis about what will happen to the sound when the length of the ruler is made longer and shorter.
  6. Do an experiment to check your hypothesis.
  7. Copy the chart shown. Record your data.
  8. What conclusions did you reach?

Length	How Sound Changed
shorter	
longer	

69

ACTIVITY

Skill Development — *Comparing and Contrasting, Hypothesizing*

Teaching Tips — The vibrating ruler will produce a humming sound. If you wish the students to hear a sound that is more distinctive, have them press the ruler less tightly against the desk top. This will cause the ruler to strike the desk top as it moves and to produce louder sounds.

Answers to Questions — **1.** A fast humming sound.   **2.** The movement of the ruler.   **3.** The sound stops.   **4.** From us. We caused the ruler to move.   **5.** The length of the vibrating ruler will change the highness or lowness of the sound. When the ruler is short, the sound will be high. When it is long, the sound will be low.
6. Change the length of the ruler by having more or less of it extend over the desk. Note the sound produced when it is made to vibrate.
7. The chart should show that the sound was higher when the ruler was shorter, or that it had more vibrations than when it was longer.
8. When we made the ruler shorter, we produced a higher sound. When we made the ruler longer, we got a lower sound.

EXTENSIONS

Reinforcement
Science Skills— Observing and Recording Data

Take your students on a "sound hike" of your school grounds. Before taking the hike, have the students construct a chart to record their observations about the sources of the sounds that they will hear. Their charts should have at least three columns. At the top of one column they should write the heading "Natural Sounds." At the top of the second column, they should write the heading "Sounds Made by Humans." At the top of the third column, they should write "Unidentified Sounds." They will need to take their charts and pencils with them on the hike. Have the students walk without talking. After they have heard a sound, they should decide whether or not it was made by humans. Then they should write a description of the sound under the appropriate heading on their charts. After the sound hike, conduct a discussion that focuses on the following types of questions:
  1. Did they record more natural sounds or more sounds made by people?
  2. What was the vibrating object or objects that produced each sound?
  3. Did they record any sounds that came from vibrating objects that were not on the school grounds?
  4. Did they record any sounds that they had not noticed before in the school building or on the school grounds?
  5. How many unidentified sounds were recorded? Can the class make some guesses as to what might have caused them?

Reinforcement
Activity

Have the students prepare a map that shows the route that they travel on their way to or from school. On their maps they should include symbols to represent the sources of the sounds they hear. At the bottom of each map, there should be a legend that explains the symbols. Some of the students may wish to make tape recordings of the sounds they hear on their way to or from school. They can bring the recordings to class and play them for the benefit of the class. The other students can then try to identify the sounds and also the vibrating object or objects that are producing the sounds.

1

Vibrate: To move back and forth quickly.

"Ready, on your mark, get set." Energy was stored in the starter. This energy was changed to sound energy when she blew the whistle.

Sound is one of many forms of energy. Light, heat, and electricity are some other forms. Energy can be changed from one form to another. You have observed many energy changes. For example, when you use a toaster, electrical energy is changed to heat energy.

Sounds are produced when energy causes an object to **vibrate** (vi-brayt). *Vibrate* means to move back and forth **2** quickly. If you strike a drum with your hand, you use energy. The energy causes the drumhead to move. It moves back and forth quickly. These vibrations cause

70

DEVELOPMENT

1 Skill Development — The students will *read the illustrations* to locate the sources of vibrations.

2 Skill Development — As the students read the text material and look at the photographs, emphasize that vibrating objects *cause* the *effect* that we call sound.

sound. When the drumhead stops vibrating, the sound also stops.

3 Look at the pictures on page 70. What sounds would you hear if you were there? What do you think is vibrating to cause the sounds?

The woodpecker's beak moves back and forth against the tree. That causes a tapping sound. The jackhammer vibrates as it digs into the ground. When you speak or sing, your throat vibrates. Place your hand on your throat **4** and hum. What do you feel?

Many objects vibrate so quickly that their motion can't be seen. The effects of the motion can be seen by using a table tennis ball and a thread. If a vibrating object touches the ball, the ball will bounce away.

5 The metal object in the photographs below is a **tuning** (**too**-ning) **fork**. A *tuning fork* is used to tune musical instruments. It has two prongs. When the prongs of a tuning fork are hit, they vibrate. A musical tone can be made when they are struck with a rubber hammer. Energy to produce sound comes from the person striking the fork. In the picture on the left, the table tennis ball is **6** not vibrating. In the picture on the right, the tuning fork has been struck. What happened to the ball? What caused it to move?

Tuning fork: A device used to tune musical instruments.

71

Look at the pictures on page 70.

3 **Text Questions** — What sounds would you hear if you were there? *The woodpecker's beak striking the tree and the jackhammer vibrating.* What do you think is vibrating to cause the sounds? *The bird's beak and the tree; the hammer and the pavement.*

4 **Text Questions** — What do you feel? *Vibrations from your voice box, or larynx.* The larynx, which is an enlarged area of the windpipe, contains the vocal cords. When the students touch their throats, they feel the muscles of the larynx move. The muscles can change the tension on the vocal cords and produce sounds of different pitch.

5 **Teaching Tips** — If you have a tuning fork available, strike it against a rubber object, such as a rubber shoe heel, and then hold the fork against a sheet of paper. The students will hear the sounds of the vibrating tuning fork striking the paper. If you have a table-tennis ball and a length of thread, you can demonstrate the sequence of events shown in the photographs.

6 **Text Questions** — What happened to the ball? *The ball was pushed outward.* What caused it to move? *Vibrations from the tuning fork.*

Section Review

Main Ideas: Energy is the ability to do work. It causes objects to move. Sound is a form of energy produced when an object vibrates. Energy is the source of all vibration.

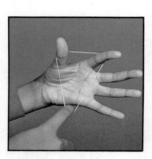

Questions: Answer in complete sentences.

1. Explain how sounds are produced. Use the words *energy* and *vibrate* in your explanation.
2. Study the picture of the rubber band. In this position no sounds come from the rubber band. What could you do to make sound come from it?
3. What one word best describes the motion of a rubber band when it is producing sound?
4. We can't see rapid vibrations, but we know they exist. Describe how the photographs on page 71 show that they exist.
5. Look at the picture of the gong above. What source of energy will make the gong ring?

72

These students are rehearsing for a concert. Notice the different types of instruments they are using. Each instrument works differently. Each instrument produces a different sound. When you finish this section, you should be able to:

☐ **A.** Name the three types of musical instruments.
☐ **B.** Explain how sound is produced by each type of instrument.
☐ **C.** Classify instruments by their vibrating parts.

One group of musical instruments is the **stringed instruments**. Some examples are the harp, violin, and guitar. Musicians produce sounds on *stringed instruments* by plucking or stroking the strings. Each stringed instrument produces a special sound. The thick strings on an instrument produce lower sounds than the thin strings.

How tight or how loose a string is will change the sound, too. Tight strings produce higher sounds. Loose strings produce lower sounds. How can musicians get

Stringed instrument: An instrument with one or more strings.

73

SECTION BACKGROUND

A vibrating object that sends out energy at regular intervals of time produces sounds that we often refer to as music. Musical sounds are produced from instruments that are categorized as being in one of three groups: string, wind, or percussion. String instruments have a string or group of strings made from metallic, synthetic, or animal fibers. The strings are stretched over a box or board that will vibrate as the strings vibrate. By using strings of different lengths, thickness, or tightness, musicians can vary the sounds they produce.

Wind instruments are either woodwinds or brass. Woodwinds produce sounds as the result of an initial vibration of a reed that causes the subsequent vibrations of an air column. Brass instruments produce sounds as the result of an initial vibration made by the player's lips that, in turn, causes an air column to vibrate. The sound from a wind instrument can be changed by varying the initial reed or lip vibrations, or by changing the length of the vibrating air column. Both lip and reed are made to vibrate when a player blows into the instrument.

Percussion instruments have solid parts, or material, stretched over a frame. The percussion player strikes the solid part, or the stretched material, and causes it to vibrate.

BASIC TEACHING PLAN

MOTIVATION

If your school district has a music instructor, that teacher might be willing to bring some instruments to class. The various types of instruments can be shown and discussed. If this is not possible, obtain pictures of various types of musical instruments. You could also display some ordinary objects that produce a "musical" sound — a piece of rubber stretched over a coffee can, various thicknesses of rubber bands, wide- and narrow-mouthed glass bottles.

MATERIALS

4 plastic straws, scissors, small glass of water

Enrichment
Research — Library

Ask the students to do some research on how a guitar and a violin are made. They should report on the number of strings each instrument has, how different notes are produced, and the function of the resonating chamber. The method by which the strings are made to vibrate in each instrument should also be explained.

different sounds from a stringed instrument? The thickness and tightness of the strings cause different sounds. The tightness of the strings can be changed by twisting the tuning pegs at the end of a guitar's neck.

Suppose you have two strings of the same thickness but of different lengths. The longer string will produce a lower sound than the shorter string. Here is how a musician can make the same string produce different sounds.

1 The top photo shows a guitar string being plucked. A low sound is produced. In the bottom photo, the same string is pressed tightly against the wood. Pressing the string against the wood shortens its length. Now when the string is plucked, a higher sound is made.

74

DEVELOPMENT

1 **Teaching Tips** — Discuss with the students the differences between the guitar in the illustration and an electric guitar. The solid-body electric guitar has a depth of only about 4 cm (1 1/2 in). It has no resonating chamber under the strings. The steel strings pass over tiny microphones that pick up the sound of their vibrations and send them to an amplifier. Knobs on the instrument control volume, tone, tremolo, and echo.

Exceptional Student
Learning Disabled
Visually Impaired

Borrow various instruments from the school and allow the students to experiment with them. Discuss how vibrations are produced on each instrument.

Wind instruments are a second type of musical instrument. They are made of either wood or metal. For this reason, they are known as woodwinds or brass. Let's look at each kind of *wind instrument*.

The photograph and diagram below show a woodwind called the clarinet. It is a hollow tube through which air can flow. On the mouthpiece, there is a thin piece of wood called a reed. Blowing through the mouthpiece will cause the reed to vibrate. These vibrations are carried through the hollow tube. They produce sound. Holes on the sides of the tube allow different sounds to be made. As a player's fingers cover and uncover these holes, high and low sounds can be made.

Saxophones, oboes, and bassoons are other instruments that have reeds. When the musician blows across a reed, it starts to vibrate. The vibrating reed causes the column of air in the instrument to vibrate. The vibrating air makes a sound.

Wind instrument: An instrument made of a hollow tube through which air can flow.

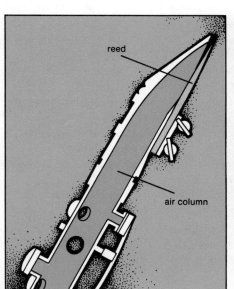

75

2 Teaching Tips — Be sure that the students understand that brass instruments differ from woodwinds in that they do not use reeds. The vibrations of the musician's lips take the place of the vibrating reed.

3 Skill Development — Have the students locate the valves on the clarinet in the *illustration*. They are the three buttonlike devices under the musician's right hand.

EXTENSIONS

Application
Activity

Discuss with the class the method by which a piano produces sound. If there is one in the school, arrange to have the class gather around it. Expose the strings so the students can see them. Point out the hammers. Let the students hit various keys and make some observations on the relationship of the sound produced to the length of string.

Perhaps a piano tuner in the community would be willing to come to the school and explain to the class how a piano is tuned. If not, it can be explained that the tension on the string is adjusted until the string produces the right note when compared to a tuning fork.

Ask the students how they would fit the piano into the classifications of instruments they have learned. A piano is a stringed percussion instrument.

Exceptional Student
Learning Disabled

Learning-disabled students with coordination problems will have difficulty with this activity. Assign partners to them.

Hearing Impaired

Have the hearing impaired student feel the vibrating straw.

Brass wind instruments are usually made of the metal brass. To play a trumpet, musicians press their lips against the mouthpiece. When musicians blow, their lips vibrate. Their vibrating lips cause the air column in the trumpet to vibrate. That makes a sound. Pressing the valves at the top of the trumpet changes the length of the air column. Changing the air column changes how high or low the sound will be.

ACTIVITY

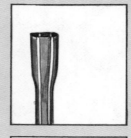

How can you change the sound of a musical instrument?

A. Obtain these materials: 4 drinking straws, scissors, small glass of water.

B. Flatten about 3 cm of one end of the straw. Rub the scissors 2 or 3 times across both sides of this end. Make a cut on each side of the flattened end. CAUTION: BE VERY CAREFUL WHEN USING THE SCISSORS. This is the reed part of the instrument.

C. Moisten the straw and blow through it. The end of the straw should vibrate and make a sound. You may have to try this a few times.

   1. What caused the sound when you blew through the straw?

   2. Would the length of the straw affect the sound of your instrument? Make a hypothesis.

D. Make several straw instruments, each of a different length. Try each one.

   3. Did you feel the vibrations of the straw?

   4. How were the sounds of longer instruments different from the sounds of shorter instruments? Compare your results with your hypothesis.

   5. How are your instruments like woodwind instruments?

76

ACTIVITY

Skill Development — *Following Directions, Cause and Effect, Hypothesizing*

Teaching Tips — It will take two or three tries before most students are able to make the reed. Students will use the side of the scissors to flatten about an inch of straw before they do any cutting. This will take a little effort since the straw has a tendency to return to its rounded shape. Students may have difficulty getting sound because they will hold the straw too deeply in their mouths. Have them experiment to find the best position.

After the activity you could do a demonstration to show the effect of the straw's length on the sound that is produced. As the class looks on, produce a steady sound and continue to snip off more and more of the end of the instrument. The sound will rise dramatically.

Answers to Questions — **1.** The vibration of the straw and the subsequent vibrations of the air within the straw. **2.** Yes. A long straw

Violin

Banjo

Cello

Saxophone

Oboe

Tuba

4 Look at the picture above. Which instruments are woodwinds? Which are brass? Which are stringed instruments?

Can you think of an instrument that is not played by plucking strings or blowing through an air column? How about drums and cymbals? These are examples of **per-**

5 **cussion** (per-**kuh**-shun) **instruments.** *Percussion instruments* produce musical sounds when hit. They are hit either by hand or by some other part of the instrument. They may be made of a solid material or materials stretched over a container. A cymbal is made of solid metal. A drum is a container with material stretched over

Percussion instrument: An instrument that produces a musical sound when hit.

77

Enrichment
Science Skills— Comparing and Contrasting

Students can make two different-sized tambourines out of paper plates and elbow noodles. Then they can compare the sounds produced.

A. Obtain two large and two small paper plates, stapler, and small elbow noodles.

B. Half fill one large and one small paper plate with noodles.

C. Staple the other matching plates on top of the first plate.

D. Shake both instruments and compare the sounds you hear.

1. Which tambourine made the louder sound?
2. What vibrated to produce the sound?
3. What supplied the energy to produce this vibration?

will make a different sound than a short straw.   **3.** Yes. I could feel the straw vibrating against my lips.   **4.** Longer instruments made lower sounds than shorter instruments.   **5.** Woodwind instruments produce sound when a thin reed is made to vibrate.

4 **Text Questions** — Which instruments are woodwinds? *Oboe, saxophone.* Which are brass? *Tuba.* Which are stringed instruments? *Cello, violin, banjo.*
5 **Teaching Tips** — Ask the students to imagine how they could make their own percussion instruments from everyday materials. They may be interested in trying this at home and bringing in their instruments. They could compare the sounds produced by their creations.

Application
Activity

This activity is appropriate for students who can locate needed materials, organize them, and follow directions. Have students assemble materials at some appropriate location in the school or classroom to make flowerpot chimes following these directions:

A. Obtain six clay flowerpots of different sizes, six pieces of heavy cord, and a broomstick.

B. Place the end of one cord through the hole at the bottom of one pot. Knot the end of the cord so that it does not slip through the hole.

C. Do this for the other cords and pots.

D. Hang the pots upside down by tying the other ends of the cords to the broomstick.

E. Tap each pot with a pencil to produce different sounds.

6

it. Both drums and cymbals cause vibrations when they are hit.

Bands and orchestras use several types of drums. A drummer can change how high or low the drum sounds by turning knobs. A tight drumhead vibrates faster than a loose one. It also makes a higher sound. The sound of a kettledrum can be changed before or while it is being played. Look at the kettledrum on the left. Before it is played, the tightness of the drum can be changed by turning the knobs at the top. The pedal at the base can be used to tighten the drumhead while it is being played.

Section Review

Main Ideas: Classifying musical instruments.

Type of Instrument	Example	What Vibrates	What Causes Vibration
1. String	Violin	Strings	Plucking or stroking strings
2. Wind **a.** Woodwind	Clarinet	Reed, Air Column	Blowing across reed
b. Brass	Trumpet	Lips, Air Column	Blowing into mouthpiece
3. Percussion	Drum	Drumhead	Hitting drumhead

Questions: Answer in complete sentences.

1. Name three main types of musical instruments.
2. Give an example of each type of these instruments. How is sound produced by each type of instrument?
3. What are two types of wind instruments?
4. For each type, tell what part vibrates.
5. Tell what type of instrument each of these is: **a.** clarinet **b.** trumpet **c.** cymbal **d.** drum **e.** violin **f.** tuba **g.** banjo **h.** harp

78

---

6 **Skill Development** — Students should *observe* the pedal at the bottom of the kettle drum.

SECTION REVIEW

Main Ideas — Display previously cut-out magazine pictures of instruments and have the students classify them into categories.

Answers to Questions
1. String, wind, percussion
2. String, violin; strings are bowed to make them vibrate. Wind, saxophone; player's lips or a reed is made to vibrate when air is blown through it. Percussion, drum; drumhead or solid part is struck to make it vibrate.
3. The two types of wind instruments are woodwind and brass.
4. Woodwind — reed, air; brass — lips, air
5. a — woodwind; b — brass; c — percussion; d — percussion; e — string; f — brass; g — string; h — string

SUGGESTED WORKSHEET MASTER
for sections 4–1 and 4–2
p. T–65j

Both the radio and the lamp in the photograph below are turned on. The radio is sending out sound energy. The lamp is sending out light energy. Anyone standing nearby can hear the radio and see the light. What would happen if the radio and the lamp were covered? When you finish this section, you should be able to:

☐ **A.** Explain how sound travels.
☐ **B.** Compare how sound energy and light energy travel.

If you covered the radio and lamp with a box, you would notice two things. First, the sound would not seem as loud. Second, you could not see the light from the lamp through the box. Both the sound and light are changed by an object placed in their paths. The box allows some sound to pass through. But no light can pass through the box.

What would happen if the box had holes in it? You could see light passing through the holes. The sound would be louder because it would pass through the holes.

Both sound and light energy spread out from a source. The sound energy spreads out from the speaker in the radio. The light energy spreads out from the light bulb. In what direction does the energy spread out?

SECTION BACKGROUND

Sound and light share some common characteristics. Both are forms of energy. Sound waves and light waves radiate outward in all directions from their source. The movement of each can be limited by obstacles placed in its path.

Sound and light are quite different with respect to the requirement of a medium for transmission. Sound energy can only be transmitted through a medium (gas, liquid, or solid). Light energy does not require a medium for transmission. Light can travel through a vacuum. Sound and light differ significantly with respect to the speed with which they move. The speed of sound depends on the characteristics of the medium through which it passes. The speed of sound in dry air at 0° Celsius is 330 meters/second (1,100 ft/second). Light travels so fast as to be virtually instantaneous. Light travels at 300,000 kilometers/second (186,000 miles/second).

79

BASIC TEACHING PLAN

MOTIVATION

You may wish to use the photographs as the basis for a demonstration of the effect of blocking the movement of energy. If you do, point out that there is another form of energy being blocked by the barrier besides sound and light. Indicate that heat is being produced by both sources and that it also is moving outward in all directions.

Text Questions — In what direction does the energy spread out? *All directions.*

Have the students bring in clean, empty tin cans and some stones. In the playground area of the school, divide the class into small groups. The students should place the stones in the tin cans. Have one student shake the cans. Have other students see how far they can get from the student shaking the can and still hear the sound of the rattling stones. Have them place a barrier, such as a line of students, between the shaker and the listeners. Ask them how that affects their perception of the sound. Tell the shaker to go just around the corner of the building to test for distance again. What effect does putting a closed door between the shaker and the listeners have on the sound?

How does sound spread from its source? A school basketball game is being played. The referee blows his whistle to call a foul. The players hear the whistle. They stop playing. The fans hear the whistle, too. Those sitting near the court hear the sound. So do those sitting high up in the bleachers. The source of the sound is the vibrating air passing through the whistle. The sound spreads out in all directions. No matter what the source of the sound, it will spread out in all directions. But when a barrier is placed in front of the source, the sound is stopped. This is why the whistle cannot be heard as well outside the gym. A barrier also keeps unwanted noise from being heard inside the recording room above.

Light also spreads out in all directions. When a lamp is turned on in a dark room, light reaches all parts of the room. Some light reaches the ceiling, floor, and walls. **2** What would happen if there were a barrier in front of the light source?

The fact that both sound and light energy spread out in all directions is important. If they didn't, you could not light a room by turning on an overhead light. You wouldn't hear a radio that was in the corner of a room. This spreading out of energy can also be a problem. It could be a problem if you wanted a lot of light or sound to

80

DEVELOPMENT

1 **Teaching Tips** — If it is convenient, take the students outside and ask them to blow a whistle from various distances and to describe the intensities of the sounds.

2 **Text Questions** — What would happen if there were a barrier in front of the light source? *Depending on the nature of the barrier, the light would be blurred or totally blocked.*

reach a certain spot. Look at the photos below. They show how sound and light can be aimed.

There are many ways to direct sound energy and light energy. Flashlights, car headlights, and spotlights all aim light. This is done by bouncing the light energy off a shiny surface. This causes most of the energy to leave in one direction instead of spreading out. When you cup your hands over your mouth to shout, you send sound energy in one direction.

3
4
Sound and light both spread out in all directions. But they travel at different speeds. Light always travels at the same speed. It travels at 300,000 km/sec (186,000 mi/sec). The speed of sound in air depends on the temperature and moisture of the air. The speed of sound in dry air at 0° Celsius (32° Fahrenheit) is 330 m/sec (about 1,100 ft/sec).

5
The speed of sound is often compared to the speed of a jet plane. Some jets travel at the same speed as sound. Others travel at twice the speed of sound.

Jets that travel faster than the speed of sound cause **sonic booms** (sah-nik boomz). These are very loud sounds. *Sonic booms* that reach the ground can cause buildings to vibrate. They can vibrate so much that glass and walls may crack.

Sonic boom: Loud sound produced when a jet is moving faster than sound.

The speed of light is so fast that it is difficult for humans to develop a concept of its magnitude. One way to help your students develop a sense of its extraordinary speed is to have them use the information in this section to make some calculations concerning how far they could travel in a given period of time, if they could travel at the speed of light (an impossibility but an interesting idea). Have the students select various time intervals (e.g., 1 second, 5 seconds, 1 minute), and then have them make calculations of the distance they could theoretically cover if they could travel as fast as light.

81

3 **Skill Development** — Use the information on this page that *compares* the speeds of sound and light to help students understand that these forms of energy are very different with respect to speed.

4 **Teaching Tips** — The speed of light is so extraordinarily fast that it is instantaneous to our eyes. You can help students get a sense of this by using a world map that has a distance scale. Select two points (e.g., your community and London, England). Have a student find the distance between them. Using the figure for the speed of light, determine how many times light could travel back and forth between those points in just one second.

5 **Teaching Tips** — As you discuss the speeds of sound and light, help students get a sense of how far sound can travel from your school into the surrounding area in one second. Pick a reference point about 300 to 400 meters from the school. Tell the students that sounds produced in the school can reach that point in one second.

Reinforcement
Science Skills—Comparing and Contrasting

This activity should be done in the school playground.

A. Have the students choose partners, one of whom goes to the opposite end of the playground. One of the partners claps hands loudly near his or her head. The sight of the hands clapping precedes the sounds made.

B. Then have students form groups of three students. Have two students stand back to back, close to each other. They will clap their hands alternately, each one clapping as soon as the sound of the partner's clap is heard, for a total of 20 claps. The other student should measure the length of time this takes.

C. Repeat this activity with the partners at opposite ends of the playground. In order to rely on sound only, the partners' eyes should be closed. The length of time for the second set of 20 claps should be longer.

Supersonic: Faster than the speed of sound.

A jet that flies faster than the speed of sound is called **supersonic** (soo-per-**sah**-nik). A *supersonic* jet has been made that carries many people. This jet is called the *Concorde*. The *Concorde* can fly from London to New York in just over three hours. It would take a regular jet almost seven hours for the same trip.

Section Review

Main Ideas: Comparing Sound and Light

	Sound	Light
Difference:	Travels at 330 m/sec	Travels at 300,000 km/sec
Likenesses:	Both forms of energy Both spread in all directions Both may be aimed	

Questions: Answer in complete sentences.

1. Describe how sound and light travel.
2. Name two things that sound and light have in common.
3. What is one way in which sound differs from light?
4. Give an example of a way sound can be aimed. Explain how your example works.
5. Can light be aimed? Explain how.
6. At a night launching of a space rocket, which would you notice *first* at blastoff, the roar of the engines or the light from the exhaust? Explain.

82

SECTION REVIEW

Answers to Questions
1. They spread out from their sources in all directions.
2. Sound and light are both forms of energy that spread out in all directions, and they both can be aimed at an object.
3. Sound must travel through a medium. Light does not need a medium.
4. The students should give an example, such as the megaphone. The sides keep the sound from spreading out in all directions.
5. Yes. Headlights, spotlights, and flashlights all cause light from a source to be reflected from surfaces behind the light source.
6. You would notice the light from the exhaust first, since light travels much faster than the sound coming from the engines.

SUGGESTED WORKSHEET MASTER
for sections 4–2 and 4–3
p. T–65k

CHAPTER REVIEW

Science Words: Unscramble the letters to find the correct terms. Then write their definitions.

1. RYGENE
2. USSIONCREP TENMSTRUIN
3. DOWINDOW
4. GUNTIN ROFK
5. NIWD RUSTMINETN
6. DEGSTRIN TUSRMINENT
7. TRASBEVI
8. NOSCI MOBO

Questions: Answer in complete sentences.

1. A musician plucks a guitar string and a sound is produced. What happens to this string? What is the source of energy?

2. What type of instrument is each of the following: **a.** drum **b.** banjo **c.** clarinet? How is each used to produce sound?

3. Look at the photograph of the girl with the gong on page 72. What type of instrument is the gong? Give a reason for your answer.

4. When a rocket is launched, both sound and light are produced. What are two things that these forms of energy have in common?

5. Match the cause in the first column with its effect in the second column.

Cause	Effect
1. vibrating object	a. produces sonic boom
2. tightened strings on guitar	b. produces sound
3. jet traveling faster than sound	c. produces lower sound
4. loosened drumhead	d. produces higher sound

83

EXTENSIONS

Reinforcement
Science Skills — Vocabulary

To improve the students' ability to use the glossary/index quickly and efficiently, have them list the page numbers on which the following subjects are discussed: energy, vibrations, stringed instruments, wind instruments, percussion instruments, sonic boom, and supersonic jet.

CHAPTER REVIEW

Science Words — 1. Energy — The ability to do work. **2.** Percussion instrument — Made of solid material stretched over a frame. **3.** Woodwind — Wind instrument that uses a reed. **4.** Tuning fork — A device used to tune musical instruments. **5.** Wind instrument — A hollow-tube instrument through which air can flow. **6.** Stringed instrument — An instrument with one or more strings. **7.** Vibrates — Moves back and forth quickly. **8.** Sonic boom — Loud sound produced when an airplane is moving faster than sound.

Answers to Questions
1. The string vibrates. The musician's fingers.
2. **a.** Percussion. The drumhead is struck and vibrates. **b.** Stringed. The strings are plucked and vibrate. **c.** Woodwind. The reed and air column vibrate.
3. Percussion: It vibrates when hit.
4. They move in all directions, forms of energy, can be aimed.
5. 1. b; 2. d; 3. a; 4. c

SUGGESTED WORKSHEET MASTER
p. T–65l

SUGGESTED TEST MASTERS
p. T–65d,e

CHAPTER 5

CHAPTER OBJECTIVES

1. Describe how sound waves travel and compare the movement of sound waves through various media.
2. Describe sound waves in terms of intensity.
3. Describe the pitch and frequency of sound waves.
4. Explain how sound waves can be reflected and absorbed, and give examples.
5. Describe how the phonograph, the telephone, and the telegraph function.

SECTION BACKGROUND

A sound wave is the alternate pressing together and spreading apart of molecules. The crowding together of molecules is compression. The spreading out of molecules is rarefaction.

Sound travels fastest through a solid that has elastic qualities. The sound of a dental drill is transmitted clearly through the bones of the skull. Liquids also conduct sound. Two objects struck together under water produce sound waves that travel through the water to a swimmer below the surface. This transmission of sound waves in water enables sonar operators on submarines to monitor the movements of ships by listening for their engines.

Sound energy cannot travel through a vacuum. The moon has almost no atmosphere, so astronauts communicate with each other through radio signals.

MATERIALS

A ticking watch, a meter stick

Exceptional Student
IEP Chapter Goal

At the end of this chapter, the student will state one example of sound traveling through matter and one example of sound reflecting.

SOUND WAVES

5-1.
Sound and Matter

84

The dolphin shown on page 85 was part of an experiment. A scientist covered its eyes. But this did not keep the dolphin from "talking." Microphones placed in the water picked up its sounds. This experiment shows that sound can travel through water. When you finish this section, you should be able to:

BASIC TEACHING PLAN
MOTIVATION

It is very probable that many students have seen a calliope, such as the one in the photograph, at a circus or a fair. Ask students: Have you seen this instrument before? *Answers will vary.* What is it called? *A calliope.* Students may wonder about its name. The instrument was named after the Greek muse Calliope, which means "beautiful voice." Ask students to describe its sound and to think about how its sound is made. The piercing tones of a calliope are made by steam whistles which are tuned to a scale. When the keys on the keyboard are struck, compressed air from steam boilers passes through the whistles. Invented in 1855, the calliope was traditionally used at fairs and gatherings because its sound could be heard from very far away.

☐ **A.** Explain how *sound waves* travel.
☐ **B.** Explain and give examples of matter through which sound travels.
☐ **C.** Compare how sound travels through different types of matter.

1 Sound energy moves from place to place. Vibrations travel from the dolphin through the water. When you hear a bird's song or a friend's voice, you hear vibrations that travel through air.

2 Sound travels in **waves**. A *sound wave* is a vibration that moves through matter. Think of this. Pretend you have dropped a pebble into a quiet body of water. You can see ripples spreading out. Sound travels through air much like ripples move through water. A sound wave starts where the vibration is produced. It spreads in all directions. But sound waves are not exactly like waves

Sound wave: A vibration that moves through matter.

85

DEVELOPMENT

1 **Teaching Tip** — Many of the students have seen dolphins performing acrobatic tricks on television programs or perhaps during visits to aquariums. They may not have thought very much about the ability of dolphins and other sea creatures to communicate over long distances. You may want to use the photograph and opening text material to get students to speculate about the meanings of the sound messages that are being sent. Very few students may be aware of the ability of water to transmit sound. The discussion of dolphin communication should start them thinking about the significance of water as a medium for the transmission of sound.

2 **Teaching Tips** — The text compares sound waves with the ripples that occur after a pebble hits water. You can show this phenomenon by filling a plastic container with 3 cm (about an inch) of water. Place the container on an overhead projector to show the waves that occur in the water as you drop small pebbles into it. The class will also hear the sound each pebble makes as it hits water.

The students have compared sound waves to the compression and release of the coils of a spring. The movement of waves through water may be illustrated by using a long rope. Tie one end of the rope to a doorknob. Tie a piece of yarn to the midpoint of the rope. Have a student grasp the free end of the rope and move it up and down. Observe the movement of the piece of yarn. It goes up and down as the wave passes it.

Bring in a coil and have the visually impaired student feel the coil bunching up and spreading out.

T–86

produced in water. Instead of an up-and-down motion, sound waves travel back and forth. Compare a sound wave to the movement of a coiled spring. Look at the **3** picture below. If you push the end of a spring, you cause a wave to move through it. The spring's coils do two things. They bunch up together and then spread out. **4** The bunching up and spreading out travels from one end of the spring to the other. Sound waves travel like that, too.

When you hear a bird's song, you hear sound waves **5** that have traveled through air. Air is made of particles. The vibrations made by the bird cause the air particles to bunch up together. Then those air particles spread out.

86

3 **Skill Development** — Be sure that the students *observe* that the vibration moves from left to right along the spring and that the coils move from side to side. Point out that the coils return to their original position after the wave moves past them.

4 **Teaching Tips** — An important point for you to keep in mind as you carry out the discussions of sound waves is that the molecules of the gases in the air move from side to side. Note how this is a different type of motion from that of water molecules as a wave moves through water. The water molecules essentially move up and down.

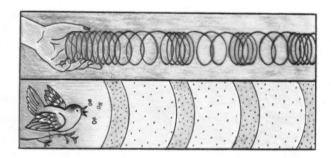

Now those air particles next to them bunch up. When those particles spread out, the next group bunches together, and so on. This bunching and then spreading out of air particles describes how a sound wave travels.

Most of the time you hear sound waves that travel through air. But you can also hear sounds in water. Try tapping two stones together underwater. The vibrations caused by the stones make the water particles vibrate. The sound wave moves through water instead of air.

Matter through which sound can travel is called a **medium**. Air and water are **media**. Solids are also good sound *media*. Test this yourself. With one finger, tap **6** very gently on your desk. What do you hear? Now place

Medium: Matter through which sound can travel.

Media: More than one medium.

87

EXTENSIONS

Reinforcement
Activity

Have the students tie a string to a spoon so that the spoon is balanced in an almost horizontal position. Have them tap the spoon gently with a pencil and listen to the sound that is made. Now have the students hold the free end of the string against one of their ears and tap the spoon again. The sound will be stronger since the sound waves are now reaching the ear through the string as well as through the air. Shorten and lengthen the string and see how the sound is affected.

5 Teaching Tips — Some students may be curious about what is meant by the use of the term *air particles*. You may wish to mention that the air is made up of a number of different gases including oxygen, nitrogen, carbon dioxide, and others. The smallest particles of these gases are molecules. When we speak of the particles of the air moving, we are really referring to the molecules of the various gases.

6 Text Questions — What do you hear? *The tapping sound*.

EXTENSIONS

Application
Activity

Conduct the following demonstration with the students:

A. Provide a small diameter garden hose and two metal funnels. Insert the stems of the funnels into each end of the hose.

B. Have one student go as far out of the room as possible with one end of the hose. Tell the student to hold the funnel near his or her ear.

C. Have another student speak softly into the funnel at the other end of the hose.

D. Ask the student who is out of the room to return and to repeat what was heard so that the class becomes aware that the sound traveled through the tube and around corners.

Stethoscope: An instrument used to hear heartbeats.

your ear on your desk top. Gently tap the desk again. What difference do you notice?

The wood on your desk is a good *medium* for sound. When you tapped, sound waves traveled through the wood to your ear. Wood is a solid. Solids carry sounds very well. Long ago, Native Americans would put their ears to the ground. They could find out if buffalo were near. Why do you think that worked?

Has your doctor ever listened to your heartbeat with a **stethoscope** (steth-uh-skope)? Sound travels very well through a *stethoscope*. When the round disc on its end is placed on your chest, the disc vibrates as your heart beats. The vibrations send sound waves through the air in the rubber tubes to the doctor's ears. The sound of your heartbeat is heard by the doctor. The air in the tubes contains many gases. Gas is a medium for sound.

88

7 **Teaching Tips** — Sound will travel through any medium that will vibrate. If the molecules are very far apart, however, transmission of energy from one molecule to another slows down. Molecules of a gas are farther apart than are molecules of a solid such as steel, so sound travels much more slowly through air than through solids.

8 **Text Questions** — What difference did you notice? *The tapping sound became louder.*

9 **Text Questions** — Why do you think that worked? *The buffalo's hoofs caused vibrations when they hit the ground. The sound waves were carried through the solid ground.*

10 **Skill Development** — Have the students *read an illustration* by locating the tubes that contain air in the photograph that shows the stethoscope in use. Both the single tube and the double tube are hollow and contain air.

What would happen if there were no matter for sound waves to travel through? This question was studied by Robert Boyle during the 1600's. He did something to find out if sound could travel without air. Boyle placed a bell, which could be rung, under a sealed glass jar. He rang the bell. The sound was loud enough to be heard through the glass. Then, using a pump, he removed the air inside the glass jar. He created a **vacuum** inside the jar. Space that does not contain matter is called a *vacuum*. He rang the bell again. What do you think happened? Although Boyle could see the bell vibrating, he could not hear a sound. With no air inside the jar, no air particles could vibrate. Boyle concluded that sound cannot travel in a vacuum. Since then, other scientists have done Boyle's experiment and had the same result.

Vacuum: Space that does not contain matter.

ACTIVITY

How does sound travel in different media?

A. Obtain these materials: ticking watch, meter stick.

B. Place your ear flat against one end of the meter stick. Have your partner hold the ticking watch against the other end.
   1. What did you observe?

C. Now put the meter stick down. Have your partner hold the watch one meter away from your ear.
   2. What did you observe?
   3. What were the two different media?
   4. What difference did you notice in steps **B** and **C** above?
   5. Write a short paragraph that sums up how sound travels in different media.

89

11 Teaching Tips — Ask your class if they have heard of the term *vacuum* and if they have, in what connection. You might discuss vacuum packaging and the use of a vacuum for insulation purposes.
12 Skill Development — Students are asked to understand the *effect* of a vacuum on the transmission of sound energy.

ACTIVITY

Skill Development — *Observing, Comparing and Contrasting, Concluding and Generalizing*

Answers to Questions — **1.** You could hear the sound through the meter stick. **2.** The sound seemed louder when it came through the meter stick. It was not as loud when it came through the air. **3.** Wood and air. **4.** The sound was louder through the meter stick. **5.** Sound is able to travel through wood. Sound travels better through a solid than through a gas (air).

Enrichment
Research — Library

Students should research the use of the radio for purposes of communication on the moon. In their study, they should compare the characteristics of radio and sound waves. Students could investigate the contents of the life-support backpack that astronauts wear.

Sound travels at different speeds in different media. Look at the chart below. What is the speed of sound in water, in wood, and in steel? Sounds travel faster in solids than in liquids. Sounds travel slowest in gases.

Medium	Speed of Sound
air	344 m/sec (1,135 ft/sec)
water	1,450 m/sec (4,790 ft/sec)
wood	3,050 m/sec (10,100 ft/sec)
steel	5,002 m/sec (16,500 ft/sec)

13 Lightning and thunder occur at the same time. However, light travels much faster than sound. The light reaches your eyes before the sound reaches your ears. The longer it takes for you to hear thunder after a flash of lightning, the farther away the storm.

Section Review

Main Ideas: Sound travels in waves as it moves through matter. Sound cannot travel in a vacuum. Media through which sound travels can be solids, liquids, or gases. Sound waves travel fastest through solids and slowest through gases.

Questions: Answer in complete sentences.

1. Compare the movement of a sound wave to pushing or pulling a coiled spring.
2. Give three examples of media through which sound can travel.
3. Can sound travel through a vacuum? Explain your answer.
4. Look at the chart above. In which medium does sound travel the fastest? Which is the slowest?
5. Look at the picture on page 88. At what place is the sound of the heartbeat traveling through a solid? At what place is it traveling through gases?

90

13 Teaching Tips — You may want students to share their observations concerning the time difference between when they see lightning and when they hear thunder. Most will realize that as a thunderstorm approaches, the interval between thunder and lightning gets smaller. The sound of the thunder is delayed by the amount of time it takes for sound to travel the distance from the lightning bolt to our ears.

SECTION REVIEW
Answers to Questions
1. A sound wave is caused by vibrations that make air molecules bunch together and then spread out. This alternate bunching and spreading out pattern is like the movement of a spring.
2. Air, water, wood
3. No. There are no air molecules to vibrate.
4. Sound travels fastest in steel and slowest in air.
5. When it goes through the round part of the stethoscope held against the boy's chest. It travels through gases in the tubes.

Do you yell and cheer at school basketball games? Have you noticed the many kinds of sounds that you hear? Some are louder than others. Sounds can be low or high. When you finish this section, you should be able to:

☐ **A.** Explain what causes sounds to be loud or soft.
☐ **B.** Explain what causes sounds to be low or high.
☐ **C.** Describe how loud noises affect people.

When you cheer at a basketball game, the sound of your voice is louder than when you whisper. The loudness or softness of a sound is called its **intensity.** Sounds that are loud have a high *intensity.* Soft sounds have a low intensity.

When you cheer, the sound you produce has a lot of energy. This energy is carried by air particles over long distances. When you whisper, the sound has less energy. Air particles still carry your voice, but over a shorter distance. The intensity of a sound depends on how

Intensity: The loudness or softness of a sound.

91

SECTION BACKGROUND

The intensity of a sound is a measure of the amount of energy carried by sound waves. The intensity is determined by the distance that air molecules are moved from their rest position. This distance is called the amplitude of vibration. For example, a violin string that is vigorously bowed will cause air molecules to move a greater distance and thus, the amplitude of the waves and the intensity of the sound are high. The unit of measure for sound intensity is the decibel.

Frequency is the quality of sound that measures the number of vibrations an object makes per second. A normal human ear can respond to frequencies of 20 to 20,000 vibrations per second (hertz). Pitch describes the highness or lowness of a sound, and it has a direct relationship to the frequency.

Each musical note has its own pitch. Middle C has a frequency of 256 hertz (scientific scale). The frequencies of other notes are expressed as a ratio to the frequency of middle C. Musicians can change the pitch of their instruments. String instrument players can vary the pitch of their instruments by altering the length of the strings. Wind instrument players can change the length of the air column that vibrates within their instruments.

BASIC TEACHING PLAN

MOTIVATION

One way to create interest in this lesson is to use a sound effects record as a stimulus for discussion of the relationship between energy and loudness. Sound effects records are readily available in record stores or libraries. Typically, they include sounds such as lions roaring, guns shooting, birds chirping, and jets taking off and landing. Don't tell the students which sounds you are going to play. Play a soft sound and ask the students to identify it and also indicate the source of the vibrations. Then play some loud sound effects and continue the discussion. After they have heard a variety of loud and soft sounds, have the students compare the energy sources that produced the different sound waves.

DEVELOPMENT

1 **Teaching Tips** — If you have a tuning fork available, you can demonstrate that using a lot of energy (striking it harder) results in a louder sound.

MATERIALS

6 bottles (same size), water, grease pencil, ruler or wooden stick

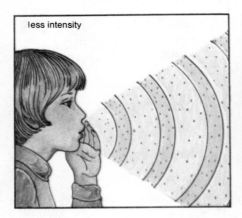

less intensity

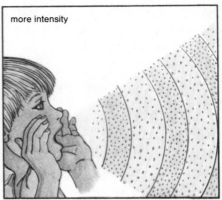

more intensity

EXTENSIONS

Reinforcement
Activity

Provide some old phonograph records and hand lenses. Let the students examine the records to see if they can detect the wavy patterns in the grooves, using the hand lenses. The irregularities in the grooves are what cause the needle to vibrate when the record spins at a high rate of speed. To demonstrate the effect on the sound produced by differences in the speed of the vibration, play the records at speeds other than those that were intended. A 45 RPM record played at 33 RPM will cause the needle to vibrate more slowly that it should, and the sound will be of a lower pitch. Playing a 33 RPM record at 45 RPM will cause the pitch to be much higher than intended.

2 strongly an object vibrates. Strong vibrations make large sound waves. Large sound waves make intense or loud sounds. Soft sounds are made when an object does not vibrate strongly. The sound waves are smaller. They make less intense, or softer sounds.

3 Sounds differ in another way. They can be high or low. The highness or lowness of a sound is called **pitch**. The sounds produced by a flute have a high *pitch*. Sounds from a tuba have a low pitch.

4 The pitch of a sound depends on how fast the object vibrates. The number of vibrations per second can be

Pitch: The highness or lowness of a sound.

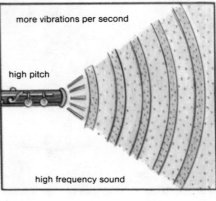

more vibrations per second

high pitch

high frequency sound

fewer vibrations per second

low pitch

low frequency sound

92

2 Skill Development — A tuning fork vibrates so quickly that it is difficult to *observe* the *effect* of increased energy on the amplitude of vibration. To illustrate the effect of increasing the energy of sound on the motion of water, strike a tuning fork lightly and ask the students to *observe* the loudness. Repeat this and quickly immerse the ends of the tines in a pan of water so that they reach just below the water's surface. The water will be slightly disturbed. Now repeat this but strike the tuning fork very sharply. The students will clearly *observe* an *effect* that can be explained by a specific *cause*, i.e., the tuning fork tines moved a greater distance in the second instance and thus the water molecules were moved a greater distance.

3 Skill Development — Use a set of tuning forks or a pitch pipe so that students can evaluate the pitch of sounds. Ask the students to shut their eyes. Select three or four tones and produce them in random order. Have the students put them in their correct sequence from highest to lowest tone. Then have the students open their eyes and discuss any differences in opinion that they might have had.

counted. This is called **frequency**. Something that vibrates very fast makes a high-pitched sound. Humans can hear sounds that have a *frequency* of 15 to 20,000 vibrations per second. Do you know where middle C is on a piano? It has a frequency of 256 vibrations per second. Higher notes have a higher frequency.

The boy in the picture is blowing air into the bottles. Each bottle produces a different pitch. That is because the air column in each bottle is different. When the boy blows into the air column above the water, it vibrates. Look at the bottle with the most liquid. Its air column is shortest. This makes its pitch higher. The frequency in **5** this bottle is higher. Which bottle would have the lowest pitch? If you said the one without liquid, you are right. It also has the lowest frequency.

Frequency: The number of vibrations made in one second.

93

EXTENSIONS

Enrichment
Science Skills— Finding Cause and Effect

Invite the school nurse or doctor to your class to discuss the effects of loud sounds on a person's hearing. You may wish to have the students prepare questions in advance for the guest.
  Possible questions are:
  1. What parts of the ear can be damaged by very loud sounds?
  2. Can prolonged exposure to loud sounds cause headaches or other illnesses?
  3. How can we protect ourselves from exposure to very loud sounds?

4 **Teaching Tips** — Bring in a guitar to illustrate ways of changing the pitch of a sound and to help in differentiating between the terms *intensity* and *pitch*. Show the students that pitch is determined by the thickness of the strings, the position of the fingers, and the tension of the strings. Explain that intensity can be increased by plucking the strings more vigorously.

5 **Text Questions** — Which bottle would have the lowest pitch? *The one without liquid because the air column is longest in that bottle.*

EXTENSIONS

Enrichment
Research — Library

Ask the students to find the following:

A. The meaning of the words *soprano*, *alto*, *tenor*, and *bass*. They will find that soprano is the highest singing voice of women and young boys; that alto is the lowest range of the female singing voice; that tenor is the highest range of the male singing voice; and that bass is the lowest range of the male singing voice.

B. Which of these singing voices produces sound waves of the highest frequency? the lowest frequency?

C. How can singers make their voices sound very loud? very soft? Does the loudness of the sound affect the frequency or pitch of the sound produced?

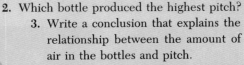

ACTIVITY

Changing pitch and intensity

A. Obtain these materials: 6 bottles of the same size, water, grease pencil, a ruler or wooden stick.

B. Number the bottles 1 through 6 and line them up in a straight row.

C. Add water to the bottles, putting the least in bottle 1 and the most in bottle 6.

D. Tap each bottle gently with the stick to create a different pitch. Adjust the amount of water in each to create the notes of a musical scale.

1. Which bottle had the most air?
2. Which bottle produced the highest pitch?
3. Write a conclusion that explains the relationship between the amount of air in the bottles and pitch.
4. What can you do to change the intensity of the sounds you create?

94

ACTIVITY

Skill Development — *Comparing and Contrasting, Finding Cause and Effect, Concluding and Generalizing*

Safety Tips — If the students work in groups, allow enough space for each group to ensure that the bottles can be safely tapped.

Answers to Questions — 1. The bottle with the least amount of water.   2. The bottle with the shortest air column or the most water.   3. As the amount of air within the bottle increases, the pitch becomes lower.   4. The bottles could be tapped with more force.

6   **Teaching Tips** — To demonstrate that it is the column of air that is vibrating and not the glass, ask several students to wrap their hands around a bottle and blow across the top. Ask the class to notice that the sound is produced even though the bottle is not vibrating.

Can a sound be low-pitched and loud? Can a sound be low-pitched and soft? The answer is yes. Choose a piano key that has a low pitch. If you hit this key hard, the intensity is high. It sounds loud. If you hit the same key gently, the intensity is low. It sounds soft. On a piano, how could you make a high-pitched sound with high intensity?

7

We are usually more aware of sound intensity than sound pitch. Sound intensity can be measured with a sound-level meter. The picture below shows a sound-level meter. Intensity is measured in units called **decibels** (des-ih-belz). The higher the *decibel* number, the louder the sound. Look at the chart below. It lists kinds

8

Decibel: Unit of measurement of sound intensity.

9

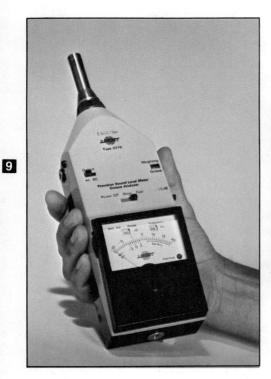

Cause	Decibel Level	Effect
Jet plane engine	160	Damage to hearing
Thunder	110	
Traffic	80	Annoying
Vacuum cleaner	60	
Automobile	45	Acceptable
Whisper	15	
Breathing	0	

95

EXTENSIONS

Enrichment
Activity

Take the students on a short field trip around the school grounds or perhaps the local community to make measurements of sound levels. You will need to borrow a sound-level meter for this activity. Possible sources for the meter are the community public health department, high school physics department, recording studio, airport, or a regional office of the U.S. Occupational Safety and Health Administration (OSHA).

On the trip, have students record the decibel readings at various locations. On their return to the classroom they can prepare bar graphs to represent their data.

7 **Text Questions** — On a piano, how could you make a high-pitched sound with high intensity? *Strike a high-pitched key very hard.*

8 **Teaching Tips** — If the power of the average faintest audible sound (the threshold of hearing) is set at zero, a sound with ten times the power of this standard is set at one bel. A sound with 100 times the power of the standard is set at two bels. The decibel unit is 1/10 of a bel.

9 **Teaching Tips** — The intensity of rock music can range as high as 100 decibels. Students should be warned of the possible hearing damage as a result of listening to loud rock music. Rock musicians have had their hearing damaged as a result of overexposure to the high decibel sounds.

Noise levels attained by modern machines can pose serious health problems. Have half of the class do library research to discover what are some of the things that cause dangerously high noise levels and what is done to help lower noise levels. Such things as car mufflers, changing flight paths, jet planes, and insulating compartments that astronauts travel in (rocket engines at blastoff may generate sustained noise levels of over 175 decibels) may be mentioned. The rest of the class can do research on what the effects of high noise levels are on humans and other animals.

Reports can be accompanied by posters with pictures cut from old magazines to illustrate results of the research.

10 of sounds. It also lists their decibel numbers. Which sound has the lowest intensity? Which sound has the highest intensity? Which sound measures 45 decibels? What is the decibel level of a whisper?

Sounds at readings near 0 can barely be heard. Sounds between 60 to 100 decibels are annoying to people. Sounds above 130 decibels can be dangerous. Constant listening to such loud sounds can cause hearing damage. Do you listen to loud sounds often?

Section Review

Main Ideas: Sounds can change in pitch and intensity.

Type of sound	How sound is made	Effect
low intensity	less energy	Sound doesn't travel far.
high intensity	more energy	Sound travels farther.
low pitch	lower frequency	Sound is lower.
high pitch	higher frequency	Sound is higher.

Questions: Answer in complete sentences.

1. Explain what causes a sound to be loud or soft.
2. What is pitch? How is the frequency of a sound related to pitch?
3. How can you make a low-pitched sound that has a high intensity? How can you make a low-pitched sound with low intensity?
4. Give two examples of sounds that measure over 100 decibels.
5. What can constant listening to sounds of high intensity do to people?

96

10 **Text Questions** — Which sound has the lowest intensity? *Breathing*. Which sound has the highest intensity? *Jet plane engine*. Which sound measures 45 decibels? *Automobile*. What is the decibel level of a whisper? *15*.

SECTION REVIEW

Answers to Questions
1. The intensity of a sound depends on the amount of energy used to make the sound. If very little energy is used to make a sound, the sound will be soft.
2. Pitch describes the highness or lowness of a sound. If an object has many vibrations per second (its frequency), it has a high pitch.
3. Low pitch sound, high intensity — strike a low pitch key or string with much strength. Low pitch sound, low intensity — strike the same object more gently.
4. Thunder and a jet plane engine
5. Sounds of high intensity can damage a person's hearing.

Mark is bouncing a ball against the wall. As soon as the ball hits the wall, it bounces right back. Sound bounces off objects in the same way that Mark's ball bounces off the wall. When you finish this section, you should be able to:

☐ **A.** Describe two effects that can occur when sound waves strike an object.
☐ **B.** Describe how sound affects people.

When we say that a sound is **reflected** (re-**flek**-ted), we mean that a sound wave has bounced off an object. What would happen if the ball struck the wall at an angle? The tennis ball would be *reflected* in the way shown in the top drawing. Sound waves behave in the same way. The bottom drawing shows how sound waves would be reflected from a wall.

5-3.

Sound Waves Reflect

Reflected: Bounced off of something.

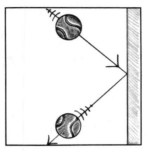

97

BASIC TEACHING PLAN

MOTIVATION

The motivation draws a parallel between the behavior of a ball striking a surface and the behavior of sound striking a surface. Demonstrate to the students that the angle at which a ball hits a surface determines the angle at which it bounces back. Use a tennis ball to show this. If you toss the ball against the floor at an angle it will bounce off at the same angle. Use the term *reflected* in your discussion of what occurs.

SECTION BACKGROUND

Sound waves can be reflected from objects. If a sound is reflected from an object, we may hear an echo. In order for an echo to be heard clearly, you must stand at least 9 m (30 ft) from the reflecting surface. At this distance, the sound will have enough time to reflect and travel back to your ears without interference from the original sound. This interference can occur because the original sound persists in our brain for about 1/10 of a second after the cessation of the sound. Since sound travels about 33.6 m (110 ft) in 1/10 of a second, you must stand at least 30 m from the reflecting surface to be able to distinguish your echo from the original sound.

Echoes can be disturbing in some settings. In a large auditorium, sounds are reflected from the walls, ceilings, people, and furniture. This is known as reverberation. Too much reverberation is unpleasant to our ears, but a slight amount gives a fullness to the sounds being produced. Consequently, acoustic engineers try to design auditoriums so that the shape of the room controls echoes. Sometimes, sound-absorbing materials are placed on surfaces in such rooms to further control reverberation.

Echoes are very useful to bats and some other animals that have a different range of hearing than humans. Bats can produce ultrasonic waves (above 20,000 hertz). Using these sounds, bats produce echoes that guide them in the dark.

MATERIALS

EXTENSIONS

Reinforcement
Activity

If there is a high, smooth, exterior wall on a building on your school grounds, take the students outside to study echoes.

A. On your trip outside, take along an object or objects that can produce a sharp, loud, distinct sound, such as two blocks of wood and a meter stick.

B. When you are by the wall, have the students clap the two pieces of wood together at various distances from the wall. Use the meter stick to find the closest distance at which you can detect an echo.

If you have no convenient area outside to do the above activity, then provide a ball and a pillow.

C. Have two students stand at opposite ends of the room. Tell them to bounce the ball off the floor at various angles. The angle at which it bounces up will be the same as the angle at which it was thrown to the floor.

D. Put the pillow on the floor and tell the students to throw the ball into it. It will not bounce back. This is what happens to sound in a room with curtains, drapes, and rugs. It does not bounce off the walls and floors but is absorbed by the above-mentioned materials.

Echo: A sound reflected from an object.

1

Ultrasonic: Sound frequency that is higher than 20,000 vibrations per second.

98

A sound that is reflected from an object like a wall is an **echo** (eh-ko). You must stand at least 9 m (30 ft) from the wall to hear an echo. This allows time for the sound to hit the wall and be reflected before the next sound is heard. If you are closer, the echo will not be heard as a separate sound. It will mix with other sounds being made. Sometimes, the sound is reflected from many objects. Many echoes are heard.

Lazzaro Spallanzani was an Italian scientist. He lived in the eighteenth century. He wondered how bats could fly in the dark and not bump into anything. He did experiments to find out. He covered a bat's ears. The bat bumped into things as it flew. He felt that the bat's ability to fly at night had something to do with sound. But the bat did not seem to make noises when it flew. Actually, bats do make sounds. As a bat flies, it makes **ultrasonic** (ul-truh-**sah**-nik) sounds. These are sounds that are too high to be heard by the human ear. The sounds are reflected from objects. The echoes are heard by the bat.

DEVELOPMENT

1 **Teaching Tips** — Students could conduct a survey at home and/or at school to determine which rooms or areas would produce the best echoes. Discuss how these areas could be changed so that more sound is absorbed.

2 The bat can tell where the objects are when it hears the echoes. So the bat can fly in darkness without bumping into the objects. The chart below shows the range of sound heard by humans and other animals.

3

Hearing Ranges of Animals	Vibrations per Second
Dog	15 to 50,000
Crocodile	20 to 5,000
Human	15 to 20,000
Porpoise	150 to 150,000
Robin	250 to 21,000
Bat	1,000 to 120,000
Moth	3,000 to 150,000

4 Look at the chart. Find the range of sound heard by humans. Find the range for bats. Notice that we can hear sounds produced by just 15 vibrations per second. Bats **5** cannot. But above 20,000 vibrations per second, we cannot hear. Those are vibrations in the ultrasonic range.

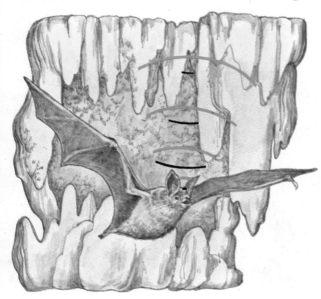

99

---

2 **Teaching Tips** — The bat's method of locating objects in the dark is called *echolocation*. A dolphin has an organ called the *melon* on its head that produces sound to aid it in its orientation in the water.

3 **Skill Development** — Students can *interpret* the *chart* to determine which animals can hear sound in the ultrasonic range.

4 **Teaching Tips** — The bat produces sound through its nose and mouth and receives reflected sound through its sensory apparatus. Included in this apparatus are the *tiagus* (a lobe at the base of each ear) and the *nose leaves* (membranous structures near the nostrils and ears in some species).

5 **Teaching Tips** — Ultrasound is used in fields such as: oceanography (echo sounder); the military (underwater detection devices); medicine (detection of tumors); industry (cleaning equipment and detection of internal flaws in machinery).

EXTENSIONS

Enrichment
Research — Library

The bat is only one of the animals that guides itself by the use of ultrasonic echoes. Have the students use the library to find out how other animals do so, how high a frequency they use, and how they produce the vibrations. Remember that the information students have obtained tells the frequencies of the sounds produced by the animals, not the range of the frequencies to which the animals are sensitive.

Exceptional Student
Learning Disabled

Locate a place in your school in which you can make an echo. Allow the student to experiment with making echoes.

EXTENSIONS

Application
Science Skills — Comparing and Contrasting

Have the students bring in various materials to test their sound-absorbing properties. Before starting, have the students make a chart listing the various materials. Ask them to include in the chart their predictions about the sound-absorbing properties of each material.

A. Set an alarm clock so that it will ring in one minute.

B. Place the alarm clock in an empty wastebasket.

C. Listen to the intensity of the ring.

D. Line the sides and bottom of the wastebasket with one of the materials (these may be cloth, paper, cork, cotton, Styrofoam, etc.).

E. Set the clock again and place it in the wastebasket. Listen again for the intensity of the ring.

F. Repeat for all the materials.

G. Compare the results with the predictions.

Acoustics: The study of sound and how it affects people.

6 Acoustics (uh-**koo**-sticks) is the study of sound and how sound affects people. People who plan buildings like concert halls study *acoustics*. They try to keep down noise pollution. Noise is a form of pollution when it disturbs people in their daily activities. There are many sources of noise pollution in our lives. Radios, traffic, airplanes, and machines all produce loud noises. These noises may even be harmful. There are several ways to control noise pollution. One is to stop the source of the noise. Another is to put up sound barriers. The barrier is placed between the source of the noise and the people nearby. This is sometimes done at airports. The noises made by machines can be reduced, too. The noisy parts are covered with something that takes in the sound.

Noises may also be caused by echoes. Echoes are helpful to a bat. But echoes can disturb people. Echo sounds can mix with other sounds. Mixing makes these other sounds unclear. **7** Probably there is a place in your school where echoes occur. Do you know where? Echoes occur in large, empty rooms, such as gyms. They occur in rooms without drapes or rugs.

100

---

6 **Skill Development** — The text material dealing with acoustics can give you an opportunity to discuss noise pollution with the students. You may wish to ask them if they produce noise pollution with loud yelling, the playing of phonographs or stereos, and so on. Ask them how they can limit noise pollution in their own environment.

7 **Text Questions** — Do you know where? *Echoes probably occur in the school auditorium or gymnasium.*

8 **Teaching Tips** —You may be able to acquire a square of ceiling tile that is of the type that is commonly used for its sound-absorbing qualities. Discuss where such tiles would be used and why their structure is especially suited for their purpose.

9 **Text Questions** — How can the room be changed to prevent echoes? *Put drapes on the windows, a rug on the floor, cork tiles on the ceiling, and add cushioned furniture.*

8 There are ways to control echoes. Certain materials used on walls, ceilings, and floors stop sounds from being reflected. These materials **absorb** (ab-**sorb**), or take in, the sound. Soft materials, such as cloth drapes and rugs, *absorb* sound. Materials with tiny holes, such as cork, break up sound waves. The sound waves cannot be reflected. Ceiling tiles are often made of materials with tiny holes. People help absorb sounds, too. When a large room is filled with people, echoes are not heard. Look at **9** the picture on page 100. How can the room be changed to prevent echoes?

Absorb: To take in.

Section Review

Main Ideas: Sound may be reflected or absorbed. Reflected sound can cause echoes. People study acoustics to control echoes and noise.

Questions: Answer in complete sentences.

1. Study the picture on page 98. Then answer the following questions:
   a. How would the time between the sound and the echo change if the girl were farther away from the wall? (Use the words *reflect* and *echo* in your answer.)
   b. What is the source of the sound? In which direction is it traveling?
   c. What is the medium for the sound waves?
   d. What is reflecting the sound waves?
2. What are some ways in which the echoes in a large room can be reduced?
3. Explain how bats can fly at night and not bump into things.
4. Using the chart on page 99, answer these questions: What is the range of sounds heard by a moth? How is this range different from a dog's?

101

EXTENSIONS

Reinforcement
Activity

A person who works with acoustics has to be aware of the way sound is reflected off different materials and of the effect the direction of sound waves have when they strike a surface. To demonstrate this, provide two large paper cones and a metal tray. One cone will be used as an ear trumpet, the other as a megaphone.

A. Have one student stand next to an open doorway with the megaphone.

B. Have the other student who is holding the ear trumpet stand on the other side of the wall. They should both face the metal tray, which is held upright by them so that it will serve as a sound reflector.

C. The student with the megaphone whispers very softly into the megaphone, directing the sound at the tray.

D. Can the student with the ear trumpet directed at the tray pick up the sound? Move the tray until the sound is as loud as possible.

E. Place a sound-absorbent material, such as Styrofoam, on the tray and observe the difference.

SECTION REVIEW

Answers to Questions

1. **a.** If she were farther away from the wall, it would take longer for the echo to reach her. The sound waves would have to travel a longer distance before they were reflected.   **b.** The source is the girl talking. It is traveling in all directions.   **c.** The medium is the air.
   d. The wall is reflecting the sound waves.
2. Drapes, rugs, ceiling tiles, and other materials that absorb sound could be used to reduce echoes in a large room.
3. Bats produce ultrasonic waves as they fly. The waves reflect off objects. Bats hear the echoes and can tell how far away the objects are.
4. Moths hear sounds in the range of 3,000 to 150,000 vibrations per second. A dog hears sounds in the range of 15 to 50,000 vibrations per second. A moth hears sounds in a much wider range of frequencies. It hears sounds of both lower and higher frequency than the dog.

SUGGESTED WORKSHEET MASTER
for sections 5–2 and 5–3
p. T–65p

SECTION BACKGROUND

Humans were unable to convey the sound of the human voice over long distances until the late 1800s. The invention that made it possible to transmit and receive sound waves over long distances was the telephone. The telephone is a device that can pick up sound waves in the air and convert them to a changing pattern of electric current. When you speak into the transmitter of a telephone, a metal diaphragm vibrates in the same pattern as the sound waves. The pattern is carried by an electric current to the telephone receiver.

Edison's invention of the phonograph enables us to make permanent recordings of sound waves that can be played back at a later time. The modern phonograph speaker and the telephone receiver both convert a changing pattern of electric current to sound waves in the air.

Although the telephone requires wires to transmit and receive messages, radio and television transmissions do not. The invention of the wireless radio set the groundwork for many types of wireless transmissions. Transmitters and receivers that operate without wires are able to do so because sound waves spoken into the appropriate equipment can be converted into electromagnetic (radio) waves. These travel at the speed of light and do not require a medium for transmission. A receiver of these waves, such as a common radio or television, converts them back into sound waves.

MATERIALS

5-4.

Sound Messages

Diane went to the phone. She dialed several numbers. A moment later she heard a ring. Then she heard a clear, familiar voice. "Bonjour," said the voice. "Hello, Grandma," said Diane. "I'm leaving for the airport now. I'll see you in Paris in just a few short hours!"

The world is a much smaller place since the telephone was invented. When you finish this section, you should be able to:

☐ **A.** Describe the events that occur when you use a telephone to send and receive messages.
☐ **B.** Use a diagram to explain how a changing pattern of electricity can cause a phonograph speaker to produce sound waves.

The sound energy of spoken words can be changed into electrical energy. That energy can travel through wires across the country. And it takes less time than it takes for you to read this sentence.

102

BASIC TEACHING PLAN
MOTIVATION

You may wish to begin this section by initiating a general discussion of the dependence we presently have on the telephone as a medium of communication. Do this by drawing a chart on the board with two columns. The first column should have the heading "Benefits" and the second should have the heading "Problems." Ask the students to contribute ideas for each column. See if any students feel that it would be preferable to be more independent of the telephone.

A variation of this discussion could be to ask the students to make some predictions about how our communications systems in the future may be different from the ones presently in use (picture phones or phones that could fit into a wrist watch).

People have always wanted to send messages to others who were not close by. A messenger traveled on horseback for days to bring a letter. But on May 24, 1844, Samuel Morse changed all that. He sent a message through wires using a **telegraph** (tel-uh-graf). The *telegraph* could not send the sound of a person's voice. Instead it sent a pattern of electrical current that stood for the letters and numbers. A person sending a message would first write it out. Then a telegraph operator would change each letter in the message into a code. The code was made up of clicks and pauses that the operator would tap out on the telegraph. The machine sent out a pattern of electric current that was like the pattern of the clicks and pauses.

When the current reached a telegraph station, it was changed back into the clicks and pauses. The receiving telegraph operator would then write out the message. The telegraph produced many changes. People could now send messages in a matter of minutes, instead of weeks. That was great, but something was missing. It was the sound of the human voice.

Telegraph: A device for sending messages using a code.

103

EXTENSIONS

Application
Activity

Several concepts learned in this unit are combined in this activity. If possible, locate an exposed metal pipe in the classroom. It may be a heating or a plumbing pipe. Students will find that messages tapped out lightly at one end of the pipe will carry long distances. Those students who are receiving the message can try resting a wooden ruler on the pipe and putting the other end of the ruler next to one of their ears to amplify the sound. Use the Morse Code signals given on page T–65q to transmit messages.

DEVELOPMENT

1 **Teaching Tips** — If you have time, construct the basic telegraph that is detailed in the Interunit pages of Unit 4 (p. T–161p). Students could observe the simplicity of its construction. It was only with the invention of more powerful electromagnets that the invention of the telegraph was possible. Students could also use the Extension on the next page to learn the Morse Code.

EXTENSIONS

Enrichment
Activity

Have the students listen to Morse Code messages. Provide them with a copy of the International Morse Code found on page T–65q and ask them to see how well they can decode messages that you or someone else in the class sends. You can prepare the code messages in advance by recording them on audio tape.

2 "Mr. Watson, come here; I want you." Those seven words made up the first voice message carried by a telephone. Alexander Graham Bell spoke those words in 1876. Mr. Bell's chat with Mr. Watson took place over the distance between two buildings. Now we use the telephone to send voice messages from city to city and from country to country.

In a telephone, sound waves in the air are changed into a pattern of electrical energy. The electrical energy is sent through wires. Modern telephones come in all shapes and sizes. All of them work in about the same **3** way.

The part of the telephone you speak into is called the **transmitter** (trans-**mit**-ter). Inside the *transmitter* is a metal disc. When you speak, the metal disc vibrates. It vibrates in the same pattern as your voice does. This pattern is carried by the electricity in the telephone **4** wires. The electricity travels through the wires to the telephone **receiver** (ri-**see**-ver). The *receiver* is the part of the telephone through which you hear. At the receiver, the electricity goes to a second metal disc. It vibrates, too. The original sound is then heard by the listener.

Just a year after Mr. Bell spoke to Mr. Watson, something else happened. Thomas Edison made the first phonograph.

For Edison's phonograph, sounds were recorded on a record. The record was a cylinder. It had grooves on it.

Transmitter: The part of the telephone you speak into.

Receiver: The part of the telephone through which you hear.

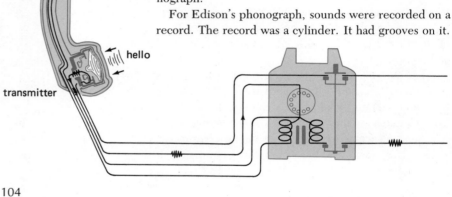

receiver

hello

transmitter

104

---

2 **Teaching Tips** — As Bell was experimenting with a telegraph set, he heard the sound of a plucked steel spring in another room where Watson was working. Realizing that a musical tone was transmitted, he and Watson worked on improvements to invent the first telephone in the ensuing months.

3 **Teaching Tips** — If you can obtain an old telephone, this would be a good time to take it apart in front of the class.

4 **Skill Development** — You can emphasize the skill of *sequencing* by writing each step of the transmitting and receiving processes on individual strips of oak tag. Do not put the strips in their correct order. Have students come forward and place them in their proper sequence.

In the grooves was tinfoil. The singer sang into a horn. The vibrating horn caused a needle to vibrate. The vibrating needle moved through the grooves. It made a pattern on the tinfoil. To play the record, it was placed on a phonograph. A needle on the phonograph moved through the grooves on the record. The pattern on the tinfoil caused the needle to vibrate in the same pattern. These vibrations caused the phonograph speaker to vibrate in the pattern of the real voice.

5 To make a record today, a spiral-shaped groove is cut into a flat disc. Sound waves cause a needle to move from side to side in the groove. The needle cuts a pattern along the walls of the groove. The disc is covered with metal. The metal disc is made into a mold. The mold stamps the pattern onto plastic records. A record is placed on a record player. As it spins, a needle moves through the groove. The needle picks up the pattern of vibrations that is cut into the groove. The pattern travels through a wire to a speaker. In the speaker the pattern changes back to sound. Then the music is heard.

105

EXTENSIONS

Enrichment
Science Skills — Vocabulary

To help students understand that sound waves are transmitters of energy you may wish to introduce the term *sympathetic vibration*. You will need to take your class to some location in the school where there is a piano.

A. Open the piano so that its strings are exposed. Press down the loud pedal to free the strings. Have the students stand close to the piano. Tell them to sing various notes loudly with their voices directed at the piano strings.

B. The string that has the same natural frequency as the note being sung will vibrate and "sing" the note back. The string is vibrating sympathetically. Energy has been carried from the students to the piano strings by the compressions and rarefactions of the sound waves.

C. Try using a piece of heavy paper rolled into a cone shape as a megaphone to direct the note toward the string. Does that increase the response of the string?

D. Ask the students why a glass made of very fine crystal can shatter if exposed to a sustained note of high frequency.

5 **Teaching Tips** — Explain that modern recordings are made by a complex process. Records are not a simple reproduction of a song played by a group of musicians. It is possible to mix and blend a number of separate recordings so that, for instance, it can sound as though a vocalist is accompanying himself.

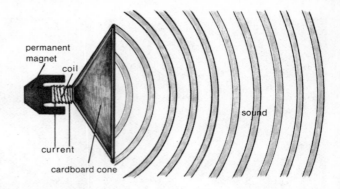

permanent magnet
coil
current
cardboard cone
sound

EXTENSIONS

Enrichment
Activity

The Edison phonograph that utilized cylindrical records was a very popular consumer item in its time. Recently, it has been a popular item for antique collectors. Many collectors have both the phonograph and the cylindrical records. You may be able to locate someone in your community who would be willing to bring such a phonograph and records to your classroom. If this is possible, you will be able to show the students the source of the phonograph's energy (a hand crank), the needle, the speaker, and the grooves on the records.

6 The telephone receiver and the speaker of a phonograph work the same way. Look at the diagram above. Sound waves in air can be produced by electricity that **7** moves through a wire. Notice the current flowing through the wire. In a phonograph, the vibrations of the needle change the current. In a phone, the sound vibrations that enter the transmitter change the current. When the current is strong, the magnet pulls very hard. The speaker cone moves back and forth, since the elec-

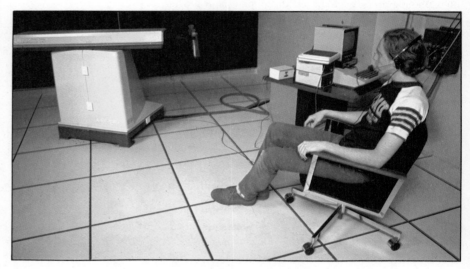

106

Exceptional Student
Learning Disabled
Visually Impaired

Bring in an old telephone and unscrew the receiver to expose the transmitter. Explain how it vibrates. This will help the learning-disabled student to understand how a telephone works. The visually impaired student, if allowed to feel the transmitter, will be able to "visualize" how it works.

Visually Impaired

Bring in a record and have the student feel the grooves.

6 **Skill Development** — Students are asked to *compare* and *contrast* the telephone receiver with the speaker of a phonograph.
7 **Teaching Tips** — Be sure that the students understand that it is not the sound waves themselves that move through the wires. Rather it is a changing electrical current that is produced from the sound waves.
8 **Skill Development** — If you have access to a small stereo system, you may wish to display it at this point. Have the students study the text material on the following pages and then *compare* and *contrast* the original Edison phonograph with a modern phonograph.

ACTIVITY

Can you make a working model of Edison's phonograph speaker?

A. Obtain these materials: a phonograph, an old unneeded 33-RPM record, paper of various thicknesses and sizes, scissors, tape.

B. Make 2 or 3 paper cones of various sizes. Have your teacher place a sewing needle through the end of the cone.

C. Lightly hold the cone so that the needle is on the grooves of a turning record.
   1. What did you hear?
   2. What is causing the cone to vibrate?
   3. Make a hypothesis to explain how speeding up the record changes the sound from your speaker cone. Test the hypothesis. Write your conclusion.

tric current keeps changing. The movement of the speaker cone produces sound waves in the air in front of it. Those sound waves travel to your ear.

Telephones and phonographs have come a long way since Bell and Edison. All ways of sending messages have improved. Telephone messages between distant countries used to travel through wires under the ocean. Now the sound waves are changed and transmitted by satellites in space. The photograph shows a satellite. It makes voices sound clear even over long distances.

8 Phonographs have also improved greatly. Speakers have become more powerful. At the same time they have gotten smaller. Tape recorders that pick up the slightest change in sound are used. Even computers can be made to "hear" sound. There are computers that work only when given a command from one person's voice, like the one on page 106.

EXTENSIONS

Reinforcement
Activity

Students could have visual proof that the telephone converts sound waves into an electric current by doing the following investigation:

A Obtain an old telephone transmitter, a 3-volt battery, and a flashlight bulb.

B. Connect the microphone of the transmitter in a series circuit with the battery and the bulb.

C. Exert pressure on the diaphragm (sheet of flexible material) of the microphone. Vary the amount of pressure used.

D. Discuss how the force of our sound waves exerts pressure on the diaphragm to cause it to vibrate. Material (carbon granules) inside the transmitter allows the current to pass through.

ACTIVITY

Skill Development — *Finding Cause and Effect, Hypothesizing, Concluding and Generalizing*

Teaching Tips — Be sure that you use a phonograph record that no one wants, since it will be scratched in the process of doing this activity.

Safety Tips — Caution the students on the use of the needles.

Answers to Questions — **1.** Sounds (music or voice).   **2.** The curves in the record grooves cause the needle to vibrate. The vibrating needle causes the cone to vibrate. The cone is producing sound waves in the air.   **3.** Hypothesis — Increasing the speed of the record will increase the pitch of the sounds produced. Conclusion — Increasing the speed of the record increases the frequency of the vibrations.

Have the students do some library research on communications satellites. They will find that these are very useful devices. *Passive communications satellites* such as *Echo 1* and *Echo 2* were constructed with metallic surfaces for reflecting signals. Signals were beamed from a *transmitting station*, reflected from the satellite, and received by another station. *Amplification* was necessary because the signal was weak. This system could not handle large amounts of information, so it was not too useful commercially.

Active communications satellites, such as *Telstar I*, *Relay I*, and *Syncom 2* operate differently. They receive transmitted signals, amplify them, and retransmit at different frequencies. *Intelsats 1*, *2*, and *3* are active satellites, positioned about 35,200 km (22,000 mi) over the equator. Their speeds are synchronized with the earth's rotational speed so they appear to be stationary.

These are but a few of the satellites that have been launched into orbit.

Section Review

Main Ideas: A telephone changes sound waves into electrical energy. It also changes electrical energy back into sound waves. A phonograph changes the vibrations on a phonograph record into sound waves in air.

Questions: Answer in complete sentences.

1. What is a telephone transmitter? What does it do?
2. What is a telephone receiver? What does it do?
3. Explain each of the steps that happen as a telephone changes sound into electricity, then back into sound.
4. How were the sound waves from human voices recorded on Edison's phonograph?
5. How was sound produced when a record was played on Edison's phonograph?

People in Science

Cyril Harris

Cyril Harris is famous for his work in the field of acoustics. He is a physicist with a great interest in music. Many of the world's concert halls and theaters owe their fine sound to Dr. Harris. His job is to work with builders of music halls. Dr. Harris decides where the seats and stage should be to reduce the noise and echoes.

Dr. Harris grew up in Hollywood, California. His interest in sound started when he was very young. At the age of 12, he began building radios. Dr. Harris studied acoustics in college and has a Ph.D. in physics. He has taught acoustics for 30 years. Dr. Harris is an expert in reducing noise on city streets. He has also helped in the designing of hearing aids. Dr. Harris protects his own hearing by wearing ear plugs whenever he travels on planes or trains. He even wears them when he sleeps.

108

SECTION REVIEW

Answers to Questions
1. A telephone transmitter is the part of the telephone into which you speak. It changes sound waves to a pattern of electricity.
2. A telephone receiver is the part of the telephone through which you hear. It changes a pattern of electricity into sound waves.
3. When you speak, a metal disc in the transmitter vibrates. The vibrations are changed into a changing pattern of electricity. The pattern is carried by electricity in the telephone wires. When the electricity reaches a receiver, it causes another metal disc to vibrate. This produces the sound waves that we hear.
4. The person spoke into a horn. The vibrating horn caused a needle to vibrate and make grooves on a tinfoil cylinder.
5. When the tinfoil cylinder was turned with a needle in the groove, the needle vibrated. These vibrations were transmitted to a speaker, which vibrated and produced sound.

CHAPTER REVIEW

Science Words: Match the terms in column A with the definition in column B.

Column A	Column B
1. Sound wave	A. Bounced
2. Medium	B. Vibrations per second
3. Vacuum	C. Loudness or softness
4. Intensity	D. A vibration that moves through matter
5. Pitch	E. Space without matter
6. Frequency	F. A reflected sound
7. Decibel	G. Matter through which sound can travel
8. Echo	H. The part of the telephone you speak into
9. Reflected	I. Unit of sound intensity
10. Transmitter	J. Highness or lowness

Questions: Answer in complete sentences.

1. What are two things that can happen when sound waves strike an object?
2. How is a sound wave like a coiled spring?
3. Robert Boyle did an experiment using a bell placed in a vacuum. What was the hypothesis that he was testing? What were his results?
4. The moon does not have any air. If one of two astronauts on the moon's surface struck a rock with a hammer, would the other astronaut hear it? Explain.
5. A person at a baseball game sees the bat hit the ball before hearing the sound. Explain why this is so.
6. Lazzaro Spallanzani experimented with the night flight of bats. What were his results?
7. Can a sound get louder without changing its pitch? Explain.

109

EXTENSIONS

Enrichment
Research — Library

This section of the chapter gives you an excellent opportunity to have students learn more about three exceptional American inventors: Samuel Morse, Alexander Graham Bell, and Thomas Edison. Ask the students to do library research to find out about their lives and accomplishments. Focus their research with these questions:

1. When did each of these inventors live?
2. What kind of childhood did each of these men have?
3. What were some of their other accomplishments? (These need not be inventions only. Samuel Morse, for example, was a talented artist.)
4. For each of these men, name the invention that is considered to be his most important.
5. How did the major inventions of these men change the lives of people?

CHAPTER REVIEW

Science Words
1. D   2. G   3. E   4. C   5. J   6. B   7. I   8. F   9. A
10. H

Answers to Questions
1. The sound can be reflected or absorbed.
2. Sound energy causes the air molecules to bunch up and spread out as the vibrations move out from the source of the sound. A coil that is pushed and pulled moves in a similar manner.
3. Boyle's hypothesis was that sound does not travel in a vacuum. A bell could not be heard when rung in a jar without air.
4. No. Sound cannot travel in a vacuum.
5. Light travels faster than sound.
6. He found that bats produce ultrasonic sounds that reflect off objects. The bats listen for echoes to tell where the objects are.
7. Yes. Pitch depends on the frequency of the sound wave. Intensity depends upon how much energy produced the sound.

SUGGESTED TEST MASTERS
p. T–65f, g, h

EXTENSIONS

Enrichment
Research — Library

To enable students to pursue further their understanding of wave characteristics, they could investigate the terms *compression* and *rarefaction*. Interested students could set up a "Slinky" model of sound waves to explain these terms to the class. In addition, they could illustrate the terms *wave length, amplitude,* and *frequency*. Their report should include a labeled diagram of a transverse and a longitudinal representation of sound waves.

Studying the vibration of strings

A. Obtain these materials: 3 guitar strings of different thicknesses, 3 metal screw eyes, board at least 15 cm by 60 cm, 2 15-cm lengths of wood molding, set of masses.

B. Insert the 3 screw eyes at the edge of the board so that they are equal distances apart. Attach the guitar strings to the screw eyes. Stretch them over the lengths of molding as shown.

C. Stretch 1 string over the board. Add masses to it until you get it tight enough to produce a tone when plucked. CAUTION: KEEP YOUR HEAD AWAY FROM THE STRING AS YOU TIGHTEN IT. It may snap. Add 100 g to the string to increase its tightness. Pluck the string. Add another 100 g. Pluck again. Add a third 100-g mass and pluck.

   1. Record your observations.

D. Remove 100 g at a time. Pluck the string each time.

   2. Record your observations.

   3. Write a conclusion based on 1 and 2 above.

E. Now attach 2 other strings to the board. Place a *total* of 300 g of mass on each string. Pluck each string.

   4. Record your observations.

   5. Write a conclusion for this investigation.

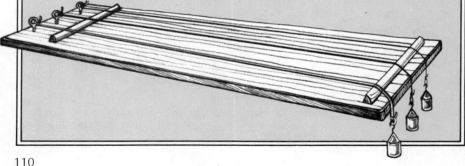

110

INVESTIGATING

Science Skills — *Finding Cause and Effect Relationships, Concluding and Generalizing*

Teaching Tips — It is easier to start the screw eyes in the wood if you make small nail holes first.

Safety Tips — Caution students again against having their faces close to the strings as they are tightened. They may snap and break with force.

Answers to Questions
1. Adding weights increases the tautness of the string. This in turn makes the pitch higher.
2. Removing weights makes the string less taut and lowers the pitch.
3. The more tension there is on a string, the higher will be its pitch when it is plucked.
4. The thicker the string, the lower the pitch.
5. The pitch of the sound produced depends upon the tightness of the string, the length of the string, and the thickness of the string.

CAREERS

Sonar Operator ▶

How do ships stay clear of other ships? The **sonar operator** listens to sound waves that travel through the ocean. The *sonar operator* also studies pictures of the sound waves on a screen. The sonar operator can tell the difference between the sounds made by ship engines and those made by whales. By sending out sound waves the specially trained sonar operator can tell what objects are in the water by their echoes.

◀ Piano Technician

When a famous player strikes the keys of a grand piano, will lovely music result? That might depend on the work of the **piano technician** who tuned the piano. Pianos are instruments that have many parts. Changes in weather may change the length of the strings inside the piano. This changes the pitch that is heard. Specially trained *piano technicians* tighten or loosen the strings. They also replace broken piano keys.

111

Application
Research

Students may be interested in finding out about other careers involving sound. Radio and television reporters and announcers write stories to be read on the radio or television or read announcements that other people have written. They need good speaking voices and an understanding of working with magnetic tape-recording equipment.

People who service television sets, stereo phonographs, and radios learn how to repair these complex devices. Introduction of new electronic machines, such as video-cassette recorders, increases the number of machines that need skilled technicians to service them. A college degree is not usually needed for either of these careers, although at least two years of technical training is necessary.

CAREERS

Teaching Tips — Information on training for a job as a sonar operator may be obtained by writing to the U.S. Navy or U.S. Coast Guard.

Piano tuners can learn their trade in different ways. Sometimes a father will pass the knowledge on to his children. A piano tuner might be willing to teach others the techniques. Information may also be obtained by contacting a music school or the music department of a university.

UNIT 3 SENSING AND MOVING

	SECTION	BASIC SCIENCE SKILLS	ACTIVITY MATERIALS STUDENT/GROUP	EXTENSIONS	
CHAPTER 6 YOUR SENSES	**6-1** p.T-114 Sense Organs	*Reading illustrations* of cells p.T-115 *Classifying* body systems p.T-116 *Reading illustration* of smelling p.T-116	graph paper, pencil	● Enrichment pp.T-115, T-116, T-117, T-118	
	6-2 p.T-119 Taste	*Classifying* tastes p.T-119	5 food samples, blindfold, paper, 2 paper cups, water, pencil, 10 toothpicks	● Enrichment p.T-120 ● Application pp.T-120, T-121, T-122	
	6-3 p.T-123 Hearing	*Reading illustration* of hearing p.T-126	blindfold, paper, pencil	● Reinforcement p.T-125 ● Enrichment pp.T-124, T-126, T-127	
	6-4 p.T-128 Sight	*Reading illustration to compare* two images p.T-130	mirror, paper, pencil	● Reinforcement p.T-129 ● Enrichment pp.T-130, T-131 ● Application p.T-132	
	6-5 p.T-133 Touch	*Comparing* a camera to your eye p.T-132	paper clip, ruler	● Reinforcement p.T-136 ● Enrichment pp.T-135, T-137, T-138 ● Application p.T-134	
CHAPTER 7 BONES AND MUSCLES	**7-1** p.T-139 Bones	*Comparing* the skeleton to a car frame p.T-140 *Observing* large and small bones p.T-141 *Reading illustration* of bones p. T-141		● Reinforcement p.T-143 ● Enrichment pp.T-142, T-144 ● Application pp.T-140, T-141	
	7-2 p.T-145 How Bones Join	*Comparing* X rays of children's and adult's hands p. T-145 *Reading illustration* of ligaments p.T-147	paper, pencil	● Reinforcement p.T-148 ● Enrichment p.T-146 ● Application pp.T-147, T-149	
	7-3 p.T-150 Muscles	*Inferring* the reason for blinking p.T-151 *Comparing* voluntary and involuntary muscles p.T-154	3 books	● Reinforcement p.T-152 ● Enrichment pp.T-153, T-154 ● Application p.T-151	
	7-4 p.T-155 Kinds of Muscles	*Observing* the shape of muscle cells p.T-156	paper, pencil	● Reinforcement p.T-157 ● Enrichment pp.T-156, T-159 ● Application pp.T-158, T-160, T-161	

EXTRA ACTIVITIES/ DEMONSTRATIONS	WORKSHEET MASTERS	EVALUATIONS
• Photographs p. T-114 • Onion skin p. T-115	Sense Organs and the Brain (AH) p. T-111j	Section Review p. T-117
• Lemon tasting p. T-119 • Food tasting p. T-120		Section Review p. T-122
• Sound effects record p. T-123 • Vibrating ruler p. T-124 • Model ear p. T-126	Hearing (SK) p. T-111k	Section Review p. T-127
• Depth perception p. T-128 • Camera p. T-132	Sight (AC) p. T-111l	Section Review p. T-132
• Mystery box p. T-133	Your Senses (SK) p. T-111m	Section Review p. T-137 Chapter Review p. T-138 Test Masters pp. T-111d,e,f
• Chicken bones p. T-139 • Bone cross section p. T-140		Section Review p. T-144
• Playing p. T-145 • Moving joint pp. T-146, T-147	How Bones Join (SK) p. T-111n	Section Review p. T-149
• Phys Ed Teacher p. T-150 • Tensing hands p. T-153	Muscles (SK) p. T-111o	Section Review p. T-154
• Muscle tissue p. T-155 • Investigating your blind spot p. T-160	Bones and Muscles (SK) p. T-111p	Section Review p. T-158 Chapter Review p. T-159 Test Masters pp. T-111g,h,i

BOOKS FOR STUDENTS

Amstutz, Beverly. *The Fly Has Lots of Eyes*, Union, Ky: Precious Resources, 1981

Cosgrove, Margaret. *Your Muscles & Ways to Exercise Them*, (illus.), New York: Dodd, 1980

Merrill, Margaret W. *Skeletons that Fit*, illus. by Pamela Carroll, New York: Coward, McCann & Geoghegan, 1978

Prince, J. H. *How Animals Move*, (illus.) New York: Elsevier-Nelson, 1981

Rahn, Joan Elma. *Eyes & Seeing*, (illus.), New York: Atheneum, 1981

Tudor, Tasha. *Tasha Tudor's Five Senses*, (illus.), New York: Platt & Munk, 1978

Ward, Brian. *The Ear & Hearing*, (illus.) New York: Franklin Watts, 1981

—*The Eye & Seeing*, New York: Franklin Watts, 1981

—*The Skeleton and Movement*, New York: Franklin Watts, 1981

FILMS

Across the Silence Barrier, 57 min, Time-Life Films

Bones and Structure, 22 min, ABC Wide World of Learning

Eyes and Vision, 10 min, Britannica

Healthy Skin, 11 min, Coronet

Mechanics of Life: Bones & Joints, 8 min, Captioned Films for the Deaf

Muscles and Bones of the Body, 11 min, Coronet

The Senses and Perception, 18 min, Britannica

Your Nervous System, 11 min, Coronet

FILMSTRIPS

The Muscular System, Britannica

The Skeletal System, Britannica

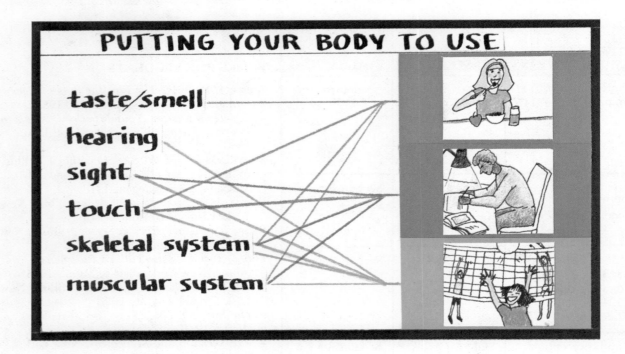

BULLETIN BOARD

The purpose of this bulletin board is to allow your students to understand the connection between their everyday activities and their body systems. At the beginning of the unit, ask the students to write three activities that they do each day and to draw a picture of themselves carrying out one of those activities. As the unit progresses, you could use each student's illustration on a different day and connect the activity with the sense or system involved.

FIELD TRIP IDEAS

To a Physical Therapy Unit

Make arrangements with your local hospital to visit its physical therapy department. Ask the therapist to describe how the nervous, skeletal, and muscular systems are interrelated and how damaged systems can be restored or improved through therapy. Students should observe the various pieces of equipment used and ask the therapist the purpose of each. Perhaps the therapist could chart the progress of several patients.

To the Nurse's Office

In small groups, students could visit the nurse's office to investigate how the nurse examines students' vision and possibly, hearing. Ask the nurse to explain the structure and function of the eyes and ears, the nature of various disorders of these organs, and the kinds of tests to detect these conditions. Students as a class could then discuss the routine for healthy care of their eyes and ears.

YOUR SENSES

Read each question. Choose the best answer. Write the letter of your choice on the line at the right.

CHAPTER OBJECTIVES

1. The part of a cell that controls its functions is the
   a. cell membrane.   c. cytoplasm.
   b. nucleus.   d. nerve.

   1._____   1. **b** (1)

2. Which of the following statements is *not* true?
   a. Every cell can produce other cells just like itself.
   b. Cells produce energy for the body.
   c. All cells are the same size and shape.
   d. Blood carries waste products away from the cells.

   2._____   2. **c** (1)

3. Muscle tissue is made of
   a. muscle cells.   c. blood and nerve cells.
   b. muscle and bone cells.   d. blood cells.

   3._____   3. **a** (1)

4. Body systems are made up of
   a. cells.   c. organs.
   b. tissues.   d. the senses.

   4._____   4. **c** (1)

5. The main organ of the nervous system is the
   a. brain.   c. nose.
   b. heart.   d. nerves.

   5._____   5. **a** (2)

6. Which of the following is *not* true about the nervous system?
   a. It makes it possible for us to smell, touch, taste, hear, and see.
   b. It controls the other body systems.
   c. It gives the body its shape.
   d. It sends messages from the brain to the muscles.

   6._____   6. **c** (2)

7. If you smelled smoke, you would look for a fire
   a. before the olfactory nerve senses the smell.
   b. before the message reaches the brain.
   c. after the message has reached the brain.
   d. while the message is traveling along the olfactory nerve.

   7._____   7. **c** (2)

8. Odors are first sensed by the
   a. nerve cells in the nose.   c. brain.
   b. olfactory nerve.   d. bone in the nose.

   8._____   8. **a** (2)

9. The sense organ for taste is the
   a. tongue.   c. taste bud.
   b. ear.   d. nose.

   9._____   9. **a** (3)

10. __d__ (3)

10. The taste nerves
   a. only sense sweet and salty tastes.
   b. only sense bitter and sour tastes.
   c. send messages from the brain to the taste buds.
   d. send messages from the taste buds to the brain.

10. _____

11. __b__ (3)

11. When you eat a piece of bread while smelling pizza,
   a. the pizza may smell like bread.
   b. the bread may taste like the pizza.
   c. the auditory nerve will send a message to the brain.
   d. none of the above will happen.

11. _____

12. __c__ (3)

12. The taste buds that respond to sugar are located
   a. along the sides of the tongue.
   b. at the back of the tongue.
   c. on the tip of the tongue.
   d. on the back, sides, and tip of the tongue.

12. _____

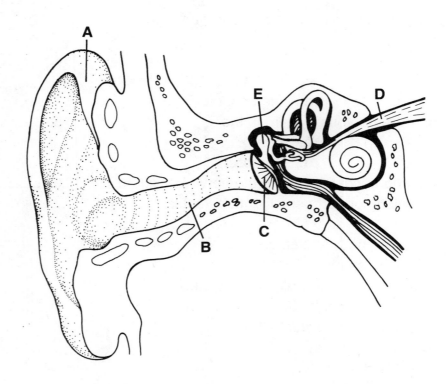

Look at the picture above. Then answer questions 13 and 14.

13. __a__ (4)

13. The part of the ear that picks up sound is
   a. A.   b. B.   c. D.   d. E.

13. _____

14. __d__ (4)

14. Part C is the
   a. outer ear.   c. ear canal.
   b. small bones.   d. eardrum.

14. _____

Name _____ Date _____

15. The part of the eye that changes size by opening and closing   15. _____
    is the
    a. pupil.   c. lens.
    b. iris.   d. diaphragm.

16. Nearsightedness causes images to be focused   16. _____
    a. behind the retina.   c. directly on the retina.
    b. in front of the retina.   d. on the optic nerve.

17. The sense of touch does not tell you if something is   17. _____
    a. hard.   c. round.
    b. cold.   d. sweet.

18. The largest sense organ we have is the   18. _____
    a. skin.   c. nose.
    b. hand.   d. foot.

19. The fingertips are more sensitive than the back of the hand   19. _____
    because they
    a. have fewer touch receptors.
    b. have more touch receptors.
    c. do not have any touch receptors.
    d. have none of the above.

20. Is the sentence below true? If it is false, tell which words can   20. _____
    be used in place of the underlined words to make the sentence
    true.
    When your hand touches something hot, receptors send a
    message to the spinal cord.
    a. The sentence is true.   c. to the arm bone.
    b. to the muscles.   d. to your hand.

Name_____ Date _____

CHAPTER OBJECTIVES

BONES AND MUSCLES

TEST 7
CHAPTER

Read each question. Choose the best answer. Write the letter of your choice on the line at the right.

1. _d_ (1)

1. Which of the following is *not* a function of the skeletal system?
    a. to support the body
    b. to protect some of the body organs
    c. to allow the body to move
    d. to send messages to the muscles

1. _____

2. _b_ (1)

2. The group of bones that surrounds and protects the brain is called the
    a. breastbone.   c. jawbone.
    b. cranium.   d. collarbone.

2. _____

3. _c_ (1)

3. The pelvis is made up of the
    a. ribs and hipbones.
    b. ribs and backbone.
    c. hipbones and backbone.
    d. hipbones and jawbone.

3. _____

4. _a_ (1)

4. The vertebrae protect the
    a. spinal cord.   c. brain.
    b. heart and lungs.   d. knee.

4. _____

5. _a_ (2)

5. A joint is
    a. a point where two bones meet.
    b. the padding at the end of bones.
    c. a strong band that holds the bones in place.
    d. tough cords controlled by muscles.

5. _____

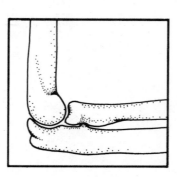

6. _b_ (2)

6. The picture that you see above shows
    a. a ball-and-socket joint.   c. a pivot joint.
    b. a hinge joint.   d. an immovable joint.

6. _____

Permission to reproduce this page is granted to users of HOLT SCIENCE 5   Holt, Rinehart and Winston, Publishers

Name_____ Date_____

7. A ball-and-socket joint is located 　　　7._____ 　　7. **b** (2)
   a. in the knee.
   b. in the shoulder.
   c. in the finger.
   d. where the head meets the neck.

8. Joints in the skull are 　　　8._____ 　　8. **c** (2)
   a. hinge joints.　　c. immovable joints.
   b. pivot joints.　　d. none of the above.

9. Cartilage is a soft substance that is 　　9._____ 　　9. **a** (3)
   a. what babies' bones are made of.
   b. found only in adults.
   c. found in the skin.
   d. found in none of the above.

10. The strong bands of tissue that hold bones in place 　10._____ 　10. **c** (3)
    are called
    a. joints.　　c. ligaments.
    b. tendons.　　d. muscles.

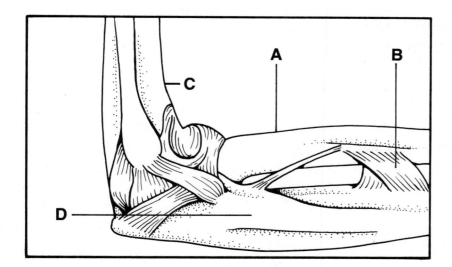

11. Look at the picture above. Which letter shows the ligaments? 　11._____ 　11. **b** (3)
    a. A　　c. C
    b. B　　d. D

12. Cartilage in a joint 　　12._____ 　　12. **b** (3)
    a. is found only in babies.
    b. keeps ends of bones from rubbing together.
    c. keeps the bones together.
    d. joins muscles to bones.

13. _c_ (4)

13. Every movement you make is caused by

    a. bones.   **c.** muscles.

    b. blood.   **d.** joints.

13. _____

14. _d_ (4)

14. Voluntary muscles control the movement of the

    a. stomach.   **c.** heart.

    b. intestines.   **d.** leg.

14. _____

15. _a_ (4)

15. Which of the following statements is <u>true</u> about involuntary muscles?

    a. You do not have to think about controlling them.

    b. They do not contract.

    c. You can move them when you want to.

    d. They are all attached to bones.

15. _____

16. _a_ (4)

16. As the biceps muscle contracts,

    a. it pulls the bones of the lower arm upward.

    b. it pushes the bones of the lower arm downward.

    c. it pulls the bones of the upper arm upward.

    d. it pushes the bones of the upper arm downward.

16. _____

17. _d_ (5)

17. A cardiac muscle cell

    a. has many nuclei.

    b. has dark and light bands across it.

    c. is voluntary and spindle-shaped.

    d. is involuntary and has one nucleus.

17. _____

18. _a_ (5)

18. Smooth muscles are located in

    a. the stomach.   **c.** the tongue.

    b. the heart.   **d.** the triceps.

18. _____

19. _c_ (5)

19. Which type of muscles can cause bones to move?

    a. smooth   **c.** skeletal

    b. cardiac   **d.** all of the above

19. _____

20. _a_ (5)

20. Blood carries oxygen and food to

    a. all the muscle cells.

    b. only smooth muscle cells.

    c. only cardiac muscle cells.

    d. only skeletal muscle cells.

20. _____

Name_____ Date _____

Sense Organs and the Brain

You are learning how your nervous system controls your reactions. In this at-home activity, you and a partner will measure the time it takes for a person to react.

A. Obtain these materials: a meter stick and nontransparent tape, such as masking tape.

B. Wrap the tape around the meter stick so that one piece is lined up with the 30 cm mark and the other with the 40 cm mark.

C. One partner should sit with his or her writing arm resting on a desk. The arm should extend beyond the edge of the desk to a point midway between the wrist and elbow.

D. The other partner should stand holding the meter stick at the 100 cm mark. The meter stick should hang within the grasp of the seated partner at the 30 cm mark.

E. The seated partner should concentrate on the 40 cm tape mark and be ready to snap his or her fingers shut on that mark when the meter stick begins falling.

F. The standing partner should release the stick without warning. The seated partner should grab the stick. Measure how far the stick fell from the 30 cm mark.

G. Switch places and repeat the above steps.

H. What you measured was the reaction distance. To find the reaction time use the table shown.

I. Record your results on the chart below.

	Distance	Time
You		
Partner		

DISTANCE OF FALL (cm)	TIME OF FALL (s)
1	0.045
2	0.064
3	0.078
4	0.090
5	0.101
6	0.110
7	0.120
8	0.128
9	0.136
10	0.143
11	0.150
12	0.157
13	0.163
14	0.169
15	0.175
16	0.181
17	0.186
18	0.192
19	0.197
20	0.202
21	0.207
22	0.212
23	0.217
24	0.221
25	0.226
26	0.230
27	0.235
28	0.239
29	0.243
30	0.247
31	0.252
32	0.256
33	0.259
34	0.263
35	0.267
36	0.271
37	0.275
38	0.279
39	0.282
40	0.286

QUESTIONS

1. Who had the faster reaction time? _____

2. How did your senses and muscles work together in this

   activity? _____

   _____

Name _____ Date _____

Hearing

Label the numbered parts of the drawing. Then match them with the correct definitions.

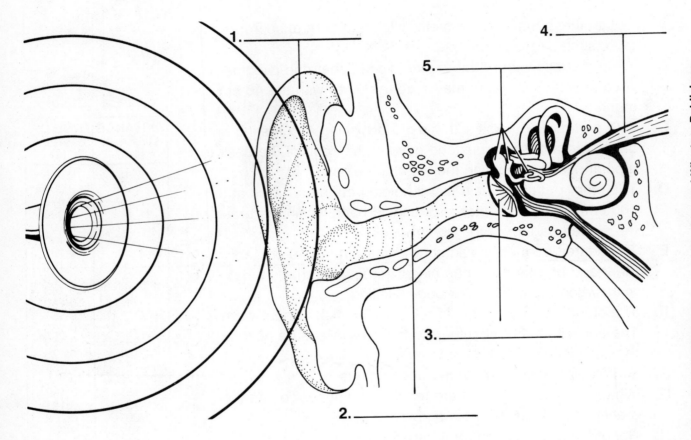

_____ **A.** The part of the ear that gathers sound vibrations

_____ **B.** The nerve that carries sound messages to the brain

_____ **C.** A narrow tube inside the ear that carries sound vibrations into the head

_____ **D.** Parts of the ear that pick up the vibrations from the eardrum and pass them on to the nerve cells

_____ **E.** The part of the ear at the end of the ear canal

Name_____ Date_____

Sight

The drawings below are optical illusions. Can you answer the questions correctly?

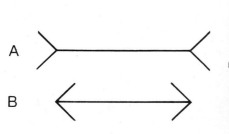

A

B

Which line is longer?

_____

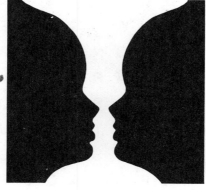

What do you see in the picture?

_____

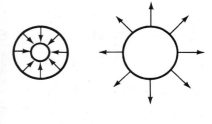

Which circle is bigger?

_____

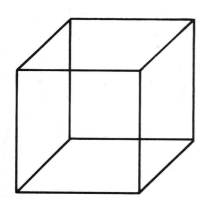

Which face of the cube is

closest? _____

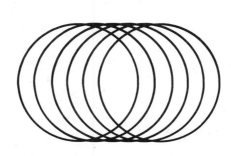

Which side is the opening

on? _____

In which direction is the person looking?

_____

The full moon can cause an optical illusion, too.
A. Measure the full moon when it is low in the sky by holding a ruler up to it. Close one eye and read its length.
B. Later the same night, repeat step A. Did the moon look the same size both times?

Name_____ Date_____

Your Senses

In the word search below, find the vocabulary words hidden horizontally, vertically, diagonally, and backwards.

```
O R G A N A C D L M N G R S N
P L R C T Y O N M W X S R B E
B L F T N S T L B O N T L O R
G O L A U S T U T A R U L D V
Q U I N C T F E G N S T E Y O
C E L M L T O R G N T A S S U
E M E B E R O N E R S T E Y S
U B U L U E T R F O O A Q S S
S L M N S T I S Y X Y Z O T Y
S M I N T A S T E N E R V E S
I N E P R Q E N M G E C E M T
T S U U S L L E C E V R E N E
B T A S T E B U D S C D V E M
F G K L U M N R E C E L M E M
C E L L M E M B R A N E T I S
```

After you have found all of the words, match them with their definitions.

1. Tiny, living parts of the body _____
2. Outside covering of an animal cell _____
3. The part of the cell that controls its function _____
4. Cells that carry information from parts of the body to the brain _____
5. A group of cells that work together _____
6. Groups of tissue that work together _____
7. Groups of organs that work together _____
8. System that controls all the other systems in the body _____
9. Nerve that carries smell messages to brain _____
10. Parts of the body that smell, taste, hear, see, and touch _____
11. Groups of cells on your tongue that pick up taste messages _____
12. Nerves that carry taste messages _____

Permission to reproduce this page is granted to users of HOLT SCIENCE 5   Holt, Rinehart and Winston, Publishers

Name _____ Date _____

How Bones Join

A. The objects below move in the same way joints in your body move. Describe which type of joint moves like the object shown. Give an example of that kind of joint.

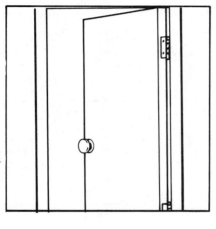  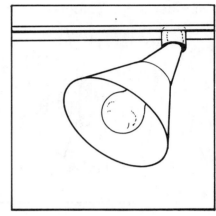

_____   _____   _____

_____   _____   _____

_____   _____   _____

B. Identify the bones below and tell what they do in your body.

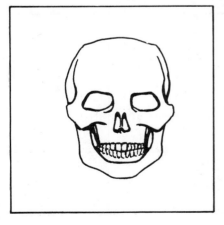 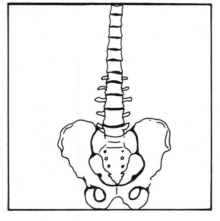 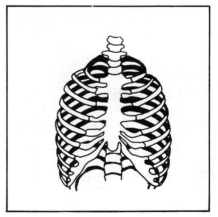

_____   _____   _____

_____   _____   _____

1. What holds the bones together in a joint? _____

2. What keeps the bones from rubbing together? _____

Name_____ Date_____

Muscles

Identify the type of muscle shown in each picture by writing its
name in the blank below it. In the blank below the name write
whether it is a voluntary or involuntary muscle.

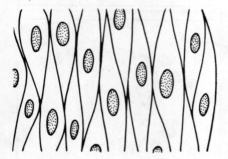

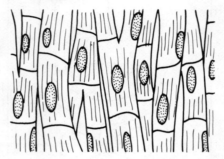

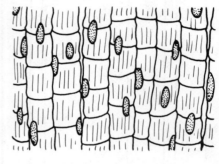

A. _____ B. _____ C. _____

_____ _____ _____

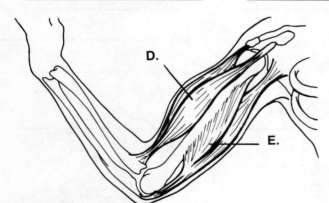

Identify the two large muscles in the
upper arm.

D. _____

E. _____

QUESTIONS

1. Describe what the muscles shown in the picture do when you bend your arm.

_____

2. Describe what the muscles do when you straighten your arm. _____

_____

3. What is the source of energy for your muscles? _____

4. How does the source of energy reach your muscles? _____

_____

5. What does it have to be combined with for the energy to be released? _____

Name _____ Date _____

Bones and Muscles

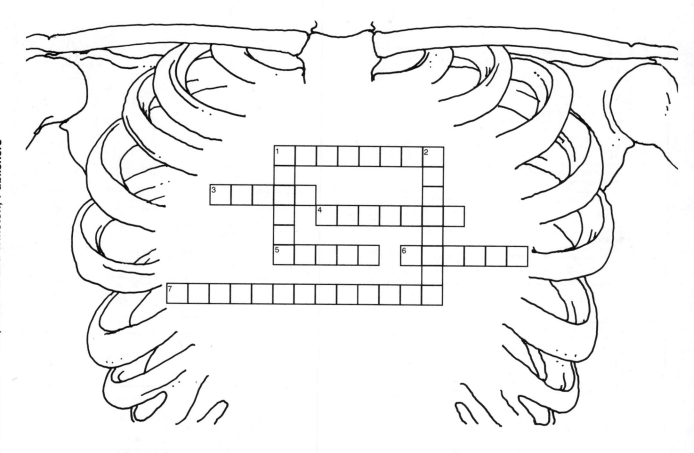

Use the clues below to complete the puzzle.

ACROSS

1. Muscles that contain large cylinder-shaped cells
3. A joint that allows the bones to move around and back
4. A type of muscle that makes up the heart
5. A joint that allows the bones to move back and forth or up and down
6. A tough cord that attaches muscle to bone
7. A joint that allows the bones to move in many directions

DOWN

1. A type of muscle containing long, thin, pointed cells
2. A strong band that holds bones in place at a joint

Name_____ Date_____

Sense Organs and the Brain

AT HOME WORKSHEET

You are learning how your nervous system controls your reactions. In this at-home activity, you and a partner will measure the time it takes for a person to react.

A. Obtain these materials: a meter stick and nontransparent tape, such as masking tape.

B. Wrap the tape around the meter stick so that one piece is lined up with the 30 cm mark and the other with the 40 cm mark.

C. One partner should sit with his or her writing arm resting on a desk. The arm should extend beyond the edge of the desk to a point midway between the wrist and elbow.

D. The other partner should stand holding the meter stick at the 100 cm mark. The meter stick should hang within the grasp of the seated partner at the 30 cm mark.

E. The seated partner should concentrate on the 40 cm tape mark and be ready to snap his or her fingers shut on that mark when the meter stick begins falling.

F. The standing partner should release the stick without warning. The seated partner should grab the stick. Measure how far the stick fell from the 30 cm mark.

G. Switch places and repeat the above steps.

H. What you measured was the reaction distance. To find the reaction time use the table shown.

I. Record your results on the chart below.

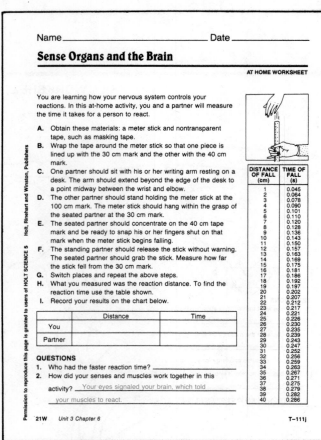

DISTANCE OF FALL (cm)	TIME OF FALL (s)
1	0.045
2	0.064
3	0.078
4	0.090
5	0.101
6	0.110
7	0.120
8	0.128
9	0.136
10	0.143
11	0.150
12	0.157
13	0.163
14	0.169
15	0.175
16	0.181
17	0.186
18	0.192
19	0.197
20	0.202
21	0.207
22	0.212
23	0.217
24	0.221
25	0.226
26	0.230
27	0.235
28	0.239
29	0.243
30	0.247
31	0.252
32	0.256
33	0.259
34	0.263
35	0.267
36	0.271
37	0.275
38	0.279
39	0.282
40	0.286

	Distance	Time
You		
Partner		

QUESTIONS

1. Who had the faster reaction time? _____
2. How did your senses and muscles work together in this activity? __Your eyes signaled your brain, which told__ __your muscles to react.__

Name_____ Date_____

Hearing

CLASSIFYING   SKILL WORKSHEET

Label the numbered parts of the drawing. Then match them with the correct definitions.

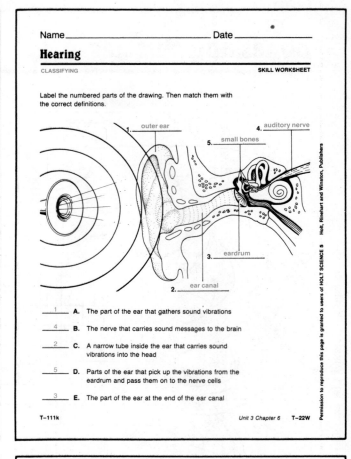

_1_ **A.** The part of the ear that gathers sound vibrations

_4_ **B.** The nerve that carries sound messages to the brain

_2_ **C.** A narrow tube inside the ear that carries sound vibrations into the head

_5_ **D.** Parts of the ear that pick up the vibrations from the eardrum and pass them on to the nerve cells

_3_ **E.** The part of the ear at the end of the ear canal

Name_____ Date_____

Sight

ACTIVITY WORKSHEET

The drawings below are optical illusions. Can you answer the questions correctly?

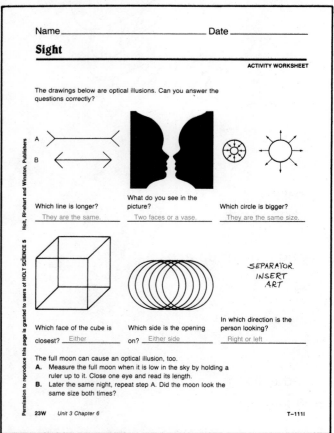

Which line is longer? __They are the same.__

What do you see in the picture? __Two faces or a vase.__

Which circle is bigger? __They are the same size.__

Which face of the cube is closest? __Either__

Which side is the opening on? __Either side__

In which direction is the person looking? __Right or left__

SEPARATOR INSERT ART

The full moon can cause an optical illusion, too.

A. Measure the full moon when it is low in the sky by holding a ruler up to it. Close one eye and read its length.

B. Later the same night, repeat step A. Did the moon look the same size both times?

Name_____ Date_____

Your Senses

BUILDING SCIENCE VOCABULARY   SKILL WORKSHEET

In the word search below, find the vocabulary words hidden horizontally, vertically, diagonally, and backwards.

```
O R G A N A C D L M N G R S N
P L R C T Y O N M W X S R B E
B L F T N S T L B O N T L O R
G O L A U S T U T A R U L D V
Q U I N C T F E G N S T E Y O
C E L M L T O R G N T A S S U
E M E B E R O N E R S T E Y S
U B U L U E T R F O O A Q S N
S L M N S T I S Y X Y Z O T Y
S M I N T A S T E N E R V E S
I N E P R Q E N M G E C E M T
T S U U S L L E C E V R E N E
B T A S T E B U D S C D V E M
F G K L U M N R E C E L M E M
C E L L M E M B R A N E T I S
```

After you have found all of the words, match them with their definitions.

1. Tiny, living parts of the body __Cells__
2. Outside covering of an animal cell __Cell membrane__
3. The part of the cell that controls its function __Nucleus__
4. Cells that carry information from parts of the body to the brain __Nerve cells__
5. A group of cells that work together __Tissue__
6. Groups of tissue that work together __Organ__
7. Groups of organs that work together __Body system__
8. System that controls all the other systems in the body __Nervous system__
9. Nerve that carries smell messages to brain __Olfactory nerve__
10. Parts of the body that smell, taste, hear, see, and touch __Sense organs__
11. Groups of cells on your tongue that pick up taste messages __Taste buds__
12. Nerves that carry taste messages __Taste nerves__

Name_____ Date_____

How Bones Join

CLASSIFYING   SKILL WORKSHEET

A. The objects below move in the same way joints in your body move. Describe which type of joint moves like the object shown. Give an example of that kind of joint.

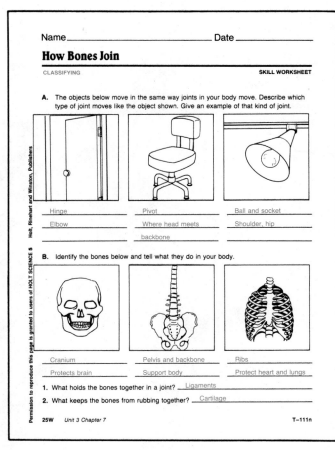

Hinge   Pivot   Ball and socket
Elbow   Where head meets   Shoulder, hip
                         backbone

B. Identify the bones below and tell what they do in your body.

Cranium   Pelvis and backbone   Ribs
Protects brain   Support body   Protect heart and lungs

1. What holds the bones together in a joint? __Ligaments__
2. What keeps the bones from rubbing together? __Cartilage__

25W   Unit 3 Chapter 7   T–111n

Name_____ Date_____

Muscles

CLASSIFYING, FINDING CAUSE AND EFFECT   SKILL WORKSHEET

Identify the type of muscle shown in each picture by writing its name in the blank below it. In the blank below the name write whether it is a voluntary or involuntary muscle.

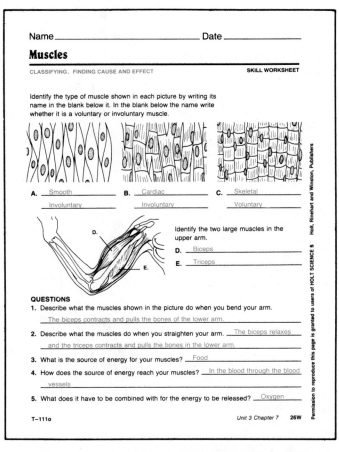

A. Smooth   **B.** Cardiac   **C.** Skeletal
     Involuntary   Involuntary   Voluntary

Identify the two large muscles in the upper arm.

D. Biceps
E. Triceps

QUESTIONS
1. Describe what the muscles shown in the picture do when you bend your arm.
   __The biceps contracts and pulls the bones of the lower arm.__
2. Describe what the muscles do when you straighten your arm. __The biceps relaxes__
   __and the triceps contracts and pulls the bones in the lower arm.__
3. What is the source of energy for your muscles? __Food__
4. How does the source of energy reach your muscles? __In the blood through the blood__
   __vessels__
5. What does it have to be combined with for the energy to be released? __Oxygen__

T–111o   Unit 3 Chapter 7   26W

Name_____ Date_____

Bones and Muscles

BUILDING SCIENCE VOCABULARY   SKILL WORKSHEET

```
        ¹S K E L E T O¹L
        M            I
     ²P I V O T      G
     O    ⁴C A R D I A C
     T            M
  ⁵H I N G E  ⁶T E N D O N
     I            N
  ⁷B A L L A N D S O C K E T
```

Use the clues below to complete the puzzle.

ACROSS
1. Muscles that contain large cylinder-shaped cells
3. A joint that allows the bones to move around and back
4. A type of muscle that makes up the heart
5. A joint that allows the bones to move back and forth or up and down
6. A tough cord that attaches muscle to bone
7. A joint that allows the bones to move in many directions

DOWN
1. A type of muscle containing long, thin, pointed cells
2. A strong band that holds bones in place at a joint

27W   Unit 3 Chapter 7   T–111p

UNIT OVERVIEW

Unit 3 is a life science unit about our senses, muscles, and bones. The cells of our bodies are grouped into tissues. Tissues are made up of similar cells. Tissues are grouped into organs. In an organ, several tissues work as a unit to perform a function. Organs are combined into organ systems. These systems are responsible for specific functions within the body. The organs of the nervous system control all of the other body systems. The body is made aware of its environment through the five senses (sight, taste, touch, smell, and hearing).

The nose is the sense organ of smell. The olfactory nerve sends smell messages to the brain. The sense of smell is closely linked to the sense of taste, which uses the tongue as its sense organ. The eyes, the sense organs of sight, receive images, which are relayed to the brain by the optic nerves. The skin is the largest organ and it is the sense organ of touch. Sensory nerves send messages to the brain through the spinal cord.

The skeletal system supports, protects, and helps the body move. Joints allow bones to move when pulled or pushed by muscles. Ligaments connect the bones together, while tendons join the voluntary skeletal muscles to bones. Involuntary muscles control those body processes that are automatic, such as digestion and breathing. Cardiac muscles keep the heart beating without our having to think about it.

Exceptional Student IEP Unit Goal

At the end of this unit, have the student list one function of each of the five senses and of the muscular and skeletal systems.

SENSING AND MOVING

UNIT OPENER

This is a photograph of the Twyla Tharp dancers performing a dance routine called "Bakers Dozen." You can ask the students the following questions as motivation: What senses do these dancers use to dance? *Sight to see the dance steps and hearing to listen to the rhythm of the music.* What parts of their bodies do they need for these senses? *Eyes and ears.* What other parts of their bodies do they use? *Their arms and legs.* What causes the movement of their arms and legs? *Their brains tell their muscles to move their bones in certain ways.*

UNIT 3

LEARNING CENTER

A suggested title for the Learning Center is "Senses, Muscles and Bones." A display of photographs showing people using their senses and muscles can be set up. You may wish to maintain a file of the Extensions and Worksheet Masters that the students can work on independently.

The following Extensions are especially suitable for the center. All of the materials needed for these Extensions should be available in the center: odor survey, page T–116 (ammonia, nail polish remover, shampoo, cologne, vanilla extract, fruit juice, pencil, paper); colored food, page T–120 (colored vanilla pudding, bread, juices, potatoes); ball toss, page T–129 (blindfold, small ball); leg bone, page T–148 (calf leg bone); chicken foot, page T–152 (chicken foot); optical illusion, page T–160 (index card).

In addition, you may wish to keep a file of related research topics in the center. The following Extensions are recommended: nervous systems (page T–115); tongue (page T–119); hearing (page T–124); ear care (page T–127); laser (page T–130); anesthetics (page T–137); artificial joints (page T–141); helmets (page T–143); arthritis (page T–147); muscular dystrophy (page T–158); Careers (page T–161).

CHAPTER 6

CHAPTER OBJECTIVES

1. Describe the parts of an individual cell and how cells are organized into tissues, organs, and organ systems.
2. Describe the parts and functions of the nervous system, and how the sense of smell functions.
3. Identify the taste areas of the tongue, and how smell and taste are related.
4. Describe the parts and functions of the ears and the eyes.
5. Identify the parts of the nervous system that provide the sense of touch.

SECTION BACKGROUND

The human nervous system consists of the central nervous system (the brain and the spinal cord) and the peripheral nervous system (all the nerves in the body outside the brain and the spinal cord). The brain receives stimuli that have been carried by nerve cells (neurons) from the sense organs. The brain interprets the information and reacts by sending commands to various parts of the body. Humans have five senses: sight, smell, hearing, taste, and touch. The nose is the sense organ of smell. Small nerve endings in the mucous membrane that lines the nose receive stimuli and transmit the smell message to the olfactory nerve. The olfactory nerve sends the smell message to the brain, where it is interpreted as "smell."

MATERIALS

graph paper, pencil

**Exceptional Student
IEP Chapter Goal**

At the end of this chapter, have the student name the main nerve in each of the five sense organs.

YOUR SENSES

6-1.

Sense Organs

114

Being good at a sport takes a lot of effort. Whether leaping, throwing, passing, or catching, you must be able to control the movements of your body. Knowing how your body works will help you to control it. When you finish this section, you should be able to:

BASIC TEACHING PLAN
MOTIVATION

You may want to introduce this lesson by displaying magazine photographs of various athletes who are using their bodies in active ways. Engage the class in a discussion of what seems to make some athletes better than others. Try to focus the discussion on the necessity for such qualities as strength, agility, and the ability to recognize a threatening situation and to react quickly and properly. Indicate to the students that they will begin learning how the brain picks up information from the outside world, and how the body reacts to the information it receives from the brain.

□ **A.** Describe some parts of a cell.

□ **B.** Describe how cells, tissues, and organs work together in body systems.

□ **C.** Describe what the nervous system does.

□ **D.** Trace the path that messages of odors take from the nose to the brain.

1 Every living thing is made of one or more **cells** (selz). The *cell* is a tiny living part of a plant or animal. Most cells are smaller than the period that ends this sentence. Your body is made of almost 3 trillion (3,000,000,000,000) cells.

2 Each of your cells has an outside covering called a **cell membrane** (**mem**-brayn). Inside the cell is a **nucleus** (**nyoo**-klee-us), which is round in shape. The *nucleus* controls all the activities of a cell.

Each cell is able to produce more cells that are just like it. Food and oxygen are carried to the cells through the blood. Cells are able to use the food and oxygen to produce energy for your body. The blood also carries waste products away from the cells.

Using microscopes, scientists have found that cells have different shapes and sizes. They have also found that cells doing the same job are usually found together. **Nerve cells** have the job of carrying information, or messages, from parts of the body to the brain. The picture below shows a *nerve cell* as seen under a microscope.

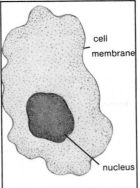

cell membrane

nucleus

Cell: Tiny living part of the body.

Cell membrane: Outside covering of a cell.

Nucleus: The part of the cell that controls its activities.

Nerve cell: Cell that carries information.

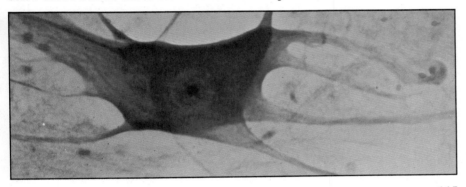

115

DEVELOPMENT

1 **Teaching Tips** — If the students have never seen a cell and if you happen to have a small microscope available, you may want to make a slide of tissue from an onion. Use a small amount of iodine to stain the cells.

2 **Skill Development** — Have the students practice *reading illustrations* by locating the various parts of a cell on the diagram.

3 **Teaching Tips** — Tell the students that their bodies are made of cells and that different parts of the body are composed of different types of cells. Be sure that they understand that the photograph at the bottom of the page is of just one type of cell.

Enrichment
Science Skills — Measuring and Recording Data

Have students conduct a survey to find out what odors people like and dislike. Class members can bring in samples of ammonia, nail polish remover, shampoo, cologne, vanilla extract, and fruit juice.

A. Divide the class into a research group and a survey group. The research group should prepare paper cups containing equal amounts of each substance. They should label the cups with numbers and prepare a key for themselves. They should also prepare a survey form for each member of the survey group.

B. Each member of the survey group will smell each sample and rate the odor as pleasant or unpleasant. They can record their ratings on the survey forms. They should wait a few minutes between samples to prevent sensory fatigue.

C. The research group should collect the survey forms and make a chart to summarize their data. The chart can serve as an audiovisual aid when they report back to the class.

Tissue: Group of cells that works together.

Organ: Group of tissues that works together.

Body system: Groups of organs that work together.

Nervous system: The system that controls all other systems in the body.

Sense organs: Parts of the body that are sensitive to smell, taste, hearing, sight, and touch.

Besides nerve cells, the body has muscle cells, blood cells, bone cells, and other types of cells. Groups of cells working together to do one kind of job form **tissue** (tish-oo). For example, nerve cells join together to form nerve *tissues*. Certain tissues work together to form an **organ** (or-gun). The heart is an *organ* made of various tissues. Some tissues that make up the heart are blood, muscle, and nerve tissue.

4 Organs work with other organs to form a **body system** (sis-tum). The body has many systems. Systems enable us to move, eat, and get rid of wastes. Each *body system* is composed of organs, which are composed of tissues, which are composed of cells.

5 There is one system that controls all other body systems. It is called the **nervous** (nerv-us) **system**. The brain is the major organ of the *nervous system*. This system also consists of nerves that carry information to and from the brain. A third part of the system, the **sense organs**, receives the information that is carried along the nerves to the brain. Through the *sense organs*, the body knows, or senses, what is going on around it. These parts of the body respond to smell, taste, hearing, sight, and touch. Let's examine the nose, which is the organ for the sense of smell.

Contained in the nose are many nerve cells. These cells respond to odors. You can smell the odor of food

6
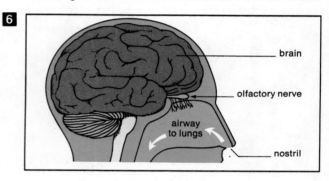

116

4 **Skill Development** — Students are introduced to the ways in which the systems of the body are *classified*.
5 **Teaching Tips** — List a number of stimuli (bright light, loud noise, cold, sour taste) and discuss the body's responses.
6 **Skill Development** — Have the students *study the illustration* and follow the path that smell information takes.

cooking even when it is cooking in another room. How does the smell message get to your brain? When you breathe in, air enters your nose. On its way to your lungs, the air passes nerve cells in your nose. These nerve cells are branches of one main nerve called the **olfactory** (ol-fak-tore-ee) **nerve**. The *olfactory nerve* carries smell messages from your nose to your brain. The drawing on page 116 shows how.

7 How might your sense of smell be a safety device for your body? Suppose your olfactory nerve picked up the smell of smoke in a building on fire. It would send the smell message to your brain. Your brain would send back a message that causes you to leave the building. So your sense of smell acts as a safety device for your body.

Your brain may receive a smell message that it understands as pleasing. Then it sends a message to other parts of your body to cause you to move closer to the smell. The smell of freshly baked cookies might cause such a response.

Olfactory nerve: The nerve that carries smell messages to the brain.

Section Review

Main Ideas: The body is composed of living cells. Cells, tissues, and organs work together in body systems. Information is received by the sense organs and carried by the nerves to the brain, which is the major organ of the nervous system.

Questions: Answer in complete sentences.

1. What parts make up a body system?
2. What is the olfactory nerve?
3. What three parts does the nervous system consist of?
4. Make a diagram of a living cell and label its parts.
5. While sitting in the living room, you smell dinner cooking in the kitchen. How does your brain receive the smell message?

Nervous System
Controls other body systems
Receives and transmits information
Enables us to smell, touch, taste, hear, and see
Causes muscles to move

117

EXTENSIONS

Enrichment
Activity

Have the students do some comparison shopping for four or five well-advertised colognes or perfumes. The lists should include colognes marketed for men and women. Comparison shopping can be done by visiting retail stores in person or by monitoring advertisements.

It is important that the students compare equal volumes of the substances. The students should prepare charts showing data such as brand names, store names, total prices, and prices per unit volume.

7 **Text Questions** — How might your sense of smell be a safety device for your body? *Have the students speculate about this. Essentially, it serves as a sort of early warning system. Since the nose senses chemical particles in the air, we can tell a lot about things even before we get near them. In the case of food, we smell it before we taste it.*

SECTION REVIEW

Answers to Questions
1. Cells, tissues, and organs make up the body systems.
2. The olfactory nerve is the nerve that carries smell information to the brain.
3. The nervous system is composed of sense organs, nerves, and the brain.
4. Have students refer to the diagram on page 115.
5. Air containing the odor enters the nose. Nerve cells pick up the smell message and carry it to the olfactory nerve. The olfactory nerve carries the message to the brain.

SUGGESTED WORKSHEET MASTER
p. T–111j

EXTENSIONS

Enrichment
Research— Library

You may wish to have a group of students engage in an independent study project that compares the ways humans and animals detect odor. Instruct your students to do the following:

A. Select five animals with obviously different odor-sensing organs.

B. Do library research as preparation for the writing of one paragraph on the sense of smell for each animal.

C. Make a labeled diagram of the odor-detection organ of each animal.

D. Make a chart that compares the odor-detection organs of the animals and of humans.

Some interesting animals that the students may wish to use for comparison with humans are elephants, snakes, snails, bloodhounds, salmon, dolphins, and honeybees.

How quickly does your nose detect an odor?

Seconds	Number of people
15	
30	
45	
60	
75	
90	
105	
120	
135	
150	
165	
180	

A. Obtain these materials: graph paper, pencil.

B. Your teacher will pour some perfume into a saucer. Half the class will observe. Half the class will record data. Then you will switch roles.

C. As an observer, shut your eyes when the teacher tells you to do so. Raise your hand when you first notice the odor. Keep your hand raised until it is counted.

D. Prepare a data chart, like the one shown, for your work as a recorder. Over one row, write "Seconds." Over the other row, write "Number of people." Count and record the number of people who have their hands raised at each 15-second interval.

E. Prepare a graph, like the one shown, using the data from your chart.

1. With what sense organ was the odor detected?
2. How long did it take the first observer to notice the odor?
3. Why did observers take different amounts of time to detect the odor?
4. Write a paragraph that sums up the results shown in the chart and on the graph.

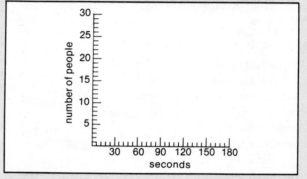

118

ACTIVITY

Skill Development — *Recording Data and Hypothesizing*

Teaching Tips — Shut the windows in your classroom so that air currents will not affect the results of the activity.

Answers to Questions — **1.** Nose (nerve cells in the nose). **2.** The first observers will probably detect the odor in 10 to 20 seconds. **3.** The differences in the detection times were due to the distances of the students from the perfume and the acuteness of the smell detectors in their noses. **4.** The students closest to the perfume smelled it first. As time went on, other students who were farther away smelled it. Some people who were the same distance away as others did not smell it as fast. They may have had allergies, a cold, or an impaired sense of smell.

This girl has just tasted the lemon. How do you think it tasted? The expression on her face should tell you the answer. You probably have bitten into a lemon. How would you describe its taste? When you finish this section, you should be able to:

☐ **A.** Identify four basic taste areas of the tongue.
☐ **B.** Explain how the brain receives taste messages.
☐ **C.** Describe how the senses of taste and smell work together.

1　There are four basic tastes that most people recognize. They are sweet, sour, salty, and bitter. Many foods have just one taste. A lemon, for example, tastes sour. Some foods combine two or more of the basic tastes. Barbecue sauce has both a sweet and a sour taste. Other foods have tastes that seem to be neither sweet nor sour, neither salty nor bitter. Pepper and other spices are examples of such foods.

The sense organ for taste is the tongue. In the tongue are groups of nerve endings called **taste buds**. When you chew food, tiny bits of it enter the *taste buds* through openings in the tongue. Taste buds for each of the four tastes are located in different areas of the tongue.

Taste buds: Groups of cells on the tongue that are sensitive to taste.

SECTION BACKGROUND

The tongue is the sense organ of taste. Located on the tongue are tiny bumps called taste buds. Each taste bud contains a pore through which small portions of dissolved food materials pass. Within the taste bud is a nerve ending that is stimulated by this dissolved material. The nerve endings are connected to the taste nerve, which transmits information to the brain. Sweet and salty tastes are detected near the tip of the tongue. Sour tastes are sensed along the sides of the tongue. Bitter tastes are picked up at the back of the tongue.

The sense of taste and smell are closely related. When we are eating, smell information, as well as taste information, reaches the brain. Smell information arrives first. The ability of the brain to receive and respond to smell information quickly may serve to protect us from ingesting foods that have "gone bad."

MATERIALS

5 food samples, blindfold, paper, 2 paper cups, water, pencil, 10 toothpicks

119

BASIC TEACHING PLAN

MOTIVATION

When you start this section, you may wish to bring a lemon to class. Cut it into several slices and have various students taste them. Ask the students who did the tasting to express their reactions.

Text Questions — How do you think it tasted? *Awful.* How would you describe its taste? *Sour.*

DEVELOPMENT

1　**Skill Development** — Have students volunteer the names of various foods and discuss whether they should be *classified* as sweet, sour, salty, or bitter.

EXTENSIONS

Enrichment
Research— Library

Some students may wish to research the structure and functions of the tongue. They can answer the following questions:
1. What is the structure of the tongue?
2. How is the tongue used for taking in food?
3. How does the tongue function in the perception of taste?
4. How is the tongue used in speech?

They will discover that the tongue is a muscular organ important in the ingestion of food, the perception of taste, the articulation of speech, and the cleansing of the inner sides of the teeth.

Application
Activity

The color of food seems to have a significant effect on how we expect it to taste. Our sense of sight can actually alter our sense of taste in this way.

Have some students prepare familiar foods, but have them change the foods' colors so that they will be different from what our minds associate with these foods. Half of the students could be assigned to be food preparers, and the other half could be tasters. Suggestions could be coloring vanilla pudding, bread, juices, and potatoes.

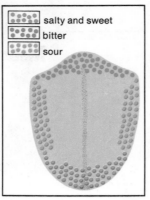

Taste nerves: Nerves that carry taste messages to your brain.

Taste buds that respond to sweetness are on the tip of the tongue. Some of the taste buds for saltiness are also there. Along the sides of the tongue are taste buds for sourness. Those for bitterness are at the back of the tongue. **2**

The sense of taste is part of the nervous system. When food enters the taste buds in the tongue, **taste nerves** pick up the messages. The *taste nerves* send the messages from the taste buds to the brain. The brain responds with a sweet, sour, salty, or bitter taste.

Look at the photographs of the boy eating. Each food has one or more taste. What taste messages are being sent to his brain about each food? **3**

The senses of smell and taste affect one another. When you chew food, odors from the food reach the olfactory nerve in the nose. While you are tasting the food, you are also smelling the food. Often you are smelling food when you think you are tasting it. That's why food seems tasteless when you have a cold. With a cold, passages in your nose are closed. Food odors cannot reach the olfactory nerve. Because you cannot smell it, food is less tasty.

120

2 **Teaching Tips** — Have three food samples available for tasting. Blindfold four students. Two of the students should hold their noses as they taste the foods, and the other two should not. Ask each of the tasters to describe the foods they are tasting. Discussion of the results will serve as a good introduction for the next page.

3 **Text Questions** — What taste messages are being sent to his brain about each food? *Lollipop — sweet; grapefruit — sour; salted peanuts — salty; radish — bitter.*

4 **Teaching Tips** — Be sure to emphasize the importance of taste as a safety device for the body. Ask students to provide accounts of their experiences in detecting foul food.

ACTIVITY

How can you test your sense of taste?

A. With a partner, obtain these materials: blindfold, paper, 2 paper cups with water, pencil, 10 toothpicks.

B. Your teacher will give you five food samples, each in a numbered paper cup. Decide who will be the taster. Make a chart like the one shown to record the taster's observations.

C. Blindfold the taster. The taster should hold his or her nostrils closed.

D. With the flat end of the toothpick, pick up a small amount of one food sample. Place the food sample on the taster's tongue.

E. Tell the taster to spread the sample around with the tongue. Then ask the taster to identify the type of taste and name the food.

F. Repeat steps **D** and **E** with each food sample. Have the taster drink some water after each sample to clear the taste buds. Use a new toothpick each time.

G. Switch places with the taster. Repeat the activity with your partner recording.

1. Were there any food samples the tasters could not identify? Make a hypothesis that explains why the tasters had trouble identifying those foods.

2. Were these food samples easy to identify? Explain.

3. Would the results be the same if the tasters had their eyes open? Why were the tasters asked to wear a blindfold?

4. Why were they asked to hold their nostrils closed?

5. Write one paragraph summarizing the data in your chart. Use the words *taste buds*, *taste nerves*, and *brain* to explain the results.

Food Sample	Food Identified
1.	
2.	
3.	
4.	
5.	

121

Application
Science Skills — Comparing and Contrasting, Recording Data

The students have seen numerous commercials on TV that make claims that cereal X tastes better than other cereals. Similar claims are made for cookies, soft drinks, peanut butter, chocolate candies, and chocolate additives for milk. Students could gather various products and conduct taste tests to determine class preferences.

ACTIVITY

Skill Development — *Comparing, Contrasting, and Recording Data*

Teaching Tips — You will need to prepare five food samples in paper cups for each group. The following selections will work well: honey (sweet); sour cream (sour); salted potato chips ground into tiny pieces (salty); instant coffee grains (bitter); barbecue sauce (sweet and sour). Place one-half teaspoon of each sample in a different paper cup, totaling five cups for each group. Label the cups 1 through 5 for each group.

Answers to Questions — **1.** Holding the nostrils closed meant that the sense of smell was not involved. The sense of taste is affected by the sense of smell. **2.** Most people can easily identify potato chips because they know the taste very well. **3.** The blindfold prevented them from seeing the food and deciding what it tasted like before they tested it. **4.** With the nostrils closed, no odor information reached the brain. Only the taste buds picked up information. **5.** The taste buds picked up the information. The taste nerves carried the information to the brain.

EXTENSIONS

Application
Research — Library

Some students can conduct a newspaper research project to collect articles written about the use of synthetic flavorings in foods. They will discover that some flavorings used in bacon, breakfast cereals, fruit juices, and dietetic foods have possible negative side effects.

5 Since smell and taste work together, it is possible to fool the brain by smelling one food while eating another. What would happen if you ate a slice of raw potato while smelling an apple? Which food would you taste? The potato slice would taste like an apple. The brain picks up the smell message more quickly than the taste message. The odor from the apple is picked up before the taste of the potato. So the potato tastes like an apple.

The sense of smell can be a safety device for you. If food is spoiled, your sense of smell will detect the odor on the first bite. If the odor from the food is very bad, you will notice it as you bring the food to your mouth.

Section Review

Main Ideas: The sense of taste is a function of the nervous system. Taste buds and taste nerves are located in the tongue, a sense organ. They pick up and send taste messages to the brain, which interprets, or explains, the messages. Messages of taste often work with messages of smell.

Questions: Answer in complete sentences.

1. What are the four basic tastes? In what sense organ are they found?
2. When you bite into food, you know before you chew it how it tastes. Why?
3. Look at the drawing of the tongue on page 120. Where are the taste buds located for: a. saltiness, b. bitterness, c. sourness, d. sweetness?
4. Why does food seem tasteless when you have a head cold?
5. Trace the route of taste from the first bite of food to the brain's response.
6. Look at the photographs on page 120. Name each food and the part of the tongue that tastes it.

122

SECTION REVIEW

Answers to Questions
1. Sweet, sour, salty, and bitter. The tongue.
2. You smell food before it gets into your mouth. Taste also depends on the odor of the food. You also see the food and remember its taste.
3. Salty—tip; bitter—back; sour—sides; sweet—tip.
4. If you have a cold, your nose can become clogged. Smell information does not reach your brain. Taste depends on smell as well as the taste buds picking up taste information.
5. As you bring food to your mouth, you smell it. When you chew it, the taste buds pick up taste information. The taste nerves carry the information to the brain. The brain tells us how the food tastes.
6. Lollipop - tip; grapefruit - sides; nuts - tip; radish - back.

How would you like to baby-sit for this infant? She is certainly making a big fuss! Do you think you ever cried like this? When babies cry, they are trying to tell adults something. If you baby-sit, you know you can find out what babies need by listening to their sounds. When you listen, you hear. Your sense of hearing is one of the ways you receive information. When you finish this section, you should be able to:

☐ **A.** Describe the parts of the ear.
☐ **B.** Describe how sound messages travel from the outer ear, through the head, and to the brain.

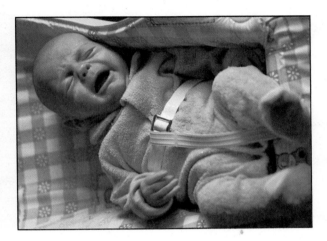

Our sense of hearing tells us what is happening outside our bodies. A baby's cry, the ringing of a doorbell, and the honking of a car horn all tell us something different. But not everybody has a good sense of hearing. Some people need hearing aids to pick up sound. Hearing aids make sounds louder. They are very small, as you can see from the photograph on the right.

123

SECTION BACKGROUND

The three regions of the ear are the outer ear, the middle ear, and the inner ear. The nerve in each ear that carries information about sound to the brain is the auditory nerve.

The outer ear consists of the visible portion of the ear and the external ear canal. Sound waves enter the outer ear and are directed to the eardrum, in the middle ear. The eardrum vibrates in response to the sound waves that strike it.

The middle ear contains three very small movable bones. The hammer, a bone connected to the eardrum, vibrates in response to the movement of the eardrum. The anvil is connected to the stirrup, which transfers the vibrations to the inner ear.

The inner ear contains the cochlea, which has the shape of a snail shell, and the semicircular canals. The cochlea contains fluid and nerve endings. The vibrations of the fluid stimulate the nerve endings. These nerve endings transmit impulses to the auditory nerve, which carries the message to the brain.

MATERIALS

blindfold, paper, pencil

BASIC TEACHING PLAN

MOTIVATION

Obtain a record of sound effects and play it at the beginning of class. Such records are common items in record stores and libraries. Play a sound effect at a low volume and ask students to identify it. Then increase the volume. This can begin a discussion of how our ears respond to sound waves.

EXTENSIONS

Enrichment
Research — Library

You may wish to have some students do research that compares the organs of hearing in humans with those in a variety of animals. They may also be able to find information concerning the acuteness of the hearing sense in certain animals. Some animals that you can suggest are elephants, bats, whales, birds, and dolphins.

Exceptional Student
Hearing Impaired

If appropriate, ask the hearing-impaired students to tell the rest of the class how they use other senses to compensate for their inability to hear.

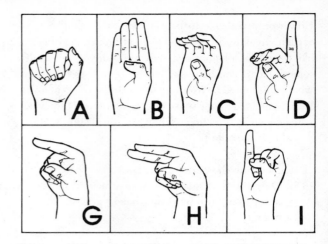

1 Some people who do not hear sound have learned to understand finger spelling. This method makes use of the fingers to form the letters of the alphabet. Whole conversations of words and phrases are spelled out. Sign language is different from finger spelling. It makes use of hand and arm gestures that stand for words and phrases. Lipreading makes use of the sense of sight, rather than the sense of hearing. This skill requires people to watch the shapes and movements of the lips of those speaking. It is possible, then, for people without the sense of hearing to understand the sounds around them.

People who do have the sense of hearing are not able to hear all sounds. Many sounds made by animals are out of the range of human hearing. There are, however, a great many sounds that people can hear. You have already learned how sound is made.

Vibrate: To move back and forth.

2 A sound is made when something **vibrates** (vi-brayts). When something *vibrates*, it moves back and forth. A vibrating object makes the air around it vibrate. The air **3** carries the sound vibrations in all directions. How do sound vibrations in the air become sounds you hear?

124

DEVELOPMENT

1 **Teaching Tips** — You may wish to ask the students if they have ever seen anyone using sign language to interpret spoken language to deaf people. TV shows, such as *Sesame Street*, illustrate this skill.

2 **Teaching Tips** — You may want to do a quick demonstration to show students that the effect we call hearing begins with a specific cause — the vibration of an object. You can place a plastic ruler on the desk top so that a portion of it extends over the edge. By pressing down firmly on the part that is on the desk and pulling on the free end and releasing it, you will cause the ruler to vibrate and produce a "humming" sound.

3 **Text Questions** — How do sound vibrations in the air become sounds you hear? *Use this question to stimulate a discussion.*

ACTIVITY

Are two ears better than one?

A. With a partner, obtain these materials: blindfold, paper, pencil.

	Right	Wrong
Ears uncovered		
Right ear covered		
Left ear covered		

B. Make a chart that is organized like the one above. Use it to record your data. Have your partner sit down. Place the blindfold on your partner.

C. At a distance of about 3 m from your partner, clap your hands. Ask your partner to point to where the sound came from. Repeat this 10 times. Try several different locations, including some that are near your partner's head.

   1. How many correct responses did your partner make?

D. Now have your partner press a cupped hand tightly over the left ear. Repeat step C.

   2. How many correct responses were made?

E. Now have your partner uncover the left ear and press a cupped hand tightly over the right ear. Repeat step C.

   3. How many correct responses were made?

F. Switch places with your partner and then repeat the activity.

   4. Write a sentence that sums up the results of having both ears uncovered.

   5. Having two ears may be a safety device for humans. Explain.

125

Reinforcement
Activity

A demonstration of water waves can be used to reinforce the idea of sound waves.

A. Fill halfway with water an oblong heat-resistant glass dish.

B. Place it on a sheet of white paper on an overhead projector.

C. At one end of the dish, repeatedly tap the surface of the water with the eraser end of a pencil. A series of water waves will form and spread outward from the pencil.

Tell the students that the pencil is like a sound source. The water waves spreading out from the vibrating source are like sound waves in air. The sound waves reach the eardrums and cause them to vibrate.

ACTIVITY

Skill Development — *Recording Data, Concluding, and Generalizing*

Teaching Tips — If you have access to a large room in the building, such as the cafeteria or the gymnasium, you may wish to do the activity there. You will want to get the working groups as far apart from one another as possible.

Answers to Questions — 1. Answers will vary. 2. Probably fewer correct responses were made when either one or the other ear was covered. 3. Probably fewer correct responses were made when either one or the other ear was covered. 4. When both ears were uncovered, we could point to the source without making mistakes. 5. Two ears rather than one enable humans to judge the direction that sounds come from.

EXTENSIONS

Enrichment
Research — Library

The people listed below are talented musicians who, because they are blind, depend solely on their ability to hear. Read the descriptions given below of Mr. S, Mr. C, Mr. F, and Mr. W without telling their real names. Let the students do some detective work for a few days to find out the names of the musicians. At the end of the allotted time, have the students submit their answers. If recordings by these musicians are available, play selections for the class at the conclusion of the research.

1. Mr. S. (George Shearing) — born in 1919 in England; jazz pianist; composed "Lullabye of Birdland."
2. Mr. C. (Ray Charles) — born in Georgia in 1932; plays piano, alto saxophone, and other instruments; blues singer.
3. Mr. F. (José Feliciano) — born in 1945 and raised in New York City; plays guitar, banjo, harmonica, and other instruments.
4. Mr. W. (Stevie Wonder) — born in 1950 and raised in Detroit; plays piano and other instruments; sings and composes; his name before he went into show business was Stevie Judkins.

Exceptional Student
Visually Impaired

Borrow a model of an ear from an ear doctor. Allow the visually impaired students to gently feel the model. If no model is available, compare the shape of the ear to a funnel.

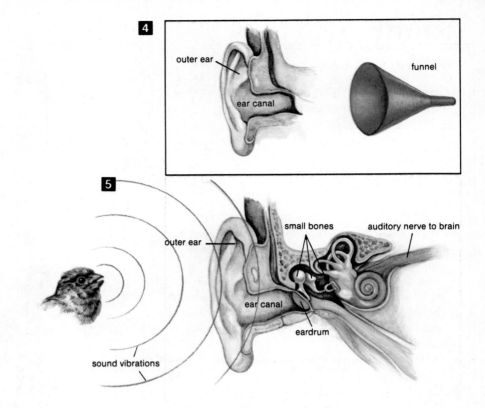

Outer ear: The part of the ear that gathers sound vibrations.

Ear canal: A narrow tube inside the ear that carries sound vibrations into the head.

Sound vibrations are picked up by one of your sense organs, the ear. Let's trace the path of a sound message from the air to your brain.

The ear you see when you look in a mirror is not your whole ear. It is the part of your ear called the **outer ear**. Your *outer ears* gather sound vibrations. Your outer ears work like funnels. They direct the sound vibrations into another part of your ear called the **ear canal**. Your *ear canal* is a narrow tube that begins at the inner side of the outer ear. The ear canal carries the sound vibrations into your head.

126

4 **Skill Development** — Ask your students to *compare* the shape and function of the funnel and outer ear as they examine the first *illustration*.

5 **Skill Development** — Guide your students through the path of a sound message as they examine the second *illustration* on this page.

At the end of your ear canal is the **eardrum**. The sound vibrations that have traveled through the ear canal then strike the *eardrum*. The eardrum also starts to vibrate. The vibrations from your eardrum pass along to nearby bones. These bones are very tiny. They begin to vibrate.

Around the small bones are nerve cells. The nerve cells carry the message about the vibrations to one main nerve. This nerve is called the **auditory** (aw-dih-tore-ee) **nerve**. The *auditory nerve* carries the sound message to your brain. When the brain receives the message, you know you have heard a sound.

Eardrum: The part of the ear at the end of the ear canal.

Auditory nerve: The nerve that carries sound messages to the brain.

Section Review

Main Ideas: Sound is picked up by the outer ear and sent to the eardrum, which vibrates. Nerve cells carry the vibrations to the auditory nerve, which carries them to the brain.

Questions: Answer in complete sentences.

Use this information to answer questions 1–6:
Anne Marie is outside roller skating. She hears her mother call, "Anne Marie, come in for dinner."

1. How did the sound vibrations reach Anne Marie?
2. What parts of Anne Marie's ears gathered the sound vibrations?
3. After the vibrations were gathered, they were directed into a narrow tube. What is that tube called?
4. Vibrations traveled along the narrow tube to the eardrum. What happened to Anne Marie's eardrum when the sound vibrations struck it?
5. Where did the sound message go from her eardrum, and how did it get there?
6. When did Anne Marie actually hear the sound of her mother's voice?

127

EXTENSIONS

Enrichment
Research — Library

Interested students could do research on ear care. The ear is a delicate organ that can be damaged easily by infection or injury. After students have finished their research work, they could make a poster on ear care. The following pointers on ear care should be included on the poster:

1. Never strike another person on the ear. This could break the eardrum and/or cause a deformity of the ear lobe.
2. Never put any object into the ear. This can injure the ear canal and even the eardrum. Do not try to remove wax. You may push it farther into the ear. Plugs of wax should be removed only by a doctor.
3. Loud sounds can harm the ear and cause loss of hearing. Use ear plugs to protect the ears from loud noises.
4. See a doctor when you have a severe earache.
5. Have a routine physical examination once a year. Doctors always inspect the ears as part of the examination.

6 Teaching Tips — You may wish to tell the students that the bones in the ear are called hammer, anvil, and stirrup. Tell the students that placing objects in their ears can break or puncture the eardrums. If this occurs, the sound message is stopped because the vibrations are not passed along.

SECTION REVIEW

Answers to Questions
1. The sound vibrations traveled through the air.
2. The outer ear.
3. The ear canal.
4. The eardrum started to vibrate.
5. The vibrating eardrum passed the vibration along to nearby bones. The bones vibrated and passed the vibration farther into the ear to the auditory nerve. The auditory nerve carried the sound messages to the brain.
6. When the message reached her brain.

SUGGESTED WORKSHEET MASTER
p. T–111k

SECTION BACKGROUND

The eyes receive light rays and transmit information to the brain by way of the optic nerves. The eyeballs fit into protective sockets in the skull. The iris (the colored part of the eye) contains muscles that control the size of the pupil. The pupil is the clear part of the iris through which light passes. The lens is a flexible portion of the eye beyond the iris. Light rays from objects that pass through the lens are focused on the retina to form an image. The retina is a layer of tissue on the inner surface of the eye that contains nerve cells.

The point at which the optic nerve enters the retina has no nerve cells. This location is known as the blind spot.

Nearsightedness is caused by an eyeball that is too long and/or a lens that is too rounded. In either of those conditions, the image formed is focused in front of the retina.

Farsightedness is caused by an eyeball that is too short and/or a lens that is too flat. In these cases, the image is focused behind the retina.

MATERIALS

mirror, paper, pencil

6-4.
Sight

This baseball pitcher is throwing a curve ball. It takes great skill to send a baseball curving toward home plate. Seconds after this photograph was taken, the batter swung at the curve ball and hit it out of the ball park. The batter's eyes provided him with the information he needed to hit that home run. It takes almost perfect vision, or eyesight, to hit a curve ball with a bat. When you finish this section, you should be able to:

☐ **A.** Trace the path of light through the parts of the human eye.
☐ **B.** Compare nearsightedness with farsightedness.
☐ **C.** Compare some parts of the eye to parts of a camera.

128

BASIC TEACHING PLAN
MOTIVATION

One eye receives an image that is slightly displaced in space from the image picked up by the other eye. The brain interprets these two images and tells us where the object is. Ask the students to put a pencil in one hand and then to hold their arms out in front of them. Then tell them to point the index finger of the hand without the pencil toward their other hand. Next tell them to try to touch the pencil point to the finger with one eye shut. Students should then try it with both eyes open. Discuss how using both eyes helps us.

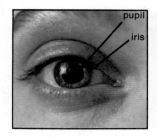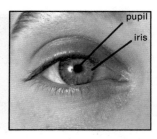

Your eyes are the sense organs for sight. When you see an object, such as a baseball, your eyes receive the light reflected from or given off that object. Eyes provide the brain with the information needed to see. Like the ears, the eyes have parts. The colored part of the eye is called the **iris** (**eye**-rus). In the center of the *iris* is an opening called the **pupil** (**pyoo**-pul). The *pupils* look like black dots. Light enters the eyes through the pupils.

1   When the light is dim, the pupil appears larger than when the light is bright. But it is not the pupil that changes size. It is really the iris that changes size by opening and closing. In dim light, the iris opens to let more light enter the eye. In bright light, the iris closes a little to stop too much light from entering. If too much light enters, parts of the eye can be damaged.

After light enters your eye, it passes through a part of the eye called the **lens** (lenz). When the light passes through the *lens*, a pattern appears on the back of the eye. The pattern is an upside-down picture of the object you are looking at.

On the back of the inside of the eye are nerve cells. These nerve cells carry the message about the pattern to one main nerve. This nerve is called the **optic** (**op**-tik) **nerve**. The *optic nerve* carries the sight message from the inside of your eye, or sense organ, to your brain. The brain changes the upside-down pattern so that you see the object right-side up.

When the lens of the eye forms a pattern, or image, on

Iris: The colored part of the eye.

Pupil: The opening in the center of the iris.

Lens: The part of the eye that changes light from an object into a pattern.

Optic nerve: The nerve that carries sight messages to the brain.

129

DEVELOPMENT

1 **Teaching Tips** — Explain that the pupil appears dark because the inside of the eye is dark and the pupil is clear. Compare this fact to looking into a dark room through a window. The window also appears to be dark.

EXTENSIONS

Enrichment
Research — Library

In recent years, the invention of the laser has had a tremendous impact on the work of the eye surgeon. Some students may be interested in contacting an eye surgeon, in addition to doing library research, to find out how the laser is used in eye surgery. They will find that it has enabled surgeons to make repairs in the interior of the eye without actually entering the eye with traditional surgical instruments. The most common operation is the reattachment of a detached retina.

The students will find that eye surgeons are now able to reattach the retina, using a beam of laser light that is directed through the pupil.

2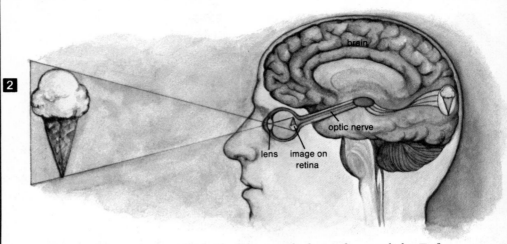

the back of the eye, the lens is focusing light. To focus an image of an object means to make it sharp and clear. The lens becomes thinner to focus light coming from far objects. It becomes thicker to focus light coming from near objects.

Nearsightedness: Difficulty in seeing faraway objects.

Retina: The back part of the eye, where images are focused.

3 If you wear glasses, your vision problem may be **nearsightedness**. *Nearsightedness* is difficulty in seeing objects that are far away. Objects far away are not clear because the images are not focused on the back part of the eye, which is called the **retina** (**reh**-tih-nuh). They are focused, instead, in front of the *retina*. That's why objects far away look fuzzy to nearsighted people.

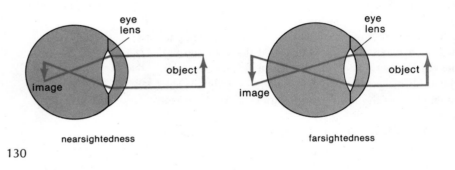

130

---

2 **Skill Development** — Ask students to look at the *illustration* and *compare* the image of the ice cream cone on the back of the eye with the image that the brain receives. Ask them to point to the optic nerve and locate the lens.

3 **Teaching Tips** — This is an excellent opportunity to discuss eye care. Children and adolescents should have vision tests every year to determine the need for eyeglasses, for changes in lens prescriptions, and to discover eye diseases. Students should be aware of the need to check eye conditions, such as blurred vision, unusual redness, extreme watering, irritation, or itching. The throwing of stones and sharp pencils, fireworks, and a variety of other things can result in eye accidents. Protective goggles need to be worn when doing jobs that have the potential for injury. The danger of chemicals to the eyes should also be emphasized.

ACTIVITY

Observing changes in your eyes

A. Obtain these materials: mirror, paper, pencil.

B. Look at your eyes in the mirror. Draw a picture of the iris and pupil of one eye. Try to draw the picture the same size as your eye. Label the iris and the pupil.

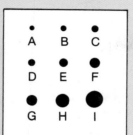

C. Look at this diagram of pupil sizes. Find the dark circle closest in size to your pupil. Write down the letter of the dark circle. Under it, write "Normal Light."

D. Your teacher will dim the lights in your classroom. Look again at your eyes in the mirror.

  1. What difference do you observe?

E. After 10 seconds, write down the letter of the circle closest in size to your pupil. Under it write "Dim Light." Your teacher will put the lights on. After 10 seconds, look at your eyes again.

  2. What do you observe now?

F. Write down the letter of the circle closest in size to your pupil. Under it write "Normal Light."

  3. Write one paragraph summing up the results. Include a sentence that answers: How does the amount of light in a room affect the size of the pupils of the eyes?

Many adults have a vision problem called **farsightedness**. *Farsightedness* is difficulty in seeing objects that are close. Here, too, the image of the object is not focused on the retina. It is focused behind the retina. Both nearsightedness and farsightedness can be corrected. Eyeglasses cause the light reflected from the object to fall directly on the retina.

Farsightedness: Difficulty in seeing objects that are close.

131

ACTIVITY

Skill Development — *Finding Cause and Effect, Comparing and Contrasting*

Teaching Tips — If you do not wish to use mirrors in this activity, simply have the students work as partners and record "pupil size" for one another.

Safety Tips — Caution students to avoid putting fingers or other objects in their eyes.

Answers to Questions — **1.** The pupil was larger in the dim light. **2.** The pupil returned to its original size. **3.** The pupil is smaller in bright light and larger in dim light. The pupil adjusts to the amount of light in a room and, therefore, protects the retina from receiving too much light.

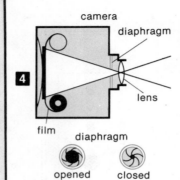

Diaphragm: Part of a camera that controls how much light enters.

If you have used a camera, you know that at the front of the camera is a clear, glass part. Light passes through this glass to the film inside the camera. Can you guess its name? If you said "lens," you are right. It does the same job for a camera that your own lenses do for your eyes. Light from the object being photographed passes through the camera. When it reaches the film, it causes chemicals on the film to react. An image is formed on the film. It is the picture you see when the film is developed. Camera film is a little like the retina of the eye.

The part of the camera that controls how much light enters is called the **diaphragm** (dy-uh-fram). The *diaphragm* is like the iris of the eye. If the light going through the diaphragm is too much or too little, the picture will be either washed out or too dark.

Section Review

Main Ideas: The eye is a sense organ. Parts of the eye are the iris, pupil, lens, retina, and optic nerve. Light from an object passes through the lens and focuses upside down on the retina. Sight messages are then carried to the brain by the optic nerve. The brain makes the image of the object right-side up.

Questions: Answer in complete sentences.

1. Define each of the following: iris, pupil, lens, retina, and optic nerve.
2. Your eyes receive the image of a tree upside down. Why do you see the tree right-side up?
3. Where is the image focused in the eye of a near-sighted person?
4. Which parts of a camera can be compared to the iris and the lens in the human eye?
5. In a dark room, what happens to your pupils and irises? Why?
6. In the bright sunlight, what happens to your pupils and irises? Why?

132

4 **Skill Development** — If an old camera is available to you, partially disassemble it and have students locate the lens, diaphragm, and the position at which the film receives the image. *Compare* the parts of the camera to those of the eye.

SECTION REVIEW
Answers to Questions

1. The iris is the colored part of the eye. The pupil is the center of the iris. The lens changes the light into a pattern on the back of the eye. The retina is the tissue on the inside of the eye and has the nerve cells that receive the image. The optic nerve carries sight messages to the brain.
2. The brain receives the information and turns it right-side up.
3. The image is focused in front of the retina.
4. The diaphragm of the camera is like the iris of the eye. The camera and the eye have a lens to focus the image.
5. The irises open, pupils get larger; more light is needed to see.
6. The irises close and the pupils get smaller in the sunlight. If too much light enters the eye, the eye can be damaged.

This student can't see. But he is reading. The book he is reading is printed in a special system that does not use ink. The system consists of raised dots, which stand for words and numbers. The student is reading by feeling the shapes of the words. Through his fingertips, he receives and sends information to his brain. When you finish this section, you should be able to:

☐ **A.** Describe the skin as a sense organ.
☐ **B.** Locate some sense receptors in the skin.
☐ **C.** Explain how touch messages are carried to the brain from the skin.

The system the young man is using to read is called the Braille system. The raised dots of the Braille system allow those without the sense of sight to make use of their sense of touch. Touch is the sense that lets us know when we have made contact with a person or an object. When

6-5.
Touch

133

SECTION BACKGROUND

Touch is the sense that tells us our bodies have made physical contact with an object. This sense tells us the shape and hardness of objects. The sense of touch also gives us information concerning warmth, cold, pain, and pressure. Within the skin are nerve endings that provide us with the feelings of pain, warmth, cold, and pressure.

The sense of touch is more acute in some parts of the body than in others. This is due to the fact that the receptors for touch are not equally distributed throughout the skin. Some areas have more receptors than other areas.

Information regarding touch is carried by nerve cells to nerves in the spinal cord, and finally to the brain. The brain transmits commands to body parts based on the touch information it receives.

MATERIALS

paper clip, ruler

BASIC TEACHING PLAN
MOTIVATION

Make a mystery box by taking a cardboard box that has a cover and cutting a hole the size of a student's hand in one side. Put an assortment of objects in the box and ask students to try to identify the objects by reaching in and touching them. Ask the students to return to their seats and write down their observations and conclusions. Discuss the kinds of information that the sense of touch provides for us.

Exceptional Student
Visually Impaired
If appropriate, have these students talk about Braille writing to the rest of the class. Ask them to discuss other ways that they rely on touch to "see."

Application
Science Skills — Classifying and Recording Data

Students could investigate the ability of individuals to distinguish differences in size by touch alone.

A. Prepare 10 squares of cardboard ranging in size from 1 to 5.5 cm (1/4 in. to 2 1/2 in.) square. The sides of the squares should increase in size as follows: 1 cm, 1.5 cm, 2 cm, 2.5 cm, . . . 5.5 cm.

B. Mark the back of each test square with a number (No. 1 is the smallest card and No. 10 is the largest).

C. Give blindfolded students an opportunity to arrange a scrambled set of test squares in order of increasing size from left to right.

The students who do this study can count the number of squares placed in correct order and use a ratio (for example, six out of ten) as a measure of success. More capable students can compute the percentages.

1 we touch, we learn the shape and hardness of an object. A great deal of human activity depends on touching. What activities do not depend on a sense of touch? Reading Braille and many other activities are possible because the skin is sensitive to touch.

Your skin is a sense organ. It is the largest sense organ of the body. The skin can pick up messages about heat, cold, pain, touch, and pressure. In the skin are many nerve cells. These nerve cells are called **receptors** (ree-**sep**-torz). Each *receptor* senses only one kind of message. In the skin are receptors for heat, cold, pain, touch, and pressure.

Look at the girl in the picture. What messages is her skin picking up about the rabbit? The receptors in her skin are picking up messages about touch, pressure, and perhaps heat from the rabbit's body.

Receptors are not evenly spread out over the skin. Some places have more receptors than others. The skin is

Receptors: The nerve cells in the skin.

134

DEVELOPMENT

1 **Text Questions** — Can you think of any activity that does not depend on your sense of touch? *Activities that solely involve the senses of sight (reading); hearing (listening to music); and smell (detecting leaking gas).*

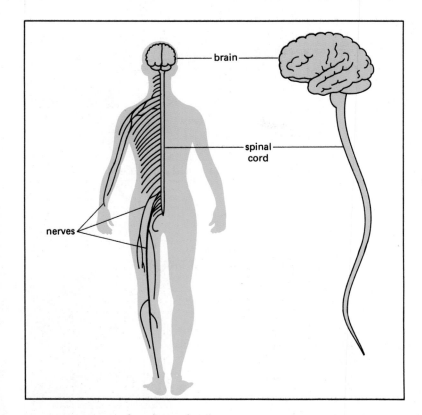

brain

spinal
cord

nerves

more sensitive in the places that have more receptors and picks up more messages there. The skin is less sensitive in places that have fewer receptors and does not pick up as many messages there. Some receptors are deeper within the skin than others.

2 Your fingertips are more sensitive than the back of your hand. There are more touch receptors there. Touch receptors lie close to the skin's surface. Pressure receptors lie deep within the skin. If you press lightly against your skin, you will feel only touch. If you press hard enough, you will cause the pressure receptors deep within the skin to react. Then you will feel pain.

135

EXTENSIONS

Enrichment
Research — Library

Students could do research on the life of Helen Keller and in particular on her use of the sense of touch as her principal method of communication. You may wish to direct the students by having them focus on such questions as:
1. Who was Helen Keller?
2. What communication problems was she born with?
3. How did she learn to communicate by using her sense of touch?
4. What methods did she use to overcome some of the problems she had?

2 **Skill Development** — You may wish to have the students gently rub the palms of their hands together and then the backs. Ask them where they think their skin seemed most sensitive to touch. Most will say that the palms were more sensitive to touch. Ask them to identify a possible cause. The cause is that there are more receptors in the palms of the hands.

EXTENSIONS

Reinforcement
Activity

Students are quite familiar with television commercials that extol the virtues of various painkillers. Overlooked in such advertisements is the possibility of dismissing the cause of the pain (which might be health- or life-threatening) by treating the symptom. Little or no mention is made of the harmful side effects, and of the development of a dependence on patent medicines that are painkillers.

To extend the students' thinking about such matters, you may wish to encourage some students to do the following:

1. Conduct a survey of the number, type, and length of the commercials for pain relievers that they observe on television over a one-week period. They will need to prepare appropriate charts to record their data.

2. As a follow-up, students could interview the school nurse or doctor to secure comments about the possible dangers of overdependence on pain relievers.

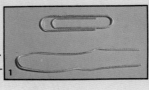

Using your touch receptors

A. Obtain these materials: paper clip, ruler.

B. Choose a partner. Decide who will be tested first. Make a chart like the one shown. Write your observations when you are the tester.

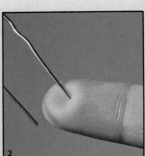

Location	1 end	2 ends	1 end	2 ends	1 end	2 ends	1 end	2 ends
finger								
palm								
hand (back)								
arm								

C. Unbend the paper clip and reshape it as shown in photograph 1. The ends of the clip should be about 1 cm apart. The person being tested should roll up a sleeve. Eyes should be closed.

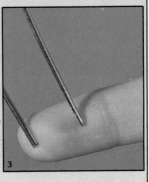

D. Gently touch one end of the clip to the person's finger as shown in photograph 2. Then touch two ends (photograph 3). Repeat 3 times.

  1. Did your partner feel one end or two ends?

E. Repeat step D on the palm of the hand, back of hand, and arm.

  2. Did your partner feel one end or two ends?

F. Switch places with your partner and repeat the activity.

  3. Where on your body did you and your partner feel the correct number of paper-clip ends?

  4. Where do you think the largest number of touch receptors are located in the body?

  5. Write a paragraph that answers: Why are some parts of the body more sensitive to touch than some other parts? Use the term *touch receptors*. Refer to your chart.

136

ACTIVITY

Skill Development — *Following Directions, Comparing and Contrasting, Recording Data*

Teaching Tips — This is the type of activity that some students may wish to repeat at home and involve adults or siblings.

Safety Tips — Tell students to be very gentle when they use the paper clip ends.

Answers to Questions — 1. The partner felt two ends. **2.** Palm, two ends; back of hand, one end; back of arm, one end. **3.** The palm and the fingertips were places where we felt two ends.
4. The palm and fingertips. **5.** Some parts of the body are more receptive to touch than other parts because they contain more touch receptors. Where there are many receptors, we can tell the difference between two objects that are touching us at only a short distance apart. Where there are few receptors, the skin does not pick up enough information to tell the difference.

The receptors are the starting points for messages that go to your brain. Other nerves take the message from the receptors to the **spinal** (spy-nul) **cord**. The *spinal cord* is a large nerve that carries the messages about heat, cold, pain, touch, and pressure to your brain.

3 What happens in your nervous system when you touch a hot stove? The heat message is received by your sense receptors. The spinal cord carries it to the brain. At the same time, the spinal cord sends a message to the muscles of your hand. You move away from the hot stove. The response happens before you have a chance to think about the heat. The swift response is a safety device against injury to your body.

Spinal cord: A large nerve that carries messages to the brain.

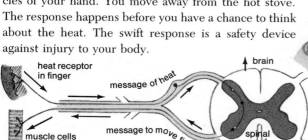

heat receptor in finger
message of heat
brain
message to move finger
muscle cells
spinal cord

Section Review

Main Ideas: Your skin is the sense organ for touch. Touch receptors in the skin gather messages about touch, heat, cold, pain, and pressure. The messages are carried to the spinal cord, a large nerve, which carries them to the brain.

Questions: Answer in complete sentences.

1. What are sense receptors?
2. Imagine you have fallen and scraped your knee. How does the message get from your knee to your brain?
3. Which part of the hand is most sensitive? Why?
4. Rewrite this sentence so that it will be correct:
   The spinal cord is a touch receptor.
5. Compare the skin, in size, to other sense organs.
6. Some receptors lie deep within the skin. Which receptors lie the deepest?

137

3 **Teaching Tips** — Emphasize the importance of the spinal cord with respect to all sensation below the neck. This makes injuries to the spinal cord extremely serious, since they impair information relays to the brain.

4 **Skill Development** — Have students follow the path of nerve messages shown in the *illustration*.

SECTION REVIEW
Answers to Questions
1. Sense receptors are nerve cells in your skin.
2. Sense receptors in the knee pick up the information, a nerve carries the information to your spinal cord, and the spinal cord carries it your brain.
3. The fingertips are the most sensitive. They contain many receptors.
4. The spinal cord carries messages that are picked up by touch receptors.
5. The skin is the largest sense organ that the body has.
6. Pressure receptors

EXTENSIONS

Enrichment
Research — Library

Students could research information concerning the discovery and the use of anesthetics. They could focus on the problems that doctors used to face when they operated on people. Then, the early forms of anesthesia and the variety of modern methods could be discussed. Motivated students could develop posters to present a summary of their investigations.

Enrichment
Research

There are animals that have some senses that are more acute than humans' senses. Students can do research on these animals to find out what they are able to detect and how they use this information to know what is going on around them. Examples of some animals and what they detect are: electric eels and electricity; insects and ultraviolet light, smoke, and infrared radiation; fish and vibrations.

SUGGESTED WORKSHEET MASTER
p. T–111m

SUGGESTED TEST MASTERS
p. T–111d,e,f

CHAPTER REVIEW

Science Words Define each of these words:

1. Cell
2. Cell membrane
3. Nucleus
4. Nerve cells
5. Tissue

What words best complete the sentences?

6. A _____ is a group of tissues that work together.
7. An organ is a group of _____ that work together.
8. A group of organs that work together is a _____ _____.
9. The body system that controls all the other systems is the _____ _____.
10. The nerve that carries smell messages to your brain is the _____.

Questions: Answer in complete sentences.

1. You are chewing on a piece of onion. How does your brain respond?
2. Name the parts of the body that make it possible for you to hear. Describe what each part does.
3. You walk into a very dark room. In about 10 seconds you see a pile of diamonds on a table.
   a. Explain why you couldn't see the diamonds when you entered the room.
   b. Explain how your brain received the message about the presence of the diamonds.
4. You reach into your pocket and pull out a coin. You know it's a dime without looking at it. How did information about the coin reach your brain?
5. Make a chart of the functions of the nervous system.
6. What are the five kinds of messages that can be picked up by receptors in your skin?

138

CHAPTER REVIEW

Science Words
1. A tiny, living part of your body.   2. Cell's outside covering.
3. Controls cell functions.   4. Carry information from parts of the body to the brain.   5. A group of cells that work together.   6. Organ. 7. Tissues. 8. Body system. 9. Nervous system. 10. Olfactory.

Answers to Questions
1. The taste buds and nose send messages to the brain. The brain recognizes the odor of an onion.
2. The outer ear gathers sound vibrations. The ear canal carries them to the eardrum whose vibrations are transferred to small bones. The auditory nerve picks up this message and sends it to the brain.
3. a. Pupils were too small.   b. They enlarged to allow more light to enter the eye; the optic nerve carried the message to the brain.
4. Skin receptors sent a message to the spinal cord, then brain.
5. See chart on pupil page 117.
6. Touch, heat, cold, pain, and pressure.

CHAPTER 7

BONES AND MUSCLES

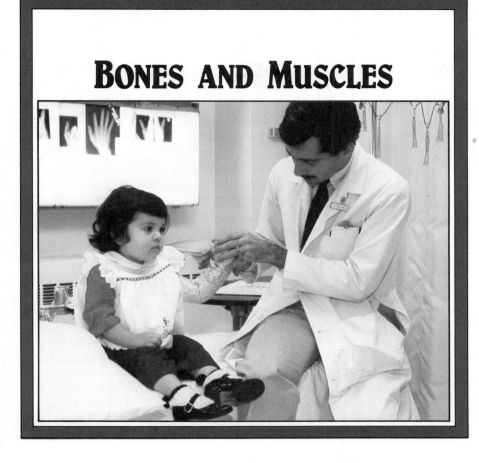

Have you ever broken a bone? The doctor is checking the plaster the broken bone is wrapped in. He wants to know if it is strong enough to keep the bone from moving. As the break in the bone heals, new cells grow. Eventually, the bone will be stronger than it was before the break.

7-1.

Bones

139

CHAPTER OBJECTIVES

1. Describe the functions of the skeletal system and identify some major bones in the human body.
2. Provide a description of a joint and compare movable and immovable joints.
3. Compare the functions of ligaments, tendons, and cartilage.
4. Describe the functions of the muscular system and compare voluntary and involuntary muscles.
5. Identify and explain how smooth, cardiac, and skeletal muscle cells differ.

SECTION BACKGROUND

The human skeletal system consists of 206 bones. The skull protects the brain and the organs in the head. The spinal column is an organized structure of bones that supports the head and protects the spinal cord (the main nerve from the brain). The spinal column consists of 33 vertebrae. The spinal column is also the point of attachment for the ribs and pelvic bones. The limbs of the body consist of the arms and legs.

Bone tissue develops from a tissue known as cartilage. The intercellular deposits of hard mineral materials, such as calcium phosphate, give bone tissue its hardness. The ability of the body to use calcium and phosphorus for this purpose depends on the presence of vitamin D in the diet. Students should learn what foods contain these minerals.

MATERIALS

**Exceptional Student
IEP Chapter Goal**

The students will be able to write two paragraphs on how the skeletal and muscular systems work.

BASIC TEACHING PLAN

MOTIVATION

You may wish to begin with a demonstration that shows that although bones are rigid, they can be softened if the minerals within them are removed. Obtain two similar chicken bones. Clean them thoroughly with soap and water. Immerse one in a jar of vinegar for four or five days. Leave the other one exposed to air. On the day of the demonstration, remove the bone from the vinegar and ask the students to describe how it is different from the other bone. It will be flexible.

Text Questions — Have you ever broken a bone? *Let students who have had broken bones describe how they were treated and the healing process.*

Application
Science Skills — Comparing and Contrasting

At this point, you may wish to demonstrate to the students the similarities and differences between the human skeleton and some animal skeletons. Students could prepare portions of the skeletons of chickens or frogs as a display to the class so that comparisons can be made between these animal skeletons and the human skeleton. After they secure portions of such animals, have them do the following:

A. Carefully remove any extraneous fleshy material from the bones. Soak the bones in hot soapy water for about two hours.

B. Use a stiff brush to scrub the bones. Then rinse them.

C. After the bones are dry, use wire and all-purpose glue to assemble the bones into a structure that resembles the way they were inside the animal.

D. Build a small platform to display the skeletal structure.

E. Use a reference book to find the names of the larger bones in the skeleton. Place numbers on small labels and glue one to each bone. Prepare a reference chart to aid in identifying the bones.

F. Students could compare analogous portions of the animal skeleton to those of the human skeleton.

What are bones made of? When you finish this section, you should be able to:

☐ **A.** Describe what the *skeletal system* does.
☐ **B.** Identify some of the bones of the body.
☐ **C.** Identify the parts of the *backbone* from a drawing of one.

1 Although your bones are strong and hard, they are made of living tissue. All living tissue can be harmed. The bones of the body are harmed if they don't receive enough food. And they can be broken if they are hit hard enough.

Bones are made of living cells and blood *vessels* (**ves**-sulz). The blood vessels carry food to the cells and carry wastes away. Bones are also made of mineral matter. The chief mineral is *calcium* (**kal**-see-um). Calcium is needed for the growth of bones. Milk is a good source of this mineral. Treated with care, a bone is able to heal and repair itself.

2 The 206 bones in the human body make up the **skeletal system**. The *skeletal system* functions in four ways. One of its functions is support of the body. The bones support the body somewhat the way beams of a building **3** support the whole building. They give the body its shape. Bones also protect the body organs that lie under them. Movement is another function of the skeletal system. Muscles attached to bones pull on the bones. Thus we are able to walk, lift, and sit. The fourth function is **4** very important. The blood that flows through the body is made in the bones.

5 Certain substances are needed for a healthy, growing skeletal system, such as yours. Because milk contains calcium, it is a natural food for young people. You need *vitamin* (**vy**-tuh-min) D also. This vitamin is added to the milk you drink. You can also get it from the sun during warm seasons. Calcium and vitamin D work together to keep bones healthy and growing straight.

Skeletal system: All the bones of the body.

Skeletal System
Support
Protection
Movement
Production of blood cells

140

DEVELOPMENT

1 Teaching Tips — On the chalkboard, list the composition of bones: living cells, blood vessels, and minerals.

2 Teaching Tips — On the chalkboard, list the functions of the skeletal system.

3 Skill Development — *Compare* the function of the skeletal system to the beams of a building or the frame of a car.

4 Teaching Tips — Have an animal bone cut in cross section to show the blood vessels.

5 Teaching Tips — Have an empty milk container available so that you can read to the students the vitamin and mineral content of milk on the label.

6 The bones that make up the skeletal system are referred to as the skeleton. Inside your body is a skeleton that looks very much like the one in the drawing. You can find some of the bones in your body by gently pressing on the surface of your skin. All of the body's bones are not shown in the drawing of the skeleton. A front view of a skeleton cannot show all the bones in the back of the skeleton. How many bones can you count on the skeleton in the drawing?

7

8

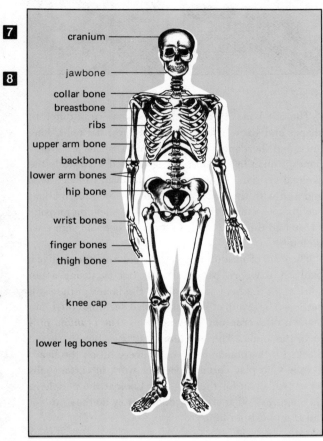

cranium

jawbone

collar bone

breastbone

ribs

upper arm bone

backbone

lower arm bones

hip bone

wrist bones

finger bones

thigh bone

knee cap

lower leg bones

141

Application
Research

Doctors can now replace many damaged joints and bones with implants of plastic or steel. Students can contact orthopedic doctors, hospitals, and supply companies to find out how these implants are made, how they are implanted in the body, and what kinds of problems people can have with them. Students may also wish to learn more about the recent developments in artificial bone material.

Enrichment
Research — Library

Students may wish to find out what an archeologist does. By examining old *National Geographic* magazines, they will find pictures of archeological digs. While reading, students will learn how archeologists use bones to describe how ancient people looked and lived. They can also find out how archeologists are able to reconstruct the bodies of ancient animals from just a few of their bones.

6 **Skill Development** — As the students will need to refer to this drawing very often in this section, it might be helpful to have them *observe* it very carefully at this time. Point out the large bones of the legs and arms and the numerous bones of the hands and feet.

7 **Text Questions** — How many bones can you count on the skeleton in the drawing? *Answers should range from 50 to 70 bones.*

8 **Skill Development** — Refer to the *illustration* on page 141, since it is important for the students to develop a good sense of where the major bones are.

Exceptional Student
Visually Impaired
Obtain a small plastic skeleton. Let these students feel the skeletal system.

You may wish to have some students learn the scientific names of particular bones of the human skeleton. Provide them with a list of scientific names and ask them to do some detective work to find out to which bones the names pertain. Here are the scientific names for some major bones:

1. *humerus* — upper arm bone
2. *ulna* and *radius* — lower arm bones
3. *femur* — upper leg bone
4. *fibula* and *tibia* — lower leg bones
5. *patella* — kneecap
6. *tarsals* and *metatarsals* — bones in the feet
7. *carpals* and *metacarpals* — bones in the hands

9

The 206 bones in the skeletal system are of different shapes and sizes. There are round ones, flat ones, long ones, and short ones. Every bone has a special job. Many bones protect important parts of the body. To study the skeletal system, let us start with the bones in the head and end with the bones in the feet. As you learn about each bone, refer to the drawing of the skeleton on page 141 to find the bone. Also, locate each bone on your own skeleton.

The skull of an adult is very different from the skull of a baby. A newborn baby's skull is not as strong as an adult's. As the baby grows older, the bones of the skull harden. The group of skull bones that surround the brain make up the **cranium** (kray-nee-um). The *cranium* protects the brain. The cranium is strong, but it can be cracked if the person receives a severe hit on the head. People who play certain sports or work in certain jobs wear protection for the cranium. Look at the people in **9** the pictures. What are they doing? How do they protect the cranium from injury?

Cranium: Group of skull bones that surround the brain.

142

9 **Text Questions** — What are they doing? *Playing football, working.* How do they protect the cranium from injury? *By wearing helmets.*

Another bone that is part of the head is the **jawbone**. Touch your chin and move your hand up toward your ear. The bone you feel is your *jawbone*. The movement of the jawbone allows you to chew food and speak.

The structure shown on the left below is a large column of bones that goes up the center of your back. It is called the **backbone**. One end of the *backbone* is connected to the head. The other end is connected to the hipbones.

The backbone is actually made up of many small bones. Gently rub your backbone with one hand. Can you feel the small bones? They are called **vertebrae** (ver-tuh-bray). The backbone has 33 *vertebrae*.

Look at the drawing of one vertebra (**ver**-tuh-bra). Each vertebra has an opening through its center. The spinal cord passes through these openings. The spinal cord is protected by the vertebrae of the backbone.

Jawbone: A bone that is part of the head.

Backbone: A column of bones that extends up the center of the back.

Vertebrae: The small bones that make up the backbone, or spine.

EXTENSIONS

Reinforcement
Research — Library

The use of a helmet to protect the cranium was discussed in this section. You may wish to have some students find out more specific information about the constructions and shapes of helmets used in various sports. Have them focus on sports such as hockey, football, baseball, boxing, racecar driving, motorcycle and motocross racing, and skiing. Students should be encouraged to do the following:
1. Make drawings of the types of helmets used.
2. Describe the nature and thickness of the padding.
3. If possible, borrow one or more types of helmets from persons who engage in these sports to show to the rest of the class.

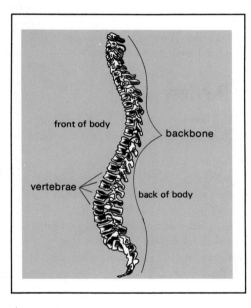

front of body

backbone

vertebrae

back of body

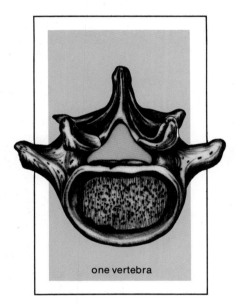

one vertebra

143

10 **Text Questions** — Can you feel the small bones? *Students should have no difficulty doing this.*

11 **Teaching Tips** — Mention that the backbone is also called the spine. You may wish to write the term *vertebrae* on the chalkboard and have the students work on its pronunciation. Have the students refer to the drawing of a skeleton on page 141 to locate the backbone and the vertebrae.

Students could research and prepare drawings that compare the skeleton of a lobster, a crab, or a grasshopper with a human skeleton. They will find that many creatures, including the ones they investigate, possess a hard body covering. This is the exoskeleton, which provides both support and protection for the soft parts of their bodies.

Ribs: Twelve pairs of bones that surround and protect the heart and lungs.

Pelvis: The hipbones and lower parts of the backbone.

Marrow: A soft substance in the hollow space of some bones.

Connected to the backbone are twelve pairs of bones called **ribs**. The *ribs* extend around to the front of the body. At the front of the body, the upper seven pairs are connected to a bone called the breastbone. The ribs form a cage that protects the heart and lungs.

Attached to the bottom of the backbone are two large hipbones. These hipbones and the lower parts of the backbone form the **pelvis** (**pel**-vis). The *pelvis* helps bear the weight of the body.

The upper parts of each leg and each arm have one large bone. The lower parts of your legs and arms have two bones. Your hands and feet have many small bones. Your hands have more bones than any other part of your body. Look at your hand. Each finger has four bones. **12** Can you find the four bones?

Many bones are hollow inside. The hollow space is filled with a soft substance called **marrow** (**mar**-roh). There are two types of *marrow*. In young people, all marrow is red. As one gets older, red marrow is found in flat bones, such as ribs. The rest of the marrow is yellow. Blood cells are produced in red marrow.

Section Review

Main Ideas: The 206 bones of the skeletal system support, protect, and move the body. They also produce blood cells.

Questions: Answer in complete sentences.

1. How do bones support and protect the body?
2. How do bones help to move the body?
3. The cranium, jawbone, backbone, and vertebrae are parts of the skeletal system.
   a. Where in the body is each bone located?
   b. What is the job of each bone?
4. Look at the drawing on page 141. Locate the ribs. From their location, can you tell their function?

144

12 Text Questions — Can you find the four bones? *This will puzzle the students a bit. They will count three bones in each finger. The fourth bone runs through the palm to the wrist.*

SECTION REVIEW
Answers to Questions
1. The bones support the body by acting as a frame to which muscles are connected. The bones are like the beams in a building. They give us shape. Bones protect various parts of the body. The cranium protects the brain. The ribs protect the heart and lungs.
2. The muscles pull on the bones to cause movement.
3. Cranium — located in the head. It protects the brain. Jawbone — located in the head. Its movement allows you to chew food. Backbone — located down the center of the back. It protects the spinal cord.
4. The ribs are connected to the backbone and wrap around like a cage. They protect the heart and the lungs.

Have you ever looked at an X ray of any part of your body? The X-ray photograph on the left shows the bones of a young child's hand. The photograph on the right shows the bones of an adult's hand. There is a difference in the way the bones join, or come together, in each hand. Do you see what the difference is? When you finish this section, you should be able to:

☐ **A.** Explain the function of *cartilage*.
☐ **B.** Identify and compare the functions of *movable joints*.
☐ **C.** Explain the function of *ligaments*.
☐ **D.** Identify one type of *immovable joint*.

You can see that the spaces between the bones of the fingers are close together in the adult's hand. In the child's hand the spaces are farther apart. They are filled with a soft substance that does not show up on the X ray. Compare the wrist areas in the two X-ray pictures. The

1

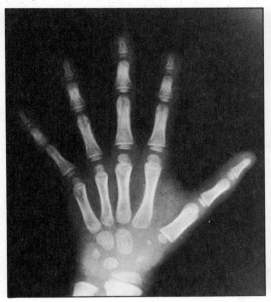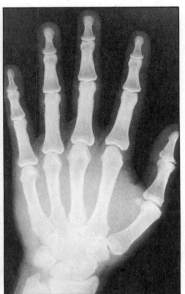

7-2.

How Bones Join

SECTION BACKGROUND

The joints of the body are the places where the bones of the skeletal system come together. There are movable and immovable joints. Most of the immovable joints are located at the junctures of skull bones. There are various types of movable joints in the skeletal system.

At a hinge joint (i.e., the elbow and the knee), the bones can move back and forth. At a ball-and-socket joint (i.e., the shoulder and hip), the end of one bone is shaped like a ball and fits into the hollow of another bone. At these joints, the bones can move in many directions. At a pivot joint (i.e., where the head joins the spine), the bones can move around and back.

Between joints is a padding of cartilage that keeps the bones from rubbing together. Bones at movable joints are held together by ligaments.

MATERIALS

paper, pencil

145

BASIC TEACHING PLAN

MOTIVATION

Use photographs of children and adults playing to stimulate a discussion of how the skeletal system of a young child is different from that of an adult. Students may think that the only difference between them is size. As they study this section, they will learn that there are large amounts of cartilage in the skeleton of a child, which are not present in the skeleton of an adult.

If you happen to have access to X rays of bones, ask students to determine which part of the body is shown. Some students who have done additional research in previous Extensions may be able to identify the bones by their scientific names.

DEVELOPMENT

1 **Skill Development** — Students should closely examine the X rays of the adult's and the child's hands to *compare* the obvious differences.

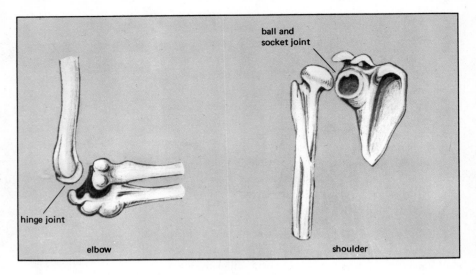

ball and
socket joint

hinge joint

elbow   shoulder

EXTENSIONS

Enrichment
*Science Skills —
Building Science Vocabulary*

Ask students to find out the difference between the *appendicular skeleton* and the *axial skeleton*. The appendicular skeleton consists of the bones of the arms and legs and the axial skeleton consists of the bones of the head, neck, and trunk.

Cartilage: A soft substance that is found where some bones meet.

Joint: The place where two bones meet.

Hinge joint: A kind of joint where the bones can move back and forth or up and down.

Ball-and-socket joint: A kind of joint where the bones can move in many directions.

146

2 child's wrist is not yet solid bone. The same soft substance lies in the wrist where the arm bones join the hand bones. There is a name for this soft substance. It is the same substance that babies' bones are made of. It is known as **cartilage** (**kar**-tih-lij). Most of your bones are hard. However, you do have *cartilage* at the end of your nose and in places where some bones meet. The place where two bones meet is called a **joint**. At some *joints*, the bones are able to move. The cartilage at the joint is like a padding that keeps the ends of the bones from rubbing together when they move.

3 You have three kinds of movable joints. One kind is like the hinge on a door. It is called a **hinge joint**. The bones at a *hinge joint* can move back and forth or up and down. The joints in your elbows and knees are hinge joints. So are the joints in your fingers and toes.

Another kind of movable joint is the **ball-and-socket joint**. At a *ball-and-socket joint*, the end of one bone is shaped like a ball. It fits into a curved space at the end of the other bone. Bones at this kind of joint can move in

2   **Teaching Tips** — Have the students touch the ends of their noses, where there is cartilage. Indicate that the outer ear is also cartilage.
3   **Teaching Tips** — Have the students move their elbow, knee, finger, and toe joints. You may wish to call their attention to the hinges on classroom cabinets and doors for comparison. Do the same for the ball-and-socket joints. They can be compared to ball-and-socket joints that can be found on track lighting and other kinds of lamps.

Exceptional Student
Visually Impaired

Direct the hands of these students to feel the joints on their own elbows, knees, and shoulders. Discuss the functions of joints.

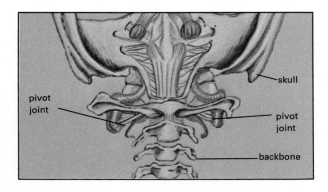

pivot
joint

skull

pivot
joint

backbone

many directions. The joints in your shoulders and hips are ball-and-socket joints.

4   A third kind of joint is the **pivot joint**. The bones at a *pivot joint* can move around and back. The joint where the head meets the backbone is a pivot joint.

5   What keeps bones from sliding off each other when they move? Bones at these three types of joints are held together by strong bands of material called **ligaments** (**lig**-uh-ments). *Ligaments* stretch across joints from the end of one bone to the end of the other. Ligaments hold

6 the bones in place. Look at the drawing below. Can you find the joint, bones, and ligaments?

Pivot joint: A kind of joint where the bones can move around and back.

Ligaments: Strong bands of material that hold bones in place at joints.

7

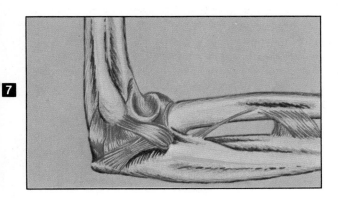

147

EXTENSIONS

Application
Research — Library

Your students have probably heard of arthritis. They may not realize that it is a serious disease, contrary to television commercials that make claims for the rather easy treatment of "arthritis pain." You may wish to have students do some research to find out about the different kinds of arthritis, the various symptoms and treatments, and the types of surgical implants that are used in severe cases.

4   **Teaching Tips** — Have the students observe that they can move their heads in many directions. This will help them understand the pivot joint.

5   **Text Questions** — What keeps bones from sliding off each other when they move? *Ligaments. Allow students to imagine how this works.*

6   **Text Questions** — Can you find the joint, bones, and ligaments? *Allow students to speculate on the purpose of each band of ligaments.*

7   **Skill Development** — In studying the *illustration* at the bottom of the page, students should understand that ligaments hold the bones in place. If this is not stressed, they may confuse them with tendons (which hold muscles to bones).

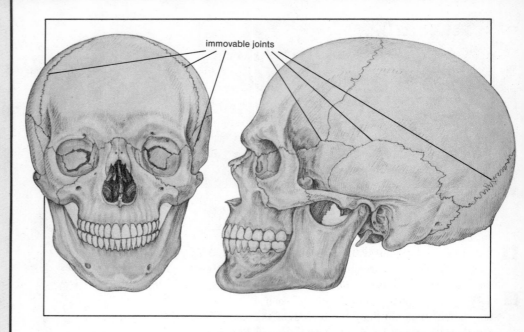

immovable joints

EXTENSIONS

Reinforcement
Science Skills — Observing

Obtain the leg bone of a calf from a local meat market. The bone should have the joint intact. Ask to have the bone split in half lengthwise. Put the bone on display and have the students identify the following:

1. cartilage
2. bone
3. ligaments
4. yellow marrow

Dislocation: A bone forced out of its usual position in a joint.

Sometimes a joint receives a sharp blow when a person falls. When this happens, one bone is forced out of its usual position, or location, in a joint. This is called a **dislocation** (dis-loh-**kay**-shun). A dislocated bone usually can be pushed back into place by a doctor.

The body has three types of movable joints. It also has one type of joint that does not permit bones to move. The body's immovable joints are part of the skull. In this diagram of a skull, you can see crooked lines.

8 These are the places of immovable joints. Eight bones surround the brain. When you were very young, the joints were slightly movable. Then, the bones on either side of the joints moved slightly. This movement allowed your brain to increase in size. As you got older, the tissue at the joints was replaced by bone. Now that your brain is full size, there is no need for these joints to still be movable.

148

8 Teaching Tips — Many students will be surprised to learn that the seemingly one-piece skull (except for the jawbone) is actually composed of many individual bones. Another location of immovable joints in the body is the area where the bones of the rib cage connect with the spinal column.

Section Review

Main Ideas: The places on the body where bones come together are joints. The body has three types of movable joints, where the bones are padded by cartilage and held in place by ligaments. Immovable joints are found in the skull.

Questions: Answer in complete sentences.

1. What is a joint?
2. List three types of movable joints. Give examples.
3. What is the difference between cartilage and ligaments?
4. Why do you no longer have movable joints around your brain?

People in Science

Augustus A. White, III

Dr. White is a scientist and doctor whose work is the treatment of people with bone and muscle injuries. He is an **orthopedic** (or-thoh-**pee**-dik) surgeon.

Dr. White studied medicine at Stanford University in California and at the Karolinska Institute in Sweden. While a professor of medicine at Yale University Medical School, he set up a special laboratory to study how the muscles cause the bones of the body to move. Dr. White is a good athlete and is interested in sports and the injuries they cause. He is the author of over 100 books and articles. Much of his writing deals with how the bones of the spine move as people use their muscles to walk, run, and lift. Dr. White has won many awards for his work. Dr. White is now a teacher of doctors at Harvard Medical School.

149

SECTION REVIEW

Answers to Questions
1. The place where two bones meet is a joint.
2. Hinge — elbow; ball-and-socket — shoulders; pivot — where the skull meets the backbone.
3. Cartilage is a soft substance that is found where bones meet. Ligaments connect bones to other bones.
4. Your brain is full size and there is no need for your skull bones to be pushed apart to provide more space.

SUGGESTED WORKSHEET MASTER
p. T–111n

SECTION BACKGROUND

The function of the muscular system is to produce movement. The human muscular system has over 600 different muscles that form approximately 50 percent of the body's weight. Muscles cover the frame of the body (the skeleton), and also line the walls of some internal organs, such as the heart and the stomach. Some muscles are attached to bones and other parts of the body by bands of connective tissue called tendons.

Voluntary muscles are muscles that can be controlled at will. Arm, leg, and neck muscles are examples of voluntary muscles. Involuntary muscles are muscles over which we have no conscious control. Examples of such muscles are those of the heart and the digestive tract.

Muscles produce movement by contracting. When they contract, they become shorter and firmer. This exerts a pulling force on bones or other body structures.

MATERIALS

3 books to be used for lifting

7-3.

Muscles

Muscular system: All the muscles of the body.

You may be surprised to learn that you have all the muscles that this body builder has. They just do not look the same on you. The bulging muscles you see on the body builder lie near the surface of the body. There are many other muscles that lie deep within the body. When you finish this section, you should be able to:

☐ **A.** Describe the functions of the *muscular system*.

☐ **B.** Locate the muscles called the *biceps* and the *triceps*.

☐ **C.** Describe the difference between *voluntary* and *involuntary* muscles.

1 Make a guess about how many muscles there are in your body. More than 100? More than 200? Your body has more than 600 muscles! They make up a body system that is called the **muscular system**. The *muscular system* makes it possible for you to move from place to place. Some muscles cause organs of the body, such as the heart, to function. Muscles acting on the blood vessels move blood through the body. Food and wastes also are moved through the body because of muscles. Muscles even connect skin to bone and skin to skin.

As you read this book, muscles are pulling on the bones of your arms and hands so that you can hold the book and turn the pages. Some muscles are pulling on the book, turning its pages. Some muscles are pulling on other bones to keep you seated upright. The small muscles around your eyes make it possible for you to read.

As you read, your eyelids move. They move down over your eyes and then back up again. You are able to blink

Muscular System
Acts on bones to move body from place to place
Acts on lungs and other organs
Moves food through digestive organs
Moves blood through blood vessels

150

BASIC TEACHING PLAN

MOTIVATION

When you begin this section, you may wish to invite a physical education teacher from your school district to visit your class. Ask your guest to comment on how long it takes to develop bulging muscles, the risks that are involved in the process, and whether muscles that have been developed to the extent commonly displayed by body builders are necessarily helpful to students who are interested in athletics. Your guest's comments on the characteristics of a good personal exercise program would also be helpful.

DEVELOPMENT

1 **Teaching Tips** — Make a list of five common activities that students do (play soccer, eat dinner). Display a picture of the muscular system of the human body on a chart or on the overhead projector. Ask the students to point to the muscles that are involved in each activity.

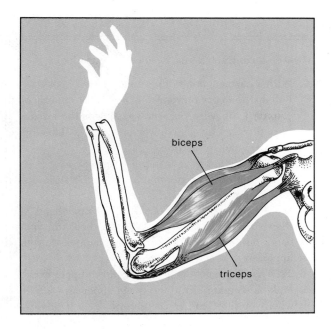

biceps

triceps

As we exercise, lactic acid builds up in muscle fibers to produce muscle fatigue. Students could do a variety of simple exercises and note how exercise produces muscle fatigue.

A. Ask students to work in pairs and in a location of the room where they will be able to view a clock with a second hand. Students should determine how many times they can make fists and immediately extend the fingers of their hands within each of four 15-second intervals. One member of the pair should record the data.

B. After one student has done the full number of trials (without resting between trials), ask the students to switch roles.

C. Now have the students repeat the activity, but this time allow a rest period of a full minute between trials. One partner should record the data. They should switch roles again.

D. Ask the students to respond to such questions as the following:

1. How did the lack of rest between the first trials affect your results?
2. Did you do better in the second trials than in the first?
3. How could you use what you learned in this exercise to increase how well you do in physical activities, such as sports, dancing, or games?

2 when you want. However, you cannot stop yourself from blinking forever. Blinking is a movement you cannot completely control.

Every movement you make is caused by muscles. Some muscles you can control. They are called **voluntary** (vahl-un-teh-ree) **muscles.** Your arm and leg muscles are *voluntary muscles.* You can move your arm and leg muscles when you want to. Look at the drawing above. It shows the muscles in the upper part of the arm. The muscle on the top side of the arm is called the **biceps** (by-seps). The muscle on the bottom side of the arm is **3** called the **triceps** (try-seps). The *biceps* and *triceps* work together to move the arm. They are voluntary muscles. Can you find your biceps and triceps?

Look at the drawing again. What are the muscles attached to? Most voluntary muscles are attached to bones.

Voluntary muscles: Muscles that can be controlled.

Biceps: The muscle on the top side of the upper arm.

Triceps: The muscle on the bottom side of the upper arm.

151

2 **Skill Development** — Have the students make observations of the number of times a partner blinks in a two- or three-minute interval. The blinking partner should be asked simply to relax and look around the room. After the students have gathered their data, ask them to *infer* what the possible reason for the blinking action is. Many will indicate that it probably keeps the eyes moist and clean. Some may wish to observe the effects of a sharp sound (such as the snapping of the fingers) on the eyes of a relaxed or unaware person. They will observe the eyes blink. They should be able to *infer* that blinking is also a protective action.

3 **Text Questions** — Can you find your biceps and triceps? *To find the triceps, tell the students to grasp the back side of their upper left arms with their right hands. They should then bend their elbows several times. They will be able to feel the muscle. To find the biceps, tell them to grasp the top side of the upper arm and bend the elbow.*

EXTENSIONS

Reinforcement
Science Skills — Observing

Obtain a chicken foot from the local meat market. Trim the skin to expose the white, stringlike tendons. Using the point of a pencil, pull on each tendon. The students will observe that some tendons bend the chicken toes and others straighten them.

ACTIVITY

How do a contracted and a relaxed muscle look?

A. With a partner, obtain these materials: 2 books.
B. Roll up the sleeve on your right arm. Put your arm on your desk top with your elbow resting on the surface. Rest the back of your lower arm on the tabletop. Observe your upper arm.
C. Make a diagram of your upper arm.
 1. Do you observe any muscles near the surface of your upper arm?
D. Have your partner put 2 books in your open hand, as shown in the photograph. With the books in your hand, raise your arm. Observe what happens to your upper arm.
 2. What happened to the shape of the upper arm?
E. Make a diagram of the way your upper arm looked when you lifted the books upward.
 3. Write a paragraph comparing how your upper arm looked at rest with how it looked as you lifted the books. Use these terms: *muscle system, voluntary, biceps*.

152

ACTIVITY

Skill Development — *Comparing and Contrasting, Concluding*

Teaching Tips — The books the students use should not be too heavy.

Answers to Questions — **1.** Yes. **2.** It started to bulge out toward the part nearest the shoulder. **3.** The muscles of the arm are part of the voluntary muscle system that allows us to move parts of our body when we want to move them. The biceps, the voluntary muscle on the top of the upper arm, bulged out when we lifted books.

Exceptional Student
Visually Impaired

For this activity, the visually impaired student should feel the upper arm as it changes position.

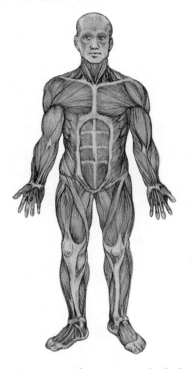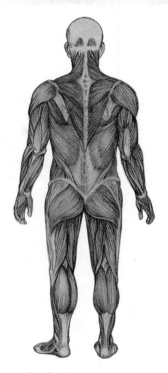

Enrichment
Activity

Body-building has become a sport that is receiving increased attention on television and in magazines. You may have some students who would be interested in locating some key muscles on magazine photographs of body builders.

To classify the major muscles, they will need to study the photograph carefully before they relate those muscles to a detailed diagram of the muscular system.

4 Some muscles are attached directly to the bones. Other muscles are attached to the bones by tough cords called **tendons** (ten-dunz). Through the *tendons*, the muscles control the movement of the bones. When the muscle contracts, or gets shorter, it pulls on the tendon. Then the tendon pulls on the bone.

5 When you want to move your arm, your brain sends a message to the muscle. The muscle shortens and becomes firm as the movement occurs. In other words, the muscle contracts. When you want to stop the movement, your brain tells the muscle to relax. When you contract your biceps, it bulges. As it shortens, it pulls the bones of the lower arm upward.

Look at the drawing above. It shows some of your body's muscles. Can you find the biceps and triceps?

Tendons: Tough cords that connect muscles to bones.

153

4 **Teaching Tips** — After having the students place their hands in a relaxed position on their desk tops, ask them to make their hands very tense and to slightly curl their fingers. They will start to see some definition of the tendons at the backs of their hands. Now have them raise their hands a few inches from the desk top and wiggle their fingers in various directions. They will be able to observe the tendons for each finger moving under the skin.

5 **Teaching Tips** — You may wish to explain that the contraction of the biceps muscle of the upper arm causes the forearm to move up. The triceps makes the forearm move down again. The biceps and triceps work alternately. When the biceps contracts to produce movement, the triceps relaxes and rests. When the triceps contracts, the biceps relaxes.

Students could research the story of Achilles, the hero of the *Iliad*.

A. Have the students do research to find out who Achilles was, what the *Iliad* is, and, most important of all, what injury Achilles received.

B. The students should also be asked to prepare a brief report on Achilles and a scientific drawing that shows where he was injured with an arrow. They should label the Achilles tendon.

SUGGESTED WORKSHEET MASTER
for sections 7–2 and 7–3
p. T–111o

Involuntary muscles: Muscles, such as the heart, that cannot be controlled.

There are some muscles in the body that cannot be controlled. They are called **involuntary** (in-**vahl**-un-teh-ree) **muscles**. *Involuntary muscles*, unlike voluntary muscles, are not attached to bones. The heart, for example, is composed of involuntary muscles. When the muscle tissues in the heart contract, blood is forced out through blood vessels. You do not have to think about controlling this muscle. It contracts and relaxes on its own.

The stomach and intestines are also composed of involuntary muscles. When they contract and relax, food is mixed and moved through the body.

The muscles that help you breathe are both voluntary and involuntary. Try holding your breath for an instant. Notice that the muscles in your chest are not moving. **7** You are controlling them. But for how long can you control them? Only for the short time that you can hold your breath.

Section Review

Main Ideas: Every movement made by the body is caused by muscles. Muscles work by contracting and relaxing. Voluntary muscles usually are attached to bones and can be controlled. Involuntary muscles are not attached to bones and cannot be controlled.

Questions: Answer in complete sentences.

1. What one word best describes the purpose of the muscular system?
2. What is the difference between the heart muscles and a leg muscle?
3. How would you describe what the biceps muscle of a weight lifter is doing as he holds up a bar?
4. Look at the drawing on page 153. Where are the tendons located? Answer in one sentence.
5. What is the difference between a tendon and a ligament?

154

---

6 **Skill Development** — Students *compare* involuntary muscles with voluntary ones.

7 **Text Questions** — But for how long can you control them? *Indicate to the students that they should not try to hold their breath, as this deprives the bloodstream of oxygen and is dangerous.*

SECTION REVIEW
Answers to Questions
1. Movement
2. The heart muscle is an involuntary muscle. The leg muscle is a voluntary muscle.
3. It is contracted.
4. Located at the ends of the muscles, tendons connect the muscle to the bone.
5. A tendon holds a muscle to a bone. A ligament holds a bone to another bone.

It takes a lot of energy to do what this gymnast is doing. She can do it because her muscles are in good condition. Well-developed voluntary muscles allow her to turn, twist, and pull her body in the direction she wants it to go. Strong biceps and triceps give her the support she needs to stand on her hands. But she couldn't come down from that position if she didn't have strong abdominal muscles. Do you know where any of these muscles are located in your body? When you finish this section, you should be able to:

☐ **A.** Identify and describe three types of muscle cells.
☐ **B.** Explain why muscle cells need blood.

Even when the athlete on the bar rests, her muscles are not totally relaxed. Because of her work she always has good muscle tone, or a certain amount of muscle contraction. When a muscle is used often, plenty of blood flows through it. Anyone sick in bed for a long period of time loses muscle tone. Without exercise, people feel

Kinds of Muscles

SECTION BACKGROUND

There are more than 600 muscles in the human body. There are three kinds of muscles — smooth muscles, cardiac muscles, and skeletal muscles. Smooth muscle fibers (muscles that line the organs) are long, thin, and pointed at each end. These muscles contract slowly and rhythmically. Smooth muscles contract when they are stimulated by nerves or by body chemicals called hormones. Cardiac muscle fibers are branched and have dark and light bands running across them. Skeletal muscle fibers (the muscles that produce the movement of bones) are long and slender. Muscle fibers are located parallel to one another and show an alternating pattern of dark and light bands when viewed under a microscope. The fibers may contain one or more nuclei.

MATERIALS

paper, pencil

155

BASIC TEACHING PLAN
MOTIVATION

If you have or can bring a microscope to class, borrow a few slides of muscle tissue from the science department of a local high school. Before you begin this section, have students look at the slides under the microscope and make diagrams of what they see. Display the diagrams at this point and have the students comment on and compare diagrams.

Text Questions — Do you know where any of these muscles are located in your body? *Biceps and triceps — upper arm; abdominal — below the navel*.

Enrichment
Research — Library

Some students may be interested in doing some research to find out how muscle fibers are able to produce energy from food. They will find that special substances in the cells, called enzymes, break down food to release its energy. The breakdown of carbohydrates and fats supplies most of the energy to the cells. The carbohydrates are sugars and starches. They are carried to the fibers by the bloodstream. A good deal of the energy that is released is in the form of heat, but some of the energy is stored for future use. It is stored in the cells as part of a substance called ATP. These letters stand for Adenosine Triphosphate.

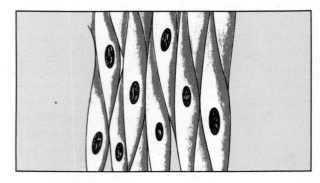

weak and tired because their muscles do not receive enough blood. In order to have good muscle tone, a large amount of blood must reach the muscle cells.

Every muscle in the body contains thousands of tiny cells. There are three types of muscles in the body. In each type, the muscle cells look different.

Smooth muscle: A type of muscle containing long, thin, and pointed cells.

One type of muscle is called **smooth muscle**. The cells of *smooth muscles* are long, thin, and pointed at each end. Look at the drawing above. It shows a group of smooth muscle cells. Do you see a dark area in the center **1** of each cell? This area is the nucleus. You learned that the nucleus controls all cell activities. Each smooth muscle cell has one nucleus in its center. The muscles in your stomach are smooth muscles.

Cardiac muscle: A type of muscle that the heart is made of.

2 Another type of muscle is **cardiac (kar-dee-ak) muscle**. The word *cardiac* means of or near the heart. Your heart is made of *cardiac muscle*. Look at the drawing at the top of page 157. The cells of cardiac muscle branch out and weave together. Each cell has one nucleus.

Skeletal muscle: A type of muscle containing long, cylinder-shaped cells with stripes across them.

The third type of muscle is called **skeletal muscle**. The cells of *skeletal muscles* are long and cylinder-shaped, like straws. They have many nuclei. Look at the drawing at the bottom of page 157. These cells have dark and light **3** bands across them. What other type of muscle has dark **4** and light bands? The tongue and lips are skeletal muscles. So are the biceps and triceps.

156

DEVELOPMENT

1 **Teaching Tips** — Point out some specific functions of the nucleus—reproduction, protein production, and storage center of chemicals that direct the basic functions of the cell. If a one-celled animal is bisected, the part with the nucleus continues to live and the part without the nucleus dies.

2 **Skill Development** — Be sure that the students *observe* how the smooth muscle cells are pointed at their ends and how the cardiac cells branch out like the limbs of a tree. It would be helpful to develop a chart to *compare and contrast* the different types of muscle cells.

3 **Text Questions** — What other type of muscle has dark and light bands? *Cardiac.*

4 **Teaching Tips** — Tell the students that tongue and lip muscles are not attached to bones but to other muscles.

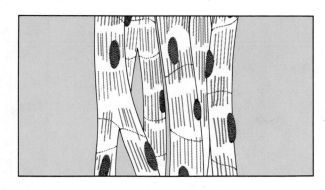

Some skeletal muscles are attached to bones by tendons. When the muscle contracts, the tendons and bones move, too. If you hold your hands palms down and wiggle your fingers, you will see the tendons on the backs of your hands move. The tendons are moved by the arm muscles pulling on the finger bones.

5 A lot of energy is needed for muscle cells to contract. The source of this energy is food carried to the muscle cells by blood vessels. The blood also carries oxygen to muscle cells. There, oxygen and food combine, energy is released, and waste products are formed. The blood carries the waste products away from muscle cells. Exercise keeps the blood supply in the muscle cells at a healthy level.

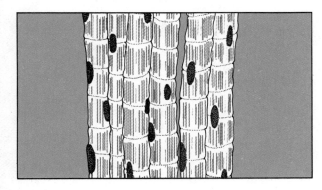

157

Reinforcement
Science Skills — Observing and Comparing and Contrasting

Bring in a cooked chicken leg and heart. Make a crosswise cut through both muscles. Display them so that students can compare the heart muscles to the leg muscles.

5 **Teaching Tips** — Depending on the background of your class, you may need to explain that blood plays a critical role in the movement of food to body cells and in the carrying away of waste products that result from energy production.

EXTENSIONS

Application
Research — Library

Have students research muscular dystrophy, a chronic, noncontagious disease characterized by the deterioration of the muscles. Its cause is unknown. Treatment for the disease is limited although substantial research is being done. Interested students can write for information to the Muscular Dystrophy Association, National Office, 810 Seventh Avenue, NY, NY 10019. In Canada, the address is 74 Victoria Street, Suite 1014, Toronto, Ontario, Canada. The students who get this information should present reports to the class.

ACTIVITY

What can you learn about your muscles?

A. Obtain these materials: paper, pencil.
B. Draw a diagram showing the type of cells found in the stomach muscles.
   1. Are these cells parts of voluntary or involuntary muscles? Explain.
C. Draw the type of cell found in the heart.
   2. Are these muscles part of voluntary or involuntary muscles? Explain.
D. Draw a diagram showing the type of cells found in the front part of the upper arm.
   3. Are these cells from voluntary muscles?
E. Make a chart that sums up information on the stomach, heart, and front upper-arm muscles.

Section Review

Main Ideas: Your body has three types of muscle cells. All muscle cells produce energy by combining oxygen with food.

Questions: Answer in complete sentences.

1. Name the three types of muscle cells.
2. Why do your muscle cells need blood?
3. What type of muscle cells are described below?
   a. thin, long, and pointed at the ends
   b. striped and branched
   c. cylinder-shaped and striped, not branched
4. When are you likely to show the most muscle tone in your arms?
   a. waving goodbye
   b. hanging from an exercise bar
   c. combing your hair

158

ACTIVITY

Skill Development — *Comparing and Contrasting and Inferring*

Teaching Tips — If you have access to some college-level biology books, you may be able to locate photographs of tissue taken from the various locations described in the Activity.

Answers to Questions — **1.** Involuntary. They are smooth muscle cells.   **2.** Involuntary. They are cardiac muscle cells.   **3.** Voluntary. They are skeletal muscle cells.

SECTION REVIEW

Answers to Questions
1. Smooth, cardiac, skeletal
2. To bring food and oxygen and carry wastes away.
3. a. Smooth, b. cardiac, c. skeletal
4. Hanging from an exercise bar

CHAPTER REVIEW

Science Words: Select the definition in column B that best fits each term in column A.

Column A

1. Cranium
2. Vertebrae
3. Cartilage
4. Ligaments
5. Joint

Column B

a. Where two bones come together
b. Bones surrounding the brain
c. Strong bands holding bones in place
d. Bones of the backbone
e. Substance that pads bones

Give an example of each of the following:

6. Involuntary muscle
7. Voluntary muscle
8. Pivot joint
9. Ball-and-socket joint
10. Hinge joint

Questions: Answer in complete sentences.

1. Give one example of how a part of the skeletal system protects some part of the body.
2. Compare voluntary muscles and involuntary muscles:
   a. What is the main difference between these two kinds of muscles?
   b. Which kind of muscle is found in the arm?
   c. Which kind of muscle is found in the heart?
3. How do cardiac, skeletal, and smooth muscle cells differ from each other in appearance?
4. Compare the muscular system and the skeletal system:
   a. What is the main purpose of each system?
   b. How is the blood related to each system?
   c. How do the systems work together to move the body?

159

EXTENSIONS

Enrichment
Activity

To review the unit, students should work in small groups to review the material. They should do the following:

A. Prepare a chart for each system of the body that was discussed. The chart should show the major function of each system.

B. Prepare a list of key words used in the sections. Next to each word, they could tell whether it is used with the nervous, skeletal, or muscular system.

The student groups could assist the teacher in reviewing the material in this unit by displaying their charts.

CHAPTER REVIEW

Science Words — **1.** b, **2.** d, **3.** e, **4.** c, **5.** a, **6.** involuntary muscle — stomach. **7.** voluntary muscle — arm. **8.** pivot joint — head. **9.** ball-and-socket joint — shoulder. **10.** Hinge joint — fingers

Answers to Questions
1. The ribs protect the heart and lungs.
2. **a.** Voluntary muscles are under conscious control while involuntary muscles are not.   **b.** Voluntary   **c.** Involuntary
3. Cardiac muscles are striped and branched. Skeletal muscles are cylinder-shaped and striped (not branched). Smooth muscles are thin, long, and pointed at the ends.
4. **a.** The muscular system enables the bones of the skeletal system to move. The skeletal system provides support and protection.
b. The blood carries digested nutrients and oxygen to each of the systems. Blood cells are manufactured by the skeletal system.
c. With each contraction of a particular muscle, a specific bone is enabled to move.

SUGGESTED WORKSHEET MASTER
p. T–111p

SUGGESTED TEST MASTERS
p. T–111g, h, i

EXTENSIONS

Application
Activity

Students can continue to explore their eyes by doing the following activity.

A. Fold a 3 x 5 card in half lengthwise and set it on edge on a table so that the fold points toward you.

B. Close one eye and look directly at the center of the card. Now look at the card with the other eye.

C. Turn the card around so that the fold is pointing away from you and repeat step B.

1. When you look at the card with one eye, does it appear to be pointed toward or away from you? (It is impossible to tell.)
2. Does it seem to change position as you stare at it? (It does.)

Exploring your eyes

Part I. Where is your blind spot?
The spot called the blind spot is the place where the optic nerve connects to nerve cells. To find your blind spot, do the following:

A. Obtain these materials: dark marking pen, white sheet of paper.

B. On the paper draw a cross and a dot as shown below.

C. Hold the sheet in front of your eyes. While staring straight ahead, close your left eye. Now, without turning your head, look at the cross. Move the paper back and forth and up and down. Keep your right eye focused on the cross and your left eye closed.

1. What do you observe about the dot?

D. Repeat the activity. This time, close your right eye and look at the dot as you move the paper.

2. What do you observe about the cross?

3. Write a paragraph that sums up the results of the activity.

Part II. What is an afterimage?
Seeing an object after it has left your view is called the afterimage.

A. Obtain these materials: index card, pen, 1 m of string.

B. Make two holes on the card. Draw a bird on one side of the card. Draw a cage on the other. Pull the string through the holes in the card.

C. Hold the string at its ends. Have someone twist the card around and around so that it will spin quickly in front of your eyes.

1. What did you observe?

2. Can you explain why cartoon characters seem to move?

160

INVESTIGATING

Skill Development — *Observing, Finding Cause and Effect*

Teaching Tips — Any part of an image that falls on the blind spot will be invisible because there are no image sensing cells in that area. Since the eyes are separated from each other by a short distance, the portion of the image that is invisible on the blind spot of one eye will fall on a slightly different location on the retina of the other eye. The brain does not sense an image until 1/10 of a second after it reaches the retina. Also, the brain senses an image for about 1/10 of a second after it leaves the retina.

Answers to Questions — Part I — 1. It becomes invisible.   2. It becomes invisible.   3. We found that there was one place for each eye where no image was formed. That spot is called the blind spot. Part II — 1. The bird looked as if it were in the cage.   2. Our brain sees an image for a short time after it leaves the eye. The next picture in a cartoon falls on the retina while the brain is still seeing the previous one.

CAREERS

Physical Therapist ▶

Physical therapists help patients who have injured muscles, nerves, joints, and bones. They teach them exercises that gradually move injured tissues. They also teach people to use artificial limbs.

Physical therapists complete a 4-year college program of anatomy, biology, and chemistry. Patience and some strength are required. Physical therapists work in hospitals, nursing homes, and schools, and in industry.

◀ X-ray Technician

X-ray technicians take pictures of parts of the body and develop X-ray film. X rays help doctors study injuries, such as broken bones, or illnesses, such as ulcers. Training can be done in a two-year college program. Students study chemistry, physics, and biology. X-ray technicians, also called radiologic (ray-dee-oh-**loj**-ik) technologists (tek-**nol**-oh-jists), work in hospitals, clinics, doctors' offices, and industry.

161

Application
Research

Students may be interested in doing research on these careers. Audiologists and speech pathologists work with people who have hearing or speaking difficulties. They decide what task, aid, or special training will help patients most. To be good at this work, a person should be patient and caring. A college degree or special training in these fields is usually required. Information can be obtained by contacting the American Speech and Hearing Association, 9030 Old Georgetown Rd., Washington, D.C. 20014

CAREERS

Teaching Tips — Additional information about careers in physical therapy may be obtained by writing the American Physical Therapy Association, 1156 15th Street, N.W., Washington, D.C. 20005.

To find out more about being in X-ray technology, students should contact the Radiological Society of North America, One MONY Plaza, Syracuse, NY 13202.

	SECTION	BASIC SCIENCE SKILLS	ACTIVITY MATERIALS STUDENT/GROUP	EXTENSIONS	
CHAPTER 8 ELECTRICITY	**8-1** p.T-164 Static Electricity	*Building science vocabulary* p.T-165 *Finding the cause and effect* of static electricity p. T-166	plastic comb, paper, pencil sharpener shavings, wool cloth 15 cm square	• Reinforcement p.T-166 • Enrichment pp.T-165, T-167, T-168	
	8-2 p.T-169 Current Electricity	*Comparing and contrasting* static and current electricity p.T-169 *Classifying* parts of a circuit p. T-172	foil, key, button, flashlight bulb, paper, socket, pencil, 2 wires 30 cm long, rubber band, screwdriver	• Enrichment pp.T-170, T-171 • Application p.T-172	
	8-3 p.T-173 One Kind of Circuit	*Comparing and contrasting* circuits p.T-174 *Reading illustrations* of circuits p. T-174	1.5 volt dry cell, 2 light bulbs in sockets, screwdriver, switch, 4 wires 30 cm long	• Reinforcement p.T-176 • Enrichment pp.T-174, T-174, T-175	
	8-4 p.T-177 Another Kind of Circuit	*Comparing and contrasting* circuit diagrams p.T-178	1.5 volt dry cell, 3 light bulbs in sockets, 7 wires 30 cm long, screwdriver, switch	• Reinforcement p.T-178 • Enrichment pp.T-180, T-181, T-182 • Application p.T-179	
CHAPTER 9 MAGNETISM	**9-1** p. T-183 Magnets	*Classifying* magnetic materials p.T-184 *Comparing* fields p.T-189	bar magnet, iron filings, plastic sheet 15 cm square	• Reinforcement pp.T-185, T-186, T-187 • Enrichment p.T-184	
	9-2 p.T-188 A Special Kind of Magnet	*Observing* a magnetic field p.T-189 *Comparing* strengths of electromagnets p.T-191	1.5 volt dry cell, iron nail, paper clips, screwdriver, switch, 2 wires 30 and 60 cm	• Reinforcement pp.T-189, T-191 • Enrichment pp.T-192 • Application p.T-190	
	9-3 p.T-193 Moving Magnets	*Following the sequence* of events in a generator p.T-194	bar magnet, compass, cardboard roll, 2 wires 90 cm long	• Enrichment pp. T-194, T-196, T-197 • Application pp. T-195, T-196	
CHAPTER 10 USING ELECTRICITY	**10-1** p.T-198 Measuring Electricity	*Classifying* and *sequencing* uses of energy p. T-200	paper, pencil	• Reinforcement p.T-199 • Enrichment p.T-200 • Application pp.T-201, T-202	
	10-2 p.T-203 Producing Electricity	*Following the sequence* in a generator and turbine p. T-204 *Cause and effect* p. T-205		• Reinforcement p.T-206 • Enrichment pp.T-204, T-205	
	10-3 p.T-207 Electricity and Environment	*Building science vocabulary* p.T-207	poster paper, marking pens, newspaper articles	• Enrichment pp. T-209, T-210 • Application pp.T-208, T-210,	
	10-4 p.T-211 Electricity in the Computer Age	*Classifying* chips p.T-212 *Finding the sequence* in how a computer works p.T-213		• Enrichment pp.T-213, T-214, T-216, T-217, T-218 • Application pp.T-212, T-215, T-219	

MAGNETISM

EXTRA ACTIVITIES/ DEMONSTRATIONS	WORKSHEET MASTERS	EVALUATIONS
• Static key p. T-164		Section Review p. T-168
• Circuit display p. T-170		Section Review p. T-172
• Series circuit p. T-173 • Dry cells p. T-176	One Kind of Circuit (SK) p. T-161k	Section Review p. T-176
• Christmas tree lights p. T-177	(AH) p. T-161l (AII) p. T-161m (SK) p. T-161n	Sec Rev p. T-181 Ch Rev p. T-182 Test Masters pp. T-162d,e,f
• Lodestone p. T-183 • Magnetic items p. T-184, p. T-187		Section Review p. T-187
• Oersted's experiment p. T-188 • Electromagnet p. T-191		Section Review p. T-192
• Galvanometer p. T-193	(AC) p. T-161o (AH) p. T-161p (SK) p. T-161q (SK) p. T-161r	Sec Rev p. T-196 Ch Rev p. T-197 Test Masters pp. T-161g,h
• Appliances p. T-198 • Appliances map p. T-199		Section Review p. T-202
	Using Electricity (SK) p. T-161s	Section Review p. T-206
• Solar Homes p. T-209	Use Checklist (AH) p. T-161t	Section Review p. T-210
• Computer Aids p. T-211	Computers (SK) p. T-161u	Section Review p. T-216 Chapter Review p. T-217 Test Masters pp. T-161i,j

BOOKS FOR STUDENTS

Arnold, Caroline. *Electric Fish*, illus. by George Gershinowitz, New York: Morrow, 1980

Asimov, Isaac. *How Did We Find Out About Electricity*, illus. by Matthew Kallmenhoff, New York: Walker, 1973

Chester, Michael. *Particles*, New York: Macmillan, 1978

DeWaard, John E. and Aron E. Klein. *Electric Cars*, Garden City, NY: Doubleday, 1977

Epstein, Sam and Beryl. *The First Book of Electricity*, illus. by Rod Stater, New York: Franklin Watts, 1978

Math, Irwin. *Wires and Watts: Understanding and Using Electricity*, illus. by Hal Kieth, New York: Scribner's, 1981

Provenzo, Eugene F. and Asterie B. *Rediscovering Electricity*, illus. by Peter A. Zorn, San Diego: Oak Tree, 1982

Schapp, Martha and Charles. *Let's Find Out What Electricity Does*, New York: Franklin Watts, 1975

Stanley, Leon R. *Easy To Make Electric Gadgets*, illus., New York: Harvey House, 1981

FILMS

Electromagnets: How They Work, 11 min, Britannica

Magnetism and Fields of Force, 13 min

FILMSTRIPS

Appliances and Other Things in Your Home: How They Work, 2 filmstrips, 2 cassettes, 16–17 min, National Geographic

Electricity and Magnetism, 1 filmstrip, 1 cassette, 14 min, National Geographic

Household Energy: The Science of Conservation, 2 filmstrips, 20 min each, Dimensions

KEY (AC)—Activity (AH)—At Home (SK)—Skill

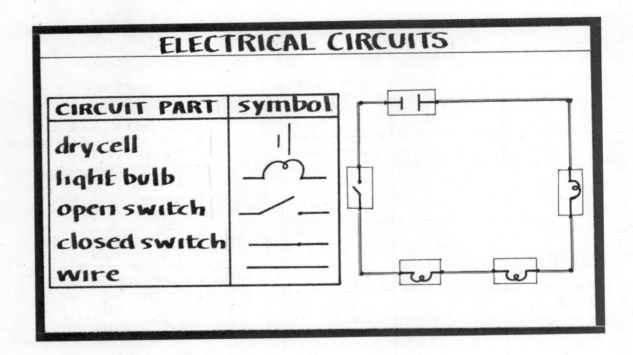

ELECTRICAL CIRCUITS

CIRCUIT PART	symbol
dry cell	
light bulb	
open switch	
closed switch	
wire	

BULLETIN BOARD

This bulletin board is designed to enable the students to become familiar with circuit symbols and diagrams and to allow them to expand their knowledge of electrical circuits. Assign a group of students to draw a set of electrical symbols to be placed on the side of the board. Using the cards, thumbtacks and yarn, students could design various circuits.

FIELD TRIP IDEAS

To an Appliance Repair Shop

Locate a small-appliance repair person in your community and arrange to visit the workshop. This trip will allow the students to see the mysterious insides of a number of appliances. Prior to the trip, have the students suggest questions they would like to ask the repair person. List these questions on chart paper. Ask the repair person to show the students how some appliances convert electrical energy to heat energy. After the trip, review the questions on the chart paper. Discuss the answers with the students.

To Understand Their School's Electrical Supply

Ask your school's custodian to take your class on an electrical tour of the school. Among items to be demonstrated should be the fuse box, any area where wires can be shown in the walls, number of outlets in each classroom, and areas where the supply of electricity needs to be greater. Ask the custodian to describe any difficulties that the school has had with its electrical system.

Name _____ Date _____

Fold Back
Answer
Key On
Line
Before
Copying.

ELECTRICITY

TEST 8

CHAPTER

CHAPTER OBJECTIVES

Read each question. Choose the best answer. Write the letter of your choice on the line at the right.

1. Static electricity is produced when
   a. objects lose all their charges.
   b. negative charges do not move.
   c. negative charges move from one object to another.
   d. positive charges move from one object to another.

   1. _____   1. **c** (1)

2. When a negatively charged object is brought near a positively charged object
   a. they repel each other.
   b. they attract each other.
   c. they both become positive.
   d. they both become negative.

   2. _____   2. **b** (1)

3. Lightning is caused when there is
   a. an absence of electrons in clouds.
   b. a buildup of electrons in clouds.
   c. a clear sky.
   d. a heavy rain.

   3. _____   3. **b** (1)

4. The electrical property of matter is called its
   a. charge.   c. current.
   b. attraction.   d. circuit.

   4. _____   4. **a** (1)

5. Which of the following is the best conductor?
   a. gold   c. rubber
   b. paper   d. glass

   5. _____   5. **a** (2)

6. The handle of a circuit switch would best be made from
   a. copper.   c. silver.
   b. aluminum.   d. wood.

   6. _____   6. **d** (2)

7. Materials that allow current to flow through them easily are called
   a. insulators.   c. switches.
   b. conductors.   d. charges.

   7. _____   7. **b** (2)

8. Which of the following is *not* true about conductors?
   a. They are used to prevent electrons from flowing.
   b. They allow current to flow through them easily.
   c. They are usually made of metal.
   d. They are used in circuit wires.

   8. _____   8. **a** (2)

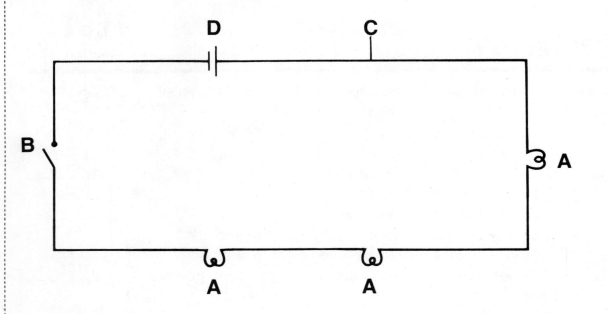

Look at the diagram above, then answer questions 9 and 10.

9. <u>**b**</u> (3)

9. The part which opens and closes the circuit is
    a. A.   **c.** C.
    b. B.   **d.** D.

9. _____

10. <u>**d**</u> (3)

10. Part D in the diagram is the
    a. bulb.   **c.** wire.
    b. switch.   **d.** dry cell.

10. _____

11. <u>**a**</u> (3)

11. Electrons are pushed through the circuit by the
    a. negative terminal.   **c.** wires.
    b. positive terminal.   **d.** switch.

11. _____

12. <u>**c**</u> (3)

12. The dry cell is used as
    a. the path of electricity.   **c.** the source of electricity.
    b. a safety device.   **d.** the conductor of electricity.

12. _____

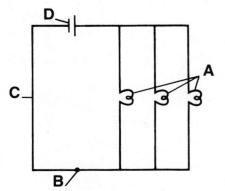

Look at the diagram above, then answer questions 13 and 14.

Name_____ Date_____

13. How many paths can the charges flow through? 13. _____ **13.** <u>c</u> (4)
    a. none   **c.** three
    b. two   **d.** six

14. The diagram shows 14. _____ **14.** <u>d</u> (4)
    a. an open series circuit.   **c.** an opened parallel circuit.
    b. a closed series circuit.   **d.** a closed parallel circuit.

15. When one bulb in a parallel circuit burns out 15. _____ **15.** <u>b</u> (4)
    a. the other bulbs will go out.
    b. the bulbs that are lit will stay on.
    c. the other bulbs will be dimmer.
    d. the other bulbs will be brighter.

16. In a parallel circuit the current has 16. _____ **16.** <u>d</u> (4)
    a. one path to follow.
    b. two paths to follow.
    c. many paths to follow.
    d. less strength than in a series circuit.

17. When the wire in a fuse melts 17. _____ **17.** <u>b</u> (5)
    a. there is a fire.   **c.** more current goes through.
    b. the current stops.   **d.** nothing happens.

18. Safety devices are used in circuits to keep wires from 18. _____ **18.** <u>a</u> (5)
    a. overheating.   **c.** breaking.
    b. becoming too long.   **d.** all of the above.

19. Tell if the sentence below is true or false. If it is false, tell which 19. _____ **19.** <u>c</u> (5)
    words can be used in place of the underlined words to make
    the sentence true.
    When a circuit breaker opens <u>the electricity flows backwards</u>.
    a. The sentence is true.
    b. the current flows stronger.
    c. the current stops.
    d. a fire starts.

20. An open circuit breaker shows 20. _____ **20.** <u>a</u> (5)
    a. that too much current is flowing in the circuit.
    b. that the circuit is a series circuit.
    c. that a new light bulb is needed.
    d. none of the above.

Fold Back
Answer
Key On
Line
Before
Copying.

Name_____ Date_____

MAGNETISM

Read each question. Choose the best answer. Write the letter of your choice on the line at the right.

1. <u>b</u> (1)

1. A magnet would *not* pick up an object that is made from
   - **a.** iron.
   - **c.** nickel.
   - **b.** tin.
   - **d.** cobalt.

1. _____

2. <u>c</u> (1)

2. Two magnets attract each other when
   - **a.** the two south poles are brought together.
   - **b.** the two north poles are brought together.
   - **c.** the south pole of one magnet and the north pole of the other are brought together.
   - **d.** all of the above occur.

2. _____

3. <u>a</u> (1)

3. A magnetic field is the area
   - **a.** around a magnet in which there is a magnetic force.
   - **b.** in which there are no lines of force.
   - **c.** in which there is no magnetic force.
   - **d.** around all the edges of the magnet.

3. _____

4. <u>b</u> (2)

4. The difference between electromagnets and regular magnets is
   - **a.** that electromagnets have a magnetic force.
   - **b.** that electromagnets can be turned on and off.
   - **c.** that electromagnets attract metal objects.
   - **d.** that electromagnets have north and south poles.

4. _____

5. <u>c</u> (2)

5. Oersted discovered that
   - **a.** compass needles always point in a north-south direction.
   - **b.** electricity flows through wires.
   - **c.** current electricity is surrounded by a magnetic field.
   - **d.** magnets have north and south poles.

5. _____

6. <u>d</u> (2)

6. A piece of iron becomes an electromagnet when
   - **a.** it has no magnetic field.
   - **b.** it is plugged in but not turned on.
   - **c.** the current is turned off.
   - **d.** a current is passed through it.

6. _____

7. <u>b</u> (3)

7. How does increasing the amount of current affect an electromagnet?
   - **a.** It becomes weaker.
   - **c.** It changes the wire.
   - **b.** It becomes stronger.
   - **d.** It has no effect.

7. _____

Name _____ Date _____

Look at the pictures below, then answer questions 8 and 9.

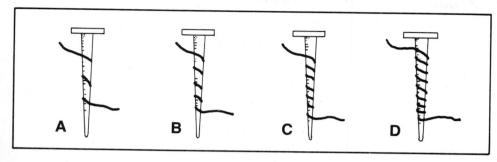

8. Which electromagnet will pick up the most nails?   8. _____   8. __d__ (3)
   a. A.   c. C.
   b. B.   d. D.
9. Adding more nails to the center of the electromagnet   9. _____   9. __a__ (3)
   a. will increase its strength.   c. will decrease the current.
   b. will decrease its strength.   d. will have no effect.
10. An instrument used to detect weak electrical current is   10. _____   10. __d__ (4)
   a. a barometer.   c. a generator.
   b. a thermometer.   d. a galvanometer.
11. When a magnet is moved back and forth inside a coil of wire 11. _____   11. __b__ (4)
   a. the magnet becomes stronger.
   b. an electric current is produced.
   c. the wire starts to move.
   d. all of the above occur.
12. Generators will *not* produce electric current if   12. _____   12. __d__ (4)
   a. the magnets stay still and the coils of wire move.
   b. the magnets whirl through large coils of copper.
   c. the magnet moves in and out of the armature.
   d. there is no energy to turn the moving parts.
13. The part of the generator that collects the current is the 13. _____   13. __c__ (5)
   a. armature.   c. metal rings.
   b. horseshoe magnet.   d. metal brushes.
14. The coil of wire in a generator is called the   14. _____   14. __a__ (5)
   a. armature.   c. current.
   b. brushes.   d. galvanometer.
15. The brushes on a generator   15. _____   15. __a__ (5)
   a. lead the current in.
   b. bring the energy in.
   c. are used to clean it.
   d. are used to crank the armature.

Name_____ Date_____

USING ELECTRICITY

Holt, Rinehart & Winston Publishers

Read each question. Choose the best answer from those listed.
Write the letter of your choice on the line at the right.

CHAPTER OBJECTIVES

1. <u>**b**</u> (1)

2. <u>**c**</u> (1)

3. <u>**a**</u> (1)

4. <u>**a**</u> (2)

5. <u>**d**</u> (2)

6. <u>**a**</u> (2)

7. <u>**a**</u> (3)

1. Which of the following converts electricity to mechanical energy?
   a. light bulb
   b. electric mixer
   c. refrigerator
   d. electric blanket

1._____

2. When you use a toaster, electricity is converted to
   a. heat energy.
   b. light energy.
   c. both of the above.
   d. none of the above.

2._____

3. An electric meter counts
   a. the number of kilowatt-hours used.
   b. the number of generators in the circuit.
   c. the number of dollars in the electric bill.
   d. none of the above.

3._____

4. Which of the following statements about a nuclear reaction is *not* true?
   a. A large amount of fuel is needed to produce energy.
   b. It releases nuclear wastes.
   c. The heat from the reaction can change water into steam.
   d. Tiny particles of matter are split apart.

4._____

5. Turbines can be made to spin by
   a. water falling on them.
   b. steam formed when oil is burned.
   c. steam formed when a nuclear reaction occurs.
   d. all of the above.

5._____

6. Fuels provide energy to turn parts of a generator by
   a. converting water to steam.
   b. causing water to fall.
   c. splitting tiny particles of matter apart.
   d. none of the above.

6._____

7. Adding harmful materials to the environment is called
   a. pollution.   c. reservation.
   b. conservation.   d. a natural resource.

7._____

Name_____ Date_____

8. One way to practice conservation is
   a. to turn off the television set when leaving the room.
   b. to use an electric blanket instead of a comforter.
   c. to burn more fuels.
   d. to leave the lights on all night.

8._____   8. _a_ (3)

9. Which of the following is *not* a way in which nuclear plants could harm the environment?
   a. Harmful wastes might be produced.
   b. They could harm plant and animal life.
   c. They could produce sulfur oxides and smoke.
   d. They could cause the temperature of streams to rise.

9._____   9. _c_ (3)

10. When the sun hits solar cells
    a. they stop working.
    b. they produce electricity.
    c. they can melt.
    d. they can become harmful to the environment.

10._____   10. _b_ (4)

11. Solar cells are made by combining
    a. iron and oil.   c. metals with coal.
    b. oil and gas.   d. metals with silicon.

11._____   11. _d_ (4)

12. Which statement about solar cells is *not* true?
    a. They are made from rare materials.
    b. Hundreds of solar cells can be hooked up together.
    c. They cause pollution.
    d. Buildings that use them can produce their own electricity.

12._____   12. _c_ (4)

13. Which statement is true about computers?
    a. They are devices that store and handle information.
    b. They store large amounts of information on disks.
    c. Silicon chips are very important in computers.
    d. All of the above are true.

13._____   13. _d_ (5)

14. After a message gets to the correct memory circuit
    a. the question can be typed in.
    b. the computer is programmed.
    c. the question goes to the computer's brain.
    d. it gets the needed information.

14._____   14. _d_ (5)

15. Computers might be used in schools
    a. to help students learn subjects independently.
    b. to keep track of names and addresses of students.
    c. to tell you when you have read a wrong word.
    d. all of the above.

15._____   15. _d_ (5)

Name _____ Date _____

One Kind of Circuit

In each space below, draw a diagram of the circuit described using the symbols given on the chart.

Chart of electrical symbols

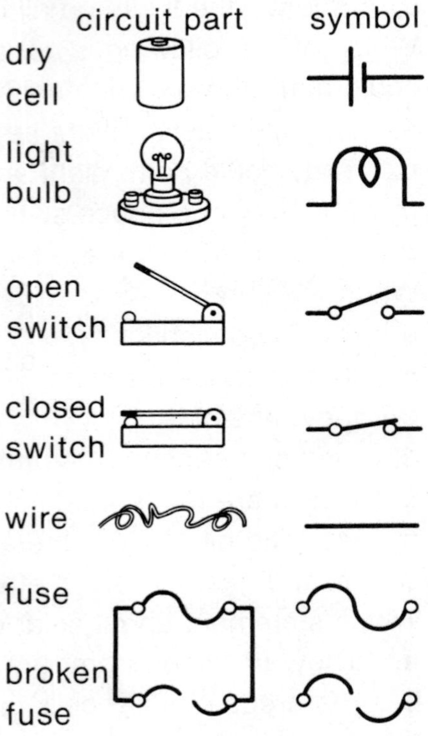

circuit part	symbol
dry cell	
light bulb	
open switch	
closed switch	
wire	
fuse	
broken fuse	

1. A series circuit with 1 dry cell, 2 light bulbs, and an open switch.

2. A parallel circuit with 2 dry cells, 3 light bulbs, and a closed switch.

3. A series circuit with 2 dry cells, 4 light bulbs, and a closed switch.

4. A parallel circuit with 1 dry cell, 2 light bulbs, and an open switch.

Name_____ Date _____

Another Kind of Circuit

You are learning how to use electricity safely. In this at home activity you will see how a fuse works. SAFETY TIP: THIS ACTIVITY MUST BE SUPERVISED BY AN ADULT.

A. Obtain the following materials: aluminum foil, 2 dry cells, 2 paper clips, scissors, screwdriver with insulated handle, socket bulb, 2 thumbtacks, wire, wooden block.

B. Place each paper clip against the underside of a thumbtack. Press the thumbtacks into the wooden block as shown. The tacks should be about 3 cm apart and upright against the wood.

C. Place a strip of aluminum foil about 5 cm long by 1 cm wide between the clips.

D. Set up the dry cells, wire, and bulb as shown.

E. Remove some insulation near the middle of the wires as shown.

F. While holding the insulated handle of the screwdriver, carefully touch the metal to the two stripped wires. Observe what happens to the aluminum.

A

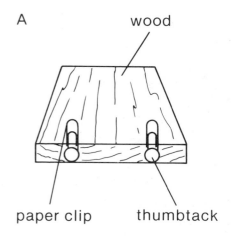

wood

paper clip   thumbtack

B

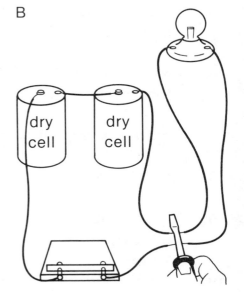

QUESTIONS

1. How did you short the circuit? _____

_____

2. Did the current travel back to the source through the

bulb or the screwdriver? _____

_____

3. What happened to the foil? Why? _____

_____

4. Why is a fuse helpful in a circuit? _____

_____

_____

Name_____ Date _____

Electricity

You are learning about the uses of electricity. In this at-home activity you will see how safe your home is electrically.
SAFETY TIP: THIS ACTIVITY MUST BE SUPERVISED BY AN ADULT

Check the answer to each question below.

		YES	NO
1.	Do all outlets have only the proper number of plugs in them?	☐	☐
2.	Are all of these plugs in safe condition? (no breaks or cracks)	☐	☐
3.	Are all cords placed where they are safe, where no one can walk or trip on them?	☐	☐
4.	Are all cords in safe condition? (no breaks or cracks)	☐	☐
5.	Do all appliances plug directly into an outlet without extension cords?	☐	☐
6.	Are large appliances with three-pronged plugs properly grounded?	☐	☐
7.	Is each large appliance plugged into its own circuit?	☐	☐
8.	Can you find the electrical service panel for your home?	☐	☐
9.	Does each fuse or circuit breaker show which circuits it controls?	☐	☐
10.	Could you turn off all of the electricity in an emergency?	☐	☐

If you have answered *no* to any of the questions above, you probably have some safety problems that should be corrected. You may be able to correct some problems yourself. If you cannot, you should contact an electrician or the electric company.

Electricity

Explain what would happen in the examples given below.

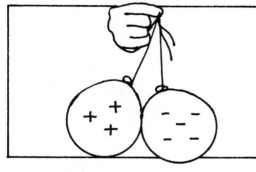

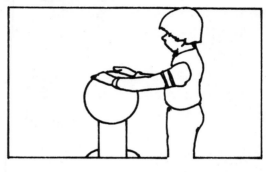

_____

_____

_____

_____

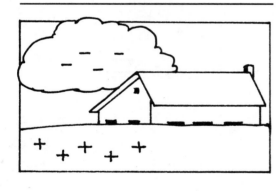

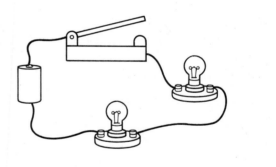

_____

_____

_____

_____

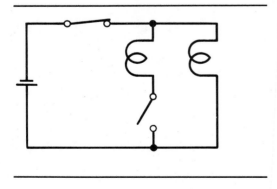

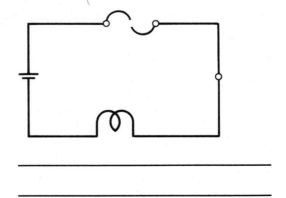

_____

_____

_____

_____

Name _____ Date _____

Moving Magnets

You are learning how magnets can be made. Here you will demonstrate how they can be destroyed. SAFETY TIP: THIS ACTIVITY MUST BE SUPERVISED BY AN ADULT

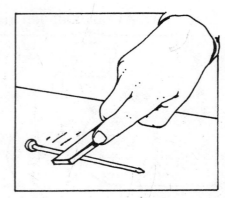

A. Obtain the following materials: bar magnet, candle, hammer, 3 iron nails, matches, paper clips, pliers.

B. Stroke one of the iron nails with the pole of the magnet in one direction only.

C. Try to pick up the paper clips with the nail.

D. Remove the clips. Then hammer along the length of the nail several times. Try to pick up the clips again.

E. Repeat steps A and B with another nail. Remove the clips.

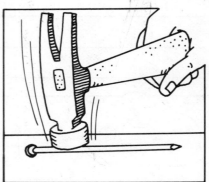

F. Stroke the nail with the pole of the magnet in both directions. Try to pick up the clips again.

G. Repeat steps A and B with another nail. Then remove the clips.

H. Hold the nail with the pliers and place the nail in the flame of a candle for about three minutes. Try to pick up the clips again.

QUESTIONS

1. How did you make the nails act like magnets?

_____

_____

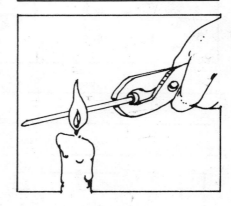

2. What happened to the nails after you hammered or heated them? _____

3. What happened to the nail after rubbing it with the magnet in both directions? _____

_____

4. What are three ways in which magnetism can be destroyed? _____

_____

_____

Name _____ Date _____

Moving Magnets

You are learning about devices that use magnetism and electricity. In this at home activity you will build one of your own, a telegraph.

A. Obtain the following materials: 1 dry cell, 2 thin iron or steel strips, a large headed nail, 2 long nails, 4 small nails, wire, wood block, wood board.

B. Hammer the large-headed nail into the center of the board.

C. Nail one metal strip near one end of the board as shown. Bend the strip back so that it doesn't touch the board when you let it go.

D. Hammer a small-headed nail into the wood under the end of the metal strip.

E. Attach a wire from this small nail to the dry cell. Attach the other wire to the dry cell. Then wrap the wire around the large nail about 40 times. Attach the loose end of the wire to the nail in the metal strip.

F. Hammer the block into the other end of the wood. Nail a metal strip to the top of the block so the strip reaches over the large nail. Bend the strip down at the center and up at the end.

G. Press down and release the key.

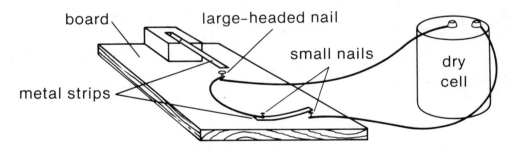

1. What happened when you pressed down on the key?

   _____

2. You have made a simple telegraph. A telegraph uses electricity to make sounds. How is the sound made?

   _____

   _____

   _____

   _____

   _____

Magnetism

1. Complete the pictures by drawing the lines of force in the diagrams below.

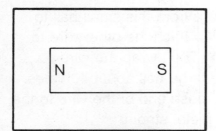 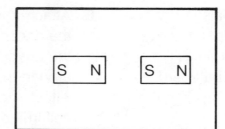 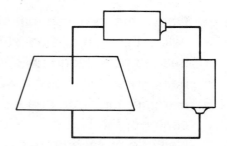

2. Arrange the letters of the electromagnets in order of increasing strength.

a.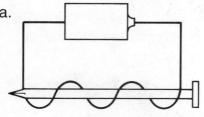

b.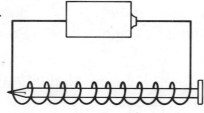

Correct
Order

_____

c.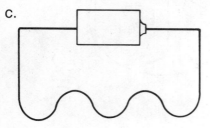

d.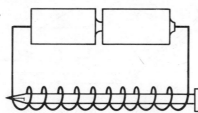

3. Use a picture to show how a magician could make a metal object float in the air using magnets.

Name_____ Date_____

Magnetism

In the word search below, find the vocabulary words hidden horizontally, vertically, diagonally, and backwards.

```
L I R W T F N A U Q T V E B T
I M P T E G V T R H O Y D G E
N R Y O N E Z O P I C O K X N
E A P G G T Q N O K Z A H I G
S Q Z E A W R T J D H N F D A
O Y W N M L B A H B K O T Q M
F I C E B S V M F O N R X L O
F P N R C L J A D T F T W A R
O Z O A Y J T R N P B C A F T
R E C T A N H T I O A H B E C
C A X O Q T I Y T L M C W L E
E T A R M A T U R E Y E J Z L
O E N R U L N I A S N D T R E
P K J A H F O D A Y T I O E Q
M A G N E T I C F I E L D U R
```

After you have found all of the words, match them with their definitions.

1. Object that picks up or attracts iron, nickel, cobalt _____
2. The ends of magnets _____
3. The space around a magnet showing magnetic force _____
4. Lines that form around a magnet

   _____

5. A magnet created by an electric current _____

6. An instrument used to detect weak electrical currents _____
7. A machine that produces current electricity using magnetism

   _____

8. A movable coil of wire found between the poles of a magnet in a generator

   _____

Name _____ Date _____

Using Electricity

1. Rewrite the terms below in their proper sequence: dam, turbine, falling water, current electricity, generator.

    _____

    _____

2. Name the kinds of energy changes that take place in each of the following: (Note: there may be more than one kind of energy.)

    record player _____

    generator _____

    video game _____

    telephone _____

3. Name three sources of electrical energy besides falling water. Then describe one problem caused by the use of each.

    Source   Problem

    _____   _____

                        _____

    _____   _____

                        _____

    _____   _____

                        _____

4. If the reading on your electric meter is 5000 kilowatt-hours for one month, and is 6500 kilowatt-hours for the next month, how many kilowatt-hours have you used?
    _____ kilowatt-hours.

5. If the cost is $.10 per kilowatt-hour, what will your electric bill be for that month? _____

Name _____ Date _____

Using Electricity

You are learning about the need to conserve energy. In this at-home activity you will observe how well you and your family use energy. Check the correct boxes to answer the questions.

		YES	NO
1.	Do you turn off the light when you are the last person to leave the room?	☐	☐
2.	Are all of the bulbs used in your home the proper brightness for their use?	☐	☐
3.	Do you make sure that all the small appliances in your home are used only when necessary?	☐	☐
4.	Do you make sure the television, radio, or record player are turned off when no one is watching or listening?	☐	☐
5.	Do you use the clothes washer and dryer only when they have a full load?	☐	☐
6.	Do you use your large appliances only at off-peak usage hours?	☐	☐
7.	Have you tried to use appliances that were designed to save energy?	☐	☐
8.	Do you set the air conditioner so that it runs at top efficiency?	☐	☐
9.	Do you use the dishwasher only when it has a full load?	☐	☐
10.	Do you follow your monthly use of electricity to see if you are conserving or not?	☐	☐

Computers

The science words below have been written in a computer code. Can you use the key below to discover what the words are? Write the words in the spaces provided.

A	Z	B	Y	C	X	D	W	E	V	F	U	G
1	2	3	4	5	6	7	8	9	10	11	12	13
T	H	S	I	R	J	Q	K	P	L	O	M	N
14	15	16	17	18	19	20	21	22	23	24	25	26

1. 5   15   17   22
___ ___ ___ ___

2. 5   24   25   22   12   14   9   18
___ ___ ___ ___ ___ ___ ___ ___

3. 7   17   16   21
___ ___ ___ ___

4. 17   26   22   12   14
___ ___ ___ ___ ___

5. 24   12   14   22   12   14
___ ___ ___ ___ ___ ___

6. 22   18   24   13   18   1   25
___ ___ ___ ___ ___ ___ ___

7. 5   9   26   14   18   1   23
___ ___ ___ ___ ___ ___ ___

   22   18   24   5   9   16   16   17   26   13
___ ___ ___ ___ ___ ___ ___ ___ ___ ___

   12   26   17   14
___ ___ ___ ___

Permission to reproduce this page is granted to users of HOLT SCIENCE 5   Holt, Rinehart and Winston, Publishers

Name_____ Date_____

One Kind of Circuit

READING ILLUSTRATIONS, SEQUENCING   SKILL WORKSHEET

In each space below, draw a diagram of the circuit described using the symbols given on the chart.

Chart of electrical symbols

circuit part	symbol
dry cell	
light bulb	
open switch	
closed switch	
wire	
fuse	
broken fuse	

1. A series circuit with 1 dry cell, 2 light bulbs, and an open switch.

2. A parallel circuit with two dry cells, 3 light bulbs, and a closed switch.

3. A series circuit with two dry cells, 4 light bulbs, and a closed switch.

4. A parallel circuit with one dry cell, 2 light bulbs, and an open switch.

T–161k   Unit 4 Chapter 8   28W

Name_____ Date_____

Another Kind of Circuit

AT HOME WORKSHEET

You are learning how to use electricity safely. In this at home activity you will see how a fuse works. SAFETY TIP: THIS ACTIVITY MUST BE SUPERVISED BY AN ADULT.

A. Obtain the following materials: aluminum foil, 2 dry cells, 2 paper clips, scissors, screwdriver with insulated handle, socket bulb, 2 thumbtacks, wire, wooden block.

B. Place each paper clip against the underside of a thumbtack. Press the thumbtacks into the wooden block as shown. The tacks should be about 3 cm apart and upright against the wood.

C. Place a strip of aluminum foil about 5 cm long by 1 cm wide between the clips.

D. Set up the dry cells, wire, and bulb as shown.

E. Remove some insulation near the middle of the wires as shown.

F. While holding the insulated handle of the screwdriver, carefully touch the metal to the two stripped wires. Observe what happens to the aluminum.

A   wood

paper clip   thumbtack

B

dry cell   dry cell

QUESTIONS

1. How did you short the circuit? _____Touching the bare wires with the screwdriver shorted the circuit._____

2. Did the current travel back to the source through the bulb or the screwdriver? _____The current traveled through the screwdriver._____

3. What happened to the foil? Why? _____The foil melted. Too much current heated the wires and the foil._____

4. Why is a fuse helpful in a circuit? _____A fuse will stop a surge of current from damaging the wires and appliances._____

29W   Unit 4 Chapter 8   T–161l

Name_____ Date_____

Electricity

AT HOME WORKSHEET

You are learning about the uses of electricity. In this at-home activity you will see how safe your home is electrically.
SAFETY TIP: THIS ACTIVITY MUST BE SUPERVISED BY AN ADULT

Check the answer to each question below.

	YES	NO
1. Do all outlets have only the proper number of plugs in them?	☐	☐
2. Are all of these plugs in safe condition? (no breaks or cracks)	☐	☐
3. Are all cords placed where they are safe, where no one can walk or trip on them?	☐	☐
4. Are all cords in safe condition? (no breaks or cracks)	☐	☐
5. Do all appliances plug directly into an outlet without extension cords?	☐	☐
6. Are large appliances with three-pronged plugs properly grounded?	☐	☐
7. Is each large appliance plugged into its own circuit?	☐	☐
8. Can you find the electrical service panel for your home?	☐	☐
9. Does each fuse or circuit breaker show which circuits it controls?	☐	☐
10. Could you turn off all of the electricity in an emergency?	☐	☐

If you have answered no to any of the questions above, you probably have some safety problems that should be corrected. If you can, you can do this yourself. If you cannot, you should contact an electrician or the electric company.

T–161m   Unit 4 Chapter 8   30W

Name_____ Date_____

Electricity

FINDING CAUSE AND EFFECT, INFERRING   SKILL WORKSHEET

Explain what would happen in the examples given below.

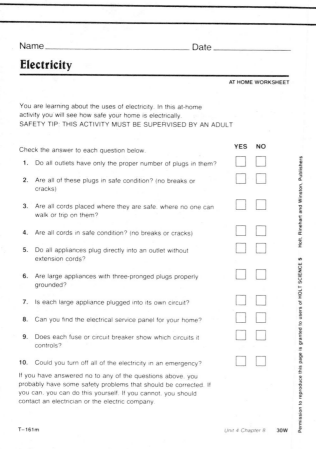

The two oppositely charged balloons would be attracted to one another.

The person would become negatively charged. His or her hair would stick out.

Lightning would travel between the cloud to the ground.

The bulb will not light up because the switch is open.

The bulb on the right will light, but the other will not, the switch is open.

The bulb will not light because the broken fuse has broken the circuit.

31W   Unit 4 Chapter 8   T–161n

T–161v

Worksheet 1 (top-left)

Moving Magnets

ACTIVITY WORKSHEET

You are learning how magnets can be made. Here you will demonstrate how they can be destroyed. SAFETY TIP: THIS ACTIVITY MUST BE SUPERVISED BY AN ADULT

A. Obtain the following materials: bar magnet, candle, hammer, 3 iron nails, matches, paper clips, pliers.
B. Stroke one of the iron nails with the pole of the magnet in one direction only.
C. Try to pick up the paper clips with the nail.
D. Remove the clips. Then hammer along the length of the nail several times. Try to pick up the clips again.
E. Repeat steps A and B with another nail. Remove the clips.
F. Stroke the nail with the pole of the magnet in both directions. Try to pick up the clips again.
G. Repeat steps A and B with another nail. Then remove the clips.
H. Hold the nail with the pliers and place the nail in the flame of a candle for about three minutes. Try to pick up the clips again.

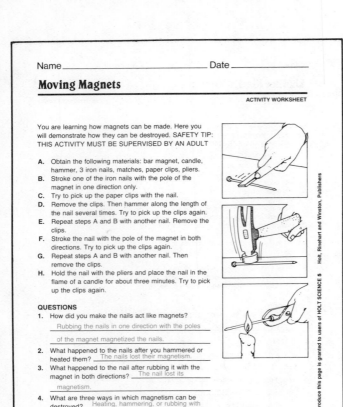

QUESTIONS

1. How did you make the nails act like magnets?
   Rubbing the nails in one direction with the poles
   of the magnet magnetized the nails.
2. What happened to the nails after you hammered or heated them? The nails lost their magnetism.
3. What happened to the nail after rubbing it with the magnet in both directions? The nail lost its
   magnetism.
4. What are three ways in which magnetism can be destroyed? Heating, hammering, or rubbing with
   the pole of a magnet in both directions will
   destroy magnetism.

Worksheet 2 (top-right)

Moving Magnets

AT HOME WORKSHEET

You are learning about devices that use magnetism and electricity. In this at home activity you will build one of your own, a telegraph.

A. Obtain the following materials: 1 dry cell, 2 thin iron or steel strips, a large headed nail, 2 long nails, 4 small nails, wire, wood block, wood board.
B. Hammer the large-headed nail into the center of the board.
C. Nail one metal strip near one end of the board as shown. Bend the strip back so that it doesn't touch the board when you let it go.
D. Hammer a small-headed nail into the wood under the end of the metal strip.
E. Attach a wire from this small nail to the dry cell. Attach the other wire to the dry cell. Then wrap the wire around the large nail about 40 times. Attach the loose end of the wire to the nail in the metal strip.
F. Hammer the block into the other end of the wood. Nail a metal strip to the top of the block so the strip reaches over the large nail. Bend the strip down at the center and up at the end.
G. Press down and release the key.

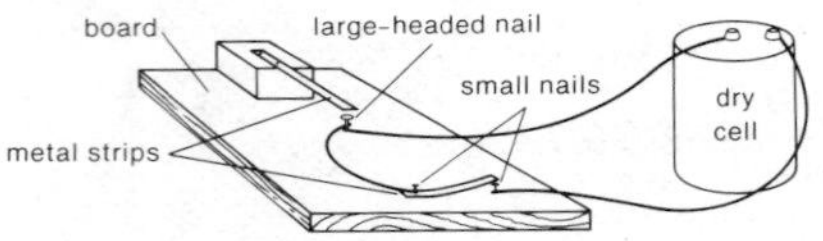

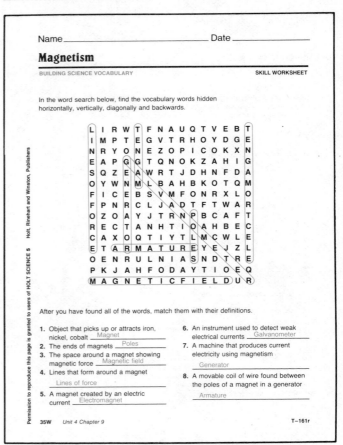

1. What happened when you pressed down on the key
   There was a clicking sound.
2. You have made a simple telegraph. A telegraph uses electricity to make sounds. How is the sound made?
   Pressing down on the key closed the telegraph circuit. The
   current made the large-headed nail into an electromagnet.
   The metal strip above the electromagnet was attracted to it.
   The magnetic attraction caused the strip to hit against the
   top of the nail and produce a sound.

Worksheet 3 (bottom-left)

Magnetism

FINDING CAUSE AND EFFECT, HYPOTHESIZING, SEQUENCING

SKILL WORKSHEET

1. Complete the pictures by drawing the lines of force in the diagrams below.

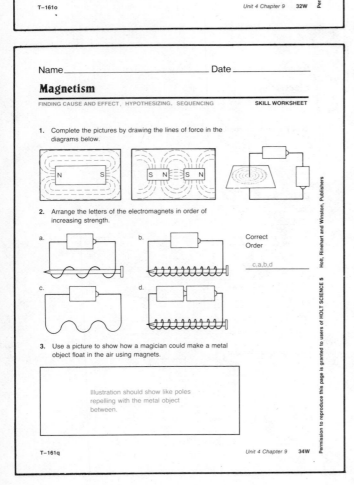

2. Arrange the letters of the electromagnets in order of increasing strength.

   Correct Order
   c,a,b,d

3. Use a picture to show how a magician could make a metal object float in the air using magnets.

   Illustration should show like poles repelling with the metal object between.

Worksheet 4 (bottom-right)

Magnetism

BUILDING SCIENCE VOCABULARY

SKILL WORKSHEET

In the word search below, find the vocabulary words hidden horizontally, vertically, diagonally and backwards.

```
L I R W T F N A U Q T V E B T
I M P T E G V T R H O Y D G E
N R Y O N E Z O P I C O K X N
E A P G G T Q N O K Z A H I G
S Q Z E A W R T J D H N F D A
O Y W N M L B A H B K O T Q M
F I C E B S V M F O N R X L O
P F N R C L J A D T F T W A R
O Z O A J J T R N P B C A F T
R E C T A N H T I O A H B E C
C A X O Q T I Y T L M C W L E
E T A R M A T U R E Y E J Z L
O E N R U L N I A S N D T R E
P K J A H F O D A Y T I O E Q
M A G N E T I C F I E L D U R
```

After you have found all of the words, match them with their definitions.

1. Object that picks up or attracts iron, nickel, cobalt _Magnet_
2. The ends of magnets _Poles_
3. The space around a magnet showing magnetic force _Magnetic field_
4. Lines that form around a magnet _Lines of force_
5. A magnet created by an electric current _Electromagnet_
6. An instrument used to detect weak electrical currents _Galvanometer_
7. A machine that produces current electricity using magnetism _Generator_
8. A movable coil of wire found between the poles of a magnet in a generator _Armature_

Using Electricity

FINDING CAUSE AND EFFECT, MEASURING, SEQUENCING   SKILL WORKSHEET

1. Rewrite the terms below in their proper sequence: dam, turbine, falling water, current electricity, generator.

   falling water, dam, turbine, generator, current electricity

2. Name the kinds of energy changes that take place in each of the following: (Note: there may be more than one kind of energy.)

   record player   electrical → mechanical → sound

   generator   mechanical → electrical

   video game   electrical → light, sound

   telephone   electrical → sound

3. Name three sources of electrical energy besides falling water. Then describe one problem caused by the use of each.

Source	Problem
fossil fuels	air pollution
solar	cloudy days block sun, expensive
nuclear	dangerous wastes, heats up water source

4. If the reading on your electric meter is 5000 kilowatt-hours for one month, and is 6500 kilowatt-hours for the next month, how many kilowatt-hours have you used?
   1500 kilowatt-hours.

5. If the cost is $.10 per kilowatt-hour, what will your electric bill be for that month?
   $150.00

T–161s   Unit 4 Chapter 10   36W

Using Electricity

AT HOME WORKSHEET

You are learning about the need to conserve energy. In this at-home activity you will observe how well you and your family use energy. Check the correct boxes to answer the questions.

	YES	NO
1. Do you turn off the light when you are the last person to leave the room?	☐	☐
2. Are all of the bulbs used in your home the proper brightness for their use?	☐	☐
3. Do you make sure that all the small appliances in your home are used only when necessary?	☐	☐
4. Do you make sure the television, radio or record player are turned off when no one is watching or listening?	☐	☐
5. Do you use the clothes washer and dryer only when they have a full load?	☐	☐
6. Do you use your large appliances only at off-peak usage hours?	☐	☐
7. Have you tried to use appliances that were designed to save energy?	☐	☐
8. Do you set the air conditioner so that it runs at top efficiency?	☐	☐
9. Do you use the dishwasher only when it has a full load?	☐	☐
10. Do you follow your monthly use of electricity to see if you are conserving or not?	☐	☐

37W   Unit 4 Chapter 10   T–161t

Computers

BUILDING SCIENCE VOCABULARY, SEQUENCING   SKILL WORKSHEET

The science words below have been written in a computer code. Can you use the key below to discover what the words are? Write the words in the spaces provided.

A	Z	B	Y	C	X	D	W	E	V	F	U	G
1	2	3	4	5	6	7	8	9	10	11	12	13

T	H	S	I	R	J	Q	K	P	L	O	M	N
14	15	16	17	18	19	20	21	22	23	24	25	26

1. 5 15 17 22
   C H I P

2. 5 24 25 22 12 14 9 18
   C O M P U T E R

3. 7 17 16 21
   D I S K

4. 17 26 22 12 14
   I N P U T

5. 24 12 14 22 12 14
   O U T P U T

6. 22 18 24 13 18 1 25
   P R O G R A M

7. 5 9 26 14 18 1 23
   C E N T R A L

   22 18 24 5 9 16 16 17 26 13
   P R O C E S S I N G

   12 26 17 14
   U N I T

T–161u   Unit 4 Chapter 10   38W

UNIT OVERVIEW

This is a physical science unit on electricity and magnetism. When matter loses or gains electrons, it acquires a static electric charge. An electric current is produced when electrons flow through a path called a circuit. A series circuit has one path through which the current flows from its source, through electrical devices, and back to the source. A parallel circuit has many paths through which the current can flow.

Magnets are made of iron, steel, or magnetite. They have the property of attracting iron, steel, nickel, or cobalt. Magnets are surrounded by lines of force known as a magnetic field. When an electric current passes through a wire, a temporary magnetic field is formed around the wire. Magnets caused by an electric current are called electromagnets.

Generators spin a coil of wire in a magnetic field to produce electricity. Energy from fossil fuels or nuclear energy is used to spin the coil of wire in a generator. Wind and solar power can be used as alternative sources of energy. Electricity from generators is carried to homes and factories, where it is used in many different ways.

We have become very dependent on electrical energy in our daily lives. Computers are making a greater impact on our lives every day. They use electicity to store information and to make rapid calculations.

Exceptional Student IEP Unit Goal

The student will explain what electricity is, name one energy resource used to make electricity, and name one type of energy derived from electricity.

ELECTRICITY AND MAGNETISM

UNIT OPENER

This is a photograph of multiple lightning strikes over Tucson, Arizona. You can ask the students the following questions as motivation: What do you think lightning is? *It is a giant electric spark.* What causes it? *The air molecules in the clouds rubbing against each other.* What does lightning strike? *It strikes the highest object.* Is this dangerous? *Very; it can start fires and kill people.* Is it useful? *No.* Is all electricity dangerous? *Only if it is not used wisely.* Is any form of electricity useful? *Yes, the kind we use in our homes.*

UNIT 4

LEARNING CENTER

A suggested title for the Learning Center is "Shocking and Attracting." Photographs of lightning, electric circuits, power plants, magnets, and computers can be used in a display. You may wish to keep a file of those blackline masters and Extensions that the students can work on independently.

The following Extensions are especially suitable for the Learning Center, and the materials for these Extensions should be available: build an electroscope, p. T–167 (regular size paper cup, small paper clip, metal foil, scissors, and tape); circuit posters, p. T–176 (poster materials); temporary magnets, p. T–187 (strong permanent magnet, paper clip, short piece of string); electromagnets, p. T–192 (1.5-V dry cell, iron nail, paper clips, screwdriver, switch, 30 cm [12 in.] piece of wire, 60 cm [24 in.] piece of wire, pencil); electric bills, p. T–202 (copies of electric bills); energy poster, p. T–210 (poster paper, labels, magazines, and photographs).

In addition, an index file of suggested research topics could be set up in the Learning Center using the following Extensions: atoms (p. T–168), lightning (p. T–170), electronics vocabulary (p. T–181), earth's magnetic poles (p. T–187), Hans Christian Oersted and Michael Faraday (p. T–194), Careers (p. T–196), earth's magnetic fields (p. T–196), hydroelectric power (p. T–204), nuclear power (p. T–205), pollution (p. T–209), solar cells (p. T–210), integrated circuits (p. T–212), computer's impact (p. T–215).

CHAPTER 8

CHAPTER OBJECTIVES

1. Explain how objects can receive a static electricity charge and describe the effects produced by bringing objects with like and unlike charges near one another.
2. Compare conductors and insulators.
3. Identify and draw a diagram of the parts of a series circuit and explain the function of each part.
4. Identify and draw a diagram of a parallel circuit and compare it to a series circuit.
5. Explain the functions of circuit breakers and fuses as safety devices in circuits.

SECTION BACKGROUND

All matter is composed of atoms. Atoms are made up of protons, neutrons, and electrons. Protons (positive charges) and neutrons are tightly bound to the nucleus. Negatively charged electrons orbit around the nucleus and are more readily gained or lost. A neutral atom has an equal number of protons and electrons. An atom with more protons than electrons has a net positive charge. An atom with more electrons than protons has a net negative charge. Most electrical phenomena are caused by atoms losing or gaining electrons.

MATERIALS

plastic comb, paper, wool and other types of cloth, dry leaves, "squiggles," table tennis balls, balloons, string, paper cups, paper clips, metal foil, scissors, tape, 15 cm (6 in.) square synthetic throw rug, key, pencil sharpener shavings

**Exceptional Student
IEP Chapter Goal**

At the end of this chapter, the student will describe two types of electricity and two types of circuits.

ELECTRICITY

8-1.
Static Electricity

164

This looks like a shocking experience! Actually, this person is very safe. If you comb your hair on a dry day, you may hear crackling sounds. Some strands of hair may stand up. Perhaps you've seen plastic sandwich wrap almost magically pulled to your hand. Each experience has the same cause—electricity.

BASIC TEACHING PLAN
MOTIVATION

If you are beginning this section on a clear day, you may wish to begin by demonstrating the buildup and release of static charge. You will need a small throw rug or runner made of synthetic material, such as nylon, and a key. Holding the key in your outstretched hand, briskly rub both feet back and forth across the rug. Then hold the key near a metal doorknob. The students will be able to hear the sound of the spark moving from the key to the doorknob. Have volunteers create sparks in this same way.

The machine shown in the photo is a Van de Graaff generator. A belt carries charges from a DC generator to the hollow metal sphere. Charges are then transferred to anything touching the sphere.

When you finish this section, you should be able to:

☐ **A.** Describe what negatively and positively charged objects are.

☐ **B.** Describe what happens when charged objects are brought near one another.

☐ **C.** Give examples of *static electricity*.

1   When an object moves, energy is present. Energy is needed for hair to stand on end. A form of energy that can produce such movement is **electricity** (ih-lek-**tris**-ih-tee). *Electricity* can cause objects to move because it produces a **force**. A *force* is a push or a pull. Electricity causes a force that pushes the strands of hair apart.

These forces were observed many years ago. About 600 B.C., a Greek named Thales was looking at amber. Amber is a yellow material sometimes used in jewelry. When Thales rubbed amber with fur, some strange things happened. The amber pulled bits of feather and straw near it. Thales could not see how this happened.

Now we know more about matter than people did many years ago. Thales did not know what happened in the amber and the fur because they were changed by particles of matter smaller than the eye can see.

All matter, such as amber, fur, paper, and feathers, contains tiny electrical particles. These particles are called **charges** (**char**-jez). There are two types of *charges:* positive and negative. We can pull or rub negative charges off one object and place them on another. When an object gains or loses negative charges, the object is said to be electrically charged.

Rub a plastic comb with wool. Negative charges rub off the wool onto the comb. The comb is now negative. Then place the comb near a piece of paper. The negative charges in the paper move to the side of the paper away from the comb. This causes the side of the paper closest to the comb to become positive. The positive side of the paper is attracted to the negative comb.

Electricity: A form of 2 energy.

Force: A push or a pull.

Charge: The electrical property of matter.

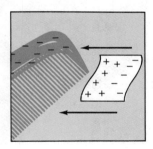

165

EXTENSIONS

Enrichment
Science Skills — Predicting

Some students can predict what will happen when a charged object is brought near a thin stream of running water. Then they can check their predictions by doing the following:

A. Obtain a plastic comb and a piece of wool cloth.

B. Rub the comb back and forth with the wool cloth.

C. Hold the comb about 2.5 cm (about 1 in.) from a very thin stream of water running out of a faucet.

1. What happened to the water? (It moved or bent toward the comb.)
2. Why do you think this happened? (The charged comb attracted the water.)
3. How did this compare with your prediction? (Answers will vary.)

DEVELOPMENT

1   **Teaching Tips** — One of the first things that should be discussed as students begin this unit is electrical safety. Your local power company may have safety booklets that you could give to your students. All the activities they will be doing in this unit are done with very low-powered dry cell batteries. Tell students that they should never try any of the activities with a more powerful electrical source, such as an outlet from a circuit in their school or home. Accidents that occur when people accidently touch electricity from powerful sources, such as household current, can be fatal. Since water conducts electricity, never touch anything electrical when hands or feet are wet. Never touch electrical fuses or circuit breakers that are part of building circuits. Stay away from telephone poles or other devices that are marked "High Voltage." Never stand under or near a tree during a thunder and lightning storm, since lightning frequently strikes trees.

2   **Skill Development** — Students should list and define new *vocabulary* words in their notebooks.

EXTENSIONS

Reinforcement
Science Skills — Comparing and Contrasting

Students can compare the amount of static electricity that can be built up in the hair and clothing of different people. They could contrast oily with dry hair, conditioned with non-conditioned hair, and straight with curly hair. This activity works best when the air is dry rather than humid. They can measure the amount of static electricity in their hair by measuring how much and how long their hair is attracted to their combs. Have the students comb through their hair several times. Have them compare the static electricity that can be built up in different materials, e.g., cotton, wool, and synthetic fibers. Ask students to find out whether or not using a fabric softener reduces static electricity in materials. All different types of fabric should be rubbed with the same cloth to produce static. The amount of time small pieces of paper are attracted to the fabric is a measure of the static buildup. The number of small pieces of paper attracted is another measure.

The students can make charts of their findings.

Activity

You may wish to demonstrate how like charges repel and opposite charges attract one another. You will need 2 balloons on strings and a piece of wool cloth. Rub both balloons with the wool. They will repel one another. Then rub one of the balloons with your hands. It will then attract the other balloon.

Exceptional Student
Learning Disabled

To reinforce this concept, have the student demonstrate the activity described on this page.

An object has the same number of positive and negative charges. The object may lose negative charges. It is left with a greater number of positive charges. The object is now positively charged. An object may gain negative charges. That object is said to be negatively charged.

3 Look at the photograph below on the left. The boy is holding two balloons. Both balloons have been given a negative charge. When two negatively charged objects are brought close to each other, what happens? They **repel** (rih-**pel**), or move away from, each other. The same **4** thing happens when two positively charged objects are brought close together. The balloons move away from each other. The same or like charges repel each other.

Look at the photograph on the right. One balloon has been given a positive charge. The other has a negative **5** charge. What happens when two objects with opposite charges are brought close together? The balloons move toward each other. They move this way because unlike charges attract each other.

When an object gains or loses negative charges, electricity is produced. It is called **static electricity**. Objects with *static electricity* may attract or repel each other.

Repel: To move away from.

Static electricity: A type of electricity produced when objects gain or lose negative charges.

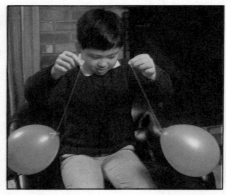

166

---

3 **Teaching Tips** — Demonstrate how a neutral object becomes charged. Draw a picture of an object such as a comb that has 10 positive (+) charges and 10 negative (MI) charges. Draw a piece of wool with 8 + and 8 MI charges. Both objects are neutral. When the wool is rubbed on the comb, 3 MI charges move from the wool to the comb. This gives the comb 13 MI charges and leaves the wool with 5 MI charges. The comb is now charged negatively (13 MI minus 10 + = 3 MI). The wool is charged positively (8 + minus 5 MI = 3 +). Draw a piece of neutral paper near the comb. Since opposite charges attract and particles of the same charge repel, the electrons in the paper will travel to the far side of the paper, and the paper will then be attracted to the comb. You may wish to cut circles out of paper to represent electrons. Draw a MI charge on each circle to indicate an electron. Put tape on the back of each circle so that you can stick them to the picture of the comb or cloth.

4 **Skill Development** — Students will understand the *cause and effect* relationship that explains static electricity.

5 **Text Question** — What happens when two objects with opposite charges are brought close together? *They attract each other*.

ACTIVITY

Producing a static electricity charge

A. Obtain these materials: plastic comb, paper, wood shavings from a pencil sharpener, piece of wool cloth 15 cm square.

B. Tear the paper into tiny pieces.

C. Rub the comb back and forth quickly with the wool.

D. Hold the comb about 2 cm above the pieces of paper.
1. What happened to the paper?

E. Repeat C and D above, but this time bring the comb near the pile of wood shavings.
2. What did you observe?
3. When you rubbed the comb with the wool cloth, which object received the extra negative charges?
4. When you brought the comb near the paper or the wood shavings, what happened to some of the negative charges that were part of the paper?
5. Explain why the objects were attracted to the comb.

They may also attract objects that do not have any static electricity.

Turn back to the photograph on page 164. The young woman received a static electricity charge from a machine. The machine was part of a science museum display. Negative charges spread out over her body. Each strand of her hair received a negative charge. What effect did those charged strands have on each other?

167

ACTIVITY

Skill Development — *Observing, Finding Cause and Effect*

Teaching Tips — For best results, this activity should be done on a cool, dry day. To expand this activity, provide the students with a variety of fabrics to rub the comb with. You could also provide other small light objects, such as bits of dried leaves, white plastic "squiggles" that are sometimes used as packing material, and a table tennis ball. Have the students pick up these objects with the charged comb.

Answers to Questions — 1. The paper got picked up.　2. The pencil shavings were attracted.　3. The comb received the extra negative charges.　4. Some of the charges moved to the side of the paper pieces away from the comb.　5. The comb had extra negative charges. When we brought it near the paper and pencil shavings, some of the negative charges that were part of the paper pieces moved away from the comb. This left one end positive. The pieces were attracted to the comb because their positive ends were pulled by the extra negative charges on the comb.

EXTENSIONS

Enrichment
Activity

The effect of static electricity may be observed using an electroscope. The students can build their own electroscope using a regular-sized paper cup, a small paper clip, metal foil, scissors, and tape.

To assemble an electroscope have the students:

A. Cut a window 2 x 3 cm in the side of the paper cup.

B. Bend the paper clip into an L shape. The bottom of the L should be 2.5 cm (about 1 in.) long. Push the top of the L through the bottom of the cup so that it sticks up 1 cm (about 1/2 in.) and secure it with tape.

C. Cut a 38 mm (1 1/2 in.) x 6.3 mm (1/4 in.) strip of metal foil and fold it over the bottom of the paper clip so that the ends hang freely together.

D. Touch the top of the paper clip with a charged object such as a comb. The foil ends will become charged and repel each other.

E. Bring other charged objects near the top of the paper clip but do not touch it. Objects with the same charge as the first object will cause the foil ends to move farther apart. Differently charged objects will cause the ends to move closer together.

F. The students should be able to find the cause and effect relationships between the charge of the object and the movement of the foil ends.

Enrichment
Research

Some of your more advanced students may wish to do research to find out more about the atomic nature of matter. Here are a few questions that you may wish to use to direct them in their research:

1. What is an atom?
2. What is a molecule?
3. What is a nucleus?
4. What are the parts of a nucleus?
5. How large is an atom?
6. How large is a nucleus?
7. How large is an electron?

Electron: The smallest negative charge.

6 Think of paper moving onto a charged comb. Negative charges are moving from place to place. These negative charges are called **electrons** (ih-**lek**-trahnz). *Electrons* are tiny. To us, they are invisible. When you produce static electricity, you are really moving electrons from place to place. Rubbing certain objects across others can cause electrons to move from one object to another. When you walk across a rug, you may rub electrons from the rug onto your shoes. Then, when you touch a metal object such as a doorknob, what happens? You may see a spark or feel a mild shock. The electrons travel from your feet through your body. The electrons then travel from your fingers to the doorknob, which causes a spark.

Clouds can sometimes build up huge numbers of extra electrons. When this happens a giant spark jumps from cloud to cloud, or from a cloud to the ground. We call such a giant spark lightning. Lightning is made of billions of electrons moving from place to place.

Section Review

Main Ideas: All matter contains negative and positive charges. Like charges repel, and unlike charges attract. Negative charges can move from object to object, causing static electricity.

Questions: Answer in complete sentences.

1. When is an object said to be electrically charged?
2. How does a negatively charged object differ from a positively charged object?
3. Give an example of how you could take negative charges from one object and place them on another.
4. What happens when a negatively charged object is brought close to a positively charged object? What happens when two negatively charged objects are brought together?
5. How is lightning an example of static electricity?

168

---

6 **Teaching Tips** — You may wish to enrich this portion of the section with a brief description of the atomic nature of matter. Background material is available in any encyclopedia under the section "Atom." You only need to discuss the protons, electrons, and neutrons, the locations of protons and neutrons in the nucleus (except for hydrogen, which does not have any neutrons), and the presence of orbiting electrons.

SECTION REVIEW

Answers to Questions
1. When it gains or loses negative charges
2. More negative charges
3. Negative charges can be rubbed or pulled off an object.
4. **a.** They will attract each other. **b.** They will repel each other.
5. Clouds build up huge numbers of electrons causing a giant spark to jump to other clouds or the ground.

Have you ever been at home when the electricity went off? Suddenly the lights go out. Heaters and fans stop. Everything gets very quiet. Can you think of other things that stop when the electricity stops? When you finish this section, you should be able to:

☐ **A.** Describe the path that electricity takes when it is used.

☐ **B.** Compare materials that allow electricity to move through them easily with those that do not.

Static electricity is produced by rubbing certain objects across others. It can also cause sparks, or charges that move through the air. Even though it is interesting, static electricity is hard to put to use. The **appliances** you see in the photograph use a form of electricity that is different from static electricity. *Appliances* such as those in your home use electricity that moves through wires.

In 1729, an English scientist, Stephen Gray, discovered that metal objects could carry electricity from one place to another. Gray was able to get short "bursts" of electricity to move through metal wires. In 1800 an Italian scientist named Alessandro Volta, shown at right, invented a new device. It let electricity move through wires for a longer time. The modern form of Volta's device is called a dry cell, or battery.

Electrical appliance: A device that uses electricity.

169

SECTION BACKGROUND

Static electricity is the result of the placement of a charge on an object. Electrons can be forced to move through materials. This movement through a material is known as current electricity. The force used to move electrons through materials is known as voltage. Voltage is also a measure of the amount of energy possessed by the electrons that are being pushed through a material. When electrons flow through a conductor, an electric current is produced. An ampere is a measurement of the amount of electrons that flow past a given point in a given interval of time. All materials resist the flow of electrons. Good conductors, such as metals, provide little resistance. Poor conductors provide high resistance. The unit that is used to measure resistance is the ohm. A closed path through which electrons can flow is called a circuit. A circuit consists of a source that provides the force to move electrons, a conductor, a switch to open and close the circuit, and an electrical device that converts electrical energy to another form of energy.

MATERIALS

aluminum foil, door key, plastic button, dry cell (1.5-volt), flashlight bulb with socket, paper, pencil, 2 pieces of wire 30 cm (12 in.), rubber band, screwdriver

BASIC TEACHING PLAN

MOTIVATION

You may wish to use the questions in the opening paragraph of this section to stimulate a discussion on how we depend on a steady supply of electricity in our daily lives. Most of your students have had the experience of being in a building when the electrical power was cut off.

DEVELOPMENT

1 **Skill Development** — The content in this section will give you an opportunity to *compare and contrast* static electricity and current electricity. Be sure the students understand that it is current electricity that is most useful to us.

EXTENSIONS

Enrichment
Research — Library

Lightning is a dramatic example of electricity. Students might wish to do some research to find out more about it. The answers to these questions can be used as a basis for reports by the students.

1. Is lightning caused by static or current electricity?
2. What are the various types of lightning?
3. Why is lightning usually accompanied by a rainstorm?
4. What are lightning rods, and why are they used?
5. Why is lightning accompanied by thunder?
6. What is produced first — lightning or thunder? Explain.

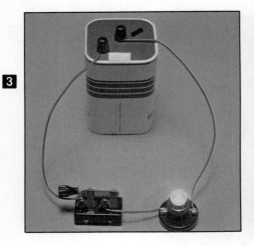 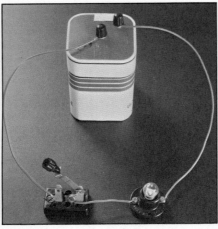

Current electricity: The flow of negative charges, or electrons.

Circuit: The path through which current electricity flows.

Since Volta's time, other scientists have found ways of moving charges through wires for even longer periods of time. When electric charges move through wire, **current electricity** is produced. *Current electricity* is the flow of negative charges, or electrons. The electrons flow in a path called a **circuit** (ser-kut).

Look at the picture above on the left. It shows a *circuit*. There are four parts to this circuit. There is a source of electric charges (dry cell), a path through which the charges flow (wires), a switch, and a user of the electricity (light bulb). In a circuit, the current flows from the source through the wires, switch, to the user of the electricity, and then it returns to the source.

When all the parts of the circuit are connected so that the current can flow, the circuit is said to be closed. When any part of the circuit is not connected, the current cannot flow. The circuit is said to be open. The switch in a circuit is often used to open or close the circuit. The circuit is open when the switch is up. When do you think the circuit is closed? Look at the picture on the right. Is it open or closed?

170

2 **Text Questions** — When do you think the circuit is closed? *When the switch is down.* Is it open or closed? *Open.*

3 **Teaching Tips** — Have some of your students assemble the circuit as shown in the photographs on this page. Have them prepare labels for each part of the complete circuit. Display the labeled circuit for the entire class to look at.

Exceptional Student
Visually Impaired

Bring in a battery, wires, a light bulb, and a switch. Without closing the circuit, allow the student to feel the path the current will follow when the circuit is closed. Point out the function of each component of the circuit.

ACTIVITY

Testing conductors and insulators

A. Obtain these materials: aluminum foil, door key, plastic button, dry cell (1.5-volt), light bulb with socket, paper, pencil, 2 pieces of wire 30 cm long, rubber band, nickel, screwdriver.

B. Make a chart like the one shown.

Item Tested	Conductor	Insulator
aluminum foil		
door key		
paper		
nickel		
rubber band		
plastic button		

1. Look at the items on the chart. Predict which ones will be insulators and which ones will be conductors. Record your predictions.

C. Connect the wire, light bulb, and dry cell as shown in the picture.

D. Hold the uncovered end of each wire to the aluminum foil.

2. What happened to the light bulb?

E. On your chart, check whether the aluminum foil is a conductor or an insulator.

F. Repeat steps D and E for each item on your chart.

3. Which items were conductors?

4. Which items were insulators?

5. Write a conclusion for this activity that compares your results with your predictions.

171

EXTENSIONS

Enrichment
Activity

Have interested students prepare sets of materials that will be needed for circuit construction in this and the following sections. They can prepare and organize the material so that each student or group of students will have a complete set.

A. Show the students how to strip insulation from the ends of standard bell wire. The wire and inexpensive wire strippers are available in hardware stores. Have the students prepare 4 or 5 lengths per set.

B. If you do not have access to small sockets, have the students construct the sockets as shown below. Prepare 3 sockets per set.

C. Each circuit set should also have three flashlight type bulbs and a fresh dry cell.

ACTIVITY

Skill Development — *Predicting, Concluding*

Teaching Tips — The light bulbs and sockets for this activity are 1.5 volt flashlight bulbs and appropriate sockets. If you have difficulty obtaining the sockets, the students can make simple sockets with a cork stopper and 3 small nails. The drawing shows how the socket is constructed and how the lightbulb and wires are attached. The wire needed for this activity is insulated copper wire and can be purchased in rolls and cut to the specified size. After cutting the wire, strip about 2.5 cm (1 in.) of insulation from the ends of each wire before distributing to each group. Graphite is the only nonmetal that will conduct electricity. Have students sharpen a pencil at both ends and test the pencil.

Answers to Questions — 1. Students should predict that metals are conductors and that nonmetals are not. 2. The light bulb went on. 3. Conductors: foil, key, nickel, graphite in the pencil. 4. Insulators: paper, rubber band, button. 5. Metals are conductors; nonmetals are not.

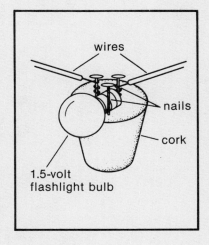

EXTENSIONS

Application
Research

Some students can visit a local hardware or electrical supply store to find out about the variety of wires sold for use in homes and factories. The students should find out which types of wires are better conductors than others and why wires are covered with insulators. Perhaps the store owner would be willing to explain this information to the students and donate samples of wires that students could bring back to show their classmates.

Conductors: Materials that allow current to flow through them easily.

Insulators: Materials that do not allow current to flow through them.

4 Some materials allow current to flow through them easily. These materials are called **conductors** (kun-**duk**-terz). Materials that allow little or no current to flow through them are called **insulators** (in-suh-lay-terz).

When people make circuits, they use *conductors* where they want electrons to move freely. Where they don't want electricity to move, they use *insulators*. The handle of a switch is made of an insulator. Can you think of a reason why?

Some materials allow very few electrons to move through them. Examples are paper, wood, rubber, and glass. They are good insulators. Can you find the insulators in the photograph? Other materials have some electrons that can be moved easily. Examples are copper, aluminum, silver, and gold. They are all metals. They are very good conductors. Copper wire is often used to wire buildings because it costs less than other metals.

Section Review

Main Ideas: Current electricity that flows through a closed circuit provides us with useful electricity. Conductors, such as metals, allow current to flow through them easily. Insulators do not.

Questions: Answer in complete sentences.

1. How is current electricity different from static electricity?
2. What is a circuit?
3. List the four parts of a circuit.
4. Compare an insulator with a conductor.
5. Identify the insulators and conductors below.
   a. rubber-soled shoes
   b. copper wire
   c. gold chain
   d. plastic switch handle

172

4 Skill Development — After the students read the top paragraph, have them go back to the photographs of the circuit to *classify* the parts of the circuit that are conductors or insulators, e.g., base of the socket and switch handle are insulators; wire is a conductor.

SECTION REVIEW

Main Ideas — Review this section with the students by asking them to make a list of all the illustrations in this section and to write one sentence for each illustration that tells what its main idea is.

Answers to Questions
1. Current electricity moves through wires. Static electricity jumps from object to object.
2. A path through which electrons flow
3. A source of electric charges (dry cells), a path through which charges flow (wires), a user of the electricity (light bulb), a switch
4. A conductor allows current to flow through it easily.
5. Insulators — a, d; conductors — b, c

One Kind of Circuit

Ed can't get the bulbs to light. He thought that perhaps he hadn't connected the battery. He checked the battery. That wasn't the problem. What do you think might be causing his problem? When you finish this section, you should be able to:

☐ **A.** Describe a type of circuit in which there is only one path for charges to flow through.
☐ **B.** Make a circuit diagram and label its four parts.
☐ **C.** Identify and describe the jobs of two parts of a dry cell.

The bulbs are part of a circuit. They are the users of the electric current. The bulbs are connected one after another. The type of circuit in which the parts are connected one after another is called a **series circuit**. In a *series circuit* there is only one path through which the charges can flow. The charges flow from the source, through the wire and each bulb, and back to the source. If the circuit has a switch, the current flows through the switch, too.

If one bulb is loose or broken, the electricity does not flow. All the lights will go out. This happened to Ed's circuit. One loose bulb had broken the circuit because the bulbs were connected in a series circuit.

Series circuit: A circuit with only one path through which charges can flow.

173

SECTION BACKGROUND

Devices that use the electrical energy in a circuit are called resistances, since they resist the flow of current through the circuit. Light bulbs, heating units, bells, and buzzers are all examples of resistances.

In a series circuit, a source of electrical energy is connected to two or more resistances, so that there is only one path through which the current can flow. An open circuit is one in which there is a break in the circuit, so that the flow of current is stopped.

The energy in a series circuit is shared by all the resistances. Adding resistances, such as extra bulbs, will dim the brightness of all the bulbs in the circuit, since the total amount of energy flowing through remains unchanged.

MATERIALS

series circuit: dry cell battery (1.5 volts), 2 miniature light bulbs in sockets, screwdriver, switch, 4 pieces of wire 30 cm (12 in.) long.

BASIC TEACHING PLAN

MOTIVATION

If you have sufficient materials available, you may wish to construct a series circuit with a number of bulbs and sockets in it. This circuit can be used to demonstrate how unscrewing one bulb will stop the flow of current. Christmas tree lights wired in a series circuit can also be used to demonstrate this.

Enrichment
Research

Batteries come in a wide variety of shapes, sizes, and materials. Students could do research to learn about the different kinds of batteries and when and why they are used. They could create charts to demonstrate their findings, comparing the various uses of batteries and how they are used.

Science Skills — Comparing and Contrasting

Have the students find advertisements in magazines about dry cells sold for transistor radios, flashlights, or calculators. Many dry cells are advertised as heavy duty or long lasting. The students can compare the prices of heavy duty dry cells and claims made about their longevity to determine if they are a better value.

1

2 Look at the pictures above. Both show a series circuit. How are the circuits different from each other? The amount of current flowing through both circuits is the same. When more bulbs are added to a series circuit, the light from each bulb is dimmer, because the users of the current must share the available current.

Scientists often make drawings or diagrams of a circuit. They use symbols to show the parts of the circuit. These symbols are shown on the chart in the margin. Scientists draw circuit diagrams in a boxlike shape.

4 The diagram below shows a series circuit. How many light bulbs are in the circuit? Is the switch open or closed? Can you point to the dry cell and wires?

3

circuit part	symbol
dry cell	||
lightbulb	⌇
open switch	⌇
closed switch	—
wire	∼

174

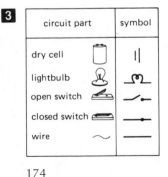 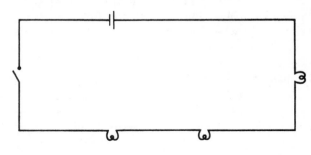

DEVELOPMENT

1 **Skill Development** — Be sure that the students take the time to *compare* and *contrast* the photographs. They should note that both circuits are complete and that the circuit with more bulbs has much dimmer lights.

2 **Text Question** — How are the circuits different from each other? *The circuit on the left has two bright light bulbs and the circuit on the right has four dim light bulbs.*

3 **Skill Development** — The short text paragraph and accompanying diagram and chart provide a good opportunity for students to practice *interpreting illustrations.*

4 **Text Questions** — How many light bulbs are in the circuit? *Three.* Is the switch open or closed? *Open.*

The source of the current shown in this section was a dry cell. Dry cells also provide current for radios and flashlights. Chemical reactions take place in dry cells. The reactions cause electrons to flow. Dry cells push these electrons through circuits. The parts of the dry cell that connect to circuit wires are called **terminals**. In a dry cell, electrons move to one *terminal*. The terminal they

Terminals: Parts of a dry cell to which wires are connected.

ACTIVITY

Exploring a series circuit

A. Obtain these materials: 1.5-volt dry cell, 2 light bulbs in sockets, screwdriver, switch, 4 pieces of wire 30 cm long.

B. Connect a series circuit as shown.
   1. Predict what will happen when you close the switch. Record your prediction.

C. Close the switch and then open it.
   2. Write down what you observed.

D. Unscrew 1 light bulb.
   3. Predict what will occur when you close the switch. Record your predictions.

E. Close and open the switch.
   4. Write down your observations.
   5. Draw and label a circuit diagram for this circuit.
   6. Write a summary for this experiment that compares your predictions with your results.

175

EXTENSION

Enrichment
Activity

Purchase or ask store owners to donate to the class a selection of regular heavy duty dry cells of the same voltage. The students can do an experiment to compare the prices and longevity of the dry cells.

A. Construct test circuits out of unused flashlight bulbs, appropriate sockets and wire. Unused bulbs must be used so that you are actually testing dry-cell power and not the longevity of the bulbs. Have the students connect each dry cell to a test circuit to find out how long each dry cell lasts.

B. The students can illustrate their results on graphs and compare the price with the longevity of each dry cell.

ACTIVITY

Skill Development — *Predicting, Observing*

Teaching Tips — Be sure that the students do not keep the circuit closed for too long, so that dry cells will not be used up.

Answers to Questions — 1. The light bulbs will all light.   2. The light bulbs lit.   3. No light bulbs will light.   4. No bulbs went on.   5. Circuit diagram showing 2 bulbs in sockets, switch, dry cell, wires.   6. If one light bulb is not in its socket, the others go out. Any break in the circuit prevents the flow of electricity.

Exceptional Student
Visually Impaired
Assign the visually impaired student to a partner for this activity.

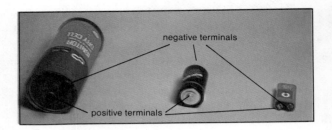
negative terminals

positive terminals

EXTENSIONS

Reinforcement
Activity

Some students can make posters for classroom display. The following topics can be illustrated and used as poster titles:
1. Conductors and Insulators
2. Parts of a Circuit
3. A Series Circuit
4. Electrical Symbols
5. Electrical Diagrams

The students should be guided to make their posters informative, colorful, and well organized.

Negative terminal: Part of the dry cell that has extra electrons.

Positive terminal: Part of the dry cell that has a shortage of electrons.

move to has extra electrons. It is called the **negative terminal**. The other terminal has a shortage of electrons. It is called the **positive terminal**. Electrons are pushed through the circuit by the *negative terminal*. They return to the dry cell at the *positive terminal*. The picture above

5 shows the terminals of three types of dry cells.

Section Review

Main Ideas: In a series circuit, there is only one path through which the charges can flow. Charges always flow from the negative terminal of a dry cell to the positive terminal. Circuit diagrams show the source of electricity and the parts through which the electricity flows.

Questions: Answer in complete sentences.

1. In what type of circuit is there only one path through which the charges can flow?
2. In the circuit described in question 1, what happens to all the light bulbs in the circuit if one light bulb goes off?
3. Draw a diagram of a series circuit that has one dry cell, 4 light bulbs, and a closed switch.
4. What happens at the negative terminal of a dry cell?
5. What happens at the positive terminal of a dry cell?
6. Describe the direction of electron flow between the terminals of a dry cell.

176

5 Teaching Tips — Provide students with dry cells of various shapes and sizes. Have them locate the positive and negative terminals. They will have to carefully inspect the covering labels on the dry cells to determine which terminal is positive and which is negative.

SECTION REVIEW

Main Ideas — Have various groups of students go to the chalkboard to develop a chart that shows the main ideas of this section.

Answers to Questions
1. Series
2. All the light bulbs go off.
3. Diagram is similar to the one in the section but has four light bulbs and a closed switch.
4. Charges leave the negative terminal and enter the circuit.
5. Charges enter the positive terminal.
6. Charges flow from the negative terminal through the circuit and reenter the battery at the positive terminal.

1 Becky is having a problem with her lamp. One of the bulbs isn't lit. Do you think the light bulbs in Becky's lamp are connected in a series circuit? When you finish this section, you should be able to:

☐ **A.** Make a labeled diagram that shows a circuit that has more than one path for current.
☐ **B.** Compare two types of circuits.
☐ **C.** Describe two safety devices used in circuits.

Becky's lamp is not wired with a series circuit. If it were, all the light bulbs would be unlit. In a series circuit, the current can't pass through a burned-out bulb to reach the others. The light bulbs in Becky's lamp are connected in a **parallel circuit**. In a *parallel circuit*, there is more than one path for the current to take.

In a parallel circuit, each light bulb is on its own path. If one light bulb is turned off or burns out, the others stay lit. The current flowing through each light bulb is separate from the current flowing through the others. In this circuit, the brightness of one bulb is not changed if other bulbs are added to or taken away from the circuit.

2 Look at the circuit diagram of a parallel circuit. Is the switch open or closed in this circuit? How many paths can the charges flow through? If one bulb burns out, what happens to the others?

In the diagram, the switch is closed. Electrons can move through the circuit. There are three paths for charges to flow through. If one bulb burns out, it will not change the current flowing through the other two.

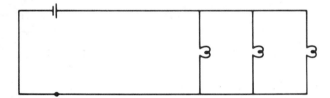

8-4.

Another Kind of Circuit

Parallel circuit: A circuit with more than one path through which charges can flow.

177

SECTION BACKGROUND

Circuits can be designed so that there is more than one conducting path for current. Resistances for such circuits are placed on separate paths, each independent of the other paths. Circuits of this type are known as parallel circuits. The advantage of parallel circuits over series circuits is that the failure of a resistance to conduct current will not affect the operation of the other resistances. If we increase the number of paths through which current can flow, the current will be increased. If there are too many paths for current to flow, there may be such an increase in current that the conductors heat up and melt. Overheating poses a fire hazard, since surrounding materials could ignite. Various safety devices can be used to protect circuits from overheating. Fuses and circuit breakers are designed to create open circuits when the level of current gets too high.

MATERIALS

dry cell battery (1.5 volts), 3 light bulbs in sockets, 7 pieces of wire 30 cm (12 in.) in length, screwdriver, switch

BASIC TEACHING PLAN

MOTIVATION

After students read the motivation, ask: Are the electric circuits in buildings series circuits? Some students will realize that series circuits would not make sense, since just one burned-out bulb would stop the current. Bring in Christmas lights that are wired in a series circuit and Christmas lights that are wired in a parallel circuit. Plug them both in and then unscrew one bulb from each circuit. Ask the students why all the lights went out in one circuit and not in the other.

DEVELOPMENT

1 **Teaching Tips** — Before students read this page, ask if they can think of a way that light bulbs could be placed in a circuit so that the loss of one bulb would not affect the others.

2 **Text Questions** — Is the switch open or closed in this circuit? *Closed.* How many paths can the charges flow through? *Three.* If one bulb burns out, what happens to the others? *They will not be affected.*

EXTENSIONS

Reinforcement
Activity

Using the blackline master from the interunit material, have the students draw diagrams of the following circuits:

1. A series circuit with 1 dry cell, 2 light bulbs, and an open switch
2. A parallel circuit with 2 dry cells, 3 light bulbs and a closed switch.
3. A series circuit with 2 dry cells, 4 light bulbs, and a closed switch
4. A parallel circuit with 1 dry cell, 2 light bulbs, and an open switch.

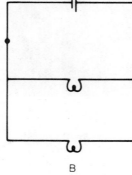

A

B

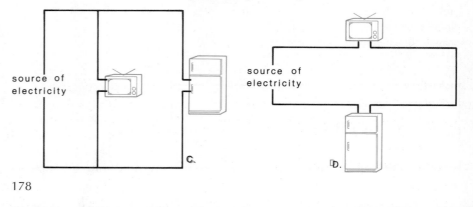

source of electricity

C.

source of electricity

D.

178

You should now be ready to compare a parallel circuit with a series circuit. Look at the two circuit diagrams in the margin.

Which of these circuits has one path for electrons? Which has two paths? Which circuit is a series circuit? Which is a parallel circuit? What would happen if one of the bulbs in circuit A burned out? What would happen if one of the bulbs in circuit B burned out?

In the diagram, circuit A is a series circuit. It has just one path for electrons. If one bulb burned out, the other bulb would also go out. Circuit B is a parallel circuit. Some charges go through one path, and some go through the other path. If one bulb burns out, the other will not be affected.

The lights and appliances in your home or school are wired in parallel circuits. When you shut off one appliance or light, the other appliances stay on. Think of the problems you might have if your home were wired with a series circuit. If just one small lamp burned out, no current would flow. All the appliances would then stop working.

Look at the two diagrams below. Which diagram is most like the circuit that your home uses? If you think that it is C, you are right. In C, if the TV is shut off, the refrigerator stays on. In D, if the TV is shut off, the refrigerator stops working.

3 **Skill Development** — The students will be *comparing* and *contrasting* the diagrams of the series and parallel circuits.

4 **Text Questions** — Which of these circuits has one path for electrons? *A.* Which has two paths? *B.* Which is a parallel circuit? *B.* Which circuit is a series circuit? *A.* What would happen if one of the bulbs in circuit **A** burned out? *The other would go out.* What would happen if one of the bulbs in circuit **B** burned out? *The other would stay on.* Which diagram is most like the circuit your home or school uses? *C.*

Exceptional Student
Learning Disabled

Have the student illustrate a series circuit and a parallel circuit to reinforce this concept.

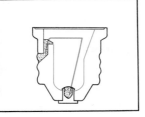

Have you ever noticed that the electrical wires in appliances sometimes get warm to the touch? All wires heat up a bit when current moves through them. Too much current passing through a wire can cause a big safety problem. Fires can start. The circuits in your home and school may have a safety device called a **fuse**. A *fuse* helps to keep wires from getting too hot. It contains a short length of wire that melts if too much current is passing through the circuit. When the special wire in the fuse melts, the circuit is no longer complete. The current stops flowing.

What if fuses were not used in circuits? The wires might get so hot that they would set fire to the ceiling, floors, or walls that they passed through. The picture above shows a fuse. The diagram shows how it looks inside. Find the wire that melts if the circuit has too much current.

Some appliances have their own fuses. If too much current is passing through the appliance, the fuse burns out. For example, a stereo might have a fuse.

In some circuits a different safety device is used to keep wires from getting too hot. This device is called a **circuit breaker**. The photograph shows the *circuit breakers* used in one home. A circuit breaker is a switch that opens the circuit if too much current is flowing.

What if a circuit breaker opens and stops the current? Someone has to find the part of the circuit that is causing the problem. After the problem is solved, the circuit breaker is closed. The current flows again.

Fuse: A safety device for circuits with a piece of wire that melts to break the circuit.

Circuit breaker: A safety device for circuits that opens a switch to break a circuit.

179

---

5   Teaching Tips — Before students read this page, ask them why it is unsafe to simply replace a burned-out fuse or to reset a circuit breaker when the electricity goes off. *Such a procedure would not solve the real problem. The burning out of a fuse or the switching off of a circuit breaker is a symptom of overheating or of some other problem in a circuit.*

EXTENSIONS

Application
Activity

Have the school maintenance person, school district electrician, or custodian take a small group of students to see the fuse box or circuit-breaker box that functions as a safety device in your school. Without touching anything the students should determine if the school power system uses fuses or circuit breakers.

They could also find out from the field trip leader whether particular fuses or circuit breakers exist for specific areas of the school. They could also ask whether particular fuses or circuit breakers produce open circuits more frequently than others, e.g., the ones that are in the circuits that provide power for kitchen equipment.

Exceptional Student
Visually Impaired

Bring in a fuse and allow the student to feel what it is. Discuss its function.

Learning Disabled

Ask the custodian to show the student the fuse box or circuit breaker that controls the school's electricity. Discuss its function.

EXTENSIONS

Enrichment

Activity

After the students have completed the activity, they can further explore circuits by making compound circuits containing both a series and a parallel circuit. In addition to the material obtained for the activity, they will need another switch. Have the students follow these directions:

A. Using the circuit from the activity, connect the new switch between the first and second light bulb.

B. With the original switch closed, predict what will happen when you close and open the new switch. Record this prediction.

C. Close and open the switch and write down your observations.

D. Write a conclusion that compares your predictions with your results.

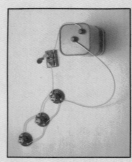

Exploring a parallel circuit

A. Obtain these materials: 1.5-volt dry cell, 3 light bulbs in sockets, 7 pieces of wire 30 cm long, screwdriver, switch.

B. Connect a parallel circuit as shown at the left.

  1. Make a diagram of the circuit. Label it.

  2. Predict what will happen when you close and open the switch. Record your predictions.

C. Close and open the switch.

  3. Write down your observations.

D. Unscrew one of the light bulbs.

  4. Predict what will happen when you close and open the switch.

E. Close and open the switch.

  5. Write a paragraph comparing your predictions with the results.

All of the circuits pictured in this chapter have shown wires connecting the source of electricity to the user. Can you imagine making a circuit without wires? How could the current travel from the source of electricity to the user?

Imagine you had some paint that contained metal. You could paint lines on a board. You could connect a battery and a bulb to the painted lines. They could carry the current. The metal in the paint would act like a conductor. This is how some kinds of circuits are made. They are stamped or printed on a board. These kinds of circuits are known as *printed circuits*. The photograph shows a printed circuit. Circuits can be printed on very tiny boards. This allows many circuits to take up a very small space. This is helpful in building machines such as computers. The printed circuits can provide many paths through which current can flow.

180

ACTIVITY

Skill Development — *Predicting*

Answers to Questions — 1. Labeled circuit diagram that includes the dry cell, 3 light bulbs, wire, and switch. **2.** All the bulbs will light. **3.** All the bulbs went on. **4.** All the bulbs will light except for the one that is not screwed in. **5.** In this activity we predicted that the bulbs would remain on if we unscrewed one bulb. The other bulbs stayed on, since there was more than one path for the current.

Section Review

Main Ideas: In a parallel circuit, there is more than one path through which current can flow. Electrical circuits sometimes contain safety devices, such as fuses or circuit breakers, to keep wires from getting too hot.

Questions: Answer in complete sentences.

1. In what type of circuit is there more than one path through which the charges can flow?
2. Compare a parallel circuit with a series circuit.
3. Why are the circuits in buildings usually parallel circuits?
4. Describe two safety devices that are sometimes used as parts of circuits. Explain how each works.
5. What is a printed circuit?

People in Science

Charles Proteus Steinmetz
(1865-1923)

Charles Steinmetz was a genius in mathematics, chemistry, and, most of all, electricity. He was born and educated in Germany. He became famous after coming to the United States in 1889.

Steinmetz was born with severe physical problems, including a deformed spine, which kept him from growing very tall. He had great difficulty walking. Steinmetz proved himself to be a true scientific thinker. One invention made it possible for people who lived far from a power plant to receive electrical power. Because of his ability, the company that Steinmetz worked for gave him all the equipment and money he wanted to do his research. Although he was so advanced in his thinking, he found time to promote the rights of all people. He also believed in good education.

181

EXTENSIONS

Enrichment
Research — Library

Have interested students do research to find out the meaning of words used in modern electronics. Some students could try to acquire some electronic devices to put on display for the rest of the class, for example:

1. Transistors (very small devices that can control the flow of current, which are commonly used in radios and televisions)
2. Semiconductors (materials used in the construction of transistors and circuits built on chips, which consist of the crystals of the elements germanium, silicon, or selenium to which impurities are added)
3. Integrated circuit (extremely small device made of chips of silicon crystals that takes the place of many circuits, and which is used in computers, calculators, and digital watches)

SECTION REVIEW

Answers to Questions
1. Parallel
2. A parallel circuit has more than one path for charges. A series circuit has only one path for charges.
3. If one appliance in a circuit burns out or is shut off, the others still receive a current.
4. The fuse and the circuit breaker are two safety devices that are used in building circuits. If too much current flows through them, they will make an open circuit. In the fuse, a piece of wire melts and opens the circuit. In the circuit breaker, too much current opens a switch.
5. A circuit printed onto a board

SUGGESTED WORKSHEET MASTERS
pp. T-161l,m

EXTENSIONS

Enrichment
Science Skills — Building Science Vocabulary

Interested students can find the definitions of the following terms:
1. Conductance (the ability of a material to conduct electrical current)
2. Resistance (the ability of a material to resist the flow of electric current)
3. Ampere (the standard unit for measuring electric current)
4. Voltage (a measure of the energy available to move a certain amount of electrical current through a circuit)
5. Ohm's law (describes the relationship between current, voltage, and resistance — the electrical current in a circuit is directly proportional to the voltage and inversely proportional to the resistance)

Science Words
What word best fits each of the following definitions?

1. A type of electricity produced when objects gain or lose negative charges.
2. The path through which negative charges flow.
3. The smallest negative charge.
4. A circuit with only one path for electrons.
5. Part of a dry cell that has a shortage of electrons.

What word best fits each of the blanks?

6. The _____ are the parts of a dry cell to which wires are connected.
7. A _____ _____ has more than one path for charges.
8. _____ and _____ _____ are safety devices for circuits.
9. _____ are materials that allow current to flow through them easily.
10. _____ are materials that do not allow current to flow through them.

Questions: Answer in complete sentences.

1. What are the four parts of a complete circuit? Draw a labeled diagram of a series circuit.
2. Why are parallel, and not series, circuits used in buildings?
3. How could you pick up papers with a plastic comb?
4. What is the difference between static and current electricity?
5. Explain how a fuse works.
6. A student doing an experiment brings a positively charged and a negatively charged balloon near each other. What will happen? What would happen if the student brought two negatively charged balloons near each other?
7. Name terminals of a dry cell.

182

CHAPTER REVIEW
Science Words
1. static electricity, 2. circuit, 3. electron, 4. series, 5. positive terminal, 6. terminals, 7. parallel circuit, 8. fuse, circuit breaker, 9. conductors, 10. insulators

Answers to Questions
1. Source of charges, path for charges, user of electricity, switch
2. If a series circuit were used, all the lights would go out and appliances would stop if one circuit burned out.
3. Rub the comb with wool or through hair to give it a charge.
4. Static electricity is the gain or loss of negative charges by an object. Current electricity is the flow of negative charges.
5. If too much current flows through a circuit, the thin wire in the fuse melts. This causes an open circuit.
6. They would attract each other. They would repel each other.
7. Positive and negative

SUGGESTED WORKSHEET MASTER
p. T–161n

SUGGESTED TEST MASTERS
pp. T–161d,e,f

CHAPTER 9

MAGNETISM

Kim is studying a stone that makes strange things happen. Paper clips, nails, and pins seem to be pulled toward the stone. The stone is called a *lodestone*. The lodestone behaves very much like something that you have probably seen before. What does it remind you of?

9-1.
Magnets

183

CHAPTER OBJECTIVES

1. Describe the properties of a magnet and locate the magnetic lines of force when like and unlike poles are brought near one another.
2. Explain how current electricity can be used to make an electromagnet.
3. Describe three ways in which the strength of an electromagnet can be increased.
4. Explain how magnetism is used to produce electricity.
5. Describe the four parts of an electric generator and explain the function of each.

SECTION BACKGROUND

Magnets are objects that attract iron, nickel, and cobalt. They are strongest at their ends, or poles. When the unlike poles of two magnets are brought near each other, they will attract; their like poles will repel.

The space around a magnet is the magnetic field. If iron filings are sprinkled around a magnet, they form a pattern of lines called lines of force. The lines of force are closest together near the poles of a magnet where the magnetic force is strongest.

The earth is a magnet, with north and south poles. A compass is a magnet that can move freely. The south pole of the compass points north and the north pole of the compass points south.

MATERIALS

lodestone, bar magnet, iron filings, string, globe, cardboard, button thread, plastic sheet 15 cm (6 in.) square

Exceptional Student
IEP Chapter Goal

At the end of this chapter, the student will state how electricity can make an electromagnet and how a magnet can be used to make electricity.

BASIC TEACHING PLAN

MOTIVATION

Borrow a piece of lodestone from a secondary school earth science teacher or from a museum of natural history. If you are able to get a sample, display it on your desk with some other rocks and minerals. Have students work out a procedure for finding out which sample is lodestone.

Lodestone means "leading stone," which indicates why the stone was used in early compasses.

Text Questions — What does it remind you of? *A magnet.*

EXTENSIONS

Enrichment
Research

Some students can do research to find out about lodestone and magnetite. Lodestone is a natural magnet found in the ground. Lodestone contains an iron ore called magnetite that has magnetic properties.

The students may be able to obtain a sample of each from a local mineral shop or museum. If a sample is obtained, dip the lodestone, or magnetite, into a pile of iron filings. The iron filings will be attracted in bunches at various places on the rock where the poles of the magnetite exist.

Magnets: Objects that pick up, or attract, iron, nickel, or cobalt.

Poles: The ends of a magnet.

When you finish this section, you should be able to:

☐ **A.** Identify and describe an object that attracts iron, nickel, or cobalt.

☐ **B.** Describe the space around an object that attracts iron, nickel, or cobalt.

☐ **C.** Compare the results of bringing like and unlike ends of magnets near each other.

The lodestone that Kim is looking at is an example of a **magnet**. *Magnets* are objects that pick up, or attract, iron, nickel, or cobalt. Objects that contain iron, nickel, or cobalt are metal. A magnet will not pick up or attract all objects. It won't attract paper, wood, plastic, tin, or rubber. Some magnets, such as lodestone, are found in nature. Others, like those shown below, are made out of steel and other metals.

The ends of a magnet are called the **poles**. Magnets are strongest at their *poles*. Magnets have two poles: a north pole and a south pole. The letters S and N show which is the north or south pole.

184

DEVELOPMENT

1 **Teaching Tips** — Have students test different objects to see whether or not they are attracted to a magnet. They could make a chart of items, predictions (as to whether or not the item will be attracted), and observations (magnetic or not).

2 **Skill Development** — Students will *classify* objects as either magnetic or nonmagnetic.

ACTIVITY

What is in the space around a magnet?

A. Obtain these materials: bar magnet, iron filings, plastic sheet 15 cm square.
   1. Predict what would happen if you sprinkled the iron filings onto the sheet covering the magnet.
B. Cover the bar magnet with the plastic sheet. Sprinkle the iron filings onto the plastic sheet, as shown.
C. Gently tap the edge of the plastic sheet.
   2. Write down what you observe. Draw a sketch of what you see.
   3. Write a summary for this activity that compares your prediction with your results.

If you sprinkle iron filings onto a sheet that covers a magnet, you will see patterns of lines like those in the pictures on page 186. These lines are called **lines of force**. *Lines of force* show that the space around a magnet has a magnetic force. The space around a magnet in which there is a magnetic force is called a **magnetic field**. **3** The lines of force show where the *magnetic field* is located. Where are the lines of force closest together?

Lines of force: Lines around a magnet that show where the magnetic force is found.

Magnetic field: The space around a magnet in which there is a magnetic force.

185

Reinforcement
Activity

Show the students a paper cup at the bottom of which is a paper clip. Then pose the following problem to the students: How can you remove the paper clip from the cup without touching the clip, turning the cup over, or placing anything into the cup?

The students should be able to conclude that a magnet can be used. The magnet will attract the clip from the outer side of the cup through the paper. The clip can be moved upward along the inner side of the cup by the magnet on the outer side. This activity shows that a magnetic attraction is not affected by nonmagnetic materials.

ACTIVITY

Skill Development — *Predicting, Observing*

Teaching Tips — The iron filings can be purchased in a hardware store. If you cannot obtain the iron filings, cut pads of steel wool into very tiny pieces and use them instead. Also, a thin piece of cardboard can be substituted for the plastic sheet. Try to avoid getting the filings on the magnet itself, because they are difficult to remove. If you don't have bar magnets, you can use horseshoe magnets, although their lines of force are not as clearly defined.

Answers to Questions — **1.** The predictions will vary. **2.** The iron filings formed a pattern of lines around the magnet. Most of the filings were lined up at the poles of the magnet. **3.** Summary should compare prediction with the result. The filings formed a pattern of lines. Most of them were pulled near the poles.

3 **Text Questions** — At what part of the magnet are the lines of force closer together? *At the poles.*

Exceptional Student
Visually Impaired

Let the visually impaired student feel the arrangement of iron filings before and after this experiment.

EXTENSIONS

Reinforcement
Science Skills — Finding Cause and Effect Relationships

Magnetic materials, such as steel paper clips, can be made into temporary magnets. These can then be used to make a compass.

A. Obtain a strong permanent magnet, a paper clip or a pin, and a short piece of string.

B. Rub the clip (pin) with one pole of the magnet, about 30 times, in one direction only.

C. Tie the string to the clip (pin).

D. Suspend the clip (pin), so that it may turn freely.

E. Have the students determine that the clip (pin) is pointing north.

1. How has the clip become magnetized? (Rubbing a magnetic material with the pole of a magnet gives it a temporary magnetic field.)
2. Why does the magnetized clip (pin) point north and south? (The poles of the magnetized clip [pin] are attracted to the magnetic poles of the earth.)

4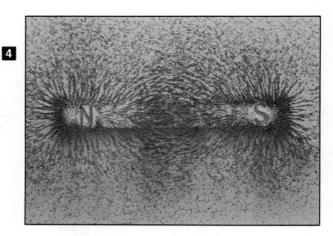

Look at the two pictures below. The picture on the left shows the lines of force around two magnets. The N pole of one magnet and the S pole of the other magnet have been brought close to each other. In the picture on the right, the N poles of both magnets have been brought **5** close to each other. How are the lines of force shown in **6** both pictures different from each other?

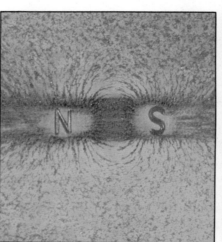
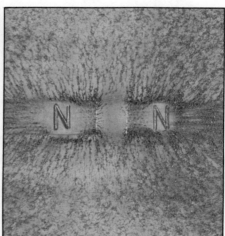

186

---

4 **Skill Development** — The text and photographs on this page will give students an excellent opportunity to *compare* and *contrast* the various patterns of iron filings.

5 **Text Questions** — How are the lines of force shown in both pictures different from each other? *In the picture on the left, there are lines of force extending from the north pole of one magnet to the south pole of the other. In the picture on the right, there are no lines of force between the north poles.*

6 **Teaching Tips** — Ask: Why do you think this is so? *Opposite poles attract, and like poles do not. Therefore, the lines of force show where there is or isn't a magnetic force.*

In the bottom left picture on page 186, the lines of force show a magnetic force from the N pole of one magnet to the S pole of the other magnet. This means that these poles of the magnets are attracting each other. N and S poles are opposite poles. Opposite magnetic poles attract each other.

In the bottom right picture, the lines of force do not show an attracting magnetic force between the two poles. The lines of force show that the magnetic force goes away from the poles. This means that the poles of the magnets are repelling each other. Two N poles are the same, or like, poles. Like magnetic poles repel each other. Do you think two S poles will attract or repel each other? If you think they will repel, you are right!

Section Review

Main Ideas: Magnets attract iron, nickel, or cobalt. Their magnetic forces are strongest at their poles. Opposite magnetic poles attract each other. Like poles repel each other.

Questions: Answer in complete sentences.

1. What is a magnet?
2. What parts of a magnet have the strongest magnetic forces?
3. How are the poles of a magnet named?
4. Compare what you observe in the lower left picture on page 186 with what is shown in the lower right picture.
5. Explain what would happen in each of the following:
   a. Bringing two north magnetic poles near each other.
   b. Bringing two south magnetic poles near each other. **c.** Bringing a north magnetic pole near a south magnetic pole.
6. What kinds of objects are attracted to magnets? What kinds are not?

187

EXTENSIONS

Reinforcement
Research — Library

Have a group of students locate the geographic north and south poles of the earth on a world globe. Then have them do library research to find out the locations of the earth's north and south magnetic poles. The students can then find the magnetic pole locations on the world globe.

7 **Teaching Tips** — If you have two bar magnets, suspend one at its center by tying a strong thread (button thread works well) around its center and attaching the free end to a horizontal support such as the top of a doorframe. Have the students predict what will happen if you bring either end of another magnet near the north and south poles of the suspended magnet. Then test the students' predictions.

SECTION REVIEW
Answers to Questions
1. Magnets are objects that pick up or attract iron, nickel, or cobalt.
2. The poles
3. North and south
4. The picture on the left shows the magnetic field where poles attract. The right-hand picture shows repulsion.
5. a. They will repel. b. They will repel. c. They will attract.
6. Magnets attract iron, nickel, or cobalt objects. They will not attract objects made of paper, wood, plastic, tin, or rubber.

SECTION BACKGROUND

Electricity and magnetism are related. Hans Christian Oersted, a Danish scientist, found that the direction of a compass needle was changed when placed near a current-carrying wire. The French scientist André Ampere later elaborated on this discovery by running a current through a coiled wire, which increased the wire's magnetic effects. The magnetic effects of a current-carrying wire can be increased by either increasing the number of coils of wire made from a conductor or by increasing the current that flows through the coil.

Another way to increase the magnetic effects of a current-carrying coil is to insert a length of soft iron inside the coil. When the current is turned on, the soft iron becomes magnetized. When it is shut off, the iron loses its magnetic properties. A magnet composed of wire coiled around a length of iron is called an electromagnet. Electromagnets are used in a wide variety of devices.

Telephones, home appliances, and specialized construction equipment for lifting and moving objects are a few examples.

MATERIALS

dry cell (1.5 volts), iron nails, paper clips, screwdriver, switch, 1 piece of wire 30 cm (12 in.) long, 1 piece of wire 60 cm (24 in.) long, magnets, compass, pieces of iron or steel, magnetic material, non-magnetic material, paper, pencil

9-2.
A Special Kind of Magnet

It is the 1780's. A young boy is carrying an armload of empty pill bottles across the room. He walks toward his father, a druggist. The boy drops a few on the floor. His father gives him a stern warning: "You'll never grow up and amount to anything if you remain so clumsy!" Little did the father realize that young Hans Christian Oersted was to become a very important scientist.

This young Danish boy soon studied at the University of Copenhagen in Denmark. He then became a famous scientist, known throughout Europe. Oersted was the first person to prove that electricity and magnetism had something to do with each other. When you finish this section, you should be able to:

☐ **A.** Explain how current electricity can be used to make a kind of magnet.
☐ **B.** Describe three ways in which the strength of this kind of magnet can be increased.

For hundreds of years before Oersted's discovery, scientists suspected that electricity and magnetism had something in common. No one was able to prove it. But Hans Christian Oersted performed an experiment that showed that magnetism could be produced by electricity. Oersted made his discovery by accident.

One day, Oersted left a compass needle near a wire through which current was flowing. A compass needle is a small magnet. The needle usually points in a north–south direction. It helps people find their direction.

188

BASIC TEACHING PLAN
MOTIVATION

You can do a demonstration of the phenomenon that Oersted observed. All you will need is a coil of bell wire (simply wrap 10 to 15 turns around a pencil and remove the pencil), a dry cell, and a compass. Place the compass at one end of the coil. Before you touch the ends of the wire to the dry cell have some students come forward to observe the compass needle. Connect the dry cell to the coil for an instant. Now connect the wire ends to opposite terminals of the dry cell. Students will see the compass needle move when electricity is flowing through the coil. The poles of the electromagnet are reversed when the terminal wire connections on the dry cell are reversed.

Whenever Oersted brought the compass needle near the wire, the needle moved in the opposite direction. This surprised Oersted, but he realized he had made an important discovery.

Oersted believed that there must be a magnetic force around a wire through which current flows. Look at the picture below. A card was placed near the wire in the circuit shown. Iron filings were sprinkled on the card. The iron filings formed lines of force around the wire. The lines of force formed a pattern of circles.

The lines of force show that there is a magnetic force in the space around the flowing current. Therefore, current electricity is surrounded by a magnetic field. How can we put this discovery to use?

189

Reinforcement
Science Skills — Observing

Since a compass contains a magnet it can also be used to find magnetic material and other magnets.

A. Obtain a compass, some magnets, pieces of iron or steel, and some magnetic materials.

B. Arrange the materials on top of a desk and slowly pass the compass around each object. Note the effect each has on the direction in which the compass is pointing.

1. What effect did the non-magnetic material have on the compass? (None)
2. What effect did the pieces of iron or steel have? (Either one or the other pole was attracted to them.)
3. What effect did the magnets have? (The poles of the compass were attracted to the opposite poles of the magnets.)

DEVELOPMENT

1 **Skill Development** — Have the students *observe* the photograph carefully. They should notice that the filings form a pattern of lines due to the magnetic field caused by the current.

2 **Teaching Tips** — Ask: What is flowing through the wire? *Electric current.* How do you know? *The wire is connected to a dry cell and the wire provides a path for charges to flow.*

You can set up the demonstration shown in the photo. You will need a dry cell, iron filings, wire, and a piece of paper.

Electromagnets are used in a wide variety of devices. Have the students research a particular device, such as a telephone, and report their findings. The following questions should be answered for each device:

1. What is the purpose of this device?
2. How are electromagnets used in this device?
3. Could permanent magnets be used in this device in place of electromagnets?
4. Are electromagnets absolutely necessary for this device to work?

Electromagnet: A magnet made with current electricity.

3 Scientists used Oersted's discovery to make magnets that could be turned on and off. They wrapped wire around a piece of steel and connected it to a source of current. That made a magnet. When they stopped the current, the magnet stopped working. A magnet that is made with current electricity is called an **electromagnet** (ih-lek-troh-**mag**-net). *Electromagnets* are found inside many devices. Tape recorders and large computers have them.

The picture below shows a large electromagnet. It is made of a huge piece of iron. It becomes an electromagnet when the person using it connects the circuit. This electromagnet is very strong. It can pick up heavy objects, such as scraps of metal.

190

3 **Teaching Tips** — Ask the students why the word *electromagnet* is appropriate for this type of magnet. *It is appropriate because it is a magnet produced by electricity.*

There are three ways to increase the strength of an electromagnet. Look at the pictures above. The picture at the upper left shows a simple electromagnet. It has one dry cell and one iron nail with wire wrapped around it 15 times. How many paper clips does the electromagnet attract? Look at the next three pictures. How does each picture show how the electromagnet has been changed?

An electromagnet can be made stronger by adding more current to the circuit. How is this done in the circuit shown in the picture at the upper right? Look at the picture at the lower left. Adding another iron nail increases the strength of the electromagnet. Look at the last picture. Wrapping the wire around the iron nail many more times also makes an electromagnet stronger.

191

EXTENSIONS

Reinforcement
Science Skills — Observing

An electromagnet has a north and a south pole. The students can conduct the following experiment to observe that the poles of an electromagnet can be reversed when the terminal wire connections on the dry cell are reversed.

A. Set up an electromagnet circuit.

B. Using a labeled magnet, determine which pole of the electromagnet is north and which is south. (Hint: The attraction or repelling of the labeled bar magnet poles will help in your determination.)

C. Reverse the wire connections at the dry cell terminals.

D. Repeat step B.

You may wish to ask the following questions:

1. How has the location of the poles changed? (The poles have reversed.)
2. How can you change the electromagnet's poles again? (By reversing the terminal connections again)

4 Text Questions — How many paper clips does the electromagnet attract? *Four.* How does each picture show how the electromagnet has been changed? *More dry cells, more wraps of wire, and another iron nail were added. The electromagnet picked up more paper clips.*

5 Text Questions — How is this done in the circuit shown in the picture at the upper right? *By adding another dry cell, which increased the amount of current.*

6 Teaching Tips — If you have dry cells, wire, and iron nails available, have some students try this demonstration. It is a variation of the activity on page 192.

7 Skill Development — Students should *compare* the strengths of electromagnets.

EXTENSIONS

Enrichment
Activity

Students can do further experiments with electromagnets. In addition to the materials used in the activity, they will need a pencil. Ask them to do the following:

A. Wrap the wire around the nail 30 times, rather than 20 times. Predict what will happen when the switch is closed and the nail is moved near the paper clips.

B. Remove the nail from the wire coil and repeat step A.

C. Place a pencil in the coil and repeat step A.

D. Write a summary that compares your predictions with your results.

Research — Library

Some students may be interested in doing additional research on one of the first practical applications of the electromagnet — the invention of the telegraph. Here are some guide questions you may wish to ask to focus their work:
1. When and where did Samuel Morse live?
2. What is the Morse code?
3. How does the telegraph operate using electromagnets?

Exceptional Student
Learning Disabled

To help the learning disabled student grasp the concept discussed on page 190, demonstrate the activity described on this page.

ACTIVITY

Experimenting with an electromagnet

A. Obtain these materials: dry cell (1.5 volt), iron nail, paper clips, screwdriver, switch, 1 piece of wire 30 cm long, 1 piece of wire 60 cm long.

B. Attach the short wire from the dry cell to one side of the switch. Make sure the switch is open. Attach the long wire to the other side of the switch.

C. Wrap the long wire around the iron nail at least 20 times. Attach the end of the long wire to the dry cell.

D. Close the switch. Move the nail near the clips.
  1. Write down the results you observed.
  2. What will happen when you open the switch?

E. Open the switch.
  3. Write down the results you observed.
  4. Write a summary for this activity.

Section Review

Main Ideas: Current electricity can be used to make an electromagnet. The strength of an electromagnet can be increased by adding more current, more turns of wire, or more nails at the center of the electromagnet.

Questions: Answer in complete sentences.

1. What important relationship did Oersted discover?
2. Look at the photograph of the electromagnet on page 190. Why couldn't a very strong bar magnet or horseshoe magnet be used for this kind of job?
3. Why do iron filings form lines of force around a wire that is carrying current?
4. How would the strength of an electromagnet containing 20 turns of wire compare with the same kind of electromagnet with 10 turns of wire?

192

ACTIVITY

Skill Development — *Predicting, Observing*

Teaching Tips — The iron nail should be at least 10 cm long. Keep switch open when not in use. If paper clips stick to the nail even after the current is shut off, it is because the nail became a weak magnet.

Answers to Questions — 1. The electromagnet picked up the clips. 2. 3. The clips fall off the magnet when the circuit is opened. 4. An electromagnet is produced when current flows through a coil.

SECTION REVIEW

Answers to Questions
1. He discovered that magnetism could be produced by electricity.
2. There would be no efficient way to release the iron objects after they were picked up.
3. Because the electric current creates a magnetic field
4. It would be twice as strong.

You have learned that electricity produces magnetism. Do you think the opposite is also true? Can magnetism be used to produce electricity? This question was on the mind of a 14-year-old boy who lived in London in 1805. His name was Michael Faraday. When you finish this section, you should be able to:

☐ **A.** Explain how magnetism can be used to produce electricity.
☐ **B.** Identify the parts of a modern machine that can be used to produce electricity from magnetism.

As a teenager, Michael Faraday had a job in a bookstore. In his spare time, he read all the science books on the shelves. As he read, he became more and more curious about electricity. Sometimes the books didn't have answers to the questions that came to his active mind. One day, he heard that a well-known scientist, Sir Humphry Davy, was going to give a speech nearby. Young Faraday went to hear the speech. He took notes on what Davy said. To show off a bit he sent Davy a copy of his notes. He hoped that the famous scientist would give him a job. Davy was very impressed with Faraday's notes. He told Faraday he could work as a helper.

Years later, Michael Faraday became more famous than Sir Humphry Davy. As a matter of fact, some scientists think that Davy's greatest discovery was Michael Faraday. In 1831, Faraday discovered that there was a way to produce electricity from magnetism.

In his experiment, Faraday used a coil of wire to make a **galvanometer** (gal-vuh-**nahm**-uh-ter). A *galvanometer* is an instrument that measures weak electric current. If current is present, the needle on the galvanometer moves. Faraday moved a magnet back and forth inside the coil of wire. When he did this, the needle on the galvanometer moved. That showed that current was present in the wire.

Galvanometer: An instrument that can measure a weak electric current.

SECTION BACKGROUND

A generator is a device that is able to convert magnetism to electricity. Michael Faraday is credited with making this discovery when he found that electricity was produced when a magnet was moved back and forth inside a coil of wire. When he connected the coil of wire to a galvanometer, a weak electric current was detected. This eventually led to the invention of the generator. Modern generators produce electricity by either moving a coil of wire through a magnetic field or moving a magnetic field so that lines of magnetic force are cut by the coil.

All generators require some form of energy to produce either the movement of the coil of wire or the magnet.

MATERIALS

bar magnets, compass, voltmeter, cardboard roll, 2 pieces of wire 90 cm (36 in.) long

BASIC TEACHING PLAN
MOTIVATION

A galvanometer is essentially a compass (a free-floating magnet) and an electric coil. If electricity is sent through the electric coil in a galvanometer, then the magnet moves. (This is the same principle that the students learned in the last section.) If you have access to a voltmeter or a galvanometer (ask a high school science teacher or your school electrician to lend you one), demonstrate how it works. Measure the voltage across the terminals of a flashlight dry cell. The galvanometer had to be invented before magnetically generated electricity could be discovered. Faraday could not have performed his experiment without a galvanometer to measure the effects.

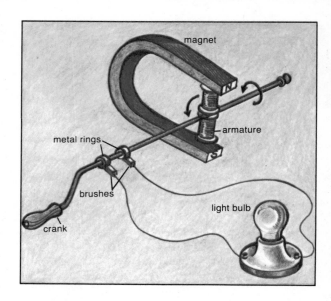

EXTENSIONS

Enrichment
Research — Library

Ask the students to find out about the lives and accomplishments of Michael Faraday and Hans Christian Oersted. The following questions may be used to direct their work:

1. When and where did each inventor live?
2. What formal education did each have?
3. When did each one become interested in science?
4. What important discovery did each one make?
5. Why are their discoveries important to us?

Generator: A machine in which current electricity is produced with magnetism.

Armature: The coil of wire in a generator.

194

How is Faraday's discovery useful to us? Look at the **1** drawing above. The drawing shows a **generator** (**jen**-uh-ray-ter). In a *generator*, current is produced with magnetism. A generator has four different parts. The first part is a coil of wire called an **armature** (**ahr**-muh-cher). It also has one or more horseshoe magnets, two metal rings, and metal brushes. The *armature* is found **2** between the poles of the magnets. Find the crank in the drawing above. When the crank is turned, the armature moves between the poles of the magnet. In large generators, the magnet moves in and out of the armature. The metal rings are connected to the end of the coil. They collect the current produced in the armature. The brushes lead the current out of the generator. The generator shown in the drawing is a small one. It is cranked by hand. It produces enough current to light one bulb.

The large generators in power plants produce the current needed to light the thousands of lights that brighten

DEVELOPMENT

1 **Teaching Tips** — An electric generator is essentially a wire coil which is turned into a magnetic field to produce electricity. This is the reverse of the process that occurs in an electric motor. In an electric motor, electricity is sent through the wire coil, which causes it to turn into a magnetic field.

2 **Skill Development** — Have the students follow the *sequence* of events in a generator that leads to the production of electricity.

3 **Teaching Tips** — It makes no difference whether the magnet moves or the wire coil moves. As long as one moves relative to the other, electricity will be produced.

ACTIVITY

Making a galvanometer

A. Obtain these materials: bar magnet, compass, cardboard roll, 2 pieces of wire 90 cm long.

B. Wrap 1 piece of wire around the cardboard roll, as shown in picture 1. Wrap the other piece of wire around the compass, as shown in picture 2. Make sure you can still see the compass needle. Leave about 30 cm of wire at each end.

1

C. Attach the ends of the wires, as shown in picture 3. Then slide the cardboard roll out of the wrapped wire.

D. Move the bar magnet back and forth inside the coil of wire. As you move the magnet, look at the compass needle.
   1. What did you observe?
   2. What caused the effect you observed?

2

E. Hold the magnet still inside the coil of wire. Look at the compass needle.
   3. What did you observe?
   4. What explanation can you give for your observation?
   5. Write a summary of the results of this activity.

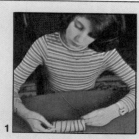
3

3 cities like the one shown in the photograph. In these large generators, current is produced by huge magnets that whirl through thick coils of copper wire. In some generators the magnets stay still. The coils of wire are the moving parts.

Not all generators produce electricity for buildings. Some cars have their own generators. Some bicycles have a generator to turn on the headlight.

195

Application
Activity

Some students can locate an old automobile generator to disassemble. A local garage may have one that the owner will donate. The students should carefully take apart the generator and locate the coil of wire and the source of magnetism.

Enrichment
Activity

After completing the activity, students can continue to experiment with a galvanometer. Instruct the students to do the following:

A. Hold the bar magnet steady and move the coil of wire back and forth around the magnet, rather than moving the magnet through the coil. (Electricity is produced both ways.)

B. With the bar magnet in the same position, reverse the coil of wire. Again move the bar magnet back and forth inside the wire. (The direction that the compass needle moves will be reversed.)

C. Use two or more magnets rather than one inside the coil. Try adding additional coils of wire. (This will produce a more sensitive galvanometer.)

D. Write a summary of what was observed and explain what happened.

ACTIVITY

Skill Development — *Observing, Cause and Effect*

Teaching Tips — After the students have completed the basic steps in this activity, encourage them to experiment with additional coils of wire and clusters of bar magnets to see if they can produce a more sensitive galvanometer (see Extension on this page). Make sure the students understand that the compass needle is making an indirect measurement of the flow of current. The compass needle is actually measuring the magnetic field produced by the current.

Answers to Questions — 1. The compass needle moved.   2. The current moving through the wire causes a magnetic field.   3. The compass needle did not move.   4. In order to produce current, the magnetic field must move across the wires in the coil.   5. Moving a magnet through a coil of wire produces a current in the wire. In this activity, we used a magnet to measure the magnetism produced by the current. Whenever we moved the magnet through the coil, we produced current.

Exceptional Student
Visually Impaired
Learning Disabled

Assign the students to partners for this activity. Before conducting this activity, make sure the learning disabled student understands why a compass points north.

Application
Research

Have interested students find out about careers in electronics technology. If possible have the students interview electronics technicians, such as television and radio technicians. The following questions may be used to direct their research:

1. What does an electronics technician do?
2. What kind of training is required?
3. What kinds of instruments do electronics technicians use in their work?
4. Are there many job opportunities for people who are electronics technicians?

Enrichment
Research

Scientists are not certain about what causes the earth's magnetic fields. They believe that there are circulating electric currents in the earth's core. Thus, the earth is like a huge electromagnet. Interested students could go to the library and do research on what causes the earth's magnetic fields. Have them find out where the electric current may be flowing and how this produces a magnetic field.

4 All generators need energy to turn their moving parts. You can't get current from a generator unless you use some other form of energy to make it move. For example, **5** the generator on a bicycle gets its energy from the rider. The generator in a car gets its energy from the gasoline that powers the engine. The engine turns the moving parts of the generator.

Section Review

Main Ideas: Magnetism can produce current electricity. A generator is a device that uses magnetism to produce electricity.

Questions: Answer in complete sentences.

1. How can you produce current electricity in the wire shown in the picture at the left? How will you know if an electric current is present in the wire?
2. What are the four basic parts of a generator?
3. Describe the sequence of events that occur when a generator is producing electricity.
4. What is the source of energy for the generator that is shown on page 194?
5. What part of a generator is made of a coil of wire?

196

4 **Teaching Tips** — Generators do not "give us something for nothing." They must have an outside source of energy to produce current.

5 **Teaching Tips** — Gasoline ignites alternately in a car's pistons causing them to move up and down. The pistons turn the crankshaft, which turns the wheels. A belt around the crankshaft is also attached to the armature of the car's generator. The armature turns as the crankshaft turns, producing electricity.

SECTION REVIEW
Answers to Questions

1. Move a magnet in and out of the coil of wire. The needle on the galvanometer will move.
2. Armature, magnet, metal rings, brushes
3. The armature moves between the poles of the magnet or the magnet moves within the armature, producing current. The metal rings collect the current and brushes take it out of the generator.
4. The hand turning the crank
5. Armature

CHAPTER REVIEW

Science Words: Unscramble each of these words. Then write its definition.

1. SELOP
2. STENGAM
3. CETNAGMI LEIDF
4. MONTEERLAAGV
5. NAGMETCOTRELE

What word fits each of the blanks in the following sentences?

6. A _____ is a machine in which electricity is produced with magnetism.
7. An object that picks up or attracts iron, nickel, or cobalt is a _____.
8. A magnet has both _____ and _____ poles.
9. The _____ of _____ are lines around a magnet that show where the magnetic force is found.
10. The coil of wire in a generator is called the _____.

Questions: Answer in complete sentences.

1. Two students are experimenting with magnets. Each has a bar magnet with labeled north and south poles. They observe that there are two ways in which they can hold their magnets, so that the magnets repel. What are these ways? Explain your answer.
2. In question 1, how can you place the poles so they will attract each other? Explain your answer.
3. What is the difference between a bar magnet and an electromagnet?
4. A student wishes to build an electromagnet. What equipment will the student need?
5. Make a labeled diagram of the electromagnet that could be built with the equipment you listed in question 4. List three ways to increase the strength of the electromagnet.
6. What is a galvanometer? What is it used for?

197

EXTENSIONS

Enrichment
Science Skills —
Building Science Vocabulary

Interested students should look up the definitions of the following terms and relate them to the concepts in this chapter:
1. Direct current (an electric current that flows in only one direction, e.g., current from a battery)
2. Alternating current (an electric current that reverses directions — usually 60 times/sec)
3. Transformer (a device for changing the voltage of an alternating current)
4. Alternator (a generator that produces alternating current)

CHAPTER REVIEW

Science Words
1. Poles,   2. magnets,   3. magnetic field,   4. galvanometer,
5. electromagnet,   6. generator,   7. magnet,   8. north and south,   9. lines of force,   10. armature

Answers to Questions
1. North-north, South-south. Like poles of magnets repel.
2. North-south, South-north. Unlike poles of magnets attract.
3. With an electromagnet you can shut off the magnetism by shutting off the electric current. This allows you to drop the iron objects where you wish to.
4. Dry cell, wire, iron nail, switch
5. Labeled diagram of electromagnet that shows the coil, the dry cell, and the iron nail. The strength of the electromagnet could be increased by increasing the current (adding more dry cells), making more coils, or adding more nails to the center of the coil of wire.
6. An instrument that can detect a weak electric current

SUGGESTED WORKSHEET MASTERS
pp. T–161q,r

SUGGESTED TEST MASTERS
pp. T–161g,h

CHAPTER 10

CHAPTER OBJECTIVES

1. Explain how electricity can be converted to at least four other forms of energy.
2. Describe how water, fuels, and a nuclear reaction supply the energy needed to turn turbines.
3. Describe ways in which the production of electricity can harm the environment.
4. Explain why solar cells offer great promise as a future source of energy.
5. Describe how information is stored (input) in and released (output) from a computer and the uses for the computer in the modern world.

SECTION BACKGROUND

Electrical energy is of limited use to us unless we have ways to convert it to beneficial forms of energy. Household appliances are devices that convert electrical energy to heat, light, sound, and mechanical energy. Mechanical energy is energy that can be used to move objects. Electric motors are able to convert electrical energy to mechanical energy.

The amount of electrical energy being used in a household is measured by a device called a watt-hour meter. The unit of measure is the kilowatt-hour. A kilowatt-hour (Kwh) expresses how many 1,000 watt units of power are used in one hour.

MATERIALS

paper, pencil

Exceptional Student IEP Chapter Goal

Using crayons and paper, the student will illustrate four resources used to make electricity. The visually impaired student will state four resources used to make electricity.

USING ELECTRICITY

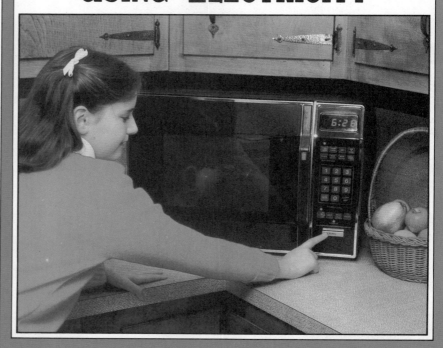

10-1.

Measuring Electricity

198

Have you boiled water lately? You know that you need plenty of heat to get the water to boil. This girl is boiling water. Do you see a flame? What kind of energy is making the water boil? When you finish this section, you should be able to:

BASIC TEACHING PLAN

MOTIVATION

Bring in a few small electrical appliances to use as a focus for a class discussion. Such things as a portable mixer, electric frying pan, or popcorn popper would be very appropriate. Ask the students to tell what function each appliance performs and what its source of energy is. Although different appliances have different functions, they all use electricity as a source of energy. Ask the students what form of energy is used in the very last step of the function of these appliances. You should emphasize that although electricity starts the appliance working, the electricity must be converted to some other form of energy before the appliance does its job.

☐ **A.** Identify four forms of energy into which electricity may be changed.

☐ **B.** Describe how the use of electricity is measured.

You have learned that electricity makes bulbs light. You have also learned that electricity can cause magnetism. The girl in the picture is using something that changes electric energy into heat energy. This oven is only one of many things that changes electricity into a **1** more useful form of energy. Can you think of other things in your home that change electricity into other forms of energy?

Televisions, electric blankets, electric guitars, and even electric corn poppers are all energy changers. Are there any electrical energy changers in your classroom? What are they?

Your classroom contains light bulbs, which change electricity into light. Some classrooms have tape recorders, which change electricity into sound.

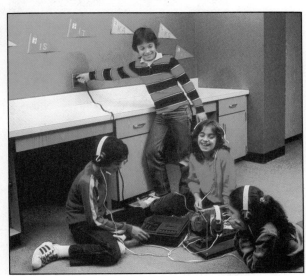

199

EXTENSIONS

Reinforcement
Research

List the following electrical devices on the chalkboard:
1. Hair dryer
2. Telephone
3. Radio
4. Electric car
5. Food blender

Tell the students to find out more about these appliances. Ask them to find out how they work and what energy conversions occur in each device.

DEVELOPMENT

1 **Teaching Tips** — Students could make a map of their classroom or kitchen at home and mark the locations of all the electrical appliances and indicate the energy conversions in each appliance.

Exceptional Student
Learning Disabled

Have the student cut out magazine pictures that illustrate electrical energy in use. The student should find at least two pictures that illustrate electrical energy being changed to:
1. Sound
2. Light
3. Heat
4. Mechanical energy

Enrichment
Activity

Your class could write to the local electric utility company to request information about where the electricity for their area is produced, what source of energy is used to produce it, how much electricity is produced, and what the peak usage time periods are. You could also request information about how the utility company copes with periods of high use. Perhaps a company representative would speak to your class.

2 The picture below on the left shows an example of electrical energy changing into heat energy. Sometimes electricity produces so much heat that light is given off, too. This happens in a toaster. Current flowing through the wires in a toaster causes the wires to get hot. The hot wires glow. This shows that electrical energy can also change into light energy.

Electricity can produce motion. The energy of motion is called **mechanical** (muh-**kan**-ih-kul) **energy.** Electrical energy is changed to *mechanical energy* by motors. For example, the motor in an electric fan causes the blades of the fan to move. The motor changes electrical energy into the mechanical energy of the moving blades.

Sometimes electrical energy can change into several forms of energy at the same time. For example, when

Mechanical energy: The energy of motion.

200

2 **Skill Development** — In examining appliances, the students will develop the skills of *classifying* forms of energy and *sequencing* them in the uses of the devices.

ACTIVITY

Measuring kilowatt-hours

A. Obtain these materials: paper, pencil.

B. On your paper draw 2 groups of 4 boxes next to one another as shown.

C. Look at the number on the electric meter in the first picture. Write the number in the first group of boxes.

D. The second picture was taken one month later. Write this number in the second group of boxes.

E. Subtract the number in the first group of boxes from the number in the second group of boxes.

   1. What is the remainder?

   2. How many kilowatt-hours were used in one month?

   3. If the cost for each kilowatt-hour is 10 cents, how much money will be owed?

your television set is on, what do you see? What do you hear? If you touch the back of the television set, what do you feel? In a television set, electrical energy changes into light, sound, and heat energy.

3 How much electricity does it take to use a toaster or run a fan? Electricity is measured in **watts**. Have you ever read the numbers on a light bulb? They tell you how many *watts* the bulb needs in order to light up. A bulb might use 100 watts. Other things in your home use much more. A larger unit is needed to measure that much electrical power. A **kilowatt** is equal to 1,000 watts. If something that uses a *kilowatt* of electricity is on for an hour, it uses a **kilowatt-hour** of electricity.

When electric current enters a building, it flows through an electric meter. The meter counts the number **4** of *kilowatt-hours* used. The meter is usually read every month to find out how much electricity was used.

Watt: A unit that measures how much electricity is needed to run an electrical appliance.

Kilowatt-hour: A unit used to measure electricity use.

201

Application
Science Skills — Measuring, Recording Data, Hypothesizing

If the electric meter for your school is in a safe and accessible location, you may wish to have some students gather daily data on the school's kilowatt-hour consumption of electricity. Such data can be recorded on a large graph that they could prepare for the classroom bulletin board. After the students have gathered and recorded the data for two or three weeks, they should start to see a regular pattern of electricity use and also be able to see days in which the amounts of electricity used change significantly. On such days, they should attempt to make a hypothesis about the causes for these variations.

ACTIVITY

Skill Development — *Measuring*

Teaching Tips — Tell the students that some electric meters have dials rather than boxes like the ones shown. In either case, they measure kilowatt-hours.

Answers to Questions — 1. 220.   2. 220 kilowatt-hours.

3. 220 x $.10 = $22.00.

3 **Text Questions** — How much electricity does it take to run a toaster or a fan? *1,000–2,000 watts*.

4 **Teaching Tips** — Ask students to find out where the electric meters in their homes or apartments are located.

Bring in copies of electric bills from your local power company. Students should note the length of time the bills cover, number of kilowatt-hours used, and whether or not there were any fuel adjustments. They could compare these bills to the one in the text. If possible, have students bring in electric bills from home and discuss why their bills differ. This activity should help the students understand the importance of energy conservation.

	For information call your representative:		Previous balance
Account number	ANNA MATTHEWS		
432127 1285 00013	at 212-473-6262	DEC 9	

Service period From To Month Day Month Day Year	Number of days	Service class	Meter readings Previous Code Present Code	Meter multiplier	Usage Kwh. or 100 Cu. ft.	Current charges
10 7 11 9 83	33	EL 1	3821 ACT 4170 ACT	1	349	55 15
10 7 11 9 83	33	GS 1	310 ACT 312 ACT	1	2	8 56

Service address	Demand in kilowatts	Sales tax included in bill
82 WASHINGTON PLAC 3B		2 45

Fuel and gas adjustments	factor	amount	Payments received through this date have been credited to your account.	
Electric	1.0790	3 77	NOV 08 1983	
Gas	1.4962	03		63 71

The picture shows a monthly bill for the use of electricity. The bill shows how many kilowatt-hours were used and the amount owed.

Section Review

Main Ideas: Electrical energy can be changed into many other forms of energy. The amount of electricity used depends on how much and how long we use it. Use of electricity is measured in kilowatt-hours.

Questions: Answer in complete sentences.

1. Electrical energy can be used to produce at least four other forms of energy. What are they?
2. Give an example of a device that will cause each energy change you listed in question 1.
3. Name three units that are used to measure how much electricity is being used. Explain what each unit measures.
4. How is the amount of electricity used by a building measured?

202

SECTION REVIEW
Answers to Questions
1. Heat, light, mechanical, sound energy. 2. Heat — electric toaster, light — light bulb, mechanical — fan, sound — doorbell. 3. The watt is the unit that measures how fast electricity is used. The kilowatt is one thousand watts. The kilowatt-hour is the amount of kilowatts used in one hour. 4. The amount of electricity used is measured by a meter that counts how many kilowatt-hours of electricity pass into the building.

The students in the photograph below are visiting an energy fair. They are learning about the many ways in which energy can be produced. Do you know where the electricity in your home comes from? When you finish this section, you should be able to:

☐ **A.** Describe the events that take place when water power is used to produce electricity.
☐ **B.** Describe the events that take place when fuel is burned to produce electricity.
☐ **C.** Explain how nuclear energy is used to produce electricity.

For thousands of years people have used falling water as a source of energy. Falling water was used to turn large water wheels. The first water wheels made were used at grain mills. Their power turned the millstones that ground the wheat into flour. Today, falling water is used to turn water wheels called **turbines** (**ter**-bynz). *Turbines* are used to turn parts of large generators in power plants.

Turbines: Wheels that are used at electrical power plants.

SECTION BACKGROUND

In order to produce electricity, the armature (coil of wire) in a generator must be moved relative to a magnetic field. To do this, a turbine is connected by a shaft to the armature. The turbine is turned by air, steam, or water pressure, which turns the armature within a magnetic field. A wide variety of energy sources are used to operate the turbines. The principal energy source is fossil fuel. The combustion of fossil fuels results in the conversion of water to steam, which in turn is used to move the turbines. In a nuclear power plant, the heat produced by nuclear reactions is used to convert water to steam.

Hydroelectric power is produced by harnessing the energy of moving water to turn the turbines. Hydroelectric power is considered a "clean" source of electrical energy since fossil fuels are not used to produce the electricity.

MATERIALS

203

BASIC TEACHING PLAN

MOTIVATION

Students should understand that electricity is something we all depend on in our daily lives. Some sources of energy are less expensive than others. Potential harm to the environment caused by different methods of generating electricity must also be considered.

Text Questions — Do you know where the electricity in your home comes from? *You may be able to acquire pamphlets that describe how your local power plant produces electrical energy. Make a rough map of your community or region on the chalkboard and ask the students to locate where they think the closest electrical power plant is.*

DEVELOPMENT

1 **Teaching Tips** — Ask the students to explain how water wheels were used to perform some other tasks. *Water wheels were also used to supply mechanical energy at sawmills, textile mills, and other early factories.*

EXTENSIONS

Enrichment
Research — Library

To generate electricity from the power of falling water, many dams have been constructed in the United States and Canada to channel river water into power plants. Students could do research on hydroelectric power as follows:

A. Use encyclopedias and the *World Almanac* to prepare a list of 20 major hydroelectric dams in North America.

B. Make a map of the United States and Canada and draw in the rivers on which these dams are located.

C. Indicate the location of each dam based on the information found.

Science Skills — Comparing and Contrasting

In this section, students learn that coal, gas, and oil are natural resources. Have a group of students develop a chart that answers the following questions about each of these resources:

1. How is it obtained from the earth?
2. Where is it commonly found?
3. How is it transported from where it is found to where it is used?
4. Which, if any, are used as fuels to produce electrical power in their community?

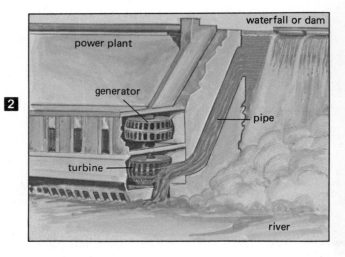

Many power plants are built near waterfalls or dams. Some of the water goes over the waterfall and down the river. Some of the water is directed into large pipes. The water moves down through the pipes to turbines in the power plant. The falling water makes the turbines spin.

204

2 **Skill Development** — The students should look at the *diagram* and note the water turning the turbine, which in turn operates the generator. They should be able to put these events in *sequence*.

3 **Teaching Tips** — You may wish to tell the students that the photograph shows the Sir Adam Beck-Niagara generating stations 1 and 2, located 12.8 km (8 mi) downstream from Niagara Falls. Tunnels containing pipes carry water from the Falls to the power station or to storage at a reservoir. The two plants produce 1,815,000 kilowatts of electricity.

A rod connected to the turbine turns. The other end of the rod connects to the magnets or coils of wire in the generator. The turning rod makes the coils or magnets turn. As a result, current electricity is produced in the generator.

A power plant that uses falling water for an energy source is called a **hydroelectric** (hy-droh-ih-**lek**-trik) plant. *Hydro* means *water*. The photograph on page 204 shows a *hydroelectric* plant at Niagara Falls, Canada.

Energy to turn turbines can also come from burning **fuel** (**fyoo**-el). *Fuel* is anything that can be burned to produce heat. Oil, gas, and coal are fuels. The heat from the burning fuel is used to change water into steam. The steam provides the energy needed to turn parts of the generator. Look at the drawing below. The water heated in the boiler changes into steam. The steam causes blades on the steam turbine to spin. The spinning blades

4

Hydroelectric plant: A power plant at which falling water is the energy source.

Fuel: Anything that can be burned to produce heat.

Enrichment
Research — Library

Have interested students find out how electricity is produced by using the energy from a controlled nuclear reaction. Focus their research with these questions:

1. What are the major parts of a nuclear plant?
2. What types of nuclear plants are being built in our state or region?
3. Where are the present nuclear plants in our state or region?
4. What do the plants use as nuclear fuel?
5. How much electricity do they produce?

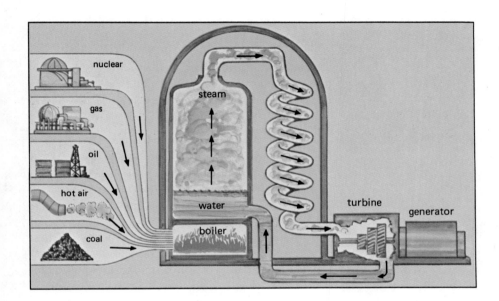

205

4   **Skill Development** — The text and illustration depict a *sequence* of *cause and effect* relationships, as follows: the combustion of a fuel or a nuclear reaction heats water and changes it to steam. The steam turns the turbine which operates the generator.

Reinforcement
Science Skills — Vocabulary

Have the students use their dictionaries to find the meaning of the prefix *hydro-* (associated with hydrogen or water), and then prepare a list of definitions for the following terms:
1. Hydroelectric
2. Hydrofoil
3. Hydrotherapy
4. Hydrosphere
5. Hydrodynamic

Ask them to add five more *hydro* words to the list and to define them.

Nuclear reaction: A reaction that occurs when tiny particles of matter are split apart.

Transmission lines: Power lines that carry electricity from its source to where it is used.

206

turn a rod that connects to the generator. As a result, current is produced.

Scientists have found that a great amount of heat is produced in a **nuclear reaction** (**nyoo**-klee-er ree-**ak**-shun). A *nuclear reaction* takes place when tiny particles of matter are split apart. The heat from the reaction can be used to change water into steam. The steam can then turn turbines to produce electricity. Only a small amount of fuel is needed to produce a lot of energy in a nuclear plant. But nuclear power has problems, as we will see in the next section.

After electricity is produced in a power plant, what happens? The electricity is sent to places where people can use it. The electricity travels through powerful **transmission lines**. Through *transmission lines*, electricity moves from its source to cities and towns. It finally reaches homes.

Section Review

Main Ideas: Turbines are used at power plants to turn parts of large electromagnets. Falling water, fuels, and a nuclear reaction can supply the energy needed to turn turbines.

Questions: Answer in complete sentences.
1. Explain the steps that take place when water power is changed into electricity. Use the diagram on page 204.
2. What are the steps that occur when a fuel is burned to produce electricity?
3. In a nuclear power plant, what provides the heat energy needed to change water into steam?
4. Is this statement true or false? Turbines push water through electric generators. Explain your answer.
5. How does electricity get to your home or school?

SECTION REVIEW
Answers to Questions
1. Falling water causes the turbine to spin, which in turn spins a rod connected to the magnets or coils of wire in a generator. The coil or magnet turns, and current electricity is produced.
2. The heat from fuels and nuclear reactions changes water into steam. The steam causes the blades of a steam turbine to spin, which causes parts of a generator to turn.
3. Heat from the nuclear reaction heats water, which produces steam that turns the turbine. The spinning turbine moves the magnets or coils of wire in the generator.
4. False. In power plants steam is used to turn the turbines. The turbines turn the parts of the generator.
5. Electricity travels through transmission lines.

Both students are mixing batter for pancakes. Compare the two methods. Which student will be finished first? Which pancakes will have a higher electricity cost? How might that electricity use be harming the environment? When you finish this section, you should be able to:

☐ **A.** Identify some of our *natural resources* and explain how they can be *conserved*.
☐ **B.** Identify some of the harmful effects that power plants have on our environment.
☐ **C.** Describe a way in which electrical energy can come directly from the sun.

The student using the electric mixer will probably be done first. That electric mixer is using electric energy that was produced at a power plant. Do power plants cause harm to the environment?

Fuels are burned for energy in many power plants. Oil, gas, and coal are often the fuels used. Oil, gas and coal are **natural resources**. A *natural resource* is something found in nature that is useful. The supplies of these natural resources are limited. We must make these supplies last. Being careful about our use of natural resources is called **conservation** (kahn-ser-**vay**-shun). A way to practice *conservation* is by using less electricity.

10-3.

Electricity and Environment

Natural resource: Something useful found in nature. **1**

Conservation: Careful use of a natural resource.

207

SECTION BACKGROUND

The depletion of nonrenewable fossil fuels has led to an interest in energy conservation and the development of alternative energy sources. Nuclear power plants can provide electrical energy at low cost. However, nuclear power plants may be hazardous to the environment and our health.

Solar energy is an alternative energy source which converts the sun's energy directly into electricity. Photovoltaic, or solar cell devices, can produce electricity from sunlight without the use of traditional fuels or nuclear energy. Whether solar cells can be developed that can provide electricity in a cost-effective manner will depend on improvements in the technology of solar cell production.

MATERIALS

poster paper, marking pens, newspaper articles

BASIC TEACHING PLAN

MOTIVATION

Display a variety of foodstuffs or manufactured articles and have the students make a list of the energy needs that were required to produce them. Students' lists might include energy to gather the raw materials needed (wood, grain, iron ore); energy needed to transport the raw materials to processing plants (trucks, trains, airplanes, ships); energy to operate the machines that produce the food products or manufacture the articles; energy used to make the wrapping materials; energy to transport them to the places they are sold; energy for the consumers to transport them; and, finally, the energy needed to cook the foods or to use the articles.

DEVELOPMENT

1 **Skill Development** — You may wish to have the students write down the new *vocabulary* terms and definitions from this section.

Application
Research

Some students can visit an electrical appliance store and talk with salespersons about recently available appliances that operate with a minimum use of electrical energy. These are the so-called energy-efficient appliances. Have them find out such things as the following:

1. What appliances are designed to be energy efficient?
2. Are they more expensive than ordinary models of the appliances?
3. How much energy do they save?
4. How do they save energy?

Pollution: The adding of harmful materials to the environment.

Sulfur oxides: Materials released when coal or oil are burned.

Do you turn off the lights when you are the last person to leave a room? Does a television remain on when no one in the house is watching? When everyone uses just a little less electricity, a great amount of energy is saved. Using less electricity conserves the supplies of natural resources.

2 People concerned with conservation are also concerned about the environment. Burning fuels to produce electricity can cause **pollution** (poh-**loo**-shun). *Pollution* is the adding of harmful materials to the environment. For example, burning coal or oil releases materials such as **sulfur oxides** (**sul**-fer **ahk**-sides) into the air. *Sulfur oxides* can cause respiratory diseases in humans.

Nuclear energy does not pollute the air with sulfur oxides and smoke. However, it can harm the environment in other ways. Nuclear reactions produce harmful wastes. These wastes are stored at power plants. Many

ACTIVITY

What are some other sources of energy?

A. Obtain these materials: poster paper, marking pens, newspaper articles.
B. Use your imagination to invent a source of energy that could power electric generators. Make sure it does not depend on burning fuel, water power, or nuclear power as an energy source. Make a labeled drawing of your invention.
  1. What is your energy source?
  2. What are its advantages? What are its disadvantages?
C. Collect local newspaper articles on the topic of energy.
  3. What energy sources are used in your area now?
  4. What energy sources might be used in the future?

208

2 Teaching Tips — Students should maintain a somewhat balanced view of the entire energy/pollution question. Be sure that the students understand that one way to limit pollution caused by energy production is for consumers to limit energy utilization.

ACTIVITY

Skill Development — *Predicting, Comparing and Contrasting*

Teaching Tips — The challenge of designing a nonfuel-powered generator may puzzle students at first. Don't be too quick to make suggestions. Instead allow them to discuss this challenge with each other. Eventually, they will suggest wind power or solar power.

Answers to Questions — 1. Wind or solar energy.   2. Advantages—Both wind and solar are pollution-free and have no fuel costs. Disadvantages—Wind doesn't blow steadily. There is no solar energy on cloudy days or at night. Both require storing electrical energy for times when no power is produced.   3. Answers will vary.   4. Energy sources would include the sun and wind.

people are concerned that these wastes could enter the air or water if something happened at the power plant. **3** Nuclear wastes can harm and even kill plants and animals. The effects of these wastes lasts for many years.

Sometimes nuclear plants pollute rivers by heating them. Such plants need a large water supply to cool off the reactors that produce the power. Cool water is removed from the river. It is pumped over the hot equipment to cool it down. The water is allowed to cool down a little. Then it is pumped back into the river.

The temperature of the river goes up. Just a small increase in the water's temperature may affect the growth of the plants and animals that live there.

Is there a way to produce electricity that does not harm the environment? There are several ways that are **4** being developed by scientists. One is to use **solar cells**. *Solar cells* produce electricity directly from sunlight. *Solar* means coming from the sun. Solar cells are made of a material called **silicon** (**sil-ih-kahn**). *Silicon* is found in many places.

Silicon is mixed with small amounts of metals. Then it is cut into thin slices. These slices are the solar cells. When sunlight hits the solar cells, electricity is produced. One solar cell, shown on the right, produces the energy needed to move a small cart. When hundreds of solar cells are hooked up together, large amounts of electricity can be made. But solar cells are more expensive than other forms of electricity.

Solar cell: A piece of silicon that can produce energy from sunlight.

Silicon: A common material found in the earth.

209

EXTENSIONS

Enrichment
Research

Frequently, there are articles and editorials in newspapers and weekly news magazines on energy production, and pollution caused by energy production. Have a group of students cut out articles on these topics and post them on a bulletin board. The articles could be classified according to their point of view — either for the production of more electricity (suggesting that the environmental risks are manageable), or against the production of more electricity (suggesting that the environmental risks are significant).

The students could also compile a list of the key arguments brought forth in the articles.

3 **Teaching Tips** — This would be an excellent opportunity to engage students in some research on the pros and cons of the nuclear power issue. Encourage them to make charts that compare the advantages and disadvantages of using nuclear power as an energy source.

4 **Teaching Tips** — Display photographs of a variety of homes that use solar energy to reduce dependence on electricity or fuels. Display the photos and have students locate where solar energy is captured.

EXTENSIONS

Enrichment
Research — Library

Solar cells can provide a non-polluting source of electrical energy. Some students could do research on the development of solar cells and their current uses. The students can then predict how solar cells may be used in the future. They could draw pictures to illustrate their predictions.

Activity

One way to reduce energy consumption is by constructing homes and office buildings that are more energy efficient. Solar energy can also be used to supply some or all of a building's energy requirements. Have a group of students begin a collection of photographs of buildings that have been designed to be energy efficient. They could mount their photographs on poster paper and write labels that explain how the buildings are energy efficient.

Each year people find ways to produce solar cells more cheaply. It may not be long before many homes and schools will have rows of solar cells on their roofs like the ones shown. Each building would produce its own electricity. Best of all, the source of the energy would be free, and it would not cause any pollution.

Section Review

Main Ideas: By limiting our use of electricity, we can conserve our natural resources. The burning of some natural resources to produce electricity can cause pollution. Nuclear energy can produce harmful wastes. Other sources of energy such as solar cells do not pollute.

Questions: Answer in complete sentences.

1. What is a natural resource? Name two.
2. How can you conserve electrical energy?
3. How does burning fuel for electricity harm the environment?
4. What is an advantage of using nuclear energy? What are two problems it causes?
5. Name something that can be used to change sunlight to electricity. What are its benefits?

210

SECTION REVIEW

Answers to Questions

1. A natural resource is something useful found in nature — coal, oil, gas.
2. Use less electricity by turning off lights and appliances that are not being used.
3. The production of electricity can result in pollution of the environment with such things as sulfur oxides.
4. Nuclear energy would allow us to conserve our natural resources of fossil fuels. The wastes from nuclear energy plants may pollute our environment and affect living things.
5. Solar cell. Solar cells produce electricity without using fuels. They can help us conserve our natural resources and not pollute our environment.

What's small enough to go through a needle's eye, but large enough to remember your name, birthday, and lots of other things? The answer is simple. A *chip* can do these things and more. Chips are found in all sorts of things. They are in watches, computers, and calculators. When you finish this section, you should be able to:

☐ **A.** Describe what a *chip* is.
☐ **B.** List the main parts of a *computer*.
☐ **C.** Describe several ways in which computers are used.

Chips are very small electric circuits. Chips are made of silicon. That's the same material solar cells are made of. If you looked at a chip under a microscope it would look like the picture on the right. The chip would look like a street map of a large city scratched onto a tiny square. The lines on a chip show different paths that electricity can take. Because chips are small, electricity can take many paths in a small space. This also means that chips can do many jobs.

There are chips that have special jobs. Certain chips have the ability to store information. These are called memory chips. Memory chips remember a certain pattern of electricity that passes through them. The pattern

Chip: A small electric circuit.

211

BASIC TEACHING PLAN

MOTIVATION

The competition within the computer industry is fierce. You could mention to your students that there is a place in California called "Silicon Valley." Ask them if they've heard of it and bring in newspaper articles relating to the competition in the field. Bring in ads from audio-electronic stores, several computerized bills, and a personal check to show the students evidence of computers in our lives. The numbers on the bottom of the check are written to be read by a computer.

DEVELOPMENT

1 **Teaching Tips** — Inform students that the technology to reproduce circuits using microscopic techniques was the revolutionary development within this field.

SECTION BACKGROUND

The modern computer is an instrument that has geometrically expanded its influence upon our lives. The need for a tool that would be capable of rapid calculations was recognized in the nineteenth century by an English mathematician named Charles Babbage. Due to the lack of mechanical skills, his conceptual drawings were unable to be realized. In the latter part of the nineteenth century, Herman Hollerith invented the first punch cards to be read by an electrical device. His computer was used for the 1890 census in the United States. Hollerith's machine was the forerunner of today's digital computer. The parts of this complex machine include: input (information can be provided by magnetic disks or drums, magnetic paper tapes or punched cards), control, storage (memory devices), processing (does calculations and directs the information to the control, storage, or output units), and output. The control, storage, and processing units are referred to as the CPU (central processing unit).

In the early part of the twentieth century, a second kind of computer was developed by Vannevar Bush at the Massachusetts Institute of Technology. Termed the analogue computer, the machine was designed to solve problems by measuring one quantity, for example the speed of a spacecraft, in terms of another quantity, such as electrical connections. Bush's perfected computer was used in military operations during World War II.

Digital computers are used to score examinations, bill customers, make election predictions, and make weather reports. Analogue computers are utilized to solve math formulas and to evaluate the efficiency of mechanical and electrical parts.

EXTENSIONS

Application
Research

Students could research the powerful influence that the integrated circuit or chip has and will have on our society. Using such sources as newpapers and magazines, students could investigate the applications of the chip in the electronics world. They could cut out the ads they find and bring them in for class discussion and display. Several students could visit an electronics store to interview a salesperson to discover the limitless variety of uses for the chip and to observe the minute size of the circuits.

2 is like a language to the chip. Other chips act like calculators. They can do arithmetic problems in seconds. Electricity flows through their circuits to come up with the right answer.

Computer: A device that stores and handles information.

Chips are very important in **computers**. *Computers* are devices that store and handle information. They do **3** this very quickly. Computers take only as much time to work as it takes for electricity to go through the circuits.

4 Computers can be big or small. Size depends on how much information they store. All kinds of things can be stored in a computer. A computer might store all the names and birthdays of the students in your school. Another computer might store the names of bicycle parts made at a plant. It would also store how many of each type were made each day.

212

2 **Skill Development** — Students *classify* chips into various categories of use.

3 **Teaching Tips** — The speed with which computers can process information is the reason why they are so important to the space program. The computers in Mission Control Center can process information within seconds. It would take scientists much longer to make these decisions.

4 **Teaching Tips** — Computers used to require much more space — an entire floor of old computers can now be placed in one room. Memory elements of a computer can be so small that they are microscopic. Computers are beginning to approach the size of a human brain.

5 Computers store large amounts of information on **disks**. *Disks* are made of magnetic tape. The pattern of magnetism stores the information.

How can people get information from a computer? **6** They must ask the computer for it. But they must ask in the computer's language. Sometimes this means typing a message on the computer's keyboard. The keyboard looks like a typewriter.

7 The keyboard is used to **input** information. You must put something into the computer to get results. If the right question is typed in, the question goes to the computer's "brain." The "brain" is its **central processing unit**, or **CPU**.

8
9 The *cpu* then sends an electric message to the correct memory circuit. There it gets the needed information.

The answer from a computer is often on a display screen. The screen is like a TV screen. A computer's answers are called **output**. The diagram shows the steps it takes to get an answer from a computer. Trace each step.

Disk: Magnetic tape that stores information in a computer.

Input: The information that goes into a computer.

Central processing unit (CPU): The "brain" of a computer.

Output: The information that comes out of a computer.

EXTENSIONS

Enrichment
Research — Library

Digital or counting computers are used to solve math problems very quickly. Students could examine the early history of basic mechanical devices that were also used to solve mathematical problems.

A. The abacus (the first device which used beads on a wood frame)

B. Pascal's calculator (gears and levers were used)

C. Babbage's computing engines

D. Hollerith's census machine (electric switches did the counting)

Students could report on how the discovery of electricity made a difference in the speed and efficiency of early computers.

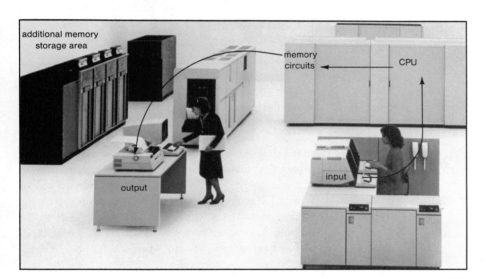

213

5 **Teaching Tips** — Tell students that the information used to be stored on cards.

6 **Skill Development** — On the chalkboard or on the overhead projector, you could sketch the *sequence* of steps. Include the additional information in your explanation.

7 **Teaching Tips** — Tell the class that a programmer must code the information for input into the computer. Information may be in the form of switches, magnetic tapes, paper tapes, or punched cards.

8 **Teaching Tips** — The CPU includes control, storage, and processing units. The other units shown in the photograph are additional memory storage units.

9 **Teaching Tips** — Explain that the computer must be kept in rooms in which temperature and humidity are controlled very closely.

EXTENSIONS

Enrichment
Science Skills — Comparing and Contrasting, Measuring

The counting part of a computer is based on the binary number system. It would be helpful to explain this method to your class. Tell the students that *bi* is a prefix that means two and the system uses only 1 and 0.

A. If possible, construct an abacus using 4 strips of wood, string, cup hooks, and washers. See figure below.

B. Using the diagram of the binary abacus, explain that each string or column represents a number twice as large as the number in the column to its right.

C. Illustrate the number 99 and various other numbers on your abacus or on a diagram of one. Write the numbers in the binary form.

D. After the students have a basic understanding, explain that a computer uses a series of electrical switches or pulses to represent numbers. The "on" position represents 1 and the "off" represents 0.

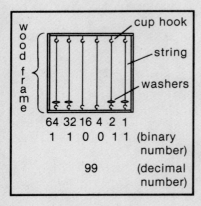

Fig. T–10–1

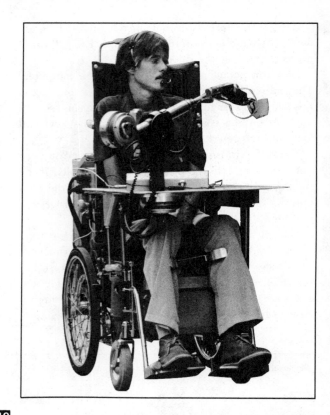

Computer program: A series of directions for a computer to follow.

Every computer is directed to do jobs a certain way. A **computer program** is a series of directions for the computer to follow. A computer can be programed to send a rocket into space. Another computer may be programed to warm a house. A computer was built into the wheelchair shown above. It has a program that listens to this man's voice. When it "hears" words such as "up" or "down," it moves the wheelchair or the cup.

The ways to use computers are almost endless. In schools they can help students learn on their own. Special language computers can "hear" whether or not a student says a word correctly.

214

10 **Teaching Tips** — Tell students that the computer program can be written in various computer languages, e.g., BASIC (for beginners), COBOL (for business problems), and FORTRAN (for scientific problems).

11 **Teaching Tips** — Stress the importance of preparing an accurate program. Tell the students that developing a program takes much more time than researching a problem on the computer.

12   Doctors can use computers to find out why a person is ill. Newspapers and books are written and printed with the help of computers. Computers often print their results on a *printout*. This is another kind of computer output, as shown below.

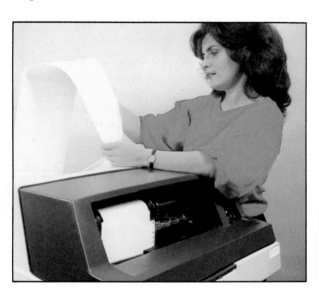

EXTENSIONS

Application
Research — Library

As computer use has been expanded into almost every area of human endeavor, your students could research the application of computers in the world. For example, computers are used in education, medical care, banking, manufacturing, space, reservations for hotels or airlines, billing, and agriculture. You could divide the class into groups, and each group could do research and present their information on one area to the class. If possible, one of the members could visit an appropriate facility in each category. Students should also consider the implication of the computer's use on the job market.

12 **Teaching Tips** — Sensors that are attached to patients can send signals to a computer. A computer can also be used in diagnoses. The computer can match symptoms and test results with corresponding patterns for different diseases.

EXTENSIONS

Enrichment
Research — Library

Computers will have a tremendous impact on our lives in the future. For example, computers will operate more and more as networks in which computers can exchange data directly with one another. A network might include terminals in banks, stores, and homes. In this way, it would be possible to do your shopping from home, and then have the cost of your purchases deducted directly from your bank account.

Many social and legal problems may arise in the future because of computers. Since it will be possible to collect and store information in large quantities, it may be difficult to protect a person's right to privacy.

Have the students go to the library and do research on how computers may be used in the future. Have them write about an imaginary day in the future that illustrates the impact that computers may have on our lives.

At home, people store important information in personal computers. Personal computers can help people plan ways to use their money and time wisely.

Section Review

Main Ideas: Silicon chips are very small electric circuits used in computers to store information and do calculations. The main parts of a computer are the input, central processing unit, memory, and output. Different computers are programed for many different jobs.

Questions: Answer in complete sentences.

1. What is a silicon chip? What is its greatest advantage?
2. What is a computer?
3. Describe how you can get information from a computer. Use these terms in your answer: input, CPU, memory circuit, output.
4. Give three examples of how people can use computers at school or at home.

216

SECTION REVIEW

Answers to Questions
1. A chip is a very small electric circuit that is made from silicon. A chip can hold a large volume of information in a small space.
2. A computer is a device to store and process information.
3. Information is then put into the computer's CPU. The CPU sends an electric message to the right memory circuit. The answer is then delivered as output on a screen or printout.
4. Computers are used to help students learn on their own, to store information, and to help people plan ways to use their money and time wisely.

CHAPTER REVIEW

Science Words: Select the definition in column B that best fits each word in column A.

Column A

1. Fuel
2. Nuclear reaction
3. Computer
4. Turbines
5. Kilowatt-hour
6. Mechanical energy
7. Chip
8. Hydroelectric plant
9. Natural resource
10. Solar cell

Column B

A. Useful thing found in nature.
B. Produces heat when burned.
C. Power plant in which falling water is the energy source.
D. Changes sunlight to electricity.
E. Reaction that occurs when particles of matter are split.
F. A device that stores and handles information.
G. Wheels used at power plants.
H. Unit of electricity use.
I. The energy of motion.
J. A small electric circuit.

Questions: Answer in complete sentences.

1. Is it possible for something to change electrical energy into other forms of energy? Explain your answer with examples.
2. All these events occur in an electrical plant that burns fuel: **a.** Turbines spin. **b.** Fuel is burned. **c.** Electricity is produced. Use these events in their correct order to explain how a power plant produces electricity.
3. What is the main problem with the electrical plants described in question 2?
4. Compare a nuclear power plant with a hydroelectric plant. How are they alike? How are they different? What are the benefits and problems of each?
5. What are solar cells? What is their source of energy?
6. What are chips? How are they useful in our lives?

217

CHAPTER REVIEW

Science Words
1. B,   2. E,   3. F,   4. G,   5. H,   6. I,   7. J,   8. C,
9. A,   10. D

Answers to Questions
1. Yes, electrical energy can be changed to heat (toaster); light (lamp); mechanical (fan); and sound (record player) energies.
2. Heat from burning fuel (b) changes water into steam which is used to spin turbines (a). The blades of the turbines turn a rod connected to the generator to produce electricity (c).
3. Pollutants from burning fuels
4. Both plants produce power by changing water to steam. Nuclear plants use a small amount of fuel to produce heat from nuclear reactions, but produce harmful wastes and may discharge heated water into streams. Hydroelectric plants produce no harmful wastes, but need a large source of water.
5. A piece of silicon that can produce energy from sunlight.
6. Small electric circuits made of silicon and used in computers.

SUGGESTED WORKSHEET MASTER
p. T–161u

SUGGESTED TEST MASTERS
pp. T–161i,j

EXTENSIONS

Enrichment
Science Skills — Measuring

You may be able to borrow a device called a voltmeter from an electrician or a teacher of secondary school industrial arts, electronics, or science. Have this person teach you how to use it. Have students use it to do the following:

A. Measure the voltage across the terminals of a dry cell. They should do this for new and used dry cells.

B. Repeat A above for a dry cell that is part of a working circuit.

C. Measure the voltage across the flashlight bulb sockets in a working circuit. (They will find that the voltage across the dry cell is equal to the sum of the voltages across each resistance.) You may wish to tell students that voltage is a measure of the energy that is pushing the electrons through the circuit. The amount of energy used up from the beginning to the end of a series circuit is equal to the total energy used in the circuit.

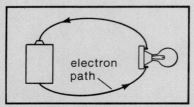
Fig. A

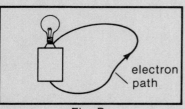
Fig. B

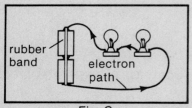
Fig. C

T–218

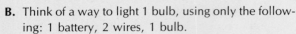

Making circuit puzzles

A. Obtain these materials: 1 rubber band, 2 D batteries, 3 pieces of bell wire (bare at each end) 20 cm long, 2 flashlight bulbs, 2 sockets.

B. Think of a way to light 1 bulb, using only the following: 1 battery, 2 wires, 1 bulb.

    1. Draw a labeled diagram of your hypothesis. What path will the electrons follow?

C. Check your hypothesis. Make the circuit.

    2. What were your results?

D. Think of a way to light 1 bulb, using only the following: 1 battery, 1 bulb, 1 wire.

    3. Draw a labeled diagram of your hypothesis. What path will the electrons follow?

E. Check your hypothesis. Make the circuit.

    4. What were your results?

F. Light 2 bulbs, using 2 batteries, 2 bulbs, 2 sockets, 3 pieces of wire, 1 rubber band.

    5. Draw a labeled diagram of the circuit.

G. Predict which of the 5 circuits shown will work. Make the circuits as shown.

    6. Compare your predictions and results.

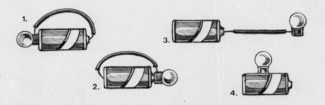

218

INVESTIGATING

Skill Development — *Following Directions, Predicting, Hypothesizing, Concluding, and Generalizing*

Answers to Questions — **1.** See Fig. A. **2.** The bulb lit. **3.** See Fig. B. **4.** If only the bulb is used and the tip makes contact with the terminal, a complete circuit is made. If the socket is used, one contact should be touching the terminal. **5.** See Fig. C. **6.** A complete circuit is made when there is a continuous piece of wire from the negative terminal to the positive terminal of the battery(ies) in the circuit. Circuits 1 and 2 will work.

CAREERS

Electrical Engineer ▶

Designing circuits no larger than your fingernail is one of the jobs of an **electrical engineer.** The *engineer* decides what kinds of circuits are needed to perform tasks and run machines. Circuits are used in computers, calculators, digital watches, and video games. Electrical engineers attend a college or university. There they study electricity, magnetism, and mathematics.

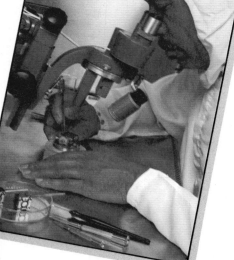

◀ Electrician

People want to be able to use their toasters without having to shut off their lights. It is **electricians** who carefully design circuits for buildings. They also install wiring, fuses or circuit breakers, and electrical sockets. *Electricians* must know about building houses so that they install wires in their proper places. Electricians usually learn their trade by working with other electricians or by going to a trade school.

219

EXTENSIONS

Application
Research

Systems analysts are responsible for the comprehensive planning of entire computer systems for companies. It is their responsibility to develop the work plan for programmers. Console operators work at the central console of a CPU and supervise the daily workings of the computer system while peripheral equipment operators work on supporting systems. Information can be obtained from The American Federation of Information Processing Societies, 210 Summit Ave., Montvale, NJ 07645.

CAREERS

Teaching Tips — Information about an engineering career can be obtained from the Engineer's Council for Professional Development, 345 East 47 St., New York, NY 10017. More information about the career of an electrician can be obtained by writing to the Institute of the Certification of Engineering Technicians, American Society of Certified Engineering Technicians, 2029 K Street NW, Washington D.C. 20006.

	SECTION	BASIC SCIENCE SKILLS	ACTIVITY MATERIALS STUDENT/GROUP	EXTENSIONS	
CHAPTER 11 CELLS AND SIMPLE ORGANISMS	**11-1** p. T-222 Classifying Living Things	*Comparing and contrasting* characteristics of living things p. T-223	paper, pencil	• Reinforcement p. T-225 • Application p. T-224 • Enrichment pp. T-223, T-225	
	11-2 p. T-226 Building Blocks of Life	*Reading illustration* of parts of a cell p. T-227		• Application p. T-227 • Enrichment pp. T-228, T-229	
	11-3 p. T-230 The Simplest Organisms	*Concluding* whether or not viruses are alive p. T-231	pond water, cover slips, pencil, slides, microscope, paper	• Reinforcement p. T-232 • Application p. T-231 • Enrichment pp. T-233, T-234	
	11-4 p. T-235 Algae and Fungi	*Classifying* seaweed p. T-235 *Building science vocabulary* by learning singular and plural p. T-236		• Reinforcement p. T-237 • Application p. T-236 • Enrichment pp. T-236, T-238	
CHAPTER 12 PLANTS	**12-1** p. T-239 Classifying Plants	*Classifying plants* p. T-240 *Finding cause and effect* in photosynthesis p. T-242	2 pots with soil, 2 lima beans, watering can	• Enrichment pp. T-240, T-241, T-242	
	12-2 p. T-243 Roots, Stems, and Leaves	*Finding cause and effect* relationship between climate and type of ground cover p. T-245	glass, water, food coloring, scissors, long-stemmed white flower, hand lens	• Reinforcement p. T-245 • Application p. T-245 • Enrichment pp. T-244, T-246	
	12-3 p. T-247 Groups of Plants	*Classifying* seeds p. T-250 *Finding cause and effect* for success p. T-251		• Reinforcement p. T-252 • Application pp. T-249, T-250, T-251 • Enrichment p. T-253	
CHAPTER 13 ANIMALS WITHOUT BACKBONES	**13-1** p. T-254 Simple Animals	*Classifying* Animals		• Enrichment pp. T-255, T-256 T-257, T-258	
	13-2 p. T-259 Animals With Shells and Spines	*Comparing* Animals	aquarium, pond snails, hand lens, pencil	• Reinforcement p. T-262 • Application pp. T-261, T-263 • Enrichment p. T-260	
	13-3 p. T-264 Arthropods	*Contrasting* Arthropods	hand lens, mealworm culture, pencil, drawing paper	• Reinforcement p. T-268 • Enrichment pp. T-265, T-266 T-267, T-269, T-270, T-271	
CHAPTER 14 ANIMALS WITH BACKBONES	**14-1** p. T-272 Fish and Amphibians	*Observing* fish p. T-274 *Contrasting* fish p. T-274 *Comparing* lives p. T-276	aquarium, paper, pencil	• Reinforcement p. T-274 • Application p. T-270 • Enrichment pp. T-273, T-275. T-276, T-277	
	14-2 p. T-278 Reptiles and Birds	*Comparing* hearts p. T-280 *Comparing* blood p. T-281	paper, pencil	• Reinforcement p. T-283 • Enrichment pp. T-279, T-282 • Application pp. T-280, T-281	
	14-3 p. T-284 Mammals	*Hypothesizing* p. T-284 *Finding cause and effect* of whales' size p. T-286		• Reinforcement p. T-288 • Enrichment pp. T-286, T-287, T-289, T-290 • Application pp. T-285, T-291	

EXTRA ACTIVITIES/ DEMONSTRATIONS	WORKSHEET MASTERS	EVALUATIONS
	• Simple Organisms (SK) p.T-219m	Section Review p.T-225
• Honeycomb p.T-226 • Exercise p.T-227 • Plant roots p.T-228 • Chlorophyll p.T-229		Section Review p.T-229
		Section Review p.T-234
• Common molds, algae, and fungi p.T-235	• Parts of a Cell (SK) p.T-219n • Puzzle (SK) p.T-219o	Sec Rev p.T-237 Ch Rev p.T-238 Test Masters pp.T-219d,e
• Plant shelf p.T-240		Section Review p.T-242
• Classroom plant p.T-243	• Reproduction (SK) p.T-219p • Losing Water (AH) p.T-219q	Section Review p.T-246
• Mosses p.T-248 • Fern p.T-249 • Cones p.T-250		Sec Rev p.T-252 Ch Rev p.T-253 T M pp.T-219f,g
• Worm chart p.T-257		Section Review p.T-258
• Mollusks and worms p.T-259 • Balloon p.T-261		Section Review p.T-263
	• (AH) p.T-219r • (SK) p.T-219s • (AC) p.T-219t	Sec Rev p.T-270 Ch Rev p.T-271 T M pp.T-231h,i
• Cartilage p.T-274 • Tadpoles p.T-276		Section Review p.T-277
• Reptile bulletin board p.T-278 • Bird feeders p.T-283		Section Review p.T-283
• Investigating p.T-290	• (SK) p.T-219u • (SK) p.T-219v • (SK) p.T-219w	Sec Rev p.T-288 Ch Rev p.T-289 T M pp.T-219j,k,

BOOKS FOR STUDENTS

Cobb, Vicki. *Lots of Rot*, illus. by Brian Schatell, New York: Lippincott, 1981

Knight, David C. *Viruses: Life's Smallest Enemies*, New York: Morrow, 1981

Laycock, George. *Bats in the Night*, Bristol, FL: Four Winds, 1981

McClung, Robert M. *The Amazing Egg*, illus., New York: Dutton, 1980

McGowen, Tom. *Album of Whales*, illus. by Rod Ruth, Chicago: Rand McNally, 1980

National Geographic Society. *Book of Mammals*, Washington, DC.: National Geographic, 1981

Rahn, Joan E. *Plants Up Close*, Boston: Houghton Mifflin, 1981

Ryder, Joanne. *The Spiders Dance*, illus. by Robert J. Blake, New York: Harper, 1981

Simon, Seymour. *Strange Creatures*, illus. by Pamela Carroll, Bristol, FL: Four Winds, 1981

Wilson, Ron. *How Plants Grow*, illus., New York: Larousse, 1981

FILMS

Insects Helpful to Man, 17 min, International

Marine Flowers, 30½ min, International

Putting Animals in Groups, 13 min, International

The Realm of Birds, 25 min, National Geographic

Unfriendly Flora and Fauna, 15 min, Centron

Warm Blooded and Cold Blooded Animals, 14 min, Coronet

FILMSTRIPS

Animals Without Backbones, series, 50 frames each, *Different Kinds of Worms, The Lobster and Its Relatives, One-Celled Animals, The Sea Star and Related Spiny-Skinned Animals, The Snail and Its Relatives*, Britannica

The Classification of Plants, 25 frames, Universal

Different Kinds of Animals, series of 6, 38 frames each, Britannica

How Worlds Begin, from the *Amazing World of Dinosaurs*, 48 frames, Disney

COMPUTER AIDS

*Animal,*Concept demo, PET, BASIC; 8K + tape, Creative Computing

KEY (AC)——Activity   (AH)——At Home   (SK)——Skill

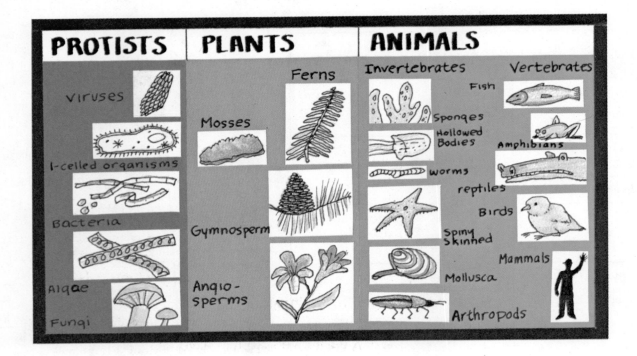

BULLETIN BOARD

This bulletin board is designed to illustrate the system scientists use to classify living things. Have the students divide the board into three sections using colored paper. The first section could be entitled "Protists," the next section "Plants," and the third "Animals." As the students progress through the unit, have them write the title of each major category of organism in its proper section and post up drawings or photographs of typical organisms under the title. For example, the section entitled "Plants" could be divided into mosses, ferns, cone-bearing plants, and flowering plants, etc.

FIELD TRIP IDEAS

To a Natural History Museum

Arrange a trip to a museum of natural history or the natural history department of a university. Often class tours are available. If possible, arrange for the students to see how scientists preserve organisms. Examine and classify plant and animal specimens. The students will learn that there are many organisms in the world that have not yet been classified.

Classification Scavenger Hunt

Take the class to a nearby park, forest, or field. Divide the class into groups and give each group a field guide to wildflowers, weeds, trees, or insects. These guides are available in libraries. Inexpensive guides such as the Golden Nature guides can also be purchased in bookstores. Challenge the students to find out and identify at least ten living things, using their field guides.

CELLS AND SIMPLE ORGANISMS

TEST 11
CHAPTER

CHAPTER OBJECTIVES

Read each sentence. Choose the best answer from those listed.
Write the letter of your choice on the line at the right.

1. The largest thing that ever lived is
   a. the blue whale.   c. the dinosaur.
   b. the redwood tree.   d. the elephant.

   1. _____   1. **b** (1)

2. Which of the following is *not* a characteristic of living things?
   a. They grow and change.
   b. They need food.
   c. They all have the same structure.
   d. They come from the same kind of living things.

   2. _____   2. **c** (1)

3. Which statement is true?
   a. Plants cannot move.   c. A car moves, so it is alive.
   b. All living things can move.   d. Only animals can move.

   3. _____   3. **b** (1)

4. Animals cannot be classified on the basis of
   a. the number of legs they have.
   b. their type of body covering
   c. whether or not they have wings.
   d. whether or not they grow.

   4. _____   4. **d** (2)

5. Classifying animals makes it possible
   a. to compare different groups of living things.
   b. to study one group at a time.
   c. to find out information about a certain living thing.
   d. all of the above.

   5. _____   5. **d** (2)

6. Structures that are characteristic of all trees are
   a. thick, woody trunks.   c. needle-shaped leaves.
   b. broad, flat leaves.   d. big flowers.

   6. _____   6. **a** (2)

7. This material in green leaves takes energy from sunlight.
   a. oxygen   c. water
   b. chlorophyll   d. carbon dioxide

   7. _____   7. **b** (3)

8. The part of the cell that controls its activities is
   a. the cytoplasm.   c. the cell wall.
   b. the nucleus.   d. the cell membrane.

   8. _____   8. **b** (3)

9. The cell wall is found
   a. around the cell membrane of a plant cell.
   b. inside the cell membrane of a plant cell.
   c. around the cell membrane of an animal cell.
   d. inside the cell membrane of an animal cell.

   9. _____   9. **a** (3)

10. __c__ (4)   **10.** Which of the following is *not* true about root cells?

   a. They are long.   **c.** They have very thick walls.
   b. They are thin.   **d.** They grow quickly.

10. _____

11. __b__ (4)   **11.** Viruses can use their blueprint to make more viruses

   a. at any time.   **c.** only in dead cells.
   b. only in a living cell. **d.** if they can breathe.

11. _____

12. __c__ (4)   **12.** What is a protist?

   a. a living thing with all the characteristics of a plant
   b. a living thing with all the characteristics of an animal
   c. a living thing that may look like a plant or animal
   d. something that resembles a plant or animal but is not living

12. _____

13. __a__ (4)   **13.** The protists that are classified by their shape are

   a. bacteria.   **c.** ameba.
   b. euglena.   **d.** paramecium.

13. _____

14. __c__ (5)   **14.** In what way is the euglena plantlike?

   a. It has leaves.   **c.** It has chlorophyll.
   b. It swims.   **d.** It has a stem.

14. _____

15. __c__ (5)   **15.** Which of the following is *not* true about fungi?

   a. They can grow in living organisms.
   b. They can grow on dead organisms.
   c. They have chlorophyll.
   d. They do not have roots or stems.

15. _____

16. __b__ (5)   **16.** Seaweed can be used

   a. to make cheeses.
   b. to make foods less watery.
   c. to make penicillin.
   d. to break down animal and plant material.

16. _____

17. __c__ (5)   **17.** Athlete's foot is caused by

   a. algae.   **c.** fungi.
   b. a virus.   **d.** bacteria.

17. _____

18. __b__ (5)   **18.** Spirogyra is a type of

   a. fungi.   **c.** saltwater algae.
   b. freshwater algae.   **d.** bacteria.

18. _____

Name _____ Date _____

Fold Back
Answer
Key On
Line
Before
Copying.

PLANTS

TEST CHAPTER 12

Read each sentence. Choose the best answer from those listed.
Write the letter of your choice on the line at the right.

CHAPTER OBJECTIVES

1. The chlorophyll in plants
   a. gives them their green color.
   b. is usually found in leaf cells.
   c. traps energy from the sun.
   d. does all of the above.

   1. _____   1. **d** (1)

2. During photosynthesis plants combine
   a. carbon dioxide, light, water.
   b. oxygen, light, water.
   c. carbon dioxide, oxygen, light.
   d. carbon dioxide, oxygen, water.

   2. _____   2. **a** (1)

3. Animals depend on plants for
   a. food and oxygen.
   b. carbon dioxide.
   c. water and oxygen.
   d. food and carbon dioxide.

   3. _____   3. **a** (1)

4. Food is usually made in a plant's
   a. stem cells.   c. leaf cells.
   b. flower cells.   d. root cells.

   4. _____   4. **c** (2)

5. When you eat a carrot you are eating a plant's
   a. root.   c. leaf.
   b. stem.   d. flower.

   5. _____   5. **a** (2)

6. Which of the following is *not* true about a stem?
   a. It is usually above ground.
   b. It absorbs minerals from the soil.
   c. It holds the plant's transportation system.
   d. It supports the plant.

   6. _____   6. **b** (2)

7. An example of an underground stem used as food is
   a. a white potato.   c. a radish.
   b. a head of lettuce.   d. a tomato.

   7. _____   7. **a** (3)

8. Grass prevents floods from washing away soil because
   a. it has a taproot.
   b. it has shallow, branched roots.
   c. it has an underground stem.
   d. it has a stem that grows above ground.

   8. _____   8. **b** (3)

9. <u>a</u> (3)

9. How are leaves of cactus plants adapted to the desert?
    a. They are small and waxy.
    b. They absorb more sun than ordinary leaves.
    c. They produce more chlorophyll than ordinary leaves.
    d. All of the above are true.

9. _____

10. <u>b</u> (4)

10. Ferns and mosses
    a. cannot grow in moist, shady places.
    b. reproduce from spores.
    c. have thick woody stems.
    d. appeared on earth very recently.

10. _____

11. <u>c</u> (4)

11. Which of the following is true about ferns?
    a. They do not have roots, stems, or leaves.
    b. They have roots and stems but no leaves.
    c. Their roots and stems grow underground and their leaves grow above ground.
    d. Their roots grow underground but their stems and leaves grow above ground.

11. _____

12. <u>c</u> (4)

12. Mosses cannot
    a. make their own food.   c. grow to be very large.
    b. grow on rocks.   d. grow in wet places.

12. _____

13. <u>c</u> (5)

13. Cycads are classified as
    a. ferns.   c. gymnosperms.
    b. mosses.   d. angiosperms.

13. _____

14. <u>d</u> (5)

14. All of the following are angiosperms except
    a. dandelions.   c. rosebushes.
    b. grass.   d. redwood trees.

14. _____

15. <u>b</u> (5)

15. Gymnosperms reproduce by
    a. producing seeds inside their flowers.
    b. producing seeds on cones.
    c. producing spores beneath their leaves.
    d. producing spores underground.

15. _____

16. <u>b</u> (5)

16. Plants are classified as angiosperms or gymnosperms according to
    a. their size.
    b. whether their seeds are covered or not.
    c. the type of spore they produce.
    d. whether or not they have leaves.

16. _____

ANIMALS WITHOUT BACKBONES

TEST 13
CHAPTER

Fold Back
Answer
Key On
Line
Before
Copying.

CHAPTER OBJECTIVES

Read each sentence. Choose the best answer from those listed.
Write the letter of your choice on the line at the right.

1. Invertebrates with bodies that are three cells thick are
   a. worms.
   c. mollusks.
   b. jellyfish.
   d. sponges.

   1._____   1. **a** (1)

2. Which of the following are *not* hollow-bodied animals?
   a. jellyfish
   c. oysters
   b. corals
   d. sea anemones

   2._____   2. **c** (1)

3. All invertebrates have
   a. to live in the ocean.
   c. whiplike structures.
   b. no backbones.
   d. all the above in common.

   3._____   3. **b** (1)

4. Worms that have nervous systems are the
   a. hookworms.
   c. tapeworms.
   b. flatworms.
   d. earthworms.

   4._____   4. **d** (1)

5. Which of the following is *not* true about mollusks?
   a. They have soft bodies.
   b. They are segmented.
   c. They have a heart and blood vessels.
   d. They have a digestive system.

   5._____   5. **b** (2)

6. All of these are hatchet-footed mollusks except
   a. clams.
   c. scallops.
   b. mussels.
   d. slugs.

   6._____   6. **d** (2)

7. A stomach-footed mollusk
   a. has a foot that is part of its digestive system.
   b. has a thick, muscular foot.
   c. has a foot that is divided into eight or more tentacles.
   d. has a two-part shell.

   7._____   7. **a** (2)

8. Mollusks are classified by differences in
   a. stomachs and feet.
   c. shells and segments.
   b. shells and feet.
   d. feet and muscles.

   8._____   8. **b** (2)

9. Which of the following is *not* true about the squid and the octopus?
   a. They have tentacles.
   b. They are stomach-footed.
   c. They can change color quickly.
   d. They can release a cloud of ink into the water.

   9._____   9. **b** (3)

10. _c_ (3)   **10.** Sea urchins and sea cucumbers belong to the group called   **10.** _____
    a. mollusks.   **c.** spiny-skinned invertebrates.
    b. starfish.   **d.** segmented worms.

11. _d_ (3)   **11.** Sand dollars and sea urchins both have   **11.** _____
    a. spines.   **c.** firm bodies.
    b. a heart.   **d.** all the above.

12. _a_ (3)   **12.** A starfish can pull a clam open with its   **12.** _____
    a. tube feet.   **c.** hatchet feet.
    b. spines.   **d.** tentacles.

13. _b_ (4)   **13.** When an arthropod gets too large for its exoskeleton it usually   **13.** _____
    a. stops growing.   **c.** finds a new one.
    b. grows a new skeleton.   **d.** grows an internal skeleton.

14. _b_ (4)   **14.** Hard-covered arthropods have all of the following except   **14.** _____
    a. five pairs of legs.   **c.** two body sections.
    b. one pair of antennas.   **d.** a very tough exoskeleton.

15. _c_ (4)   **15.** Which of the following is true about millipedes?   **15.** _____
    a. They always have more legs than centipedes.
    b. They always have fewer legs than centipedes.
    c. They have more legs on each body segment than centipedes.
    d. They have fewer legs on each body segment than centipedes.

16. _a_ (4)   **16.** All arthropods have   **16.** _____
    a. jointed feet.   **c.** four pairs of legs.
    b. very hard coverings.   **d.** many segments.

17. _b_ (5)   **17.** The eggs of grain beetles hatch into   **17.** _____
    a. caterpillars.   **c.** grain beetles.
    b. mealworms.   **d.** moths.

18. _a_ (5)   **18.** All of the following go through complete metamorphosis except   **18.** _____
    a. grasshoppers.   **c.** butterflies.
    b. moths.   **d.** grain beetles.

19. _d_ (5)   **19.** During the resting stage, caterpillars   **19.** _____
    a. feed constantly.   **c.** lay eggs.
    b. grow spines.   **d.** spin a cocoon.

20. _d_ (5)   **20.** Insects that go through complete metamorphosis pass through   **20.** _____
    a. one stage.   **c.** three stages.
    b. two stages.   **d.** four stages.

Name_____ Date_____

Fold Back
Answer
Key On
Line
Before
Copying.

ANIMALS WITH BACKBONES

TEST **14**
CHAPTER

Read each sentence. Choose the best answer from those listed.
Write the letter of your choice on the line at the right.

CHAPTER OBJECTIVES

1. Vertebrates have all of the following except
   a. an exoskeleton.
   b. an endoskeleton.
   c. a well-developed brain.
   d. a closed system of blood circulation.

1._____   1. **a** (1)

2. In fish, oxygen enters the blood in the
   a. lungs.   **b.** gills.   **c.** fins.   **d.** heart.

2._____   2. **b** (1)

3. The body temperature of a fish is
   a. always about the same.
   b. about the same as the temperature of the water around it.
   c. below freezing.
   d. about 37°C.

3._____   3. **b** (1)

4. Which of the following is true about fish?
   a. They hear noises and vibrations in the water.
   b. Their hearts have two chambers.
   c. They have senses of balance and of taste.
   d. All of the above are true.

4._____   4. **d** (1)

5. Both amphibians and fish
   a. are cold-blooded.
   b. live on land and water.
   c. undergo metamorphosis.
   d. have two-chambered hearts.

5._____   5. **a** (2)

6. All of the following are amphibians except
   a. frogs.   **c.** salamanders.
   b. toads.   **d.** sharks.

6._____   6. **d** (2)

7. When tadpoles become adults
   a. they grow tails.
   b. they live only in water.
   c. they develop lungs.
   d. they grow gills.

7._____   7. **c** (2)

8. Amphibians and insects both
   a. have two pairs of legs.   **c.** undergo metamorphosis.
   b. breathe through gills.   **d.** live on dry land.

8._____   8. **c** (2)

Name _____ Date _____

9. **d.** (3)   **9.** Most reptiles do *not*
   a. have a skin made of hard scales.
   b. lay eggs that are hard shelled.
   c. have a three-chambered heart.
   d. lay their eggs in the water.

9. _____

10. **c** (3)   **10.** Dinosaurs are classified as
   a. invertebrates.   **c.** reptiles.
   b. amphibians.   **d.** mammals.

10. _____

11. **a** (3)   **11.** A reptile that has a four-chambered heart is the
   a. alligator.   **c.** green turtle.
   b. snake.   **d.** lizard.

11. _____

12. **c** (3)   **12.** A rattlesnake kills its prey by
   a. outrunning and catching it.
   b. swallowing it whole.
   c. injecting a poison from its fangs.
   d. coiling around it.

12. _____

13. **b** (4)   **13.** What do birds and reptiles have in common?
   a. They have feathers.
   b. They lay eggs.
   c. They are cold-blooded.
   d. They have wings although they don't all fly.

13. _____

14. **c** (4)   **14.** Flying birds have
   a. solid bones.   **c.** hollow bones.
   b. webbed feet.   **d.** long beaks.

14. _____

15. **b** (4)   **15.** A bird that is a champion navigator is the
   a. hummingbird.   **c.** penguin.
   b. arctic tern.   **d.** ostrich.

15. _____

16. **d** (4)   **16.** Which of the following is true about the ostrich?
   a. It has large wings.
   b. It can fly.
   c. It does not lay eggs.
   d. It can run very fast.

16. _____

17. **a** (5)   **17.** How is the kangaroo different from other mammals?
   a. Its young are born before they are fully developed.
   b. It has hair.
   c. It is warm-blooded.
   d. It feeds milk to its young.

17. _____

18. Bats are classified as

    a. amphibians.   **c.** mammals.

    b. reptiles.   **d.** birds.

18. _____   18. __c__ (5)

19. A characteristic that distinguishes primates from other mammals is that

    a. they have sharp teeth shaped like chisels.

    b. they are plant-eaters.

    c. they have hooves.

    d. they have movable fingers and flat nails.

19. _____   19. __d__ (5)

20. Hoofed, plant-eating mammals have

    a. flat, sturdy teeth.   **c.** pouches to hold their young.

    b. sharp, chisel-shaped teeth.   **d.** two eyes that look forward.

20. _____   20. __a__ (5)

Cells and Simple Organisms

Match each drawing with its correct name. Choose from the list.

Virus   Euglena   Paramecium
Bacteria   Spirogyra   Fungi

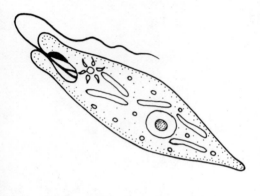

_____

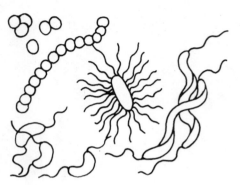

_____

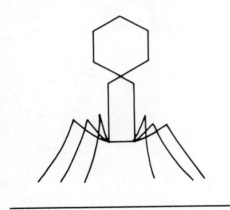

_____

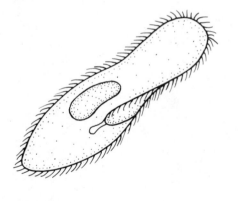

_____

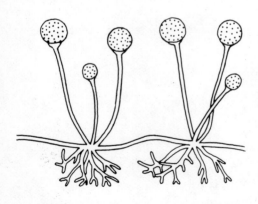

_____

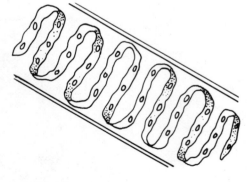

_____

Name_____ Date_____

Cells and Simple Organisms

A. Label the parts of the cell. Identify it as a plant or animal cell.

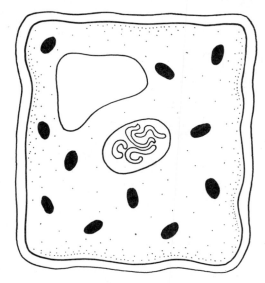

This is a _____ cell.

B. Describe how a virus attacks a cell and reproduces in it. Draw pictures to show what happens.

Cells

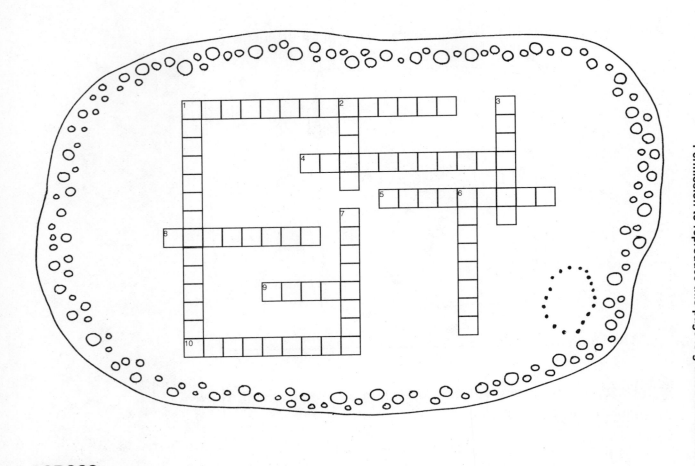

ACROSS

1. Sorting things into groups according to ways they are alike and ways they are different
4. Green material in plants that helps them make their own food
5. Part of a living thing such as a wing, leg, or leaf
8. The thin, skinlike covering of all cells
9. Group of tissues that works together
10. The liquid inside which the cell's activities take place

DOWN

1. Something that helps set one thing apart from another
2. Tiny living parts of which all organisms are made
3. The control center of a cell
6. A stiff protective layer around plant cells
7. A living thing

How Plants Reproduce

Label the two plant cycles shown below. Then cut out the stages of each. Arrange them in the proper order and paste them down onto a sheet of paper.

 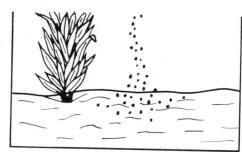

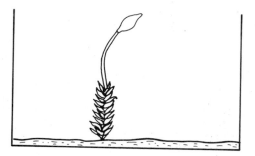 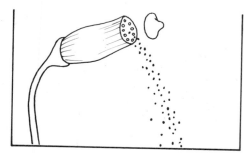

Reproduction by _____

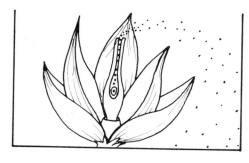 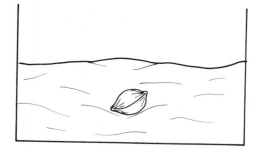

Reproduction by _____

Name _____ Date _____

Do Plants Lose Water?

You are learning about how water moves through plants. In this at-home activity you will observe how some of the water leaves the plant.

A. Obtain these materials: a small potted plant, a plastic bag, string, and a large jar with a lid.

B. Water the plant so that the soil is moist.

C. Place the pot into the plastic bag and tie the bag to the bottom of the stem.

D. Place the plant inside the jar and screw the lid on tightly.

E. Place the jar in a sunny spot for a few hours. Observe what happens inside the jar.

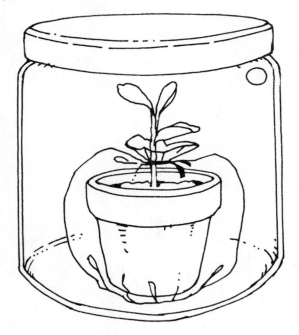

QUESTIONS

1. What happened in the jar? _____

_____

2. Why did this happen? _____

_____

_____

Name _____ Date _____

Insects

You have been studying the metamorphosis of insects. In this at-home activity, you will observe the changes a caterpillar undergoes.

A. Obtain these materials: a large glass jar with a lid, plastic bag.

B. Find a caterpillar eating a leaf. Place it into a plastic bag along with some leaves and twigs from the plant.

C. Carefully place the contents of the plastic bag into the jar.

D. Observe how the caterpillar moves and eats. If possible, watch it spin its cocoon.

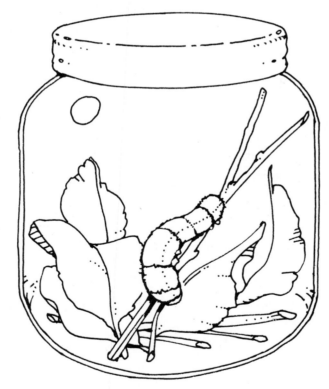

QUESTIONS

1. How many legs does the caterpillar have? _____

2. What is happening when the caterpillar is inside its cocoon?

_____

Name _____ Date _____

Animals without Backbones

Unscramble the letters to form the science words defined. Then,
use the numbered letters to solve the riddle below.

1. Animals without backbones

B R I V A T E S E N T E R

_ _ _ _ _ _ _ _ _ _ _ _
1   2   8

2. Animals with backbones

R A V B E R E T T E S

_ _ _ _ _ _ _ _ _ _
      12

3. Invertebrates with jointed legs and an exoskeleton

H O R T A P R O D

_ _ _ _ _ _ _ _
9   7

4. Hard outer covering of arthropods

N E X E L O S K O T E

_ _ _ _ _ _ _ _ _ _
     11   6

5. A series of major changes in the structure of an animal as it grows

P E M O T H O R A S M I S

_ _ _ _ _ _ _ _ _ _ _ _
    4   3   5

6. An arthropod with many body segments and one pair of legs on most segments

P I N T E C E D E

_ _ _ _ _ _ _ _
10 14   15

7. An invertebrate with a soft body, usually protected by a shell

L O M U S L K

_ _ _ _ _ _
13

Riddle: Why do people think a jellyfish is a coward?

_ _ _ _ _ _ _ _ _ _ _ _ _ _ _
1 2 3 4 5 6 7 8 9 10 11 12 13 14 15

Name _____ Date _____

Animals without Backbones

1. Cut out each box below.
2. Take all the cards from the A column and arrange them into a row face down. Arrange the B cards into another row.
3. With your partner, take turns choosing one card from Row A and one card from Row B. The object of the game is to match the animal group with its examples or features. When you make a match, keep the pair. If not, return the cards to their rows face down.
4. The partner with the most pairs wins the game.

A	B	A	B
sponge	covered with small holes	flatworm	flat bodies, often found in food
jellyfish	hollow-bodied roundworms	roundworms	round bodies, can infect people
segmented worms	earthworm	insect	fly or bee
mollusk	snail or clam	spiny-skinned animal	starfish
lobster	hard-shelled arthropod	spider	four pairs of legs

Animals with Backbones

Circle the animal that does not belong with the rest.
Then, explain why in the blank.

1. platypus   turtle   bird   cow   _____

                                              _____

2. bird   crocodile   frog   trout   _____

                                              _____

3. snake   shark   horse   ostrich   _____

                                              _____

4. penguin   bat   eagle   dog   _____

                                              _____

5. ray   frog   worm   deer   _____

                                              _____

6. shark   salamander   alligator   man   _____

                                              _____

7. barracuda   tiger   boa constrictor   elephant   _____

                                              _____

8.

                                              _____

                                              _____

Name _____ Date _____

Animals with Backbones

A. Arrange the items below in the proper order.

   1. By increasing complexity: human, kangaroo, trout, frog, snake

   _____

   2. By numbers of chambers in heart: salamander, ray, cat

   _____

   3. By ability to live in different environments: human, tuna, frog, lizard

   _____

B. Identify the type of animal described.

   4. I have hands with movable fingers with flat nails. I have hair and two eyes that look forward. I am a _____.

   5. I lay eggs and I cannot control my body temperature. I have a three-chambered heart. My skin is hard and scaly. I am a _____.

   6. I lay eggs and cannot control my body temperature. I have a two-chambered heart and my skin is usually covered with scales. I breathe through gills. I am a _____.

C. In the space below draw a picture of one of the organisms described.

Name _____ Date _____

Animals with Backbones

Find the science words hidden in the puzzle. Then match them to their definitions below.

```
M A M M A L S R T Q X B Z
A E I O U C P M S N O T R
M C T E T B J R G O N V E
P R O A R D W K V T H W P
H J L L M J B J D E F K T
I T J A D O H U L L C N I
B T K I G B R Z X E U O L
I P K I F J L P P K Y G E
A F L S G T D O H S P A S
N L W A R M B L O O D E D
S I U P N G G P L D S T Y
L V S E F S R V D N E I W
C A R T I L A G E E J D S
```

1. Cold-blooded animals that live "two lives" _____

2. Scaly, egg-laying land animals _____

3. Hairy, warm-blooded animals that nurse with milk _____

4. Firm material found in skeletons _____

5. Cannot control body temperatures _____

6. Can control body temperatures _____

7. Fish use these to breathe with _____

8. A skeleton inside the body _____

9. Major changes in the shape of an organism as it grows _____

Name_____ Date_____

Cells and Simple Organisms

CLASSIFYING   SKILL WORKSHEET

Match each drawing with its correct name. Choose from the list.

Virus	Euglena	Paramecium
Bacteria	Spirogyra	Fungi

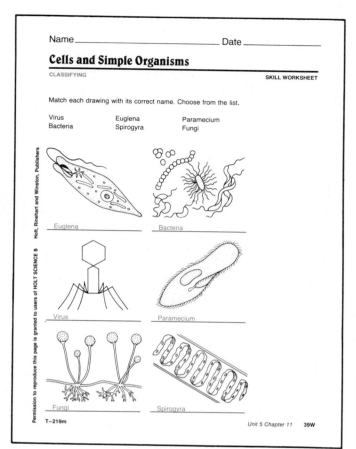

Euglena

Bacteria

Virus

Paramecium

Fungi

Spirogyra

Name_____ Date_____

Cells and Simple Organisms

CLASSIFYING, SEQUENCING   SKILL WORKSHEET

A. Label the parts of the cell. Identify it as a plant or animal cell.

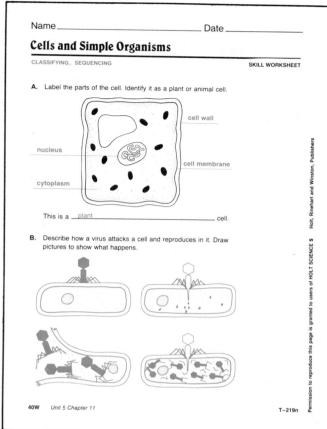

cell wall

nucleus

cell membrane

cytoplasm

This is a ___plant___ cell.

B. Describe how a virus attacks a cell and reproduces in it. Draw pictures to show what happens.

Name_____ Date_____

Cells

BUILDING SCIENCE VOCABULARY   SKILL WORKSHEET

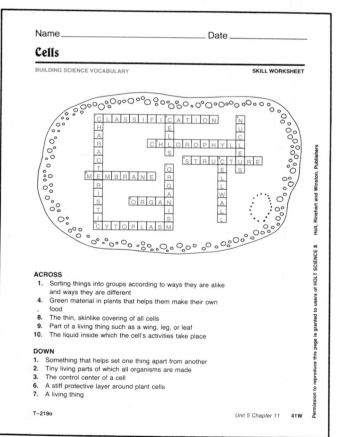

ACROSS
1. Sorting things into groups according to ways they are alike and ways they are different
4. Green material in plants that helps them make their own food
8. The thin, skinlike covering of all cells
9. Part of a living thing such as a wing, leg, or leaf
10. The liquid inside which the cell's activities take place

DOWN
1. Something that helps set one thing apart from another
2. Tiny living parts of which all organisms are made
3. The control center of a cell
6. A stiff protective layer around plant cells
7. A living thing

Name_____ Date_____

How Plants Reproduce

SEQUENCING   SKILL WORKSHEET

Label the two plant cycles shown below. Then cut out the stages of each. Arrange them in the proper order and paste them down onto a sheet of paper.

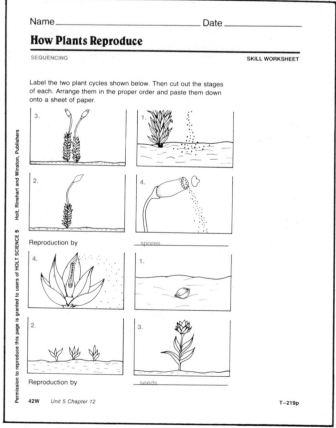

Reproduction by ___spores___

Reproduction by ___seeds___

Do Plants Lose Water?

AT HOME WORKSHEET

You are learning about how water moves through plants. In this at-home activity you will observe how some of the water leaves the plant.

A. Obtain these materials: a small potted plant, a plastic bag, string, and a large jar with a lid.
B. Water the plant so that the soil is moist.
C. Place the pot into the plastic bag and tie the bag to the bottom of the stem.
D. Place the plant inside the jar and screw the lid on tightly.
E. Place the jar in a sunny spot for a few hours. Observe what happens inside the jar.

QUESTIONS

1. What happened in the jar? Water formed along the sides.

2. Why did this happen? The water from the plant's leaves evaporated from the heat and condensed on the side of the jar.

Unit 5 Chapter 12   43W

Permission to reproduce this page is granted to users of HOLT SCIENCE 5   Holt, Rinehart and Winston, Publishers

---

Insects

AT HOME WORKSHEET

You have been studying the metamorphosis of insects. In this at-home activity, you will observe the changes a caterpillar undergoes.

A. Obtain these materials: a large glass jar with a lid, plastic bag.
B. Find a caterpillar eating a leaf. Place it into a plastic bag along with some leaves and twigs from the plant.
C. Carefully place the contents of the plastic bag into the jar.
D. Observe how the caterpillar moves and eats. If possible, watch it spin its cocoon.

QUESTIONS

1. How many legs does the caterpillar have? 3 pairs
2. What is happening when the caterpillar is inside its cocoon? It is changing into an adult.

T-219r

Permission to reproduce this page is granted to users of HOLT SCIENCE 5   Holt, Rinehart and Winston, Publishers

---

Animals without Backbones

BUILDING SCIENCE VOCABULARY

SKILL WORKSHEET

Unscramble the letters to form the science words defined. Then, use the numbered letters to solve the riddle below.

1. Animals without backbones

B R I V A T E S E N T E R
I N V E R T E B R A T E S
__ __1 __ __ __2 __ __ __8 __ __ __

2. Animals with backbones

R A V B E R E T T E S
V E R T E B R A T E S
__ __ __ __ __ __ __ __ __ __12

3. Invertebrates with jointed legs and an exoskeleton

H O R T A P R O D
A R T H R O P O D
__ __9 __ __ __7 __ __ __

4. Hard outer covering of arthropods

N E X E L O S K O T E
E X O S K E L E T O N
__ __ __ __ __11 __ __ __ __ __6

5. A series of major changes in the structure of an animal as it grows

P E M O T H O R A S M I S
M E T A M O R P H O S I S
__ __ __ __4 __ __ __ __3 __5 __ __ __

6. An arthropod with many body segments and one pair of legs on most segments

P I N T E C E D E
C E N T I P E D E
__10 __14 __ __ __ __ __15 __

7. An invertebrate with a soft body, usually protected by a shell

L O M U S L K
M O L L U S K
__13 __ __ __ __ __

Riddle: Why do people think a jellyfish is a coward?

I T   H A S   N O   B A C K B O N E
1 2   3 4 5   6 7   8 9 10 11 12 13 14 15

Unit 5 Chapter 13   45W

Permission to reproduce this page is granted to users of HOLT SCIENCE 5   Holt, Rinehart and Winston, Publishers

---

Animals without Backbones

ACTIVITY WORKSHEET

1. Cut out each box below.
2. Take all the cards from the A column and arrange them into a row face down. Arrange the B cards into another row.
3. With your partner, take turns choosing one card from Row A and one card from Row B. The object of the game is to match the animal group with its examples or features. When you make a match, keep the pair. If not, return the cards to their rows face down.
4. The partner with the most pairs wins the game.

A	B	A	B
sponge	covered with small holes	flatworm	flat bodies, often found in food
jellyfish	hollow-bodied roundworms	roundworms	round bodies, can infect people
segmented worms	earthworm	insect	fly or bee
mollusk	snail or clam	spiny-skinned animal	starfish
lobster	hard-shelled arthropod	spider	four pairs of legs

T-219t

Permission to reproduce this page is granted to users of HOLT SCIENCE 5   Holt, Rinehart and Winston, Publishers

Animals with Backbones

Name_____ Date_____

COMPARING AND CONTRASTING   SKILL WORKSHEET

Circle the animal that does not belong with the rest.
Then, explain why in the blank.

1. platypus   turtle   bird   (cow)   It doesn't lay eggs.

2. (bird)   crocodile   frog   trout   It is warm blooded.

3. snake   (shark)   horse   ostrich   It lives in the water.

4. penguin   bat   eagle   (dog)   It doesn't have wings.

5. ray   frog   (worm)   deer   It is an invertebrate.

6. (shark)   salamander   alligator   man   It has a skeleton of cartilage.

7. barracuda   tiger   boa constrictor   (elephant)   It eats plants.

8. 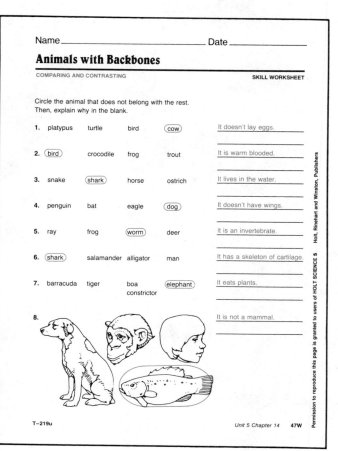   It is not a mammal.

Animals with Backbones

Name_____ Date_____

SEQUENCING, CLASSIFYING   SKILL WORKSHEET

A. Arrange the items below in the proper order.

1. By increasing complexity: human, kangaroo, trout, frog, snake

   trout, frog, snake, kangaroo, human

2. By numbers of chambers in heart: salamander, ray, cat

   ray, salamander, cat

3. By ability to live in different environments: human, tuna, frog, lizard

   tuna, frog, lizard, human

B. Identify the type of animal described.

4. I have hands with movable fingers with flat nails. I have hair and two eyes that look forward. I am a   primate

5. I lay eggs and I cannot control my body temperature. I have a three-chambered heart. My skin is hard and scaly. I am a   reptile

6. I lay eggs and cannot control my body temperature. I have a two-chambered heart and my skin is usually covered with scales. I breathe through gills. I am a   fish

C. In the space below draw a picture of one of the organisms described.

Animals with Backbones

Name_____ Date_____

BUILDING SCIENCE VOCABULARY   SKILL WORKSHEET

Find the science words hidden in the puzzle. Then match them to their definitions below.

```
M A M M A L S R T Q X B Z
A E I O U C P M S N O T R
M C T E T B J R G O N V E
P R O A R D W K V T H W P
H J L L M J B J D E F K T
I T J A D O H U L L C N I
B T K I G B R Z X E U O L
I P K I F J L P P K Y G E
A F L S G T D O H S P A S
N L W A R M B L O O D E D
S I U P N G G P L D S T Y
L V S E F S R V D N E I W
C A R T I L A G E E J D S
```

1. Cold-blooded animals that live "two lives"   amphibians
2. Scaly, egg-laying land animals   reptiles
3. Hairy, warm-blooded animals that nurse with milk   mammals
4. Firm material found in skeletons   cartilage
5. Cannot control body temperatures   cold-blooded
6. Can control body temperatures   warm-blooded
7. Fish use these to breathe with   gills
8. A skeleton inside the body   endoskeleton
9. Major changes in the shape of an organism as it grows   metamorphosis

UNIT OVERVIEW

This is a life science unit on classifying living things. Scientists classify living things according to their similarities and differences. All living things need food, grow and change, move, and reproduce. All living things are made of cells, which are composed of a nucleus, cytoplasm, and a cell membrane. Plant cells also have cell walls and chlorophyll, which uses the sun's energy to produce food.

Protists, such as bacteria, algae, and fungi have some of the characteristics of plants and some of animals. Scientists have therefore placed them in their own group.

Plants are divided into four main groups: mosses, ferns, cone-bearing plants, and flowering plants. Mosses are the simplest land plants and do not have true roots, stems, or leaves. Ferns do have roots, stems, and leaves. Both mosses and ferns reproduce by means of spores. Cone-bearing plants produce seeds but no flowers. Flowering plants are the most complex and the most successful group of plants. More than 95% of all members of the animal kingdom are invertebrates and a large majority of the invertebrates are insects. Insects belong to the phylum Arthropoda, which also includes lobsters, crayfish, and spiders. Other invertebrate phyla include the sponges, the coelenterates (jellyfish, corals), the flat- and roundworms, segmented worms, mollusks (clams, oysters, snails) and echinoderms (starfish).

The vertebrate groups are, in order of complexity, fish, amphibians, reptiles, birds, and mammals.

Exceptional Student IEP Unit Goal

At the end of this unit, the student will define cell, photosynthesis, reproduction, metamorphosis, and endoskeleton.

LIVING ORGANISMS

UNIT OPENER

This is a photograph of an orchid mantis nymph on a Malaysian orchid. Orchids and insects are much more plentiful than most people realize. There are more insects on earth than all other animals put together. The orchid family is probably the largest family of plants. To motivate the students, ask the following questions: What living things do you see in the photograph? *a flower and an insect.* How would you classify them — in the plant kingdom or in the animal kingdom? *The insect is an animal and the flower is a plant.* What are the differences between plants and animals? *Animals can move quickly and plants cannot. Plants have leaves and animals do not.* What do all living things have in common? *They all need food, grow and change, move, and reproduce.* What do you notice about the coloring of the insect? *It is similar to the plant's coloring.* How does that help the insect? *The coloring probably protects the insect from being spotted by other animals.*

UNIT 5

LEARNING CENTER

A suggested title for the learning center is "Plants and Animals." Photographs and drawings of a wide variety of plants and animals can be used as a display. You may wish to keep a file of the worksheet masters and Extensions that the students can work on independently.

The following extensions are especially suitable for the learning center. The materials for these extensions should be available in the learning center: observing onion skin, p. T-229 (microscope or magnifying glass, onion); growing and observing algae, p. T-236 (quart bottle, aquarium water, microscope slide); roots and moisture, p. T-244 (seedlings, glass tray, sponges); examining seeds, p. T-252 (seeds, hand lens); snail and light, p. T-260 (snail, aquarium, lamp, cardboard); fruit flies, p. T-269 (fruit flies, cotton, small glass jar, fruit fly medium).

In addition, an index file of suggested research topics can be set up in the learning center using the following Extensions: poisonous plants (p. T-224); Dewey decimal system (p. T-225); muscle pairs (p. T-228), immunizing (p. T-231); euglena (p. T-232); plant pigments (p. T-242); fern sori (p. T-249); science words (p. T-253); nematocysts (p. T-256); digestive system (p. T-258); giant squid (p. T-261); red tide (p. T-263); barnacles (p. T-265); molting (p. T-267); beekeepers (p. T-270); social insects (p. T-270); fish tank (p. T-275); amphibians (p. T-276); dinosaurs (p. T-279); living fossils (p. T-279); poisonous snakes (p. T-280); thecodants (p. T-283); chordates (p. T-289).

CHAPTER 11

CHAPTER OBJECTIVES

1. Describe four ways in which living things are alike.
2. Describe how scientists classify living things into groups and explain why classification is useful.
3. Describe three parts of all living cells, compare plant and animal cells, and explain how cells carry on special functions.
4. Explain how viruses and protists are classified.
5. Compare and contrast algae and fungi and how they are useful or harmful.

SECTION BACKGROUND

The most obvious and largest grouping of living things is the division into the plant and animal kingdoms. Plants do not move from place to place. Animals do. Plants have chlorophyll, which enables them to make their own food. Animals cannot make their own food. They must eat plants and/or other animals.

There are some organisms which have characteristics of both plants and animals. These organisms have been placed in the protist kingdom. This kingdom was first suggested over a century ago by the zoologist Ernst Haeckel, but it was not accepted by most biologists until the twentieth century. It is important for students to realize that classifications can and do change as new living things are discovered. This theme will run through this entire unit.

MATERIALS

paper, pencil

**Exceptional Student
IEP Chapter Goal**

At the end of this chapter, the student will state one characteristic of each of the following: cell, cell wall, virus, euglena, protist, and bacteria.

CELLS AND SIMPLE ORGANISMS

11-1.

Classifying Living Things

222

A frog jumps into the pond. The children listen. Insects buzz in the tall weeds. The dogs run through the grass. Frogs, children, weeds, and dogs are all alive. How else are some of these living things alike? When you finish this section, you should be able to:

BASIC TEACHING PLAN
MOTIVATION

Ask the students how many living things they can identify in the picture. Point out that there are many more living things that they cannot see. In a square foot of soil, scientists have counted as many as 25,000 insects, worms, and other small animals. That same square foot of soil will hold billions of bacteria and other microscopic organisms. The number of known living species of plants and animals is enormous. There are over 350,000 species of plants and over a million species of animals. New species are being discovered all the time. Some 1,000 new species of insects alone are discovered each year.

Text Questions — How else are some of these living things alike? *Students should be able to point to many similarities that link some or all of these living things. The children and the dogs need food and water, move about, and have legs. The plants also need water.*

☐ **A.** Describe four ways in which all living things are alike.

☐ **B.** Describe how scientists *classify* living things into groups.

☐ **C.** Explain why *classifying* things into different groups is useful.

1 Living things come in many sizes and shapes. They are almost everywhere on earth. Some fly high in the air; some live on the ground. Some even make their homes **2** under the ground.

Living things also swim in the sea, crawl on the sea floor, and burrow beneath it. The smallest living things can only be seen with powerful microscopes. The largest living animal is the blue whale. It is about 35 meters (115 **3** feet) long. In fact, the blue whale is larger than any other animal that ever lived, including the dinosaur. But the blue whale is not the largest living thing. That record belongs to the giant redwood tree. Redwoods grow as tall as 100 meters (330 feet).

All living things, from the smallest to the largest, share four **characteristics** (kar-ik-ter-**is**-tiks). A *characteristic* helps set things apart from others. These four characteristics set living things apart from things that are not alive. All living things need food. All grow and change. All come from the same kind of living things. All show movement. Think of any living thing. Does a dog have each of these characteristics? Do you have them?

Living things show many differences, too. A kitten has fur and four legs. A snake has scales. A bird has feathers and wings. A grasshopper has a hard outer covering. We can use these different **structures** (**struk**-cherz) to help us sort out other kinds of living things. For example, pine trees and oak trees have thick, woody trunks and many branches. These *structures* are characteristics of trees. Pines and oaks belong to a group of living things called trees.

Characteristic: Something that helps set one thing apart from another.

Structure: Part of a living thing, such as a wing, leg, or leaf.

223

Application
Research — Library

Have students do research in the library on common poisonous plants, and how to distinguish them from other plants that they resemble. For example, poison hemlock, a deadly herb, has leaves that resemble parsley and roots like those of the parsnip. The plant is sometimes mistaken for Queen Anne's Lace, a harmless weedy herb closely related to the carrot. Another familiar example of a poisonous plant is poison ivy. Have students write a report on the characteristics which distinguish these plants from harmless or useful plants that they resemble. Students should not be encouraged to try this out in the field, unless under the guidance of a knowledgeable adult.

Exceptional Student
Learning Disabled

Bring in a variety of pictures that illustrate living things. Have the student group pictures according to specific characteristics designated by the teacher. Regroup according to other characteristics. This will help prepare the student for the activity on page 224.

Visually Impaired

Bring in a variety of leaves. Have the student classify the leaves according to the characteristics they can feel, e.g., shape, size.

ACTIVITY

Classifying living things

A. Obtain these materials: paper and pencil.
B. Look at all the living things in the picture. List the ones that have wings. Make another list of the things that do not have wings.
   1. Is this a good way to group things? Why or why not?
C. Group just the animals in the picture according to their structures. Copy the chart below and use it to help you organize the animals. One animal has been done for you.

Wings	Covering	Number of Legs	Kind of Animal
yes	feathers	2	gull

   2. Which animals on your chart would scientists probably group together?
D. Compare your chart with your lists of the living things in the picture that fly and that do not fly.
   3. What living things in the picture do not show up on your chart?
   4. Are they part of another group of living things? Can you name the group?
   5. How are these living things alike?
   6. How are the living things from question 4 different from the ones on your chart? Write a short paragraph describing these differences.

224

ACTIVITY

Skill Development — *Classifying, Following Directions, Comparing and Contrasting*

Teaching Tips — First, ask students to copy the classification chart on the papers they will be using for this activity. You may wish to draw the chart on the chalkboard and ask the class to fill it in as a group.

Answers to Questions — **1.** No. The animals in each group are not similar. **2.** Gull and robin. **3.** Rose bush, grass, any other plants. **4.** Yes, plants. **5.** They do not move, they are rooted in the ground, they are green, they have flowers. **6.** Answers may include a reference to the fact that animals move about from place to place, whereas plants do not. Accept all other reasonable answers.

But pines and oaks are also different in some ways. The leaves of the oak are broad and flat. The leaves of the pine are long and needle-shaped. Pines keep their leaves all year round. Oaks lose theirs in the fall. So pines belong to a different group of trees than oaks. Which of the photographs on the right shows an oak?

We sort things into groups according to ways they are alike and ways they are different. Sorting things into groups is called **classification** (klas-ih-fih-**kay**-shun). We use *classification* every day to make looking for things easier for us. The books in a library are classified by likes and differences. But you have to be careful to pick useful likes and differences. Suppose books were classified according to the colors of their covers. Would that be helpful if you were looking for a book on a certain subject?

There are many kinds of living things, or **organisms**. It would be impossible to study all these *organisms* without classifying them. It would be like trying to find a certain book in a pile of millions of books. With classifications, we can study one group at a time. We can also compare different groups.

Classification: A way of sorting things into groups according to ways they are alike and ways they are different.

Organism: A living thing.

Section Review

Main Ideas: All living things share four characteristics. These set them apart from things that are not alive. Living things with similar structures are classified into groups. Classification helps us compare living things.

Questions: Answer in complete sentences.

1. Name four characteristics that all living things have.
2. In what ways are pine trees and oak trees alike? In what ways are they different?
3. Which of the following are grouped with gulls? **a.** robins **b.** grasshoppers **c.** catfish **d.** eagles **e.** chickadees **f.** wasps. Give a reason for each answer.
4. Why do you think scientists classify living things?

225

SECTION BACKGROUND

The cell is the unit of structure and function in all plants and animals. It is the smallest unit that can carry out the basic processes of life: respiration, digestion, growth, and reproduction.

Many living things are made up of a single cell. Examples are protozoa, bacteria, and some simple algae. Higher plants and animals are made up of many millions of cells. Though each cell in an animal or plant is a unit of life, it is specialized by form and structure to do certain jobs. Nerve cells coordinate body movements. Muscle cells do the actual work of carrying out such movements. Plant cells have developed stiff cell walls made of cellulose. Linked together in enormous numbers, these cells can support the weight of trees hundreds of feet tall.

In this sense, cells are the building blocks of life. But the analogy with bricks or other building blocks is far from perfect. Cells are building blocks that can grow, join together, work together, and repair themselves.

Cells can also reproduce, by dividing to make two new cells. There is a "blueprint" in the cell nucleus which controls cell processes, including reproduction. This blueprint is the coil of nucleic acids in the nucleus. Nucleic acids are found in every living thing.

MATERIALS

11-2.
Building Blocks of Life

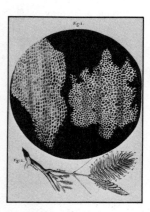

Cells: Tiny living parts, of which all organisms are made.

Membrane: The thin skinlike covering of a cell.

226

What are living things made of? A house may be built of bricks, stone, or wood. Living things are built of tiny "building blocks." Your body is made up of trillions of these building blocks. What are they? When you finish this section, you should be able to:

☐ **A.** Describe four parts of a living *cell* and the job each part does.
☐ **B.** Identify what a *cell* does by its shape.
☐ **C.** Compare and contrast plant and animal *cells*.

The building blocks of living things were discovered by an English scientist, Robert Hooke, over 300 years ago. He was looking at thin slices of cork under a microscope. Cork is made from the outer bark of an oak tree that grows in the Mediterranean area. Under Hooke's microscope, the cork showed a regular pattern of tiny, boxlike, open spaces. The pattern reminded him of tiny rooms. The Latin word for room is *cella*. He named the boxlike structures **cells** (selz).

1

All the activities of life take place in each *cell*. Every cell in your body is a living building block. Each cell takes in food and gets rid of wastes. Each cell needs oxygen. This is true of all plant and animal cells.

Food, water, and oxygen pass into the cell through the cell **membrane** (**mem**-brain). Wastes pass out of the cell through the cell *membrane*.

BASIC TEACHING PLAN
MOTIVATION

Ask students to discuss the number 300,000,000,000. How many times a million is it? *3,000.* How many times 1,000? *300 million.* 100? *3 billion.* This should give students a better idea of the sheer number of "building blocks" in the body of each one of them. Ask them to discuss the idea that each person is made up of 300,000,000,000 tiny, individual, living parts.

Text Questions — What are living things made of? *Cells.*

DEVELOPMENT

1 **Teaching Tips** — Robert Hooke was reminded of a honeycomb when he gave cells their name. Ask students if they have ever seen one. Bring a honeycomb into class for everyone to examine.

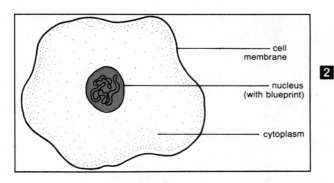

2

Near the center of each cell is the **nucleus** (new-klee-us). Packed tightly within the *nucleus* is a kind of chemical blueprint. A blueprint is a printed plan that people follow when they build something. Under a microscope, a nucleus looks like a tangled mass of string.

This blueprint controls most of the cell's activities. It controls what material the cell makes. It controls how the cell grows and what it does. When a cell splits into two new cells, the nucleus splits, too. A new copy of the blueprint forms. Now each new cell has a nucleus and an exact copy of the original blueprint.

A jellylike liquid surrounds the nucleus. This liquid fills up the rest of the cell. This is the **cytoplasm** (sight-uh-plazm). The *cytoplasm* is where the food, water, and oxygen taken in by the cell are used.

There are many kinds of cells in the human body. Think of all the cells in a girl's body that are working when she is running. Heart muscle cells are working to pump blood faster to her leg muscles. Red blood cells are bringing extra oxygen to the cells in her leg muscles. Messages from her brain are traveling through her nerve cells. These messages are going to her muscles to help control muscle movements.

Running smoothly and keeping your balance is a harder job than it looks. To do these things, it takes trillions of body cells working together as a team.

Nucleus: The part of the cell that controls its activities.

Cytoplasm: The liquid inside the cell where the cell's activities take place.

3

227

---

2 **Skill Development** — The students can use the *illustration* to review the parts of a cell and their functions.

3 **Teaching Tips** — Tell students to stand beside their desks and run quietly in place. As they exercise, direct their conscious attention to what is going on in their bodies. (Muscles flex and pull, feet are raised and lowered, each foot bends in turn, arms swing, the heart pumps faster, and so on.) Ask students what they think their lives would be like if they had to make conscious decisions to do each of these things in turn as they ran.

EXTENSIONS

Enrichment
Research — Library

Have students find out how muscles work in pairs to move the forearm. Why is a pair of muscles necessary? (Because muscles can only move the bone by contracting and pulling. Thus, the triceps muscle causes the forearm to extend, while the biceps flexes the forearm.)

Have students draw a diagram showing the arrangement of the biceps, triceps, upper arm bone and the two forearm bones and how they move.

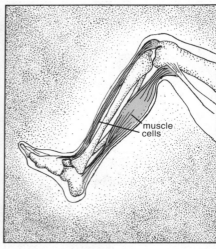

muscle cells

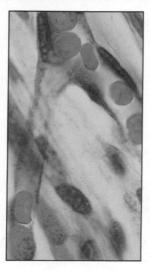

Chlorophyll: Green material in plants' cells that helps them make their own food.

Look at the drawing of the muscle cells that move the girl's leg. Muscle cells are long. When a muscle cell is doing its work, it pulls together and gets shorter. It is much like what happens when you stretch a rubber band and then let it snap back again. Why do you think muscle cells are long? Does it help them work better? **4**

Red blood cells are smaller than most body cells. They are shaped like tiny round coins. Red blood cells carry oxygen all over the body. They must pass through very small blood vessels, not much bigger than the red blood cells themselves. Does their shape fit their job?

Plant cells have special shapes and special jobs, too. **5** Root cells at the tip of a plant's roots are long and slender. Root cells grow rapidly, spreading through the ground.

Cells inside the trunk of a tree form long tubes. Through these tubes, food and water travel up from the roots to the branches and leaves.

Green leaves have special cells that contain **chloro-** **6** **phyll** (**klor**-uh-fil). *Chlorophyll* is a green material that takes energy from sunlight. Leaf cells use that energy to make their own food.

228

4 **Text Questions** — Why do you think muscle cells are long? Does it help them work better? *Yes, because they do work by contracting, getting shorter.* Does the shape of red blood cells fit their job? *Yes, they are small and round to fit through tiny, tube-shaped blood vessels.*

5 **Teaching Tips** — Gently remove a plant from its pot. To do this, hold the plant near the soil line with one hand and turn it upside down. Gently tap the pot rim against the table until the plant drops out. The students can then observe the way roots grow in soil.

6 **Teaching Tips** — Bring in a living plant and have the students observe the parts that contain chlorophyll. These parts will be green (usually the stems and leaves).

Exceptional Student
Visually Impaired

Make a three-dimensional diagram of different cells. Have the student feel the various parts. Compare the structures of the cells to their functions.

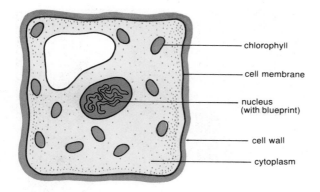

chlorophyll

cell membrane

nucleus
(with blueprint)

cell wall

cytoplasm

Chlorophyll is one thing that makes plant cells different from animal cells. Another is the **cell wall**. The *cell wall* is a sturdy, woody layer around the cell membrane of plant cells. What Robert Hooke actually saw through his microscope were the cell walls of the cork, or bark, of an oak tree. The insides of the cells had dried out.

Cell wall: A stiff protective layer around plant cells.

Section Review

Main Ideas: Cells are the building blocks of all animals and plants. Cells do many different jobs and have different shapes. All plant and animal cells need food, water, and oxygen. Plant cells have chlorophyll and cell walls, which animal cells do not have.

Questions: Answer in complete sentences.

1. Name three parts that every cell has. Explain what each part does.
2. Name two different kinds of cells in your body. Describe how each is shaped. How does its shape help it do its job?
3. Trees are tall and heavy. What structures in their cells might be useful for carrying this weight?
4. Name two things found in plant cells, but not in animal cells.

229

EXTENSIONS
Enrichment
Activity

A. Have your students scrape the insides of their cheeks with a flat toothpick and spread the scraping on a microscope slide.
B. Have them add a drop of water and a drop of tincture of iodine stain, and then cover the slide with another microscope slide.
C. Then instruct your class to examine the material through a microscope, moving the slide around until they see a clearly defined cheek cell.
D. Your students can then identify and draw the parts of the cell.

To observe plant cells, students can peel off one layer of the skin of an onion and examine it with a magnifying glass or microscope. They should draw a diagram of what they observe. They should pay particular attention to cell walls and the distribution of chlorophyll within the cells.

SECTION REVIEW

Answers to Questions
1. The membrane is the outer covering, and allows passage of food, water, and oxygen into the cell and wastes out of it; the nucleus is the cell's center and controls most of its activities; the cytoplasm is where the cell's activities are carried on.
2. Muscle cells are long because they work by getting shorter, contracting; red blood cells are small and round so that they can pass easily through blood vessels.
3. Cell walls
4. Chlorophyll, cell wall

SECTION BACKGROUND

Viruses have been called half-living things. A virus is far simpler than a cell. It is a coil of nucleic acid surrounded by a protective protein coat. Outside of the cell it infects, a virus is totally inert. It does not respire, change, or grow. Even when it penetrates a cell, it merely takes over the cell's stores of chemicals and energy in order to reproduce. The cell is killed in the process. The newly made viruses can infect other similar cells in the same way.

Euglena is a one-celled organism. Like an animal, it swims about freely. Like a plant, it uses chlorophyll for photosynthesis.

Bacteria are one-celled organisms that have cell walls as do plants. However, unlike plants almost all bacteria depend on other living things, or their remains, for food. Organisms such as viruses, bacteria, and euglenas have led scientists to create a third kingdom of living things. This is the kingdom of protists.

MATERIALS

large jar of freshly collected pond water, cover slips, glass slides, microscope, pencil, drawing paper, writing paper

11-3.

The Simplest Organisms

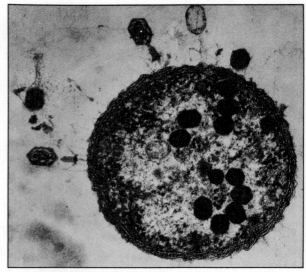

What does the picture show? Are these strange crystals or creatures from another world? Look out. Creatures like these may already be in your town. When you finish this section, you should be able to:

☐ **A.** Describe how *viruses* are like both living and nonliving things.

☐ **B.** Explain how *protists* are like both plants and animals.

☐ **C.** Explain how *bacteria* are classified.

The picture shows tiny structures that are shaped like crystals. They are attacking a living organism made of only one cell.

Each crystal is a **virus** (vy-ris). *Viruses* are real scientific puzzles. Viruses are very small. The period at the end of this sentence could hold about 50,000 viruses. Many hundreds of viruses could fit inside a single cell.

You have learned that the nucleus holds a kind of blueprint for running a cell. Most viruses are nothing more than a similar blueprint wrapped in a protective layer.

Viruses: Particles much simpler than cells. Viruses can only reproduce inside living cells.

230

BASIC TEACHING PLAN
MOTIVATION

Ask students to think about these pictures. What, besides a spacecraft, a crystal, or an extraterrestrial, can they imagine these strange shapes might be? Does it occur to any students that these viruses shown are destructive? These viruses are T_2 bacteriophage attacking a cell of *E. coli*, a common bacteria.

Virus blueprints are very different from the blueprints inside living cells. They are a master plan for just one thing: making more viruses. The new viruses will be like the ones from which the blueprints came.

This can only happen inside a living cell that a virus attacks. The virus injects its own blueprint into the living cell. The virus blueprint blocks the cell's own blueprint from working. Instead, the virus blueprint runs the cell. The cell begins making new viruses.

The cell keeps making viruses until its store of food and energy is used up. Then the cell dies. Its membrane bursts. Hundreds of viruses spill out. They can attack other cells. The diagram below shows this process.

Viruses cause many diseases in humans. Some diseases caused by viruses are smallpox, colds, polio, and flu. Smallpox and polio are very rare these days. Special medicines help the body fight these viruses.

Are viruses alive? Scientists don't agree on that. *Sometimes* might be a good answer. Viruses show signs of life only when they are inside cells. A virus is not a cell. It does not feed, grow, or breathe. It has none of the parts of a cell, except a blueprint.

Most scientists think viruses are on the borderline between living and nonliving things. By studying them, scientists are sharpening their ideas about what life is.

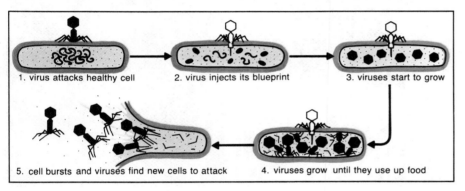

1. virus attacks healthy cell   2. virus injects its blueprint   3. viruses start to grow

5. cell bursts and viruses find new cells to attack   4. viruses grow until they use up food

231

DEVELOPMENT

1   **Teaching Tips** — Ask students what the word *virus* means to them. Most of them will probably answer that they have "had a virus" — a cold or a stomach "bug." Viruses can cause diseases. Point out that viral diseases vary greatly in severity — and vary according to the population in which they are active, as well. At the same time that polio epidemics were terrifying American parents, this disease was widespread among the people of India. However, because it was so common there, the population had built up an immunity to it, and it presented little health threat.

2   **Teaching Tips** — Ask students to recall the four characteristics of living things. The only characteristic viruses share with living things is the ability to reproduce.

3   **Skill Development** — Based on the evidence they now have, some scientists have concluded that viruses are a form of life. Ask students to use the information in the text to form their own *conclusion*. Encourage a discussion. Emphasize that science is a matter of ideas, theories, and speculation, as well as of hard fact.

EXTENSIONS

Reinforcement
Research

Challenge students to find out how euglena is classified in several different textbooks. These need not be up to date. Let them have a debate on whether a euglena is an animal, a plant, a bit of both, or an organism that should be in a group separate from either plants or animals. They should use the information from the different textbooks to support their positions. They should be made aware that there are no final right answers to this question.

Euglena: A one-celled organism that is like both an animal and a plant.

Protists: A group of living things that are not animals or plants, but have some characteristics of each.

Ameba: A one-celled animallike protist with no regular shape.

Paramecium: An animallike protist shaped like a slipper.

This picture shows another scientific puzzle. It's a **euglena** (yoo-**glee**-nuh). The *euglena* is a one-celled organism. Until recently, scientists classified all living things as plants or animals. What is a euglena?

The euglena swims through the water. So it could be an animal. But the euglena also has chlorophyll. Only plant cells have chlorophyll. So the euglena could be a plant.

4 Scientists argued about this. Then they realized that the old animal-plant classification system did not work for living things such as the euglena. Scientists made a new classification of living things called **protists** (**pro**-tists). So scientists now classify living things into three main groups: animals, plants, and *protists*.

Protists are usually very small. They may look like animals or like plants. One example of an animallike protist is the **ameba** (uh-**mee**-buh). *Ameba* comes from the Greek word that means *change*. As the picture on the left shows, amebas can be almost any shape!

The **paramecium** (par-uh-**mee**-see-um) is another animallike protist. *Paramecium* comes from the Greek word for *oblong*. A paramecium is shaped like a slipper. Both the ameba and paramecium live in water.

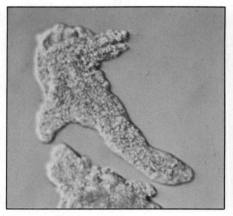 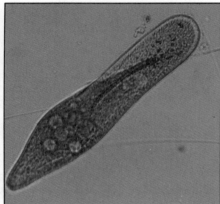

232

---

4 **Teaching Tips** — Point out to students that sometimes old classification systems break down and must be replaced by new ones. That's what happened when scientists had to invent the classification of protists for living things that were not clearly either plants or animals.

Exceptional Student
Visually Impaired

Using string, outline an ameba and a paramecium. Allow the student to feel their shapes.

ACTIVITY

Observing protists

A. Obtain these materials: large jar of freshly collected pond water, cover slips, glass slides, eyedropper, lamp, microscope, pencil, drawing paper.

B. Put a drop of water on a slide. Cover the slide with a cover slip.

C. Put the jar aside for a couple of hours in a cool, dark place. Set a high-intensity lamp next to it so that the strongest light hits the water near the top.

D. Put the slide on the microscope. Turn the microscope barrel down until it nearly touches the slide. Look through the microscope. Raise the knob slowly until you can see the water clearly. You may have to focus up and down slightly to see different organisms.

   1. How many kinds of protists can you see? Look carefully. Paramecia dart quickly in a spiral path. Amebas are harder to see because they are nearly colorless. Changing the light will help you see some organisms better.

   2. Draw the protists that you can see. Don't try to make the drawing look like a drawing in a book. Label any parts of cells that you can see.

E. Use an eyedropper to take one drop of water from the brightly lit part of the jar and one from the dimly lit part. Put one drop on each of the two slides. Label one D for dim, and the other L for light.

F. Look at the dark slide under the microscope.

   3. Do you see any organisms?

G. Repeat the observation with the light slide.

   4. Did you see more or fewer organisms on the light slide?

   5. Write down what you have learned from this activity.

233

Enrichment
Activity

Students may wish to "grow" their own garden of protozoa. Have them gather some hay or grass and steep it in hot water for about an hour. Then strain the water into a dish or a jar. After a day or so the water should become cloudy. Have the students examine some drops of it under a microscope and draw any organisms that they see. Have them examine the water each day for a week or more and draw some of the organisms that they see. Do the kinds of organisms change? Ask the students to explain what might be causing the change, and where the organisms are coming from. If the students wish to identify and learn more about their protozoa, a good reference book is *Nature Discoveries With a Hand Lens* by Richard Headstrom, published by Dover in 1981.

ACTIVITY

Skill Development — *Observing, Concluding, and Generalizing*

Teaching Tips — This may be the students' first experience with working with microscopes. They will need help preparing slides, focusing, and so on. Help students work with different samples of water until they have seen a variety of organisms. Encourage students to draw what they actually see. Explain that doing so is more important — more "scientific" — than convincing yourself that you see what you were "supposed" to see. Students should see few amebas and paramecia because they avoid light. Euglenas move toward it.

Answers to Questions — 1. Answers will vary. 2. Drawings will vary. Students should use labels, "membrane," "nucleus," and "cytoplasm." 3. Answers will vary. There should be fewer amebas and paramecia. 4. Fewer organisms were observed in bright light, since most protozoa avoid bright light and heat. Euglenas move toward light. This is a useful response for euglena, since they carry on photosynthesis.

Exceptional Student
Visually Impaired
This activity may not be appropriate for the student who has severe visual impairment.

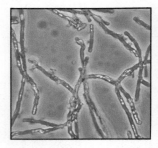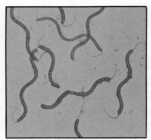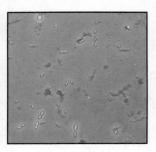

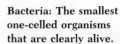

Bacteria: The smallest one-celled organisms that are clearly alive.

Another group of very small protists are the **bacteria** (bak-**teer**-ee-uh). *Bacteria* have a simple cell structure. It takes over 100 million bacteria to cover a penny. Bacteria are classified according to their shapes. Some are shaped like **rods**. Some are **spiral**. Some are **round**.

Some bacteria cause disease. Most do not. Many are necessary to life on earth. They help break down the **5** remains of dead plants and animals. This returns materials that are needed for plant growth to the soil.

Section Review

Main Ideas: Viruses are on the borderline between living and nonliving things. Protists are a group of living things that are not considered plants or animals. Bacteria are classified by their shapes.

Questions: Answer in complete sentences.
1. What are the three main groups of living things?
2. In what way are viruses like living things? In what way are viruses different from living things?
3. How is euglena like a plant? How is it like an animal?
4. How are bacteria classified?
5. Scientists have changed the classifications of some organisms. Do you think they might change them again in the future? Why or why not?
6. Name three protists you could find in pond water.

234

Have you ever picked up seaweed from an ocean beach? It feels tough and rubbery. Seaweed contains a jellylike material. This material is often added to candies and jellies to keep them from being too watery. When you finish this section you should be able to:

☐ **A.** Compare and contrast *algae* and *fungi*.
☐ **B.** List two ways that *algae* are important.
☐ **C.** Give examples of both useful and harmful *fungi*.

1   Seaweeds are called the "grasses of the sea." But seaweeds are simpler plants than grasses. Seaweeds do not have stems, roots, or leaves. They are **algae** (al-jee). *Algae* are plantlike protists that have chlorophyll. Most algae grow in water. Seaweed grows in the ocean and supplies food for many organisms in the sea. Some people eat seaweed for food. Other people use material from seaweed to thicken foods like jellies. The largest kind of seaweed is **kelp** shown on the lower right. *Kelp* grows about 35 m (115 ft) long.

2   Other kinds of algae grow in fresh water such as ponds. One kind is **spirogyra** (spy-roh-**jy**-ruh), shown below. Each strand of *spirogyra* is one cell thick. The chlorophyll you see inside each strand gives spirogyra its name which means a "turning spiral."

11-4.
Algae and Fungi

Algae: Plantlike protists that have chlorophyll and grow in water.

Kelp: The largest kind of seaweed.

Spirogyra: A freshwater alga one cell wide and many cells long.

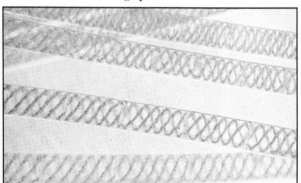

235

SECTION BACKGROUND

Algae are simple plantlike organisms ranging in size from single cells to large seaweeds hundreds of feet long. Algae possess chlorophyll and so can photosynthesize their own food — characteristics they share with higher plants. But because they lack roots, stems, and leaves, some biologists classify algae with the protists. This is the classification we use in this book. There is no complete agreement among biologists on how to classify borderline organisms, such as algae. Because biologists are always discovering new facts about living things, classifications will change.

    Fungi are another group of protists. Like plants, they grow in a fixed place. Unlike plants, they do not have chlorophyll. Some fungi grow as parasites on or in other living things. This includes the skin fungus that causes athlete's foot. Other fungi grow on dead or dying organisms. Many molds help to enrich soil by digesting the remains of animals and plants. The antibiotic penicillin is derived from the bread mold penicillium. Penicillin is made by the mold as a way of protecting itself against certain kinds of bacteria.

MATERIALS

BASIC TEACHING PLAN

MOTIVATION

Bring in examples of molds, algae, and fungi that we use in our everyday lives. Ask students how we use them. Suggested items besides those in the text include mushrooms, seaweed cakes, and diatomaceous earth.

DEVELOPMENT

1 **Teaching Tips** — Ask students to describe seaweed. Listen carefully to see whether or not they use the words "roots," "stems," or "leaves" to tell how seaweed looks. If they do, point out that seaweeds have none of these plant parts.

2 **Skill Development** — Students can *classify* seaweeds by creating a class collection. Are they surprised to find that there are many different kinds of seaweed? Go outside to a grassy area and examine the different plants present. How many kinds of grass and weeds can students find? How do these numbers compare to the class seaweed collection?

EXTENSIONS

Application
Activity

Students can grow a large supply of algae which they can then observe under the microscope. They will need a clear quart water bottle and access to an aquarium. Have them follow these directions:

A. Fill the bottle with water and let it stand overnight.

B. Take a small sample of water from a working aquarium and place it in the jar.

C. Place the jar in a sunny spot and observe it for a few days. The water should gradually turn green as the algae grow.

Enrichment
Activity

Students can strain plankton from ponds or saltwater bays. Have them do the following:

A. Make a cone of the muslin or discarded sheeting. The cone should be approximately 30 cm (12 in.) across the mouth and 50 to 60 cm (20 in. to 26 in.) long.

B. Fasten the top of the cone to a ring of coat hanger wire, and after cutting off a small piece of the cone tip, fasten the tip with heavy string to the mouth of a baby food jar.

C. Several buckets of water from the pond or bay should be poured into the mouth of the cone. Excess water will escape through the cloth and the plankton and will concentrate in the jar.

D. The plankton can then be viewed with a microscope.

E. Put a drop of water on a slide and observe it under a microscope. Draw a diagram of any organisms seen.

Exceptional Student
Visually Impaired
Learning Disabled

Bring in seaweed, grass, and a green plant. Have the student feel each. Compare and contrast characteristics.

3

Fungi: Plantlike protists that cannot make their own food.

4 Other plantlike protists are the **fungi** (**fun**-jy). Like algae, *fungi* do not have roots, stems, or leaves. Unlike algae, fungi do not have chlorophyll. Without chlorophyll they cannot make their own food.

Fungi live in or on other organisms. Some fungi grow on living organisms. Others grow on dead ones. The photographs show some different kinds of fungi.

Like some bacteria, fungi break down animal and plant matter. This helps return useful chemicals to the soil.

5

236

3 **Teaching Tips** — This interesting looking fungus is known as a coral fungus.

4 **Skill Development** — Students can build their science vocabulary by learning to distinguish the singular from the plural in the following science words: algae is the plural of alga and fungi is the plural of fungus.

5 **Teaching Tips** — Ask students whether they think that fungi can be harmful. Remind them that mushrooms are fungi. Warn them never to experiment with touching or tasting mushrooms they may find growing wild.

Molds are fungi. Some molds are harmful. Have you ever had athlete's foot? It is caused by a fungus growing on the skin of the feet. Do you think that fungus is more likely to grow on dry skin or on wet skin? Another kind of mold spoils bread. Common bread mold is shown in the photograph above.

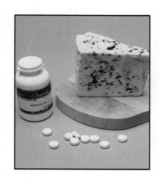

Some molds are useful. Certain molds are used to make some kinds of cheeses like the one shown. A similar mold that grows on fruits is used to make the medicine we know as penicillin. The penicillin mold makes peni-
6 cillin to protect itself from bacteria. We use it as a medicine to cure diseases caused by bacteria.

Section Review

Main Ideas: Algae are plantlike protists with chlorophyll. Most of them live in water. Fungi are plantlike protists without chlorophyll. Fungi usually live on dead or living organisms.

Questions: Answer in complete sentences.

1. How are algae like other green plants?
2. What common features of green plants do algae lack?
3. How are algae useful to us?
4. Are fungi helpful or harmful? Explain.

237

EXTENSIONS

Reinforcement
*Science Skills —
Observing, Inferring*

Have students obtain some fresh edible mushrooms. Have them cut off the stems close to the caps, place some of the caps, topside up, on light colored paper squares and some dark paper. Invert a jar or bowl over each mushroom cap to keep drafts away, and leave overnight. The next day, students will see dark or light colored powdery patterns. These are spores that have fallen from the cap which is the fruiting body of the mushroom. They will be arranged in a spokelike pattern because they fall from in between the flaps that form a radial pattern under the cap.

6 **Teaching Tips** — Tell students that prejudices against mold were one factor that helped delay the discovery of penicillin. In the early years of this century, student doctors who were growing deadly bacteria cultures in the lab occasionally found those cultures "ruined" by molds. The students were scolded by their teachers and told to improve their work! Without that attitude, penicillin might have been in use long before Sir Alexander Fleming discovered it in 1928.

SECTION REVIEW

Answers to Questions
1. Algae have chlorophyll and make their own food.
2. Algae lack roots, stems, and leaves.
3. They're used to make substances like candies and jellies firmer.
4. Fungi are both helpful and harmful; they help break down plant and animal matter to fertilize the soil; certain molds are used to make cheeses and a vital medicine, penicillin, but fungi can also cause such diseases as athlete's foot.

Enrichment
Activity

Have students obtain a slice of apple, a spoonful of cream cheese, and a small sample of jelly. Have them seal each sample in a separate plastic bag and place all the bags in a warm, dark place for several days, or until there are signs of mold sprouting on them. Have students look at the mold through a hand lens. Call their attention to the round tops on some of the threadlike growth. These are where the mold spores are produced. These fruiting bodies are often different colors in different molds.

CHAPTER REVIEW

Science Words
1. Cytoplasm
2. protists
3. viruses
4. membrane
5. algae
6. nucleus
7. euglena
8. chlorophyll
9. bacteria
10. fungi

SUGGESTED WORKSHEET MASTERS
pp. T–219n,o

SUGGESTED TEST MASTERS
pp. T–219d,e

CHAPTER REVIEW

Science Words
Unscramble the letters to find the terms that fit the definitions.

1. Cell liquid: CLAPSMTYO
2. Organisms that are not plants or animals: TIPORTSS
3. Particles that only show signs of life inside a live cell: UVRIESS
4. Thin layer covering a cell: MBMRANEE
5. Plantlike protists with chlorophyll: GAAEL
6. Control center of a cell: CUSENUL
7. A type of protist: ANUGLEE
8. Helps green plants to make food: YLLCHPHLROO
9. Smallest living one-celled organisms: TERIABAC
10. Plantlike protists without chlorophyll: GINUF

Questions: Answer in complete sentences.

1. List four ways that a cat and a euglena are alike.
2. Could classification be useful to other people besides scientists? Explain.
3. Are words in a dictionary classified? Tell how they are classified. Why do you think that words in a dictionary should be classified?
4. Are plant cells and animal cells exactly alike? Explain.
5. Plant cells that have chlorophyll are often flat and thin. Can you explain how this might help these cells do their job?
6. How does a virus make new viruses? Is this way different from the way other organisms make new organisms?
7. Why did scientists decide to classify some living things as protists?
8. Why are ameba and paramecium grouped together?
9. When might you eat seaweed? When might you eat mold?
10. How are algae and fungi alike? In what ways are they different?

238

Answers to Questions
1. Both need food, grow and change, come from the same kind of living things, and move about.
2. Yes. Classification would be useful to anyone who works with or must organize large numbers of objects, long lists, and so on.
3. Yes, they are arranged alphabetically so we can find them easily.
4. No. Plant cells have chlorophyll and cell walls. Animal cells don't.
5. Chlorophyll needs sunlight to help a plant manufacture food, and flat, thin leaves allow more sunlight to react with the chlorophyll.
6. A virus makes new viruses by entering a living cell and making new viruses until the cell bursts apart and releases the viruses. Yes, viruses are the only organisms that make new organisms in this way.
7. Scientists classify some living things as protists because they are not wholly plant nor wholly animal.
8. Because they are both single-celled animal-like organisms.
9. You might eat seaweed in candies or jellies, or mold in cheeses.
10. Algae and fungi are alike because neither has roots, stems, or leaves; different because algae have chlorophyll; fungi do not.

CHAPTER 12

PLANTS

Does your state have a flag? What colors are in it? If plants had a flag, it would be green. Trees are green. So is grass. In damp places, still smaller plants cover the ground and rocks with a green carpet. Why do you think that most of the plants you see are green? What do all

12-1.
Classifying Plants

239

CHAPTER OBJECTIVES

1. Explain how plants are able to make their own food and why all life on earth depends on this ability.
2. Describe the functions of roots, stems, and leaves.
3. Compare different root systems and types of stems and leaves.
4. Describe how mosses and ferns grow and reproduce.
5. Explain how gymnosperms and angiosperms reproduce.

SECTION BACKGROUND

All green plants have chlorophyll. Chlorophyll absorbs energy from sunlight. The plant makes use of this energy in two ways. Part of it is used to split water into hydrogen and oxygen. The oxygen is released into the air.

This process is vital to life on earth. Oxygen is constantly consumed by living things and converted into carbon dioxide. Photosynthesis replenishes the oxygen supply.

The second phase of photosynthesis uses energy from the sun to combine the hydrogen split from the water with the carbon and oxygen in carbon dioxide. This forms carbohydrates—starches and sugars. Only plants can make these basic foods. All living things depend on plants or they eat other organisms that depend on plants for food.

MATERIALS

two pots with soil, two lima beans, watering can

Exceptional Student IEP Chapter Goal

When requested by the teacher, the student will name the four main types of plants and state one characteristic of each.

BASIC TEACHING PLAN

MOTIVATION

Roses are red, violets are blue . . . Ask: How many different colors can plants be? What color do all plants have in common? *Green*. What makes plants green? *Chlorophyll*. At what time of the year are plants green? *In the spring and summer*. Does this suggest that the green color may have something to do with plant growth? *Chlorophyll, which is green, allows plants to make their own food which is used in growth*. How many different green plants do you see in the photograph? *Answers will vary*. This photograph of a temperate rain forest in Olympic National Park in Washington will give students an idea of the great variety of green plant life.

plants have that makes them green? When you finish this section, you should be able to:

☐ **A.** Explain what green plants need to make their own food.
☐ **B.** Explain why all living things depend on plants.
☐ **C.** Describe the steps in the carbon dioxide-oxygen cycle.

There are many different kinds of plants. Most of the **1** plants you know best have roots, stems, and leaves. The tiny plants that cover soil and cling to rocks do not.

Some plants, such as rosebushes, have flowers. Other plants, such as pine trees, have cones. Scientists use structures like flowers and cones to divide plants into groups. However, all plants have something in common. **2** They are green. In plant cells, the green comes from a material known as chlorophyll. Plants use chlorophyll to make their own food. *Chloro* means "green" and *phyll* means "leaf." Chlorophyll is usually found in leaf cells. Often it is in stem cells, too. Chlorophyll makes these cells look green. The photograph on the left shows how chlorophyll looks in a leaf cell.

Plants use chlorophyll to make their own food during **photosynthesis** (foh-toh-**sin**-thuh-sis). *Photo* means "light." *Synthesis* means "putting together." That's just what *photosynthesis* is: "putting together with light."

Photosynthesis: The process by which plants use light energy to make food.

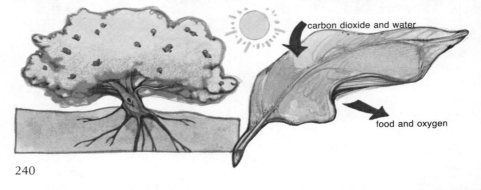

carbon dioxide and water

food and oxygen

240

DEVELOPMENT

1 **Teaching Tips** — This is a good time to expand — or start — a class plant shelf. Make sure you have an example from each of the four groups of plants that students will learn about in Section 12.3 — a moss, a fern, a flowering plant, and a cone-bearing plant, such as a seedling fir tree.

2 **Skill Development** — The students should note how scientists classify plants by their roots, stems, leaves, flowers, and cones.

ACTIVITY

Do plants need light to make chlorophyll?

A. Obtain these materials: 2 pots with soil, 2 lima beans, watering can.

B. Place 1 lima bean on soil in each pot. Cover with about 1 cm of soil. Place both pots in a sunny window. Keep the soil moist.

C. After both plants have formed green leaves, put 1 pot in a dark place. Keep both plants watered.
   1. Predict how the 2 plants will look in a week.

D. Examine the 2 plants a week later.
   2. How do your observations compare with your prediction?
   3. Which plant looks healthier? Can you explain why?
   4. What color are the leaves of the plant that has been in the dark? What is missing from these leaves?

E. Place the "dark" plant in the sun for a week.
   5. What color are the leaves of the "dark" plant after a week in the sun? Why do you think this happened?
   6. Write a conclusion about this activity. Use the terms *chlorophyll* and *sunlight*.

Chlorophyll traps energy from sunlight. Leaf cells use this energy to make food from water and carbon dioxide. Carbon dioxide is a gas found in the air. After making food, the plant releases oxygen into the air. For food to be made, light is needed. Light is also needed for the cells to make chlorophyll.

Plants use sunlight, carbon dioxide, and water to make oxygen and simple foods. These foods are sugars and

241

ACTIVITY

Skill Development — *Comparing and Contrasting; Finding Cause and Effect; Predicting; Concluding and Generalizing*

Teaching Tips — Plants must be cared for according to directions in order for this experiment to work. Appoint individual students or student committees to take responsibility for watering the plants and for moving them into and out of sunlight as directed. Ask students to label each pot according to whether it is to be the "dark" or "light" one.

Answers to Questions — **1.** Students should predict that the plant kept in the dark will not do as well as the other.   **2.** Answers will vary.   **3.** The plant in the light looked healthier. Plants need sunlight for photosynthesis and the production of chlorophyll. The plant in the dark was producing no food or chlorophyll.   **4.** The leaves would be light green or whitish, because they lacked chlorophyll. **5.** The leaves would turn a darker, healthier green, because they were getting needed sunlight.   **6.** Responses will vary.

3

carbon dioxide

oxygen

EXTENSIONS

Enrichment
Science Skills —
Comparing and Contrasting

Challenge students to discover whether the color of the light that a plant receives will affect the rate of photosynthesis in that plant. They can use lima bean seedlings such as were used for the Activity in this lesson. The students should:

A. Prepare four cardboard boxes open at the tops and bottoms. Over the tops of three of the boxes, they can place cellophane of different colors, taping it to the sides to keep it from blowing off. Red, green, and blue are good colors to try. The fourth box may be covered with clear cellophane so the plant in this box will get full spectrum light.

B. Pot the seedlings and put them together on a sunny windowsill. Do not put them over a radiator. Place a box over each seedling. Water the seedlings equally.

C. Record their results after the plants are exposed for a week and report on their conclusions. Students may want to follow this up with library research on which colors produce photosynthesis most efficiently. Generally, plants respond best to red light and least to green light.

starches, such as those found in apples and potatoes. All animals depend on plants for food. They either eat plants or they eat other animals that eat plants.

All animals also depend on plants for oxygen. Animals take in food and oxygen for energy. Their cells combine oxygen and food to make energy. Animals also produce carbon dioxide and water. The plants use the carbon dioxide and water to make oxygen and food again.

What you have just read about is the carbon dioxide-oxygen cycle. The arrows show the cycle. It is called a cycle because the steps are repeated over and over.

Section Review

Main Ideas: Plants need chlorophyll, sunlight, carbon dioxide, and water to make their food. All animals depend upon plants for food and oxygen.

Questions: Answer in complete sentences.

1. What is photosynthesis? What do plants need for photosynthesis?
2. Would a houseplant stay healthy in a dark room? Explain your answer.
3. Do meat-eating animals need green plants? Why or why not?
4. What are the steps in the carbon dioxide-oxygen cycle?

242

Exceptional Student
Learning Disabled

To help the students retain this concept, have them illustrate and discuss the carbon dioxide-oxygen cycle in common animals and plants.

3 **Skill Development** — Students will be able to *identify cause and effect relationships* in both photosynthesis and in the oxygen-carbon dioxide cycle depicted here.

SECTION REVIEW
Answers to Questions
1. Photosynthesis is "putting together with light"; it is the way plants use water, sunlight, and carbon dioxide to make sugars and starches; chlorophyll, sunlight, water, carbon dioxide.
2. No. Plants need sun for photosynthesis and the production of chlorophyll.
3. Yes, because meat-eaters may eat animals that eat only plants.
4. Plants use carbon dioxide, water, and sunlight, along with their own chlorophyll to make food; the plants give off oxygen, which is breathed in by animals; the animals breathe out carbon dioxide, which is used by plants.

Do you eat roots? Do you eat stems and leaves? When you eat a salad, you probably eat all three. Which parts of the plant are the vegetables that are shown in the photograph below? What jobs do roots, stems, and leaves do in a living plant? When you finish this section, you should be able to:

☐ **A.** Describe the basic jobs of *roots*, *stems*, and *leaves*.

☐ **B.** Compare two types of root systems.

☐ **C.** Compare the stem of a woody plant with the stem of a nonwoody plant.

Roots, such as those of the radish and carrot, are storehouses of food for the plant. That's why they are good for us to eat. After plants make food, they store it in the *roots*. Roots also keep the plant in the ground. They take up water and minerals from the soil.

The water and minerals flow upward through the roots to the **stem** of the plant. Usually the *stem* is above ground. The stem supports the part of a plant that is above ground. It is a plant's transportation system. There are two systems of tubes in the stem. One carries the minerals and water from the roots to the **leaves**. Inside the *leaves* food is made. The other tube system in the stem carries food from the leaves to the stem and the roots.

12-2.
Roots, Stems, and Leaves

Root: The plant structure that takes in water and keeps the plant in the ground.

Stem: The plant structure that carries food and water through the plant and that also gives it support.

Leaf: The plant structure that usually makes food.

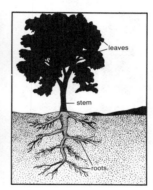

243

SECTION BACKGROUND

Roots, stems, and leaves are special structures in higher plants. Roots absorb water and dissolved minerals from the soil. They anchor the plant firmly in the ground. The roots of some plants are also used for food storage. This is true of carrots and radishes.

The part of the root that first grows out of a seed is the primary root. In some plants, such as the dandelion, sweet clover, plantain, and alfalfa, this root remains the main root of the plant. This taproot grows deep into the soil. It can supply the plant with water long after the upper part of the soil has dried out. In other plants, such as grass, the roots spread widely through the soil, forming many fine branches. For this reason, grasses are important in keeping the soil from being blown away by the wind.

Stems are specialized for conducting minerals and water up from the roots to the leaves, through a network of tubes. The veins in a leaf form the upper end of this network of tubes. Food is manufactured in the leaf by photosynthesis. Food and water are conducted downward from the leaf to the rest of the plant through another network of tubes. These two networks of tubes make up the vascular system of higher plants. In woody plants, such as shrubs and trees, the wood supports the parts of the plant that are above ground.

MATERIALS

glass, water, food coloring, scissors, long-stemmed white flower, hand lens

BASIC TEACHING PLAN
MOTIVATION

Students will find that they do eat roots, stems, and leaves.

Text Questions — Which parts of the plant are the vegetables in this picture? *Students will probably identify leaves (lettuce), roots (radish, carrot), and stem (celery).*

DEVELOPMENT

1 **Teaching Tips** — Do not water a classroom plant, such as a geranium, for four or five days, then ask students to *observe* it. They will see that the leaves hang limply, and even the stems may appear a little bent. Ask students to *hypothesize* a reason for this. The roots are no longer gathering, and the stem transporting, water to the upper stem and leaves.

Enrichment
Activity

How do growing roots react to moisture? To find out, students may start several seedlings near one end of a clear glass tray. The seedlings should be close enough to the edge of the tray so that the roots will be visible. Once the seedlings have sprouted, the soil around them should not be watered. Instead, a sponge should be placed in the soil at the other end of the tray so that just the top of the sponge is above the surface of the soil. The sponge should be kept moist. Challenge the students to explain why the roots grow the way they do.

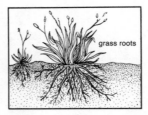

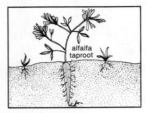

Taproot: The main root of a root system.

There are two kinds of root systems. One is shallow, with many small branches. The other has one main root. Grass has the first kind of root system. Grasses often grow on wide, flat plains. In summer, hot, strong winds blow over the plains. They dry out the ground fast after rain. The shallow roots of the grass take in water before it dries up.

The grass roots also help to hold the soil in place. Have you ever tried to pull grassy weeds out of the ground? The soil clings to the roots in a large clump. Without a cover of grass, soil may wash away in floods or blow away in dust storms.

Another plant that grows on hot, dry plains is alfalfa, shown on page 245. It has the other kind of root system. Alfalfa has one big main root, the **taproot**. Like a drill looking for water, the *taproot* digs into the ground. It may grow down 4.5 meters (15 ft) in a single season!

2

ACTIVITY

How do materials move up the stems of plants?

A. Obtain these materials: glass, water, food coloring, scissors, long-stemmed white flower, hand lens.

B. Fill a glass one-quarter full of water. Add a few drops of food coloring.

C. Trim the end of the stem of a fresh long-stemmed white flower. Put it in the glass and leave overnight.
  1. What does the flower look like the next day? Why?

D. Use the scissors to cut the stem above the water line. Look at the cut top of the stem in the glass. Use a hand lens.
  2. What do you see?
  3. What was it that transported water up through the stem?

244

Exceptional Student
Visually Impaired
The visually impaired student might need a partner to describe the stem tubes.

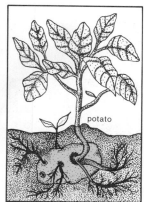
potato

The soil dries out from the top downward. There is still water deep in the ground long after the soil near the surface is dry. In hot, dry summers, the taproot of the alfalfa grows straight down fast. It grows down faster than the ground dries out!

Roots usually grow in the ground. But did you know some stems grow in the ground, too? In some plants the parts that are above ground die out each winter. If these plants grow from year to year they have underground stems. The white potato is an example of an underground stem. Food is stored in the underground stem. It is protected from the wind and cold. When spring comes, a new stem and new leaves grow up from the underground stem of the potato.

The potato is also an example of an **herb**. An *herb* is a plant that does not have a woody system to support it. The tubes that conduct water and food in herb stems are in little bundles. The bundles are scattered through the stem. Find the bundles in the diagram on the right.

In plants such as bushes and trees, the stem must survive the winter above ground. These stems have a tough, woody outside. It protects and supports the plant. The diagram on the right shows a woody stem. What is the outside layer of a tree called? A woody stem also has tubes that conduct food and water. Bundles of tubes form a circle in the stem.

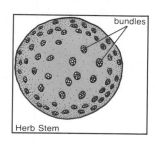
bundles

Herb Stem

Herb: A plant without a woody stem.

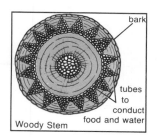
bark

tubes to conduct food and water

Woody Stem

245

Enrichment
Activity

Transpiration is the process by which water is lost by plants through pores on their leaves. If the pores on leaves are blocked, then transpiration will not occur. Students can observe this effect by doing the following:

A. Obtain two fresh leaves from a plant, plastic wrap, and petroleum jelly.

B. Wrap the base of each cut leaf with the plastic wrap and coat one leaf with petroleum jelly.

C. Place the two leaves in a warm place. Observe them after a few hours.

1. What difference is there between the two leaves? (The one without the petroleum jelly has wilted while the other one has not.)
2. Why has this happened? (The petroleum jelly has kept the leaf from losing water, so it did not wilt.)

Exceptional Student
Visually Impaired
Learning Disabled
Bring in plants with various stems and leaves. Have the student feel and compare the different types of stems and leaves. Discuss the characteristics and advantages of each.

SUGGESTED WORKSHEET MASTERS
for sections 12–1 and 12–2
p. T–219p, p. T–219q

Cactus: A desert plant.

Plants have different kinds of roots and stems. Let's examine leaves. Leaves are usually thin and wide. Thin leaves allow lots of light through to the chlorophyll. Wide leaves let each leaf catch as much sunlight as possible. Have you ever noticed how the leaves of houseplants turn toward the sun? Why do they do that? **6**

The leaves of **cactus** plants look very different from the leaves of other plants. *Cactus* plants grow in deserts, where there is very little rain. Their leaves are small and thick, and covered with a waxy coating. The smaller and thicker the leaf, the more slowly its water dries out. Desert plants must hold in as much water as they can. The waxy coat slows down water loss, too. **7**

Some cactus plants have leaves that are just long, sharp thorns. They have barrellike stems that hold lots of water. The thorns protect the stems against thirsty desert animals. The stems are green. They do the work of photosynthesis.

Section Review

Main Ideas: Most plants have roots, stems, and leaves. Some roots are shallow and others, such as taproots, are deep. Stems may be woody or nonwoody. Leaves are usually thin and wide, but desert plants have thick, waxy, or thorny leaves that slow down water loss.

Questions: Answer in complete sentences.

1. Describe two types of roots. Give an example of a plant with each type.
2. What is the usual shape of plant leaves? Are there any exceptions?
3. Name a plant with a woody stem.
4. What is an example of a plant with an underground stem? How does this kind of stem help a plant?
5. Does photosynthesis always take place in a plant's leaves? Explain.

246

6 **Text Questions** — Why do they do that? *To get the proper amount of sunlight*.

7 **Teaching Tips** — Ask students if they have ever seen a movie or a TV show in which the protagonist, lost in the desert, cuts into a cactus to obtain water, or a nature movie or program that depicts how birds and animals sometimes use cacti for water.

SECTION REVIEW
Answers to Questions
1. Shallow, with many small branches; long taproot; grass, alfalfa
2. Thin and wide; yes, cactus leaves are small and thick to hold water better.
3. Any tree, such as oak or maple
4. Potato; an underground stem stores food for the plant
5. No, in cacti, for example, photosynthesis takes place in the stem.

It is over 400,000,000 years ago. There are no animals on the land. But in wet places, tiny green plants cover the cracks in bare rocks. Do you know what they are? When you finish this section, you should be able to:

☐ **A.** Name four types of plants.
☐ **B.** Describe some examples of each type of plant.
☐ **C.** Describe how each type of plant produces more of its own kind.

Most of the plants below are **mosses**. *Mosses* are small plants that have no real roots, stems, or leaves. Mosses are often only as big as your fingernail. They grow mostly in damp, shady places.

Mosses can grow on bare rock and tree trunks. Nearly all other plants need soil to grow on. Mosses grow into the cracks in the rocks. They help break the rock down into smaller and smaller bits. Remains of the mosses mix with the bits of rock. This is one way soil is formed.

You have learned that roots and stems carry water and food to all parts of a plant. Because mosses have no real roots and stems, food and water just spread slowly from cell to cell. Without stems, mosses cannot support the weight of a heavy plant. Mosses can never be very large. They have no real roots to keep them in soil, or to dig for water. The bigger a plant is, the more water it needs.

Mosses: Small plants without real roots, stems, or leaves.

247

BASIC TEACHING PLAN
MOTIVATION

Ask students to look for signs of life in this picture. Do they think they could survive in such a landscape? Remind them that this is how the whole earth may have looked 400 million years ago. What is missing from this picture that is absolutely essential to human life? *Large oxygen-producing plants.* Tell students that more and more plant life will be added to this picture through this section.

Text Questions — Do you know what they are? *Mosses.*

SECTION BACKGROUND

Mosses are among the most primitive kinds of plant. They do not have a vascular system. Thus, minerals, food, and water must spread through the plant slowly from cell to cell. This is one reason mosses cannot grow very large. Another is that they have no stems to support a large plant structure. Mosses usually grow in moist, shady places such as low-lying meadows and bogs. Botanists think that mosses or mosslike plants were among the first plants on earth. Ferns also live in moist, shady places, but they do have roots, stems, leaves, and a vascular system. The fossil remains of the great fern forests of prehistoric times are the major source of coal.

Both mosses and ferns reproduce from spores. But the most abundant plants alive today are the seed-producing plants. Seeds can remain dormant for years — even centuries. Seed-producing plants are divided into two groups, the gymnosperms and the angiosperms. Gymnosperms, or "bare seed" plants, produce their seeds in cones. Most modern gymnosperms are conifers. These include spruces, firs, cedars, pines, and redwoods.

Angiosperms are "covered seed" plants. The seeds of angiosperms develop in a closed space within the flower. The flowers are the reproductive organ of angiosperms. The seed is often enclosed in a fleshy fruit. Animals eat the fruit and help to spread the seeds far and wide.

Angiosperms are the most widespread and successful of plants. They supply nearly all our food crops, such as grains, vegetables, and fruits.

MATERIALS

EXTENSIONS

Enrichment
Science Skills — Observation

Have students research the life cycle of a typical moss plant. Then they may gather some mosses from low-lying woodland or pasture soil. Mosses may also form a covering over the soil holding some potted plants. Have students examine the mosses with a hand lens and draw the fruiting stalks they see.

Spores: Special cells made by some living things that develop into new organisms like the organisms that made them.

Reproduction: The process by which living things make more of their own kind.

Ferns: Plants with roots, stems, and leaves, and that reproduce by spores.

Mosses do have tiny leaflike parts where food is made. They are only one cell thick. The leaflike parts are on small stalks. Rootlike structures help the stalks cling to the rocks and the ground.

New mosses grow from **spores**. *Spores* are special cells that some living things make. These cells can grow into new organisms like the organisms that made the cells. This process is the way mosses **reproduce**. When a moss plant is fully grown, it *reproduces* by spores. The little caps in the photograph show where spores are formed.

Some mosses that grow in wet places are called peat mosses. Many people use peat mosses to enrich the soil in their gardens.

Ferns are another type of plant. *Ferns*, like mosses, grow best in moist, shady places. But ferns have roots, stems, and leaves. Some ferns are tree-sized. About

248

DEVELOPMENT

1 Teaching Tips — Allow students to examine the mosses on your classroom plant shelf, or ask them to bring in samples from around their homes or outside the school. They may bring in samples similar to the moss shown, a common *Polytrichum* moss that produces its spores in a spore case covered with a "hair cap." Later in this section, they will want to compare their moss samples with some of the more advanced plants.

300,000,000 years ago, ferns were the most common type of land plant. There were great forests of ferns.

The ferns you usually see are around 1 meter (3 feet) high at the most. Only the leafy part of the plant is above ground. The roots and stem grow underground. The photograph on the bottom left of page 248 shows a common fern, the cinnamon fern. The photograph next to it shows small dark spots that form underneath the fern leaves. Each dot holds hundreds of spores. The dots break open when the spores are ripe. The spores drift in the wind. The spores are the way the ferns reproduce.

About 280,000,000 years ago, a new group of plants appeared. They were the **cycads** (sy-kadz). *Cycads* are like ferns in many ways. Some have underground stems and a crown of fernlike leaves just above the ground. Others have trunks up to 18 meters (60 feet) high, with a crown of fernlike leaves.

Cycads do not produce spores like ferns. Instead they produce **seeds**. Each *seed* contains a tiny plant and stored food. Seeds can survive for many years, sometimes centuries. When conditions are right, the seed grows into a new plant. That is how plants with seeds reproduce.

About 100,000,000 years ago, cycads replaced ferns as the most common kind of plant. Dinosaurs lived in forests of giant cycad trees like the one shown.

2

Cycads: The earliest plants that reproduced by seeds.

Seeds: The structure by which most plants reproduce. Each seed contains a complete tiny plant and stored food.

249

2 **Teaching Tips** — Remove a fern from its pot and carefully remove any soil clinging to it. Have the students examine it and observe the underground stem and roots. Students can also observe the fern spores by removing the spore cases from the fern frond and examining it under a microscope. Glycerin will break the spore case and release the spores.

Gymnosperms: Seed-bearing plants that form seeds on cones exposed directly to the air.

Today, most cycads are found in hot rain forests. They belong to a group of seed-bearing plants called **gymnosperms** (jim-nuh-spermz). *Gymnosperm* means "bare seed." Gymnosperms produce their seeds on structures called cones. The place where the seeds form on the cones is exposed to the air. That is why this group is called the "bare seed" group. The photograph on the left shows a cone. Some of its seeds have been removed.

You have probably seen some common gymnosperms. They include evergreen trees, such as spruce, fir, cedar, pine, and redwood. They are among the biggest, tallest, and oldest living trees. Bristlecone pine trees are thought to live the longest. One tree of this kind is about 4,900 years old!

Many parts of the world are covered by huge forests of evergreens. Evergreens often live in cold places. The fir forest shown below is in Alaska.

3

4

250

3 **Teaching Tips** — Ask each student to bring in as many examples of cones as he or she can.

4 **Skill Development** — Using cones that they have brought in, ask the students to devise a system of *classification* for them. Allow them to explore several different possible systems before settling on one they prefer.

Most of the plants you see around you do not belong to any of the groups mentioned so far. Common plants are not mosses, ferns, or gymnosperms. They are **angiosperms** (an-jee-uh-spermz). *Angiosperm* means "covered seed." Angiosperms are also called flowering plants. Their seeds are produced inside their flowers. Most familiar plants are angiosperms.

Grass is an angiosperm. Dandelions, rosebushes, apple trees, and daisies are all angiosperms. All flowering plants and trees are angiosperms. They produce seeds like the ones you see in the photograph. Every seed contains a tiny plant and stored food. **5**

Angiosperms: Seed-bearing plants that form their seeds inside a flower.

251

5 **Skill Development** — Ask students why they think angiosperms are the most common of all plants today. What might the fact that they have covered seeds have to do with their being so widespread? *Fruit and flowers protect the seeds and make them attractive to insects, birds, and animals, who spread the seeds widely.*

EXTENSIONS

Application
Activity

Students can make a seed viewer and compare how the seeds of different plants sprout. They should:

A. Obtain different kinds of seeds, such as vegetable, flower, and fruit seeds. Also obtain paper towels, two pieces of cardboard (approximately 30 cm square), plastic wrap, tape, and staples.

B. Moisten three or four layers of paper towels and place flat on a piece of plastic wrap. Arrange the seeds on the toweling about 6–8 cm apart. Then put another layer of plastic wrap over the top of the toweling and seeds.

C. Staple the plastic wrap, with towels and seeds inside, to a piece of cardboard. Tape the top of the cardboard to the other piece of cardboard so that the two pieces of cardboard together can serve as a stand.

D. Leave the seed viewer in a warm place and observe how the seeds sprout. You may wish to draw a picture of each seed each day to show how the different seeds sprout. It might be interesting to compare how a monocot (e.g., corn) and a dicot (e.g., bean) sprout.

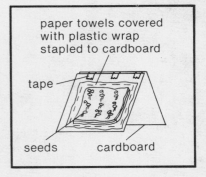

paper towels covered with plastic wrap stapled to cardboard

tape

seeds   cardboard

Exceptional Student
Learning Disabled
Visually Impaired

Bring in samples of mosses, ferns, and flowering plants. Discuss the characteristics of each.

Section Review

Main Ideas: Classifying Plant Groups

Group	Structures	Reproduce by	Examples
Mosses	No true plant organs	Spores	Peat moss
Ferns	Roots, stems, leaves	Spores	Cinnamon fern
Gymnosperms	Roots, stems, leaves	Bare seeds	Firs, pines, spruce
Angiosperms	Roots, stems, leaves	Covered seeds	Grasses, flowers

Questions: Answer in complete sentences.

1. Name four types of plants.
2. Could a moss plant grow very tall? Explain.
3. How do ferns reproduce?
4. What is the difference between gymnosperms and angiosperms? Give two examples of each.

People in Science

Barbara McClintock

Dr. Barbara McClintock has been planting corn for the last 40 years. But she is not a farmer. She is a scientist who studies how characteristics of corn plants are passed along from one year's crop to the next. At a laboratory in New York, Dr. McClintock observed that corn plants produce kernels of different colors. Sometimes they are yellow. Other times the kernels have spots of purple and pink. Dr. McClintock is discovering why the colors change. She is studying an area of science called **genetics** (juh-**neh**-tiks). *Genetics* is the study of how characteristics are passed along from one generation to the next. Dr. McClintock carefully "crosses" plants of certain colors. She examines the plants that result. Her work helps us know more about how all animals and plants pass on their characteristics to their young.

252

SECTION REVIEW

Answers to Questions

1. Mosses, ferns, gymnosperms, angiosperms
2. No, because it has no roots to anchor it or to absorb water, and no strong stem to hold it erect and transport food and water.
3. By spores
4. Gymnosperms have cones, angiosperms have flowers; pine, spruce, fir, or any other conifers; oak, rose, or any other flowering plants

CHAPTER REVIEW

Science Words

Think of a word for each blank. List the letters **a** through **l** on paper. Write the word next to each letter.

Green plants make their own food during the process of __a__.
Food making usually takes place in the __b__ of plants. Food is often stored in the __c__ of plants which also take in water. The part of the plant above the ground is usually supported by its __d__. Some plants, known as __e__, have no real roots, stems, or leaves. They reproduce by __f__. Another group of plants that reproduce in this way are the __g__, which grew as tall as trees millions of years ago. Trees such as spruce, fir, and pine belong to a plant group called the __h__, which means "bare seed." These plants produce their seeds in structures called __i__. All the flowering plants reproduce by forming __j__. They are known as the __k__. That name means "__l__ seed."

Questions: Answer in complete sentences.

1. How are sunlight and chlorophyll important to a plant?
2. Is this statement true or false: All animals depend on plants for food. Explain.
3. What does a root do? What does a stem do?
4. What is one important difference between an herb and a tree?
5. Copy the names of each of the plants listed below. Beside each name, write the plant group to which it belongs: cedar, peat moss, rose, cinnamon fern, corn, white pine, grass.
6. Explain one way mosses helped pave the way for later land plants.
7. What are spores? What are seeds?

253

EXTENSIONS

Enrichment
Research — Library

Students can use their dictionaries and other reference books to learn the meaning of these words and how they relate to the concepts of this chapter.
1. rhizome — an underground, horizontal stem
2. rhizoid — a rootlike structure at the base of a moss that anchors it and holds water
3. frond — a leaf of a fern
4. sporophyte — the spore-producing phase in the life cycle of a plant
5. embryophyte — the seed-producing phase in the life cycle of a plant

CHAPTER REVIEW

Science Words
a. photosynthesis, b. leaves, c. roots, d. stem e mosses, f. spores, g. ferns, h. gymnosperms, i. cones, j. seeds, k. angiosperms, l. covered

Answers to Questions
1. A plant cannot make its food without chlorophyll, but chlorophyll cannot work without sun.
2. True.
3. Roots gather moisture, anchor plants, and store food. Stems give support and transport food and water.
4. An herb dies to the ground over the winter; a tree does not.
5. Cedar, white pine — gymnosperms; peat moss — mosses; rose, corn, grass — angiosperms; cinnamon fern — ferns
6. Mosses helped break rock down into soil.
7. Spores are the reproductive structures of mosses and ferns; gymnosperms and angiosperms reproduce by seeds.

SUGGESTED TEST MASTERS
pp. T–219f,g

CHAPTER 13

CHAPTER OBJECTIVES

1. Explain how some simple invertebrates are classified and describe some representative organisms.
2. Describe some characteristics of mollusks and how they are classified.
3. Describe some common mollusks and spiny-skinned invertebrates.
4. Name some characteristics of arthropods and explain how they are classified.
5. Describe incomplete and complete metamorphosis of insects, and give examples.

SECTION BACKGROUND

The poriferans, or sponges, the simplest multicellular animals, are found in shallow coastal waters to great ocean depths anchored in one place. Commercial sponges are made of marine sponge skeletons.

   The coelenterates or hollow-bodied animals (corals and jellyfish) are sedentary, marine animals made of two-cell layers.

   Worms are still more complex, with three cell layers and specialized systems for digestion, circulation, and coordination. Three main groups are the Platyhelminthes (flatworms), the Nematodes (roundworms), and the Annelids (segmented worms). Many flatworms are parasites. Roundworms include the hookworms and trichina worm, whose eggs are often present in undercooked pork. Segmented worms, the most advanced group, have many similar segments containing nerves and blood vessels.

Exceptional Student
IEP Chapter Goal

When presented with the following: sponges, jellyfish, worms, animals with shells, and arthropods, the student will state two characteristics of each.

ANIMALS WITHOUT BACKBONES

13-1.

Simple Animals

254

Is this organism an animal or a plant? It may be a surprise to you that it is an animal. Some animals look like plants. They stay in one place all their lives. How can you tell it is an animal? When you finish this section, you should be able to:

BASIC TEACHING PLAN
MOTIVATION

Scientists once thought that corals were plants. Today, they are recognized as animals. Have students suggest why living things that are fixed in one place, as plants are, should still be classified as animals. Since they have no chlorophyll, they cannot be classed as plants. Ask if anyone in your class ever visited a coral reef. Only one such reef exists in the United States. It's the Pennekamp Coral Reef, off Key Largo, Florida. Corals are hollow-bodied animals with a degree of cell specialization. Among these cells are the stinging cells, which are unique to this group of animals. These cells are in the tentacles that surround the "mouth" at the open end of the hollow sac which forms the body of the animal.

□ **A.** Explain how *sponges, corals,* and *jellyfish* get their food.

□ **B.** Compare and contrast three types of worms.

There are more than 1,200,000 different kinds of animals known today. New kinds are found every year. Scientists classify these animals into two groups. One group includes all animals with backbones. These animals are called **vertebrates** (ver-tuh-brayts). *Vertebrates* include frogs, snakes, birds, cats, dogs, and humans. The other group is called the **invertebrates** (in-ver-tuh-brayts). *Invertebrates* are animals without backbones.

Sponges are a group of simple invertebrates. Most of them live in the ocean attached to rocks. Many *sponges* are shaped like vases. The body of a sponge is made up of two cell layers. They form the sides and bottom of the "vase." The top has an opening.

Sponges have small holes all over their bodies. The holes are lined with special cells. Each cell has a whiplike structure. It beats back and forth causing water to flow through the holes into the sponge. Other cells take tiny organisms out of the water for food.

Bath sponges are often made of plastic. Natural bath sponges are made from the dried bodies of sea sponges.

Vertebrates: Animals with backbones.

Invertebrates: Animals without backbones.

Sponge: A simple invertebrate that has one body opening and small holes all over its body.

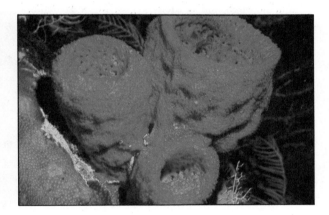

255

Enrichment
Science Skills —
Comparing and Contrasting
Obtain two or more sponge skeletons of different species from a biological supply house. The skeletons are made up of needlelike spicules, which interlock in chains because of their shapes. Have students examine the skeletons of each species with a hand lens, and a low-power microscope. They should make drawings showing the way spicules interlock in each species. Ask:
1. What do you notice about the shapes of the spicules? (Each species may have spicules of several different shapes but these shapes will be characteristic of that species.)
2. How do you think what you have learned might be used by scientists who study sponges? (As a means of separating sponges into different species.)

Exceptional Student
Learning Disabled
Bring the student to a local pet store that has saltwater tanks. Observe sea anemones, coral, and other animals discussed in this chapter. Illustrate them when back in the classroom.

DEVELOPMENT

1 **Teaching Tips** — Write the words "vertebrate" and "invertebrate" on the board. Ask students to look up the words in a dictionary (a collegiate or library reference volume, not a student dictionary). What is the root of each word? *Vertebra.* What does it mean? *To turn or change.* Can the class figure out the relationship between the idea of turning and the backbone? *The individual vertebrae of the backbone allow great freedom and fluidity of movement.* What does the prefix *in-* mean in the word *invertebrate*? *Not.* Can students think of other words in which the prefix *in-* has the same meaning? *Indecent, indirect.*

2 **Teaching Tips** — If you disassemble a sponge into its separate cells and scatter those cells about, they will migrate together and redevelop into a complete new animal. A high school junior from Florida used this fact to design an experiment for testing aboard the United States space shuttle *Columbia.* Would the sponge cells regroup in space, the student wondered, or would the lack of gravity prevent their doing so? The results, when analyzed, are expected to shed light on how an astronaut's cells might react if damaged during a space flight.

EXTENSIONS

Enrichment
Research

Students can do research to find out about the stinging cells of coelenterates or hollow-bodied animals. These cells are called *nematocysts* and they vary from animal to animal. A few of these animals have some control over firing these cells, but most of the time they are set off automatically by a kind of spring device within the cell. Some have harpoonlike projectiles, while others lasso their prey. Students can find out how scientists use these cells to classify coelenterates.

Hollow-bodied animal: A simple invertebrate with one body opening that is surrounded by tentacles.

Hollow-bodied animals are another group of simple invertebrates. They include jellyfish, corals, and sea anemones (uh-**neh**-muh-neez). Like the sponges, these animals have only one body opening. Their bodies are made up of two cell layers. Sea anemones and corals stay attached to one place. The picture on the upper left shows a sea anemone. The picture on page 254 shows a coral.

Hollow-bodied animals have fingerlike structures **3** around the open end of their bodies. These structures are called *tentacles*. When one tentacle touches a small animal, other tentacles close around the animal, too. Stinging cells in the tentacles inject a poison into the animal. The tentacles pull the animal inside, where it is eaten. Find the tentacles in the jellyfish shown above.

Worms are also invertebrates. They are more complicated than sponges and corals. Their bodies are three cell layers thick. Worms grow new parts of their bodies when they are cut apart. There are three major groups of worms. **Flatworms** have long, flattened bodies. *Flatworms*, such as the tapeworm, live inside other animals and cause disease.

Flatworm: A worm with one body opening and a long, flattened body.

256

---

3 **Teaching Tips** — Throughout the rest of this chapter, students will be learning about creatures that are progressively more and more complex. In this section they first learn about sponges, which use whiplike structures to direct food-bearing water to the insides of their bodies. The more highly developed hollow-bodied animals have tentacles that actually seize small animals.

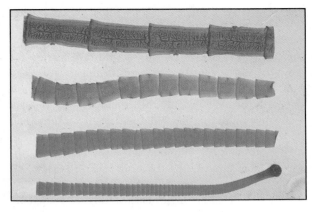

Sometimes flatworms are found in fish or meat that is bought for food. If the fish or meat is cooked well, the worms will be killed. But if it is not cooked long enough, the living worms will be eaten with the food. They will infect the person who has eaten the food. The picture shows parts of a tapeworm seen through a microscope.

Roundworms have round bodies that are pointed at both ends. They have two body openings. Food enters through one opening. Wastes go out through the other.

Many *roundworms* live inside plants and animals. Hookworms are roundworms that infect humans. They live mostly in the warmer parts of the world. Hookworms on the ground enter the body of a person through the skin of the feet. That's why it's important not to walk barefoot in areas where there may be hookworms.

Segmented worms are worms whose bodies are divided into many similar parts or sections. These sections are called segments. *Segmented worms* are more complicated than flatworms or roundworms. They have a heart and blood vessels, for example. They also have a nervous system. This allows them to sense what is around them.

Earthworms are segmented worms. Their nervous system gives them good control of their bodies as they dig through the ground.

Roundworm: A worm with a round body pointed at both ends.

Segmented worm: A worm with a body that is divided into many similar parts.

257

EXTENSIONS

Enrichment
Science Skills — Observing

Students can observe how earthworms respond to light. They will need to obtain a few earthworms. Early morning is the best time to look for them.

A. Obtain a pie plate, aluminum foil, a lamp, and earthworms.

B. Wrap a piece of aluminum foil around the pie plate so that half of it is covered.

C. Place the worms on the un-covered side of the pie plate and shine the light on them. Do the worms move? In what direc-tion? (They move away from light.) This is called negative phototropism.

4 Teaching Tips — Continue to stress the increasing complexity of each type of animal the students read about. This progression is clearly evident in the groups of worms.

5 Teaching Tips — Ask students to draw a "worm chart" on pieces of drawing paper. Then ask them to use the textbook in order to classify the worms according to their characteristic structures. Ask them which structures they will use to do this. *Number of body openings, shape of body, heart, blood vessels, nervous stystem.*

Exceptional Student
Learning Disabled
Visually Impaired
Bring in an earthworm. Make a habitat in a jar using soil and leaves. Have the learning dis-abled student observe the worm and its movements. Allow the visually impaired student to hold the earthworm and ob-serve its movements.

EXTENSIONS

Enrichment
Research

Students can do research to trace the increasing complexity of the digestive systems in animals. It begins in the sponges as a hollow area surrounded by a single layer of cells. The coelenterates or hollow-bodied animals have two layers of cells. The digestive tract becomes an enclosed tube in segmented worms. This tube becomes more and more complex in higher and higher forms of animals. Students should investigate how the various animals obtain food and what organs, if any, are involved in digestion. They can prepare a report of their findings for the class.

Each earthworm's segments—except the first and last—has four pairs of stiff bristles. The earthworm burrows by pushing its front end into the ground. Then the front bristles move to pull the earthworm further in. Now the bristles further back are in the ground. The front bristles relax. The back bristles go to work and push the earthworm deeper into the ground.

Earthworms are good for the soil. Their wastes enrich it. Their burrows let more air and water into the soil. In very good, moist soil, there may be over a million earthworms in an area the size of a big backyard! They can bring tons of soil up from under the surface. Because they move the soil at night, earthworms are commonly called "night crawlers."

Section Review

Main Ideas: Classifying Simple Invertebrates

Main Group	Structures	Features	Examples
Sponges	One body opening. Two cell layers.	Attached to one place.	Freshwater or saltwater sponges
Hollow-bodied animals	One body opening. Two cell layers. Tentacles.	Attached to one place.	Jellyfish, coral
Worms	One or two body openings. Three cell layers. Segmented worms have a heart, blood vessels, and a nervous system.	Move about.	Flatworm (tapeworm) Roundworm (hookworm) Segmented worm (earthworm)

Questions: Answer in complete sentences.

1. Name the only way sponges are like plants.
2. How do sponges get food?
3. How are hollow-bodied animals different from sponges?
4. What are the three groups of worms?
5. What does "invertebrate" mean?

258

SECTION REVIEW

Answers to Questions

1. They are fixed in one place.
2. Special cells cause water to flow through the sponge and other cells take food from the water.
3. Hollow-bodied animals have tentacles around the open end of their bodies and sponges do not.
4. Flatworms, roundworms, segmented worms
5. Without backbone

What kind of animal has its stomach on its foot? What kind of an animal can push its stomach into its food to eat? What kinds of animals have arms around their mouths? The animal you see below has its eyes around its foot. It is called a blue-eyed scallop. When you finish this section, you should be able to:

☐ **A.** Describe what structures *mollusks* have in common.

☐ **B.** Compare and contrast three different kinds of *mollusks*.

☐ **C.** Describe what structures spiny-skinned invertebrates have in common.

☐ **D.** Explain how a starfish gets its food.

Mollusks (**mahl**-usks) are another large group of invertebrates. Most *mollusks* live in fresh or salt water. Some, like slugs and certain kinds of snails, live on land.

Mollusks are like segmented worms in some ways. They have soft bodies, two body openings, a heart, blood vessels, and a digestive system. However, they are not segmented. They have a thick, muscular "foot" that moves them from place to place. Many mollusks have hard shells that protect their soft bodies. There are three kinds of mollusks. They are grouped according to the differences in their shells and feet.

13-2.
Animals with Shells and Spines

Mollusk: An invertebrate with a soft body, usually protected by a shell.

259

SECTION BACKGROUND

Mollusks are a group of invertebrates that includes oysters, scallops, clams, snails, slugs, squids, and octopuses. Most mollusks live in salt or fresh water, but a number of snails and slugs are land animals. There are three main groups. The pelecypods, or hatchet-footed mollusks (e.g., oysters, scallops, and clams), have a shell made up of two parts called valves that are hinged at the top edge. The shell is made of calcium carbonate. It is held together by muscles at the hinge. These mollusks feed by straining tiny organisms and particles from the water as it passes over internal gills. Stomach-footed mollusks, or gastropods (e.g., snails, slugs), have a muscular foot with which they can glide smoothly over vegetation, sand, or even glass. Most are vegetarians. Slugs are often pests in vegetable gardens. Head-footed mollusks, or cephalopods (e.g., squids, octopuses), are distinguished by the long arms and tentacles that encircle their heads.

The echinoderms, or spiny-skinned invertebrates, usually have a bulbous or star-shaped body. It is covered with a tough, leathery skin often studded with spines. Adult animals have bodies that show radial symmetry, that is, similar parts radiate outward from the center, like the spokes of a wheel. This can easily be seen in a starfish. These animals live on sea bottoms. Some are scavengers that help to keep the sea floor clear of dead organisms. Others, like starfish, prey on mollusks as well as on fish and other animals like themselves.

MATERIALS

aquarium with pond snails, hand lens, pencil

BASIC TEACHING PLAN
MOTIVATION

The students may find the creatures described odd; but is is likely that many of them have seen examples of them. After they have answered the questions, have the students describe the animals they have seen and where they have seen them.

Text Questions — What kind of animal has its stomach on its foot? *A snail.* What kind of animal can push its stomach into its food to eat? *A starfish.* What kinds of animals have arms around their mouths? *Squid and octopuses.*

DEVELOPMENT

1 **Teaching Tips** — Ask students to take out the worm charts they made in the last section. Ask them to compare mollusk characteristics with those of worms. Mollusks and segmented worms share several characteristics but are also quite different.

Enrichment
Activity

The students can study the snails' response to light using the aquarium from the Activity, a lamp, and a large piece of cardboard. Have the students do the following:

A. Cut a piece of cardboard so that it will divide the aquarium in half.

B. Place a lamp so that it shines only on one half of the aquarium.

1. How do the snails move in response to light? (Away from the light.)
2. How does this response help the snails survive? (This helps prevent water loss.)

Hatchet-footed mollusks make up one group. Clams, oysters, mussels, and scallops have a hatchet foot. They also have two parts to their shells. The two parts are hinged. A muscle attached to their shells can open or close the shell.

When the shell is open, the hatchet-shaped foot can stretch out. Then the muscle in the foot makes it draw together. That pulls the mollusk along the sandy bottom of the lake or ocean. These mollusks feed on tiny protists that live in the water.

Stomach-footed mollusks have one-part shells. Snails and slugs belong to this group. Most snails live in water, although some giant ones live on land. You may have seen pond snails moving on the walls of an aquarium. The foot lays down a trail of slime. The snail glides along the trail. The snail's foot is actually a part of its digestive system, too. That's where the name "stomach-footed" comes from.

ACTIVITY

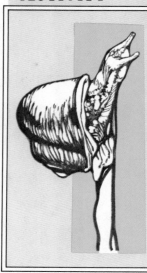

Observing snails

A. Obtain these materials: aquarium with pond snails, hand lens, pencil.

B. Observe snails crawling up the glass sides of the aquarium. Use a hand lens to see how the snail's "foot" moves.
1. Describe how the foot moves.

C. The front part of the "foot" is the snail's head. Look at it with a hand lens while the snail is moving.
2. What can you see on the snail's head?
3. What do you think these structures do?

D. Tap the aquarium glass sharply near a snail.
4. What happens?
5. Does the snail react quickly? Do you think this is a useful reaction? Why?

260

ACTIVITY

Skill Development — *Observing, Inferring, Concluding and Generalizing*

Teaching Tips — Snails can be found under leaves, rotting logs, or stones. The best time to look for them is on damp, dark days, when they are most active. They should be collected in a clean glass jar with no trace of soap or detergent which can harm them. The bottom of the aquarium should be covered with leaves, rocks, and twigs. Lettuce and parsley are excellent supplementary foods.

Answers to Questions — **1.** A wavelike motion that ripples along the length of the foot. **2.** Feelers. **3.** To inform the snail when it approaches prey; to warn of danger. **4.** The snail retreats into its shell. **5.** Yes, because it allows the snail to protect itself.

Exceptional Student
Visually Impaired

Assign the visually impaired student a partner for the activity on this page.

Head-footed mollusks make up the third group. In these mollusks, the "foot" is divided into eight or more
2 tentacles. The tentacles are arranged around the mouth of the animal. The octopus has eight tentacles that have suckers for holding on to food. The octopus has no shell. It feeds mostly on crabs. An octopus is shown above.

The squid has ten tentacles with suckers. It has a shell
3 inside its body. The squid has sharp jaws. It feeds largely on fish. The squid and the octopus can swim rapidly by
4 squirting a jet of water out of their bodies. Which way is the octopus moving? Each animal can change color quickly to match its surroundings. Both can release a cloud of ink into the water to escape from enemies.

261

EXTENSIONS
Application
Research

Students can do research to find out about the largest invertebrate, the giant squid. This enormous creature has been reported to measure 16 m (53 ft) long, including its tentacles. It is very rare, and for a long time scientists thought it was a mythical creature. The bodies of dead squid sometimes wash up on shore. This gives scientists a chance to study this creature. Students should find out where it lives and what it eats. They might also be interested in finding out how they were depicted in stories such as *Twenty Thousand Leagues Under the Sea* by Jules Verne.

2 **Teaching Tips** — With creatures like the octopus and the squid, we move on to animals about which students may have formed preconceptions. Octopuses and octopuslike creatures, for instance, are occasional "villains" in science fiction and horror stories and movies. Tell the class that octopuses are actually very unlikely villains. Marine biologists and other divers report that they appear to be quite "shy," and quickly disappear when approached.

3 **Teaching Tips** — Point out to students that squid and octopuses move about by jet propulsion, just as jet planes do. You can illustrate jet propulsion by blowing up a balloon, and without tying it, releasing it and letting it zoom about the room. The air rushing out the back of the balloon propels it just as water propels a squid or burning fuel propels a jet.

4 **Test Question** — Which way is the octopus moving? *Toward the upper right*

Students who live near the ocean can collect and observe starfish. Have the students collect starfish in plastic buckets. To observe their movement, the students should invert a few and see how they use their arms and tube feet to turn over. If a salt-water aquarium is available, they can continue their observations in school or at home.

Among the oddest of the invertebrates are the *spiny-skinned invertebrates*. Like mollusks, spiny-skinned invertebrates have two body openings, a digestive system, and a heart and blood vessels. They have firm bodies. Spiny-skinned invertebrates get their name from the spines that cover their bodies. Some are long and sharp as needles. Others are short. This group includes starfish, sea urchins, sand dollars, sea cucumbers, and sea lilies. They all live in salt water.

Starfish are the best known of the spiny-skinned invertebrates. Most have five arms spread out from the center of their bodies. The undersides of the arms are covered with many tiny, hollow tubes called tube feet. They work like suction cups.

The feet are used for walking and feeding. A starfish may wrap its arms around a mussel, as shown in the picture on the bottom left. The tube feet hold tightly to the two parts of the mussel's shell. The starfish's arms pull steadily on the shell, trying to make it open. This may go on for hours. Sooner or later, the mussel's shell muscle gets tired. It can no longer hold the shell closed. The shell opens.

Then the starfish pushes its stomach out through its mouth and into the open shell of the mussel. The soft

262

Exceptional Student
Learning Disabled
Visually Impaired

Bring to class clams and squid from a fish store, and a starfish and snail from a pet store. Allow the students to observe and touch these animals. Discuss the characteristics of each.

5   Teaching Tips — Explain to students that starfish and some other invertebrates have an ability that most higher animals lack — the ability to regenerate, or regrow, damaged or lost parts of their bodies.

6   Teaching Tips — Starfish, sea urchins, and sand dollars are commonly washed ashore and found on ocean beaches. If your students live or vacation near saltwater, they probably have specimens of these spiny-skinned invertebrates that they can bring in for the class to investigate. Evidences of such structures as the starfish's tube feet and the sea urchin's spines will be clearly seen.

body of the mussel is digested. The starfish pulls its stomach and the digested mussel back inside itself.

Because of their long, needlelike spines, sea urchins look like living pincushions. When a sea urchin dies, its spines fall off. The picture on the right shows a sea urchin. Sand dollars look like round, flattened pieces of dough. That's because their spines are very short. You can see the star-shaped pattern on a sand dollar's body in the picture on page 262. Both sea urchins and sand dollars can be found washed up on beaches.

6

Section Review

Main Ideas: Invertebrates that have shells and spines are classified as shown in the following chart.

MOLLUSKS			SPINY-SKINNED INVERTEBRATES	
Structures	**Groups**	**Examples**	**Structures**	**Examples**
Soft bodies. Two body openings. Heart and blood vessels. Digestive system. Most have a shell.	Hatchet-footed. Two-shelled.	Clam, oyster, mussel, scallop.	Firm body. Two body openings. Heart, blood vessels. Digestive system. Spines.	Starfish, sea urchin, sand dollar, sea lily, sea cucumber.
	Stomach-footed. One-shelled.	Snail, slug.		
	Head-footed. Many legs or tentacles.	Octopus, squid.		

Questions: Answer in complete sentences.

1. Mollusks are divided into three groups according to two of their structures. What are these structures?
2. In what ways are mollusks like segmented worms?
3. A starfish eats in an unusual way. How?
4. Name five structures that many mollusks have in common.
5. In what two ways does a starfish use its feet?

263

EXTENSIONS

Application
Research — Library

Have some students do some research on edible mollusks and the danger of food poisoning from the so-called "red tide," as well as on the dangers that arise from the ability of these animals to concentrate heavy metals (mercury) and other toxic pollutants sometimes found in the sea. Students may present oral reports. This can lead to a class discussion on ocean pollution.

SECTION REVIEW

Answers to Questions
1. Feet, shells
2. They have soft bodies, two body openings, a heart and body vessels, and a digestive system.
3. A starfish might eat a clam the following way: It wraps itself around the clam and slowly pulls it open; then it pushes its stomach out through its mouth and onto the open clamshell, digests the soft clam, and pulls its stomach back inside itself.
4. Soft bodies, two body openings, heart, blood vessels, digestive system; octopuses lack a shell but many mollusks have them.
5. To move, to seize and pry open its prey

13-3.
Arthropods

Arthropods: Invertebrates with jointed legs and an outer skeleton.

Exoskeleton: The hard outer covering of arthropods.

One of the animals shown below can fly. Do you think it is a bird? Why not? One animal lives on land and spins webs. The other lives in the sea. All three are related to each other. When you finish this section, you should be able to:

☐ **A.** Name three ways in which all *arthropods* are alike.
☐ **B.** Name one difference used to separate *arthropods* into five groups.
☐ **C.** Explain how a caterpillar and a butterfly can be the same animal.

There are over a million different kinds of **arthropods** (**ahr-thruh-pahdz**). Yet all *arthropods* have some things in common. They all have a hard **exoskeleton** (**ek-so-skel-uh-tun**). *Exoskeleton* means an outer skeleton.

The human skeleton is inside the body. It supports the weight of the body. Muscles are attached to the bones.

The exoskeleton of an arthropod has the same purpose. It supports the animal's weight. Muscles are attached to the inside of the exoskeleton. The exoskeleton is not made of bone. The material it is made of is like the material that makes up our fingernails. This material can be very hard. If you have ever tried to crack a lobster shell, you know that. Lobsters are arthropods.

1

2

264

Once formed, an exoskeleton cannot get larger. But the arthropod inside it is growing. When it gets too large for the exoskeleton, the exoskeleton splits. The arthropod sheds the old exoskeleton. It grows a new one as you can see in the top left picture. It takes time for the new exoskeleton to harden. During that time, the arthropod stays in one place and hides from enemies.

Arthropod means "joint-footed." That is another way that all arthropods are alike. All have several pairs of jointed feet and bodies made of several segments.

Arthropods are divided into five main groups. Each group has a different number of legs. The first group is made up mostly of animals that live in water. They have a scientific name that means "hard-covered." These animals have an especially tough exoskeleton. This group includes lobsters, crabs, crayfish, and shrimp. Have you ever eaten any of these animals?

The hard-covered arthropods have five pairs of legs. They also have two body sections and two pairs of **antennas** (an-**ten**-uz). *Antennas* are many-jointed structures on the heads of most arthropods. The everyday word for them is "feelers." But they are used for much more than feeling. They are used for smelling and sometimes for hearing. Can you find the lobster's antennas in the top right picture?

Antennas: Jointed structures on the heads of many arthropods that are used for feeling, smelling, and hearing.

265

DEVELOPMENT

1 **Teaching Tips** — The exoskeleton of arthropods also protects delicate internal organs and prevents water loss in arthropods that live on land.

2 **Teaching Tips** — Ask the students if they have ever eaten lobsters with family or friends, and one member of the group had extra trouble — or an extra-easy time — cracking the lobster shell. One lobster might have been just about ready to shed its old shell, and thus have had a thicker, harder, exoskeleton than the others; another might have had a new, thin exoskeleton.

3 **Teaching Tips** — Tiny crustaceans called *krill* serve as the main source of food for the largest animals on earth, the baleen whales. Krill are usually only 25 millimeters long. Whales can be as large as 30 meters long.

T–265

Enrichment
Activity

The webs made by orb weavers are marvels of animal design. Students can preserve a permanent record of some of these webs using a can of dark spray paint and stiff white paper. First, the spider should be frightened away from the web so that it will not be killed by the spray. It will build a new web overnight. The spider can be frightened from the web by touching one edge of the web with a small stick and making strong vibrations. Then spray the paint over the entire web. Press the paper up against the web. The web will stick to the paper and make a permanent record. Have students follow up this activity by researching the steps by which an orb weaver makes its web.

The second group of arthropods is made up of spiders and spiderlike animals. These animals all have two body sections. They have four pairs of legs and no antennas. Nearly all of these animals live on land.

4

Many spiders are useful to humans. They catch and kill huge numbers of pests such as houseflies and mosquitoes. All spiders have poison fangs. They use them to kill or stun their prey. Very few spiders are poisonous to humans.

5

Most spiders catch their prey in sticky webs. A jumping spider, such as the one shown below, can catch prey by leaping on it. It has several pairs of eyes to help it see its prey from a distance. Spitting spiders squirt long, sticky threads at nearby prey. The spiders are so fast that they can catch a resting fly before it takes off.

Ticks and mites belong to the same group of arthropods as spiders. Many are harmful to humans. Some destroy plants that we grow for food. The tick shown on the left sucks the plant's juices. Other ticks and mites burrow into the skin of humans or animals and often spread disease. Have you ever had a tick or removed one from a pet? Ticks must be carefully removed.

266

4 **Teaching Tips** — Scientists use the number of legs of various types of arthropods in order to divide arthropods into five major groups. Ask students what they think of this system of classification. Does it seem like a useful method? *Yes, because arthropods with the same number of legs seem to be related in other ways as well.* Ask: What other criteria could be used to classify arthropods? *Number of body divisions, number of antennae, method of respiration.*

5 **Teaching Tips** — Tell students that spiders do not actually eat their prey. They inject powerful chemicals into the bodies of their prey that liquify the body parts. The spider then sucks this fluid out of the prey's body.

6   The third group of arthropods is the insect group. All insects have three pairs of legs. All have three body sections and one pair of antennas.

Insects are the most numerous of all animals. There are more kinds of insects than there are animals in all the other groups put together. **7** Can you name the ones shown? Some you have certainly seen.

Why are there so many insects? One important reason is that each female insect can lay many thousands of eggs at a time. Even if only a few eggs from each batch develop into adult insects, there will still be lots of new insects!

Another reason for the high survival rate of insects is that insects eat almost anything that can be eaten. Everything we think of as food, some insect will also eat. And some insects eat things that few other animals will touch. Termites eat wood. Tobacco beetles eat tobacco leaves. The young of some moths eat cloth.

267

Enrichment
Research

Students can do research to find out about the process of molting. When an arthropod molts, it sheds its exoskeleton in order to grow. The students should try to answer these questions.

1. What functions does the exoskeleton serve? (protects internal organs, provides an anchor for muscles, prevents water loss)
2. What limitations does an exoskeleton have? (It cannot be very big since it would be too heavy to move)
3. What is the exoskeleton made of? (chitin)
4. How do arthropods make sure their new exoskeleton is large enough to allow them to grow? (They blow themselves up to above normal size so that the exoskeleton will be large)
5. What do they usually do before the new exoskeleton hardens? (Hide, because they are very vulnerable until their exoskeleton hardens)

6   **Teaching Tips** — Inform students that insects, like other arthropods, shed a series of exoskeletons as they grow larger. But winged insects do not develop wings until after they have reached full size and have molted for the last time. All arthropods are largely defenseless and vulnerable to enemies during a molt. If insects had to lose their wing parts whenever they molted, their vulnerability would increase enormously during the extra-long time it would take for new wings to grow.

7   **Text Question** — Can you name the ones shown? *Clockwise from upper left they are: velvet ant, Cecropia moth, ladybird beetles (ladybugs), praying mantis.*

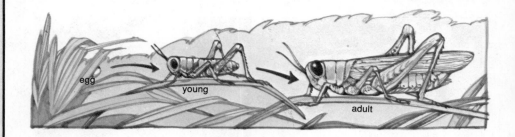

egg   young   adult

EXTENSIONS

Reinforcement

Science Skills — Recording Data

Have students make a pie chart using the data given below, showing the number of species of insects as compared to other arthropods, mollusks, vertebrates, and the remaining invertebrates.

Insects	900,000 species (approximate)
Other	
Arthropods	52,000 species
Mollusks	82,000 species
Vertebrates	38,000 species
All others	48,000 species
Total	1,120,000

Challenge the class to explain what the chart tells us about the number of insects relative to the numbers of other animals. Insects are very numerous, very successful creatures because they are extremely adaptable.

Metamorphosis: A series of major changes in the structure of an animal as it develops from its early stages to become an adult.

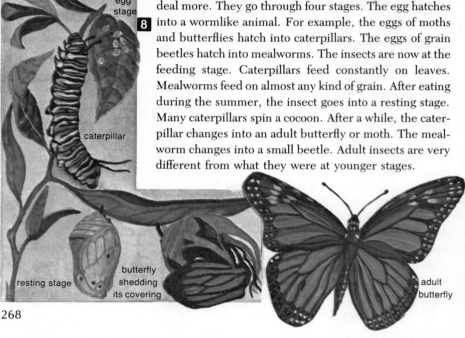

egg stage

caterpillar

resting stage

butterfly shedding its covering

adult butterfly

268

Most insects go through a series of changes as they develop from egg to adult. These changes are called **metamorphosis** (met-uh-**mor**-fuh-sis).

Some insects go through incomplete *metamorphosis*. A grasshopper egg, for instance, hatches into a very tiny grasshopper. It looks like a full-grown grasshopper, but without wings. The young grasshopper grows and sheds its exoskeleton several times. By the third or fourth time, the young grasshopper has wings. It is an adult.

Insects with complete metamorphosis change a great deal more. They go through four stages. The egg hatches **8** into a wormlike animal. For example, the eggs of moths and butterflies hatch into caterpillars. The eggs of grain beetles hatch into mealworms. The insects are now at the feeding stage. Caterpillars feed constantly on leaves. Mealworms feed on almost any kind of grain. After eating during the summer, the insect goes into a resting stage. Many caterpillars spin a cocoon. After a while, the caterpillar changes into an adult butterfly or moth. The mealworm changes into a small beetle. Adult insects are very different from what they were at younger stages.

8 Teaching Tips — Students in some parts of the country may have noticed dramatic evidence of the metamorphosis of one insect, the gypsy moth caterpillar. In the spring, they may have seen the brownish-gray clusters of eggs on the sides of trees and buildings. By summer, in heavily infested areas, one can hear the constant low crackling noise that is the sound of the caterpillars eating, and one can see the nearly leafless trees. Toward summer's end, metamorphosis is complete, and the moths emerge.

ACTIVITY

Observing Mealworms

A. Obtain the following materials: hand lens, mealworm culture, pencil, drawing paper.

B. Take a mealworm from the class culture. Use the lens to observe the mealworm carefully. Draw what you see. Label head, segments, antennas, legs.

  1. How many segments are there?

  2. How many pairs of legs are there? How many pairs of antennas?

  3. What group of arthropods do mealworms belong to? Explain your answer.

C. Look at the class culture. Use the lens. Try to find eggs, resting stage, and adult beetles.

  4. What kind of metamorphosis does the mealworm go through?

Many insects are serious pests. Some spread disease in animals and in humans.

Other insects, such as bees, are very useful. Bees visit flowers for food. As they do, the bees pick up a fine dust from the male structures of the flower. This dust is called pollen. Pollen must be carried to the female structures of the flower before a flower can make seeds. The bees carry the pollen as they go from flower to flower.

Fruit trees will not produce fruit unless their flowers produce seeds. And their flowers will not produce seeds without bees. When their fruit trees are in flower, some farmers pay beekeepers to bring their hives into the orchards.

The fourth group of arthropods is made up of **centipedes** (**sen**-tuh-peedz). The name means "a hundred legs." *Centipedes* have bodies made of many segments.

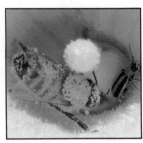

9

Centipede: An arthropod with many body segments and one pair of legs on most segments.

269

EXTENSIONS

Enrichment
Activity

Students can continue their study of metamorphosis by doing this activity using fruit flies. Have the students:

A. Obtain these materials: adult fruit flies, cotton, small glass jar, fruit fly medium (available from biological supply houses).

B. Place the fruit flies inside the jar with the medium and seal the top with a cotton plug.

C. Observe the medium each day, first for the presence of eggs, and then the presence of maggots and pupae.

D. Have the students answer the same questions in the activity for the fruit flies they have observed.

ACTIVITY

Skill Development — *Observing, Classifying, Comparing and Contrasting, Recording Data*

Teaching Tips — Mealworms can be obtained at most pet stores where they are raised as food for amphibians and other animals. They can be raised on raw oatmeal. Slices of raw potato should be added to the oatmeal to provide moisture. The mealworms can be kept in a plastic box, such as a food storage box, with holes cut in the lid for ventilation. Gauze taped over the holes will keep the insects from escaping. The box can be filled with alternating layers of food and burlap. Food layers should have 1/4 inch of oatmeal and two thick slices of potato.

Answers to Questions — 1. 13; yes. 2. 3;1. 3. Insects; three pairs of legs, one pair of antennae. 4. Complete.

9 **Teaching Tips** — Discuss the part bees play in the development of flowering plants. The photograph shows a bee covered with pollen, as well as a cucumber beetle, inside a flower.

Exceptional Student
Visually Impaired

This activity may not be appropriate for students with severe visual impairment.

T–269

Application
Research

Have students visit some bee-keepers or do research in the library on beekeeping. Provide the students with the following questions to guide their research:
1. How do beekeepers take care of bees?
2. What do the bees do during the winter?
3. Does the flavor of the honey vary with the kinds of flowers the bees visit? If so, how do beekeepers control this?

Enrichment
Research — Library

Students can do research to find out about social insects. These are insects such as bees, ants, and termites that live together in large colonies. Ask the students to find out what kinds of insects form colonies, how these colonies are organized, and what jobs the individual insects may have in the colony. They may also be interested in finding out how these insects communicate and reproduce.

Exceptional Student
Learning Disabled

Have the student cut out magazine pictures that illustrate arthropods.

SUGGESTED WORKSHEET MASTER
p. T–219r

Millipede: An arthropod with many body segments and two pairs of legs on most segments.

Most segments have one pair of legs. Centipedes can have from 30 to 340 legs. They feed on many insect pests, including horseflies and cockroaches. The picture shows a centipede that is commonly found in the United States.

Millipedes (mil-uh-peedz) are the fifth group of arthropods. Their name means "a thousand legs." *Millipedes*, like centipedes, have many body segments. Each segment has two pairs of legs. So millipedes look more "leggy" than centipedes. But actually, millipedes never have more than 115 pairs of legs, or 230 legs in all. Millipedes usually eat plants. Although many millipedes are small, some grow as long as 28 cm (11 in.). Both centipedes and millipedes have one pair of antennas.

10

Section Review

Main Ideas: Classifying Arthropods

Structures in common	Group	Special structures	Example
Exoskeleton Joint-footed Segmented body	Hard-covered	Five pairs of legs. Two pairs of antennas. Two body sections.	Lobster, shrimp
	Spiders, spiderlike animals	Four pairs of legs. Two body sections.	Spiders, mites, ticks
	Insects	Three pairs of legs. Three body sections.	Butterflies, bees, beetles
	Centipedes	Many segments. One pair of legs per segment.	Centipedes
	Millipedes	Many segments. Two pairs of legs per segment.	Millipedes

Questions: Answer in complete sentences.
1. In what three ways are all arthropods alike?
2. What one structure do scientists use to separate the five main groups of arthropods? Name the groups.
3. Draw a picture of the metamorphosis of a caterpillar.

270

10 **Teaching Tips** — Tell students that although many people think of centipedes and millipedes as creepy and revolting looking, they are actually very useful creatures. City dwellers might like to keep some centipedes as pets — they prey upon cockroaches voraciously.

SECTION REVIEW
Answers to Questions
1. Exoskeleton; several pairs of jointed legs; segmented bodies
2. Number of legs; hard-covered, spiders, insects, centipedes, and millipedes
3. Students should make a drawing similar to the one on the bottom of page 268.

CHAPTER REVIEW

Science Words: Match the terms in Column A with the definitions in Column B.

Column A	Column B
1. Hollow-bodied invertebrates	a. Changes some insects go through
2. Arthropods	b. Feelers
3. Invertebrates	c. Invertebrates with exoskeletons and jointed legs
4. Sponges	d. Supports an animal's weight on the outside of the body
5. Metamorphosis	e. Animals without backbones
6. Antennas	f. Invertebrates with one body opening
7. Spiny-skinned invertebrates	g. May cause disease if eaten in undercooked meat
8. Flatworms	h. Starfish
9. Mollusks	i. Octopus, squid, clam
10. Exoskeleton	j. Jellyfish, corals, and sea anemones

Questions: Answer in complete sentences.

1. What is different in the ways sponges and jellyfish feed themselves?
2. In what important ways are segmented worms different from flatworms or roundworms?
3. Companies that sell seeds to gardeners sometimes sell earthworms, too. Why do you think this is so?
4. Name the three main groups of mollusks.
5. What structures do mollusks have in common?
6. Is there anything strange about the stomach of a starfish? If so, explain.
7. Do arthropods need bones? Why or why not?
8. What are the five main groups of arthropods?

271

EXTENSIONS

Enrichment
Science Skills — Comparing and Contrasting

Students can compare the eyes of mollusks such as squids and octopuses with the eyes of arthropods, such as spiders and insects. These mollusks have two eyes that are remarkably similar to our eyes. Spiders commonly have eight simple eyes, and insects can have a combination of simple and compound eyes. Compound eyes have many lenses instead of just one as our cameralike eyes do.

CHAPTER REVIEW

Science Words
1. j, 2. c, 3. e, 4. f, 5. a, 6. b, 7. h,
8. g, 9. i, 10. d

Answers to Questions
1. Sponges take in food as it passes by; jellyfish sting their prey.
2. They are more complex with a heart, blood vessels, and a well-developed nervous system.
3. Earthworms aerate and fertilize soil.
4. Hatchet-footed, two-shelled; stomach-footed, one-shelled; head-footed, many legs or tentacles.
5. Soft bodies, two body openings, heart and blood vessels, digestive system.
6. Starfish extend their stomachs outward to devour prey.
7. No. Their "skeletons" are outside their bodies.
8. Hard-covered; spiders and spiderlike animals; insects; centipedes; millipedes.

SUGGESTED WORKSHEET MASTERS
pp. T–219s,t

SUGGESTED TEST MASTERS
pp. T–219h,i

CHAPTER 14

CHAPTER OBJECTIVES

1. Compare body systems of invertebrates and vertebrates.
2. Compare the body systems of fish and amphibians.
3. Describe reptiles, give examples, and explain how they are classified.
4. Compare birds and reptiles and give examples of types of birds.
5. Explain how mammals and reptiles are different and describe different types of mammals.

SECTION BACKGROUND

Fish are the first group of vertebrate animals to appear in the fossil record. There are three main groups of fish. The most primitive group includes the jawless fishes. They have no jaws, paired fins, or scales. They include hagfish, slime eels, and lampreys. Hagfish and slime eels scavenge for sick or dead fish. Lampreys attach themselves to other fish by a suckerlike mouth with teeth and suck out blood, weakening their victims. The two other groups are the cartilage fish and bony fish.

Amphibians spend the early part of their lives in water using gills to breathe dissolved oxygen in the water. As they mature, they lose their gills and develop lungs. They grow legs and become land-dwellers. Frogs and salamanders are amphibians.

MATERIALS

aquarium, paper, pencil

Exceptional Student IEP Chapter Goal

When presented with the following: fishes, amphibians, reptiles, birds, and mammals, the student will state two characteristics of each.

ANIMALS WITH BACKBONES

14-1.

Fish and Amphibians

272

This shark is not too interested in eating the fish that are swimming around it. It is sleeping! The shark and the other fish have many things in common. Can you see some of them in the picture? When you finish this section, you should be able to:

BASIC TEACHING PLAN

MOTIVATION

Text Questions — Can you see some of them in the picture? *Both are streamlined, have gills, tails, and fins and live in water.* Point out that the big difference between the two fish lies beneath their skins. The shark has no true bones as the small fish do. Sharks, skates, and rays are cartilage fish. Their skeletons are made of cartilage, not bone. They have paired fins and most are predatory. The scales of these fish resemble teeth and have a pulp cavity inside them.

Bony fishes have a skeleton made of bone. Most are covered with bony scales. Most bony fishes are ocean-dwelling, but some live in fresh water. Eels, salmon, and other migratory fish spend part of their life in fresh water and part in saltwater. They are known as anadromous fish.

A. Compare the body systems of *vertebrates* and *invertebrates*.

B. Describe the body plan of a fish.

C. Describe the life cycle of an *amphibian*.

Fish are the largest group of vertebrates, the animals with backbones. You have learned that most animals without backbones do not have an inside skeleton. Some have an exoskeleton, or a skeleton on the outside of the body. But all vertebrates have an **endoskeleton** (en-doh-**skel**-uh-tun). This is a hard framework inside the body that supports muscles and softer body parts.

Vertebrates have complex body systems. They have a nervous system with a well-developed brain. They have a closed system of blood circulation. This means that the blood stays in the blood vessels all the time.

Invertebrates have a simple blood system. An insect has a heart that acts like the rubber bulb on an eyedropper. It squeezes and opens, sending blood sloshing through the insect's body and bringing food to all cells. That is fine for an insect with a small body. But for vertebrates, blood must bring food and oxygen to trillions of cells. Blood must carry carbon dioxide and other wastes away from the cells. Red blood cells do this.

In a fish, the heart has two parts or *chambers*. Blood from all over the body comes into the first chamber. This blood carries carbon dioxide from the cells of the fish.

1

Endoskeleton: A hard support structure inside the body of some vertebrates, made of cartilage and bone.

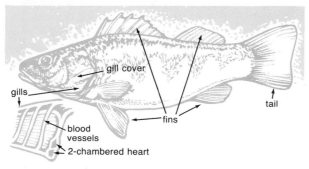

gill cover

gills

fins

tail

blood vessels

2-chambered heart

273

DEVELOPMENT

1 **Teaching Tips** — Review with students the meaning of the words *vertebrate* and *invertebrate*. Review *exoskeleton* and introduce *endoskeleton*. What do the prefixes *exo-* and *endo-* mean? *Exo-* means *outside*, *endo-* means *within*.

2 **Teaching Tips** — In this chapter, students will continue to learn about more and more complex animals. Remind them that they have already seen that worms are more complex than sponges; mollusks are more complex than worms; arthropods are more complex than mollusks, and so on. Ask the students to pick out ways that vertebrates in general are more complex than the invertebrates they have studied. Vertebrates have nervous systems, well-developed brains, closed system of circulation, and a more complex heart.

T–273

EXTENSIONS

Reinforcement
Activity

The students will have learned that primitive fish have skeletons of cartilage. Point out that all bones begin as cartilaginous structures and then, as the animal matures, special cells deposit calcium salts within the cartilage, hardening it. Have students take a wish bone from a chicken and leave it in vinegar for a week. How does the bone look? (about the same) How does it react to bending? (bends easily, feels rubbery) What has been removed from the bone? (calcium salts) What is left? (cartilage)

Gills: Structures in some water-dwelling animals that pick up oxygen from the water.

Cold-blooded animals: Vertebrates whose body temperature stays about the same as the temperature of their surroundings.

Cartilage: A firm but bendable material that forms the skeleton of some fish, and is found in many animals.

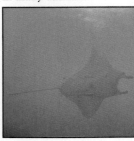

The first chamber squeezes the blood into the second chamber. The second chamber pumps the blood through blood vessels to the **gills**. Since fish live in water, they use *gills* instead of lungs to breathe. The gills pick up carbon dioxide from the blood as it passes through them. Then they pass the carbon dioxide out into the water that bathes the gills. **3**

At the same time, the gills pick up oxygen from the water. The oxygen passes to the blood around the gills. The blood travels to the body cells, carrying oxygen and food. It picks up carbon dioxide from the cells and returns to the first chamber of the heart.

Fish are **cold-blooded** animals. This means that their body temperature stays about the same as the temperature of the water around them.

Some fish have skeletons made of **cartilage** (kar-tuh-lij). *Cartilage* is a firm material, but it is not as hard as bone. Cartilage bends, while bones are stiff. The firm ridges in your ears and nose are made of cartilage. **4**

Fish with skeletons made of cartilage include sharks, skates, and rays. Most sharks have jaws lined with several rows of sharp teeth. The shark's skin is made up of sharply pointed scales of tooth-like material. In fact, sharkskin is used to make a kind of sandpaper. Only nine of the 250 kinds of sharks are dangerous to humans. **5**

Skates and rays have broad, flat bodies. As they swim through the water, they look like living kites. This is especially true of skates. They have long, sharp tails.

Fish with bony skeletons are found in almost every natural body of water. They live in oceans, lakes, rivers, and ponds. There are 25,000 different kinds of bony fish. Salmon, haddock, and trout are some of them.

Most fish have the same body plan. The body is streamlined. It is narrow at the head end, wider in the middle, and then narrower again toward the tail end. This is the best shape for moving easily through the water. Even boats have a similar shape.

274

3 **Skill Development** — If your classroom or school has an aquarium, ask the class to *observe* the fish as they breathe. Can students see the gills moving? Ask them to *compare* this movement with the movement of their own chests as they breathe.

4 **Teaching Tips** — Have students wiggle the ends of their noses or bend their ears with their fingers so they can feel how flexible cartilage is. Can they bend their fingers as easily as they can bend the rim of their outer ears? *No. Except at joints, fingers cannot be bent.*

5 **Teaching Tips** — Ask students to figure out what fraction of sharks are dangerous to people. *9/250.* Can they figure this out as a percentage? *Less than 4%.* Ask the students why, given such a low figure, do people seem to be so afraid of sharks? Are people unfair to these animals? If so, could this unfairness threaten sharks in any way?

Fish have two sets of paired fins. They are like the four legs of land-living vertebrates. The paired fins of the fish are used for swimming. In addition to the paired fins, many fish have other, unpaired fins. There may be one or two on a fish's back, one on its bottom, and one on its tail. Can you find the fins on this fish?

Fish have a good sense of balance and of taste. They can hear noises and vibrations in the water. Sound travels very well through water. You may have noticed this if you have ever swum underwater.

The next group of vertebrates is the **amphibians** (am-fib-ee-unz). *Amphibian* means "two lives." Most amphibians do live two lives. They spend the early part of their lives in the water. They get their oxygen from the water through gills. As adults, they have lungs and live on land. Amphibians include frogs, toads, and salamanders. Like fish, they are cold-blooded.

Amphibians: Cold-blooded vertebrates that must live in or near water. Amphibians lay their eggs in water.

ACTIVITY

Observing fish

A. Obtain these materials: aquarium with several fish, paper, pencil.
B. Watch the fish as they swim through the water. Look at how their tails and fins move.
  1. How does a fish push itself through the water?
  2. Can a fish turn? How?
  3. Can a fish stop? How?
C. With a pencil, gently tap one side of the aquarium below the water level.
  4. How do the fish respond?
D. Hold a sheet of paper against one side of the aquarium. Tap gently on the paper with a pencil.
  5. How do the fish respond? What sense are they using? Explain your answer.

275

EXTENSIONS

Enrichment
Research — Library

Have the students identify the fish in your fish tank by looking them up in a guidebook. Have them make an identification card for each species with a drawing of the fish, the common and scientific names of the fish, and information about its habitat, feeding habits, etc.

Activity

Students can observe how fish react to light. They can use the same set-up that was used in the activity. They will also need a lamp or flashlight.

A. Place the lamp above the tank and turn it on. After a few minutes observe where the fish are in the tank.

B. Move the lamp so that it shines on only one side of the tank and again observe the location of the fish after a few minutes.

  1. Did the fish move toward or away from the light?
  2. Did it make a difference if the light was on the top or sides?
  3. Why do you think the fish show this reaction to light?

ACTIVITY

Skill Development — *Observing, Hypothesizing*

Teaching Tips — You may want students to wait a few minutes between steps B and C. If fish hear several taps in relatively quick succession, they will no longer display the same reaction.

Safety Tips — In the interests of the safety of the fish, do not let students put their hands or other objects in the tank.

Answers to Questions — 1. With fins and tail. 2. Yes, by twisting its body in the direction it wants to go. 3. Yes, by "backpedalling" with its fins. 4. By coming over to the spot where you tapped. 5. They head toward the spot where you tapped; their sense of hearing, since they can no longer see the person tapping.

Exceptional Student
Visually Impaired
If the students cannot observe the fish in the tank, have them hold a fish from a fish market and demonstrate how it moves, turns, and stops.

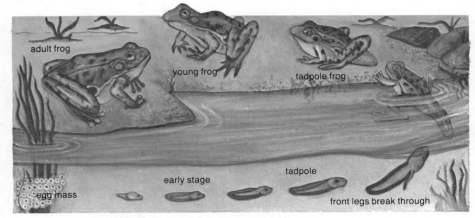

adult frog
young frog
tadpole frog
egg mass
early stage
tadpole
front legs break through

EXTENSIONS

Enrichment
Research

Although amphibians need to keep their skins moist to live, they do not necessarily live near large bodies of water. Students can do research to find out how amphibians are adapted to live out of water. For example, there are tiny frogs that live inside plants called bromeliads. Bromeliads have leaves that catch and hold water which the frogs use to stay moist. Another species of frog survives in the desert by remaining buried in the sand surrounded by a moist mucous layer.

Living "two lives" means amphibians go through a big change. Like insects, they undergo a metamorphosis.

The eggs of frogs and toads hatch into young called **6** *tadpoles*. Tadpoles live in the water. They have gills and tails. After a while, the tadpoles begin to change. Their tails disappear. Bumps develop on the sides of their bodies. These become front and hind legs. The animals lose their gills and develop lungs.

Now the tadpoles must come up to the surface for air. Soon they move onto land as adults. This life cycle takes **7** over two years for a bullfrog. Leopard frogs go through it in about three months.

Even though adult amphibians can live on land, they must stay near water. They have thin skins. They take in water through their skins from damp air. In a sense, amphibians use their skins to "breathe in" water. Only near a pond or in swampy places is the air moist enough for this. In dry air, amphibians would lose water rapidly through their skins. Then they would die.

Amphibians have a more complex heart than fish do. It has three chambers. As in all vertebrates, the blood carries food and oxygen to the body cells. The three-chambered heart does a somewhat better job of this than the two-chambered heart of fish.

276

6 **Teaching Tips** — In springtime, it is easy to catch tadpoles in ponds and swampy areas. Bring one to the classroom — or ask a student to — and observe it as it turns into the adult form. Have the class keep records of its growth from day to day. Be sure students add fresh pond water to its tank regularly, and provide a stone or other place for it when it can no longer breathe underwater.

7 **Skill Development** — Ask the class to *compare* the life cycle of an amphibian with the life cycle of an insect that undergoes metamorphosis. Carefully review the steps in each process.

Land-living animals need a better working heart and blood system than fish do. They use more energy as they move about. That's because their bodies are not supported by water. A land animal weighs more than a water animal of the same size. Think of how much lighter you feel in a bathtub full of water. You can feel your weight return as the water goes out of the tub.

8

Land-living animals also have a well-developed nervous system. A frog has a larger brain than a fish.

Section Review

Main Idea: Classifying Some Cold-blooded Vertebrates

Main Groups	Structures	Subgroups	Examples
Fish (water)	Endoskeleton. Well-developed brain, nervous system. Closed circulation. Gills. Fins. Two-chambered heart.	Bony Cartilage	Salmon Shark
Amphibians (water/land)	Endoskeleton. Well-developed brain, nervous system. Closed circulation. Gills/lungs. Fins/legs. Three-chambered heart.		Frog, toad

Questions: Answer in complete sentences.

1. What is the main difference between a vertebrate and an invertebrate animal?
2. Explain what a closed system of circulation is.
3. Describe the shape of a fish. How does this shape help a fish swim?
4. What does the word "amphibian" mean? Why are some vertebrates called amphibians?
5. Describe the life cycle of a frog.

277

EXTENSIONS

Enrichment
Activity

The students can measure how much weight an object seems to lose when it is supported by water. Have the students do the following:

A. Obtain these materials: any small solid object, a tub of water, and a spring scale.

B. Use the spring scale to measure the weight of the object.

C. Place the object so that it is totally under the surface of the water and weigh it again.

1. What was the weight of the object when it was not in the water?
2. What was the weight of the object when it was in the water?

---

8 **Teaching Tips** — Ask students if they've ever noticed the phenomenon referred to here — that of feeling lighter in a bathtub full of water and heavier after they've gotten out. Ask if anyone has experienced the same phenomenon on other occasions, such as when swimming.

SECTION REVIEW

Answers to Questions
1. Vertebrates have backbones, invertebrates do not.
2. Blood is always in the heart or blood vessels.
3. Narrow at the head and tail and wider in the middle; it's the best shape for moving through water.
4. "Two lives"; because they spend the first part of their lives in water, the second on land.
5. Frogs hatch from eggs in water, have gills, and breathe water like fish; gradually they lose their gills, grow lungs, legs; they come out on land and live in marshy, swampy places; they lay their eggs in water.

Unlike amphibians, reptiles are true land animals. Although some are excellent swimmers and spend a good part of their lives in water, all reptiles breathe air throughout their lives. All reptiles lay their eggs on land.

Like fish and amphibians, reptiles are cold-blooded. Their body temperature remains about the same as that of their surroundings. In very hot weather, reptiles must seek shade. In cold weather, they become sluggish. They cannot survive freezing temperatures for more than a few minutes.

Birds are warm-blooded vertebrates. All birds have feathers. In flying birds, the feathers help guide streams of air over and beneath the wings as they beat. Flying birds have light, hollow bones and powerful wing muscles.

Feathers also help insulate the bird's body. They can act as a blanket to hold in body heat. If the bird becomes too hot, the feathers can be raised to allow some body heat to escape. Unlike cold-blooded animals, birds can live almost everywhere in the world.

Even flightless birds have wings and feathers. Penguins have stiff feathers that are slicked down against their skin by a coating of natural oil. The oil makes the feathers waterproof. The stiffness of the feathers make the flipperlike "wings" of the penguins efficient swimming tools.

MATERIALS

paper, pencil

14-2.

Reptiles and Birds

Reptiles: Cold-blooded vertebrates that lay their eggs on land and have thick skins made of scales or plates.

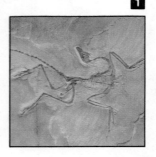

The animal shown in this rock lived 150 million years ago. What is it? It had feathers and wings like a bird. But it also had a long, bony tail, and teeth in its jaws. Scientists think it was the first bird. When you finish this section, you should be able to:

☐ **A.** Explain why *reptiles* are true land animals.
☐ **B.** Name the structures that allow *birds* to fly.
☐ **C.** Compare and contrast *reptiles* and *birds*.

Reptiles (**rep**-tylz) are true land animals. Like amphibians, they are cold-blooded and lay eggs. Like amphibians, most *reptiles* have a three-chambered heart. Many reptiles spend all of their entire lives on land. They lay their eggs on land.

Reptiles, unlike amphibians, have a skin of hard plates or scales. They do not lose water from their skins. So they can live in dry places—even in deserts.

Amphibian eggs are soft and jelly-like. They dry out easily. They must be hatched in water. The eggs of reptiles have a tough shell and do not dry out easily.

Millions of years ago, most animals were reptiles. Dinosaurs of all shapes and sizes roamed the land. Reptiles with wings soared through the air and dove for fish. Unlike modern birds, these flying reptiles had beaks with teeth. Their wings were covered with leathery skin, not feathers. Other reptiles swam in the seas. They had

278

BASIC TEACHING PLAN
MOTIVATION

Ask students whether they agree with scientists who think Archaeopteryx may have been the first bird. Or do they think this animal should be classified as a reptile? Tell them that its name comes from two Greek words, *archaeo* (primitive) and *pteryx* (wing). Archaeopteryx was smaller than a present-day crow. Only four archaeopteryx fossils have been found, the first during the nineteenth century in Solnhofen, Bavaria.

DEVELOPMENT

1 **Teaching Tips** — What do students think of when you say *reptile*? *Many answers may reflect the widespread feeling that reptiles are repulsive or slimy. Actually, snakes are dry and move gracefully.*
2 **Teaching Tips** — Design a reptile bulletin board. Start with the earliest reptiles. Ask students to look up ancient reptiles, such as dinosaurs, and draw pictures of them. Tack the pictures at the top of a large bulletin board.

fish-shaped bodies with tails and fins. Their scientific name means "fish-lizard." But they were not fish. They had lungs and breathed air.

Today, these animals no longer exist. Only three main groups of reptiles are still living: the turtles, the alligators and crocodiles, and the lizards and snakes.

Turtles are easily recognized by their hard, protective shells. A few kinds live on land, but most live in water.

The most famous is the green turtle. Adult green turtles weigh up to 400 kilograms (880 pounds). Many feed on plants along the Atlantic Ocean shore of Brazil, in South America. Every few years, the turtles head out to sea. They swim across the Atlantic to a small island only 10 kilometers (6 miles) wide. Somehow the turtles find it. There, they mate and lay their eggs on the shore. **3**

After hatching, the young turtles head straight for the sea, even when it is hidden by sand dunes. Eventually, the young turtles cross the ocean to the same beaches in Brazil that their parents came from.

How do they do it? The turtles may get clues from the position of the sun. They may use chemical clues like changes in the taste of the water they swim in. How they travel is a fascinating scientific puzzle. **4**

Crocodiles and alligators are reptiles. They also spend a lot of time in the water. Their strong jaws and razor-sharp teeth make them fierce and dangerous hunters. Crocodiles and alligators are the only reptiles that have a four-chambered heart.

5

279

EXTENSIONS

Enrichment
Research — Library

Students can do research to prepare a report on the dinosaurs. They should investigate the kinds of dinosaurs, their sizes, what they ate, what their surroundings looked like, what may have caused them to become extinct, and so on. Some of your students may want to report on recent evidence that some dinosaurs may have been warm-blooded, cared for their young, and were quite agile.

Research — Library

Turtles, crocodiles, and alligators are sometimes known as living fossils. This means that animals very much like those living today existed millions of years ago. The students can do research to find out what the ancient forms of these animals looked like, what they ate, and how they lived. The students can then formulate a hypothesis that explains why these animals remained unchanged for such large periods of time.

3 **Teaching Tips** — Using a large-scale map, ask students to locate Brazil and Ascension Island. Have them trace the migratory route of the green turtle. How many students have ever traveled so far?

4 **Teaching Tips** — Ask students if they know how scientists learned so much about the migrations of animals like the green turtle. Scientists didn't always know the facts. Years ago, for instance, people believed that some migratory birds simply hid and slept in the underbrush all winter and then reappeared in the spring. Direct observation has taught scientists much about migration. Banding birds and animals helped them trace precise routes. Today, scientists also make use of modern technology to study animal habits. In some cases, researchers have fastened tiny radio transmitters to animals and have kept track of their movements that way.

5 **Teaching Tips** — Point out to the class that although we consider crocodiles and alligators fierce and dangerous, these creatures do seem to exhibit mild natures in some cases. Alligator and crocodile mothers are very careful with their offspring. When the mothers move their babies, they pick them up gently and carry them in their mouths.

Exceptional Student
Learning Disabled
Visually Impaired

Take the students to visit a pet store that has turtles, snakes, and lizards. Have them hold and observe the reptiles and discuss the characteristics of each.

Application
Research — Library

There are only four kinds of poisonous snakes in the United States—the coral snake, copperhead, water moccasin, and rattlesnake. Have students do research to report on these snakes, how they can be identified, habits, first-aid treatment for bites, and the use of antivenom in their treatment.

280

The four-chambered heart is more complex than the three-chambered heart. It works better. Animals with a four-chambered heart have a richer supply of oxygen in their blood. They can be more active and use more energy. That's important for animals that must run on land or fly through the air. **6**

Snakes and lizards make up the third group of reptiles. Scientists classify them together because they are alike in so many ways.

You might think that there is one big difference between them—that lizards have legs and snakes do not. But in fact, that's not true. Some lizards have no legs. One that has no legs is the worm lizard. Another is the glass snake, shown above. In spite of its name, the glass snake is really a lizard. Why? Because its eyelids can move. True snakes cannot move their eyelids. This is one of the few real differences between lizards and snakes.

Snakes kill their prey in three different ways. Some snakes swallow an animal whole, while the animal is still **7** alive. Their jaws "unhinge" so that their mouths can open very wide. The smooth green snake kills in this way. Some snakes kill by coiling around an animal until the animal can no longer breathe. The boa constrictor kills in this way. The middle photograph shows a boa. These snakes also swallow their prey whole. Some snakes, such as the rattlesnake, kill by injecting poison from their fangs into their prey.

The largest snakes in the world are constrictor (squeezing) snakes. Pythons and anacondas reach a length of 9 meters (30 feet).

Most lizards are less than half a meter (20 inches) long. They eat insects and small animals. One lizard, the Komodo dragon of southeastern Asia, is much bigger. It **8** grows to a length of about 3 meters (10 feet). It can outrun and catch small pigs and even deer. Watching a Komodo dragon run is like looking back into the past. Perhaps small dinosaurs ran like them to catch their prey.

6 **Skill Development** — Students can *compare* the four-chambered hearts of alligators and crocodiles with the three-chambered hearts of the other reptiles.

7 **Teaching Tips** — Point out to the students that snakes very often find their prey not by using their poor vision but by using their ability to detect changes in heat.

8 **Teaching Tips** — Finish your reptile bulletin board by adding pictures of present-day turtles, alligators and crocodiles, and snakes and lizards. Be sure to include a Komodo dragon, so the class can see the similarity between some of the dinosaurs of ages past and the reptiles we know today.

Another group of vertebrates is the **birds**. *Birds* lay eggs, but in almost every other way, they are different from the vertebrates we have seen so far.

All birds have feathers and wings. Even those birds that do not fly have feathers and wings. An ostrich, for example, may be 2.5 m (8 ft) tall and weigh about 160 kg (350 lb), so its small wings are useless for flying. But ostriches can run almost 50 km (30 mi) an hour. They use their powerful legs to protect themselves against enemies.

Even penguins have wings and feathers. Their wings act like flippers. They can swim as fast as seals.

Flying birds have light, hollow bones. Their wing feathers are made to "catch" the greatest possible amount of air. Powerful wing muscles move the wings up and down in a twisting motion.

Birds are **warm-blooded** animals. A bird's body temperature stays the same no matter how cold or hot the air or water is. Unlike cold-blooded animals, birds can be active even in very cold weather. A bird's feathers help it keep warm.

10

Warm-blooded animals: Vertebrates whose body temperature does not change.

281

EXTENSIONS

Application
Activity

The students may wish to go on a bird walk. Using bird identification books obtainable from the library, they could find out how many types of birds they can spot and identify in an afternoon. It would be helpful to invite an experienced bird watcher to go along with the students. They may wish to bring along binoculars so that they can spot the birds without disturbing them.

9 **Teaching Tips** — Ask: Did birds like penguins and ostriches ever fly? *Yes, ancestors of these modern flightless birds flew.* Have students look up information about the early ancestors of penguins and ostriches.

10 **Skill Development** — Ask students to *compare* the trait of warm-bloodedness with that of cold-bloodedness, and list the advantages and disadvantages of each.

EXTENSIONS

Enrichment

Science Skills — Comparing and Contrasting

Students can learn about the concept of convergent evolution by comparing the eating methods of flamingos and baleen whales. Convergent evolution means that organisms with different ancestors become more alike because they have adapted to the same environment. Since they both feed by straining tiny organisms from the water, the beak of a flamingo is very similar to the mouth of a baleen whale. The most obvious difference between them is, of course, size.

ACTIVITY

Where do some birds migrate?

Arctic tern

A. Obtain these materials: tracing paper, pencil.

B. The map below shows the summer and winter homes of the arctic terns. They are the champions of bird migration. Trace the map onto tracing paper.

  1. The terns leave their northern home in late summer and head across North America to the Atlantic Ocean. With an arrow, show this.

  2. The terns fly across the ocean to Europe. Show this part of their trip.

  3. Then the terns head south across Europe to Africa. Draw an arrow to show this.

  4. The terns fly over Africa to their winter home. Draw this as well.

  5. Where is their winter home?

C. The arctic tern's fall migration is 17,700 kilometers long. The birds fly north again in the spring.

  6. What is their round trip each year?

D. These birds are adapted to their long trip. Look at the picture on the left.

  7. What do you notice about the bird's tail?

  8. From the bird's bill, what do you think it eats?

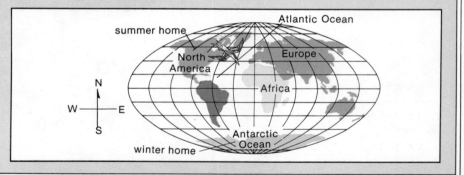

282

ACTIVITY

Skill Development — *Reading Illustrations, Following Directions, Observing, Inferring*

Teaching Tips — Students may want to trace the migration route on a globe using tape to show the flight path.

Answers to Questions — **1. 2. 3. 4.** Their map should resemble the map on page 282, with arrows pointing east across North America and the Atlantic Ocean to Europe, and then South across Europe and Africa to the Antarctic Ocean. **5.** The Antarctic Ocean. **6.** 35,400 km. **7.** It is forked-shaped. **8.** Fish.

There are about 8,500 different kinds of birds. The **11** ostrich is the largest bird. The fairy hummingbird is the smallest. It is only 5½ centimeters (2¼ inches) from head to tail. All hummingbirds are small. Their wings can beat as many as 75 times per second. This makes the humming noise that gives these birds their name. Because of the fast wingbeat, hummingbirds can hang almost motionless in the air as they use their long beaks to suck nectar, a sweet liquid, from flowers.

Birds are good navigators. Some birds fly at night using the stars to guide them. But how birds make long migrations is still puzzling.

Section Review

Main Idea: Classifying Reptiles and Birds

REPTILES			
Group	**Structures**	**Features**	**Example**
Turtles	Scales. Shell. Three-chambered heart. Legs. Teeth.	Cold-blooded. Lay eggs. Navigate.	Green turtle
Crocodiles, alligators	Scales. Four-chambered heart. Legs. Teeth.	Cold-blooded. Lay eggs.	Crocodile, alligator
Snakes, lizards	Scales. Three-chambered heart. May be legless.	Cold-blooded. Lay eggs.	Komodo dragon, rattlesnake

BIRDS
Structures
Feathers. Wings. Hollow bones. Four-chambered heart.
Features
Warm-blooded. Lay eggs. Navigate.

Questions: Answer in complete sentences.

1. What does "warm-blooded" mean? How is it different from "cold-blooded"?
2. What three structures do birds have that reptiles do not have?
3. What are two reasons that make it possible for reptiles to live entirely on land, something that amphibians cannot do?

283

EXTENSIONS

Reinforcement
Research — Library

Scientists believe that birds evolved from reptiles. They did not, however, evolve from the flying reptiles such as the pteranodons. They evolved from a type of dinosaur known as the thecodonts. The students can do research to find out what these reptiles looked like, how they lived, and why it is believed birds evolved from them.

11 **Teaching Tips** — Students can easily study birds and their characteristics by attracting them to a bird-feeding station. Elaborate equipment is not necessary; feeders made from coffee cans and plastic milk containers do the job. Emphasize that once birds come to depend upon a winter-feeding station, food should be offered until spring. Otherwise, birds may starve.

SECTION REVIEW

Answers to Questions

1. That an animal's temperature stays about the same, regardless of the temperature of air or water; cold-blooded animals grow warmer and cooler with outside changes.
2. Wings, feathers, hollow bones
3. Thicker skins, which don't dry out so easily; tougher eggs that do not dry out so easily

Mammals are the highest class of vertebrates. Like birds, they are warm-blooded and air-breathing. Unlike birds, mammals have hair, give birth to live young, and nurse their young with milk produced by the mammary glands.

Hair serves as insulation for mammals. Mammals can grow thick coats of hair in cold weather, and shed some in warm weather. Some mammals, such as human beings, can further regulate their body temperature by sweating. Increased sweating helps cool the body by evaporation. Other mammals cool themselves by panting, which allows evaporation from the mouth.

Mammals are adapted to live in every environment on earth: ice pack, desert, prairie, jungle, mountain, ocean, fresh water. One group, the bats, has taken to the air. Prolonged care of the young, a highly developed brain, and keen senses have made mammals one of the most successful groups of animals.

MATERIALS

14-3.

Mammals

Here's a living puzzle. What animal has a bill and webbed feet like a duck, but no feathers or wings? What lays eggs with tough, leathery shells that are similar to reptile eggs? What animal is covered with thick hair and feeds milk to its young? One animal has all these characteristics. When you finish this section, you should be able to:

☐ **A.** Compare and contrast *mammals* with birds.
☐ **B.** Compare and contrast *mammals* with reptiles.
☐ **C.** Explain why *mammals* can live in so many different places.

1   The animal shown is a duck-billed platypus. It lives in Australia and on Tasmania, a nearby island.

In some ways, the platypus is like a reptile. In some ways, it is like a bird. But the platypus is different from both of these groups. Scientists classify the platypus as a **mammal**. The platypus has hair. All *mammals* have hair or fur. In winter, some mammals grow thick coats of hair for warmth.

Unlike reptiles, the platypus is warm-blooded. Mammals are warm-blooded. The platypus feeds milk to its young. This is a characteristic of all mammals.

Mammals: Vertebrates that have hair and feed milk from their bodies to their young.

284

BASIC TEACHING PLAN

MOTIVATION

Can students figure out what this animal is? Perhaps some can come up with its name. *Duck-billed platypus.* Tell the students about another egg-laying mammal called a spiny anteater. This tiny creature also lives in Australia. When they were first discovered, many people thought that they were a hoax. They are known as *monotremes*.

DEVELOPMENT

1   **Skill Development** — Ask students to locate the islands of Australia and Tasmania on a map or globe. Ask: What kind of land forms are they? *Islands.* Ask students to *hypothesize* what this might have to do with the fact that the majority of the most primitive mammals are limited to these two places. These mammals were isolated and therefore protected from other animals that might have competed with them or preyed on them.

The young of mammals live and grow in the mother's body until they are ready to be born. But the platypus is different from other mammals. The platypus lays eggs and the young hatch from them. The platypus is probably a very early mammal. That is why it looks like a kind of "halfway" animal.

The next group of mammals is the pouched mammals. Kangaroos and opossums are pouched mammals. The young of pouched mammals begin life in the mother's body. But they are born before they are ready to live in the outside world. They are tiny and very weak. They crawl to the mother's pouch and settle down inside it. There, they get milk. They are protected until they are big enough to move on their own.

In all the rest of the mammals, the young get food from the mother's blood stream before they are born. They are not born until they are completely developed. This allows mammals to live in places all over the earth.

Bats are the only mammals that fly. The structure of their front limbs has changed to support their wings. The wings are made of skin. Four very long fingers hold the skin outstretched. The thumbs are hooked. Some bats, like the ones shown, eat fruit. Some eat insects.

Meat-eating mammals have sharp teeth for cutting and tearing. Claws are used for catching and holding prey, and for digging and climbing.

285

2 **Teaching Tips** — Bats are interesting animals. Point out that they have extremely keen hearing, and navigate and find food through echolocation. A bat constantly emits a stream of high-pitched sounds, which bounce off nearby objects, thus serving as a guide to flight.

3 **Teaching Tips** — Ask students to describe the way in which these meat-eaters indirectly depend on plants for food.

Enrichment
Research — Library

Students can do research to find out about the evolution of sea mammals. At one time the ancestors of modern whales and seals lived on land. Evidence of this can be found by examining the skeletons of certain whales. They have the vestiges of hip bones that were once needed for the hind legs. These creatures evolved adaptations to a life in the water. The students can report their findings to the class.

Rodents: Mammals with chisel-like teeth.

5

Many mammals live in the sea. The front limbs of walruses and seals are flippers. These animals have a fish-like tail. Dolphins and whales have fish-like bodies and fins. Some of these mammals are also meat-eaters.

Mammals like mice and squirrels are **rodents.** *Rodents* have sharp teeth shaped like chisels. They are used for cutting and gnawing. Rodents reproduce very quickly, and they live almost everywhere. They dig, run, leap, hop, climb, and swim. There are even squirrels that glide. The picture shows a gray squirrel.

Hoofed mammals, such as cows, eat plants. They have flat, sturdy teeth for chewing and crushing tough plants. Their hoofs help them to run fast to escape enemies.

4

286

4 **Skill Development** — Students can describe the *cause and effect* relationship between the fact that whales live in water and are the largest animals that ever lived.

5 **Teaching Tips** — Tell the students that hoofed mammals are divided into two groups. Animals in the group that includes horses, rhinoceroses, and tapirs have an odd number of toes on each foot. Animals in the group that includes cattle, pigs, sheep, antelopes, giraffes, and hippos have an even number of toes on each foot.

Elephants are also plant-eaters. They are the largest living land mammals. Like other plant-eaters, they have broad teeth for grinding food. The tusks are actually a pair of upper teeth that have grown very long. The elephant's trunk is an extension of its nose and upper lip. It can pick up huge logs, and gently move tiny twigs without breaking them.

Primates are the most intelligent of the mammals. *Primates* have hands with movable fingers and flat nails instead of claws. They can pick up small objects and handle them with skill. This is a great advantage in looking for food and for making and using tools. Both eyes of the primates look forward. This makes it easier for them to judge how far away things are. Monkeys, chimpanzees, and humans are primates.

As you have seen, mammals live almost everywhere on earth where life is possible. They live in the cold of the Arctic and in the world's highest mountains. They live in the heat of jungles and deserts. Some live in the water and have bodies like fish. Mammals have hair or fur at some time in their lives. Even the young of whales and dolphins have fur before they are born. Some mammals can even fly. But they all breathe air, are warm-blooded, and feed milk to their young.

Primates: The most intelligent mammals.

287

EXTENSIONS

Enrichment
Science Skills — Classifying

Have students do a written report on how scientists try to measure the intelligence of different mammals. What methods do they use? Have students describe their own thoughts about the testing methods and perhaps suggest ideas of their own for testing animal intelligence. Since scientists do not completely agree on what intelligence is or how to test it, the students should be allowed to speculate freely, but should be prepared to defend their ideas.

6 **Teaching Tips** — Point out that although elephants are the largest of land animals, and that although a herd of rampaging elephants can do enormous damage to a field of crops or a village, elephants are nonetheless gentle and intelligent animals. They take devoted care of their young; adults will "adopt" orphans, help crippled members of a family group to find food and water, and so on.

7 **Teaching Tips** — Primates are the most advanced of all mammals. Some scientists even claim a measure of success in teaching chimps and other primates to communicate with humans through signs and pictures.

EXTENSIONS

Reinforcement
Activity

Students will have learned in this section that mammals have a unique way of cooling their bodies when they become over-heated — by evaporation. Water evaporating on a body surface such as the tongue or the skin cools the surface. Have students dip one hand in warm water. Then have them wave both their dry hand and their wet hand in the air. What do they notice? (The wet hand feels cooler.) Why? (Water is evaporating from it.) How do mammals cool themselves by evaporation? (Sweating or panting)

Main Ideas: Mammals are warm-blooded vertebrates with fur or hair that feed milk to their young.

MAMMALS			
Group	**Structures**	**Features**	**Examples**
Pouched mammals	Pouch.	Born undeveloped. Develop in pouch.	Opossum, kangaroo
Flying mammals	Fingers form "wings."	Can fly.	Bats
Meat-eating mammals	Sharp teeth. Claws.	Catch prey for food.	Cheetah, cat
Sea-living mammals	Flippers. Fins.	Swim in ocean. Most eat meat.	Walrus, seal
Rodents	Sharp teeth shaped like chisels.	Can gnaw. Reproduce quickly.	Squirrel, mouse
Hoofed mammals	Hoofed feet. Flat teeth.	Eat plants.	Cow, horse
Elephants	Tusks. Trunk.	Largest mammal. Eat plants.	African elephant
Primates	Developed hands, eyes.	Most intelligent mammal.	Chimpanzee, human

Questions: Answer in complete sentences.

1. Does the platypus seem like a bird in any way? Why do scientists classify it as a mammal?
2. Name three ways in which reptiles and mammals are different.
3. Do any mammals live in the sea? Why don't scientists classify whales and dolphins as fish?
4. Name two advantages that primates have over other mammals.

288

SECTION REVIEW

Answers to Questions
1. Yes, it lays eggs. Because it feeds milk to its young and is warm-blooded.
2. Reptiles lay eggs, almost no mammal does; reptiles are cold-blooded, mammals are warm-blooded; reptiles have scales, mammals have hair.
3. Yes; because whales, dolphins, and so on bear their young alive, nurse them, are warm-blooded.
4. They have hands with movable fingers so they can pick up small objects; their eyes look forward, which improves vision.

CHAPTER REVIEW

Science Words: Think of a word for each blank. List the letters **a** through **v** on paper. Write the word next to each letter.

Animals with backbones are called ___a___. All of them have a hard framework within the body. This is called the ___b___. Some fish are bony and some are supported by a substance known as ___c___. All fish breathe through ___d___. Their body temperature changes with the temperature around them. That means that fish are ___e___. Animals that live "two lives" are ___f___. They undergo a big change known as ___g___. Instead of a two-chambered heart like the fish have, the amphibians have a ___h___ heart. Snakes, alligators, and turtles are three kinds of ___i___. ___j___ have a hard, protective shell. Although all ___k___ are legless, there are some ___l___ that do not have legs either. ___m___ and ___n___ are the only reptiles with a four-chambered heart. A bird is considered ___o___ because its body temperature always stays the same. Birds are covered with ___p___. Most of them fly with their ___q___. Many birds have ___r___ bones that also help them to fly. Animals that are covered with fur and that feed their young milk are called ___s___. These animals live in many places, even in the ___t___, where the walruses and seals live. Mammals with sharp teeth shaped like chisels are the ___u___. Monkeys belong to the group known as the ___v___.

Questions: Answer in complete sentences.

1. How do scientists use the backbone to help them classify different kinds of animals?
2. Describe how fish get oxygen.
3. Why do we say that frogs live "two lives"? Give details.
4. Which is a true land animal, a toad or a snake? Explain.
5. What is one way that all reptiles and all birds are alike?
6. How do wings help birds to fly? How do feathers and hollow bones help them?
7. Most birds can fly, but only one kind of mammal can. Name two other ways mammals are different from birds.

289

EXTENSIONS

Enrichment
Research — Library

Students can do research to find out about primitive organisms, such as acorn worms and sea squirts, or tunicates. The students can investigate what group of organisms each belongs to and why. They will learn that scientists are not sure whether to classify them as chordates, invertebrates, or somewhere in between. They should draw their own conclusions using the facts they discover.

CHAPTER REVIEW

Science Words
a. vertebrates, **b.** endoskeleton, **c.** cartilage, **d.** gills, **e.** cold-blooded, **f.** amphibians, **g.** metamorphosis, **h.** three-chambered, **i.** reptiles, **j.** turtles, **k.** snakes, **l.** lizards, **m.** crocodiles, **n.** alligators, **o.** warm-blooded, **p.** feathers, **q.** wings, **r.** hollow, **s.** mammals, **t.** ocean, **u.** rodents, **v.** primates

Answers to Questions
1. All animals with backbones belong to the group called vertebrates.
2. Through the gills
3. Frogs are amphibians. They live in the water and on land.
4. A snake; it can live far from water and lays eggs on land.
5. All lay eggs.
6. Wings beat against the air and keep the bird aloft. Wing feathers "catch" the greatest possible amount of air. Hollow bones are light.
7. Mammals give birth to live young and have hair.

SUGGESTED WORKSHEET MASTERS
pp. T–219u,v,w

SUGGESTED TEST MASTERS
pp. T–219j,k,l

T–289

EXTENSIONS

Enrichment
Activity

Scientists very often use dichotomous keys to identify organisms. These keys ask a series of yes-and-no questions that lead the scientist to the proper identification while eliminating other animals. After they have completed the investigation, have the students develop a dichotomous key using the organisms in it.

Classifying plants and animals

A. Obtain these materials: paper, pencil, reference book.

B. Using the clues below, match each organism pictured with its correct group. Then unscramble the letters for its name.

Clues:

1. Hunts for food on the forest floor at night. Thin, moist skin. Lays eggs in water.

2. Hunts in the desert at night. Scaly skin. Lays hard, leathery eggs.

3. Has fins and fish-like tail. Mother pushes newborn to surface of water to breathe, and nurses young.

4. Warm-blooded. Triangle-shaped scales made of hair. Mothers nurse young.

5. Has hinged leaves and small white flowers. Leaves snap shut when insects walk on them.

6. Grows on trunks of dead trees. Uses wood for food.

Groups:

Angiosperms: USNEV TRYFLAP   Reptiles: NADDEB COGEK
Fungi: EFBEATESK ROUSMMOH   Mammals: INPHOLD
Amphibians: RITGE DESLAAMARN   GANPLINO

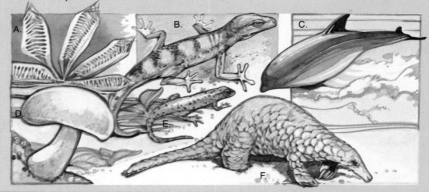

290

INVESTIGATING

Skill Development — *Inferring, Classifying*

Teaching Tips — The students may need several reference books to find all of the organisms. An encyclopedia of natural history will be most helpful.

Answers to Questions — **1.** Tiger Salamander (E.)   **2.** Banded Gecko (B.)   **3.** Dolphin (C.)   **4.** Pangolin (F.)   **5.** Venus Flytrap (A.) **6.** Beefsteak Mushroom (D.)

CAREERS

Beekeeper ▶

A **beekeeper** cares for colonies of honeybees. The best time to start beekeeping is in the spring when fruit trees and dandelions begin to bloom. In the early fall, the *beekeeper* checks each bee colony to see that it has at least 23 kilograms (50 pounds) of honey and several frames of pollen. A person who wants to become a beekeeper should work with a skilled beekeeper and read books about the subject.

◀ Wildlife Manager

A **wildlife manager** works to preserve and manage animals in public forests, wildlife refuges, and privately owned land. *Wildlife managers* plan conservation programs and organize surveys to find out the number of animals in given areas. They work to provide environments where animals will reproduce. An interest in animals and a background in science is needed for this work.

291

EXTENSIONS

Application
Research

The students may be interested in doing research to find out about a career in taxonomy. These scientists classify newly discovered organisms by studying their characteristics. Modern taxonomists use computers and sensitive biochemical tests to aid them in their identifications. Information on this and other careers is available from the National Science Foundation, 1800 G St. N.W., Washington, D.C. 20550.

CAREERS

Teaching Tips — For more information on careers in wildlife management, contact the Fish and Wildlife Service, Dept. of the Interior, C. St. N.W., Washington, D.C. 20240. For additional career information on beekeeping, contact the Dept. of Agriculture, Independence Avenue S.W., Washington, D.C. 20250.

SECTION	BASIC SCIENCE SKILLS	ACTIVITY MATERIALS STUDENT/GROUP	EXTENSIONS	
15-1 p.T-294 Day, Night, and the Seasons	*Building science vocabulary* p.T-296 *Reading illustrations* p.T-297	chalk, flashlight, sheet of black construction paper	• Reinforcement pp.T-295, T-298 • Enrichment p.T-297 • Application pp.T-296, T-298	
15-2 p.T-299 The Moon	*Reading illustrations* p.T-300 *Observing* and *predicting* shape of the moon p.T-303 *Hypothesizing* p.T-303	lamp, orange	• Reinforcement p.T-301 • Enrichment pp.T-300, T-301, T-302, T-304 • Application p.T-303	
15-3 p.T-305 The Sun	*Sequencing* of energy production in the sun p.T-306 *Comparing and contrasting* lunar and solar eclipses p.T-307	pencil, tape, cardboard (20 cm square), watch, compass, marking pen	• Reinforcement p.T-309 • Enrichment pp.T-307, T-308 • Application p.T-306	
16-1 p.T-310 The Inner Planets	*Hypothesizing* p.T-312 *Observing* diagrams p.T-312 *Observing* mosaic photograph p.T-313	graph paper, pencil, ruler	• Reinforcement p.T-314 • Enrichment pp.T-312, T-315, T-316 • Application pp.T-311, T-313	
16-2 p.T-317 The Outer Planets	*Comparing and contrasting* orbits of Pluto and Neptune p.T-320		• Enrichment pp.T-318, T-319, T-320, T-321	
16-3 p.T-322 Asteroids, Meteors, and Comets	*Classifying* celestial bodies p.T-322	basketball, clay, meter stick	• Reinforcement p.T-323 • Enrichment p.T-324	
16-4 p.T-325 Travel in the Solar System	*Reading illustrations* and *sequencing* with space shuttle photographs p.T-327		• Reinforcement p.T-329 • Enrichment pp.T-327, T-329 • Application pp.T-326, T-328	
17-1 p.T-330 The Stars	*Hypothesizing* p.T-331 *Sequencing* star history p.T-335 *Building vocabulary* p.T-335	sheets of graph paper, colored pencils or markers	• Enrichment pp.T-332, T-335, T-336 • Application pp.T-331, T-333, T-334	
17-2 p.T-337 Constellations	*Reading illustrations* of constellations p.T-338 *Finding main ideas* p.T-338 *Inferring* p.T-339	black construction paper, clear tape, flashlight, safety pin, scissors, shoebox, tracing paper	• Reinforcement pp.T-338, T-339 • Enrichment pp.T-338, T-340, T-341 • Application pp.T-339, T-340	
17-3 p.T-342 The Universe	*Reading illustrations* of galaxies p.T-343	graph paper, pencil	• Reinforcement p.T-347 • Enrichment pp.T-343, T-344, T-346, T-347, T-348 • Application pp.T-345, T-346,	

CHAPTER 15 THE EARTH, MOON, AND SUN

CHAPTER 16 THE SOLAR SYSTEM

CHAPTER 17 THE STARS AND BEYOND

EXTRA ACTIVITIES/ DEMONSTRATIONS	WORKSHEET MASTERS	EVALUATION
• Seasonal change photos p. T-295 • Four seasons bulletin board p. T-297	• Day, Night, and the Seasons (SK) p. T-291k	Section Review p. T-298
	• Eclipse (SK) p. T-291l • The Moon (AH) p. T-291m	Section Review p. T-304
	• The Sun (SK) p. T-291n	Section Review p. T-308 Chapter Review p. T-309 Test Masters pp. T-291d, e
		Section Review p. T-316
• Relative sizes of Jupiter and Earth p. T-318	• Planets (SK) p. T-291o • Revolutions (AC) p. T-291p	Section Review p. T-321
		Section Review p. T-324
• Balloon and water rockets p. T-326	• Travel Through the Solar System (AC) p. T-291q • Solar System (SK) p. T-291r	Section Review p. T-328 Chapter Review p. T-329 Test Masters pp. T-291f, g
	• The Stars (SK) p. T-291s	Section Review p. T-336
• Observing stars p. T-339	Constellations (AC) p. T-291t	Section Review p. T-341
• Investigating— Building and using an astrolabe p. T-348	• The Universe (SK) p. T-291u	Sec Rev p. T-346 Ch Rev p. T-347 Test Masters pp. T-291h, i, j

BOOKS

Berger, Melvin. *Comets, Meteors and Asteroids*, illus., East Rutherford, NJ: Putnam, 1981

Blumberg, Rhoda. *The First Travel Guide to the Moon: What to Pack, How to Go, and What to See When You Get There*, illus. by Roy Doty, New York: Four Winds, 1980

Fields, Alice. *Satellites*, illus. by Mike Tregenga, New York: Franklin Watts, 1981

Ford, Adam. *Spaceship Earth*, New York: Lothrop, Lee & Shepard, 1981

Gardner, Robert. *Space: Frontier of the Future*, illus. by Jeffrey Brown, Garden City, NY: Doubleday, 1981

Knight, David C. *The Moons of Our Solar System*, illus. by Ellen Cullen, New York: Morrow, 1980

Simon, Seymour. *The Long View into Space*, illus., New York: Crown, 1979

Taylor, Jeffrey G. *A Close Look at the Moon*, illus., New York: Dodd, 1980

Veglahn, Nancy. *Dance of the Planets: The Universe of Nicolaus Copernicus*, New York: Coward, 1979

Zim, Herbert. *The New Moon*, New York: Morrow, 1980

FILMS

The Astronomer, 16 min, International

Constellations, Guides to the Night Sky, 11 min, Indiana University

Man Looks at the Moon, 15 min, Britannica

The Milky Way, 14 min, Captioned Films for the Deaf

Planetary Motions and Space Travel, 10 min, BFA

Stars: Parts I and II, 9 min each, Sterling

Star Salesman, 20 min, Agency for Instructional Television

The Star Seekers, 9 min, Sterling

The Stars Through the Seasons, 14 min, Coronet

FILMSTRIPS

Astronomy, set of 4, United Learning

Earth and Stars, set of 3, Creative Visuals

An Introduction to the Amazing Universe, 2 sound, 11–14 min each, National Geographic

COMPUTER AIDS

Ursa, Tutorial, Apple, BASIC, 32K + DOS 3.2, Creative Computing

KEY (AC)——Activity   (AH)——At Home   (SK)——Skill

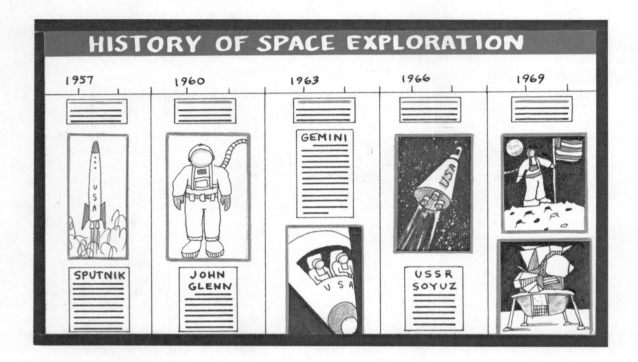

BULLETIN BOARD

This bulletin board is designed to illustrate the history of space exploration. Cover the bulletin board with sheets of colored construction paper. A string stretched across the top of the board will represent a time line of the events and dates of space explorations. Assign three-year time spans to groups of students, starting from 1957. The students should research the important events in space exploration that occurred in their time span, and write the date and event on an index card to be attached to the board. Then the students should draw pictures and write reports about the events to be displayed underneath the time line.

FIELD TRIP IDEAS

To an Observatory

Make arrangements to visit an observatory. Ask the technicians to show the students how the telescopes, cameras, and tracking equipment are used to observe the heavens. Point out the reasons why observatories are often located far from town and on the tops of hills and mountains.

Stargazing

If possible, make arrangements to have a nighttime stargazing field trip in the schoolyard or other suitable location. This would be a good activity to involve adults. Star maps are available in almanacs and many local newspapers. Challenge the students to find the prominent constellations and planets.

Name _____ Date _____

Fold Back
Answer
Key On
Line
Before
Copying.

THE EARTH, MOON, AND SUN

TEST 15
CHAPTER

CHAPTER OBJECTIVE

Read each sentence. Choose the best answer from those listed.
Write the letter of your choice on the line at the right.

1. During one rotation of the earth, most places on earth pass through

    a. four seasons.
    b. one daytime and one nighttime.
    c. one week.
    d. the nighttime.

    1. _____   1. **b** (1)

2. The change of seasons is caused by the

    a. rotation of the sun.
    b. rotation of the earth on its axis.
    c. tilt of earth's axis.
    d. moon's revolution.

    2. _____   2. **c** (1)

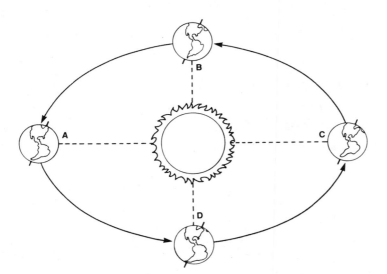

Look at the diagram above. Then answer questions 3 and 4.

3. Which letter shows the vernal equinox?

    a. A
    b. B
    c. C
    d. D

    3. _____   3. **b** (1)

4. The season shown at letter C is

    a. summer.
    b. fall.
    c. spring.
    d. winter.

    4. _____   4. **d** (1)

5. Which of the following is *not* true about the moon?

    a. It is a satellite.
    b. It revolves around earth.
    c. It produces its own light.
    d. It is rocky and barren.

    5. _____   5. **c** (2)

6. A maria can best be described as

    a. deep and wet.
    b. flat and smooth.
    c. a bowl-shaped hole.
    d. a forest area.

    6. _____   6. **b** (2)

7. <u>a</u> (2)

7. The entire lighted surface of the moon faces us when the moon

7. _____

    a. is full.   **c.** is new.

    b. is a quarter of the way.   **d.** causes a solar eclipse.

8. <u>a</u> (2)

8. The phases of the moon are caused by

8. _____

    a. the revolution of the moon around the earth.

    b. the rotation of the earth on its axis.

    c. the revolution of the earth around the sun.

    d. the rotation of the sun on its axis.

9. <u>a</u> (3)

9. For a solar eclipse to occur,

9 _____

    a. the moon has to pass between the earth and the sun.

    b. the earth has to pass between the moon and the sun.

    c. the sun has to pass between the earth and the moon.

    d. the moon has to be a crescent.

10. <u>c</u> (3)

10. A solar eclipse is visible from

10. _____

    a. anywhere on earth.

    b. the area where the earth's shadow falls.

    c. the area where the moon's shadow falls.

    d. any area where there is daylight.

11. <u>d</u> (3)

11. During a lunar eclipse, the moon may appear to be

11. _____

    a. white.   **c.** black.

    b. yellow.   **d.** red.

12. <u>a</u> (3)

12. A shadow of earth is cast on the moon during

12. _____

    a. a lunar eclipse.   **c.** the new moon phase.

    b. a solar eclipse.   **d.** the full moon phase.

13. <u>c</u> (4)

13. An area of the sun where gases have cooled is called

13. _____

    a. a maria.   **c.** a sunspot.

    b. a solar flare.   **d.** a corona.

14. <u>c</u> (4)

14. The nuclear reaction in the sun's core is the change from

14. _____

    a. oxygen to helium.

    b. helium to hydrogen.

    c. hydrogen to helium.

    d. hydrogen to oxygen.

15. <u>d</u> (4)

15. The surface of the sun is called

15. _____

    a. the atmosphere.   **c.** the corona.

    b. the core.   **d.** the photosphere.

16. <u>a</u> (4)

16. Solar flares seem to affect things on earth such as

16. _____

    a. radio messages.   **c.** the amount of hydrogen in the air.

    b. sunspots.   **d.** the composition of the core.

Name_____ Date_____

Fold Back
Answer
Key On
Line
Before
Copying.

THE SOLAR SYSTEM

TEST 16
CHAPTER

CHAPTER OBJECTIVES

Read each sentence. Choose the best answer from those listed.
Write the letter of your choice on the line at the right.

1. Our solar system is made up of
   a. only the nine planets.
   b. the nine planets, their moons, and the sun.
   c. the inner planets, their moons, and the sun.
   d. the nine planets and the sun.

   1. _____   1. **b** (1)

2. The order of the inner planets as they move from the sun is
   a. Mercury, Venus, Earth, Mars.
   b. Venus, Mercury, Earth, Mars.
   c. Mars, Earth, Mercury, Venus.
   d. Earth, Mercury, Mars, Venus.

   2. _____   2. **a** (1)

3. Scientists believe that earth is the only inner planet that
   a. has volcanoes.   c. has a moon.
   b. has clouds.   d. has water.

   3. _____   3. **d** (1)

4. The red planet that has ice caps at its poles is
   a. Mars.   c. Mercury.
   b. Venus.   d. Earth.

   4. _____   4. **a** (1)

5. Scientists believe that the giant spot on Jupiter may be
   a. a large sea.   c. a very large crater.
   b. a long-lasting storm. d. a huge volcano.

   5. _____   5. **b** (2)

6. The planet that is now farthest from the sun is
   a. Uranus.   c. Pluto.
   b. Neptune.   d. Jupiter.

   6. _____   6. **b** (2)

7. Which of the following is *not* true about Jupiter?
   a. It is the largest planet.
   b. It is an outer planet.
   c. It has one moon.
   d. It is covered by bands of clouds.

   7. _____   7. **c** (2)

8. The planet with a thousand rings is
   a. Saturn.   c. Pluto.
   b. Uranus.   d. Mercury.

   8. _____   8. **a** (2)

9. Which planet takes the most time to revolve around the sun?
   a. Earth   c. Jupiter
   b. Pluto   d. Saturn

   9. _____   9. **b** (3)

10. __a__ (3)

10. The two planets with orbits that overlap are
   a. Neptune and Pluto.   c. Saturn and Jupiter.
   b. earth and Mars.   d. Uranus and Neptune.

10. _____

11. __a__ (3)

11. Earth and Mars are almost identical in
   a. time needed for one rotation.
   b. time needed for one revolution.
   c. climate.
   d. amount of rainfall.

11. _____

12. __d__ (3)

12. The planet with the slowest rotation time is
   a. Pluto.   c. Mars.
   b. Mercury. d. Venus.

12. _____

13. __c__ (4)

13. Most asteroids move through space between
   a. Jupiter and Saturn.   c. Mars and Jupiter.
   b. earth and its moon.   d. Mercury and Venus.

13. _____

14. __b__ (4)

14. Chunks of iron and metal that move through space and hit the earth's surface are called
   a. meteoroids.   c. asteroids.
   b. meteorites.   d. comets.

14. _____

15. __c__ (4)

15. Which of the following is *not* true about comets?
   a. They are made of ice and rock.
   b. They get smaller each time they come near the sun.
   c. They complete one orbit around the sun every year.
   d. Their tails stream away from the sun.

15. _____

16. __a__ (5)

16. The booster rockets of the space shuttle
   a. place satellites in orbit.
   b. orbit the earth.
   c. carry astronauts to the moon.
   d. launch space probes.

16. _____

17. __c__ (5)

17. The biggest advantage of the space shuttle is
   a. it uses less fuel for lift-off than other rockets.
   b. it does not need rockets for lift-off.
   c. it can be reused.
   d. all of the above.

17. _____

18. __a__ (5)

18. A rocket moves forward when
   a. it pushes exhaust backward.
   b. it pushes exhaust forward.
   c. it pushes exhaust from side to side.
   d. there is no exhaust at all.

18. _____

THE STARS AND BEYOND

TEST 17
CHAPTER

CHAPTER OBJECTIVES

Read each sentence. Choose the best answer from those listed.
Write the letter of your choice on the line at the right.

1. The speed of light is
   a. 75,000 km/sec (46,500 mi/sec).
   b. 150,000 km/sec (93,000 mi/sec).
   c. 300,000 km/sec (186,000 mi/sec).
   d. 600,000 km/sec (372,000 mi/sec).

   1. _____   1. __c__ (1)

2. The star that is closest to the earth after the sun is
   a. Sirius.   c. Betelgeuse.
   b. Proxima Centauri. d. Polaris.

   2. _____   2. __b__ (1)

3. The stars with the highest temperatures are
   a. blue.   c. yellow.
   b. red.   d. orange.

   3. _____   3. __a__ (1)

4. A star's magnitude depends on
   a. size.   c. distance from earth.
   b. temperature. d. all of the above.

   4. _____   4. __d__ (1)

5. Stars release energy from reactions that change
   a. hydrogen to helium.
   b. oxygen to nitrogen.
   c. helium to hydrogen.
   d. hydrogen to a gas.

   5. _____   5. __c__ (2)

6. When a star becomes a white dwarf, its magnitude
   a. increases.
   b. decreases.
   c. remains the same.
   d. cannot be predicted.

   6. _____   6. __b__ (2)

7. Which of these does *not* happen when a star is forming?
   a. The particles of matter move closer together.
   b. Its temperature rises.
   c. Its temperature becomes lower.
   d. Nuclear reactions take place.

   7. _____   7. __c__ (2)

8. The remains of stars that have died
   a. may combine with other matter to form new stars.
   b. fall to the earth.
   c. disappear forever.
   d. become comets.

   8. _____   8. __a__ (2)

9. __b__ (3)   **9.** Quasars give out   9. _____
   a. less energy than stars.
   b. more energy than stars.
   c. the same amount of energy as stars.
   d. no energy at all.

10. __a__ (3)   **10.** Quasars can be detected by devices that pick up   10. _____
   a. radio waves.   **c.** X-rays.
   b. light waves.   **d.** black light.

11. __b__ (3)   **11.** Scientists think that a black hole is a place that pulls in   11. _____
   a. hydrogen.
   b. material from collapsed stars and light.
   c. space shuttles.
   d. material from old comets.

12. __d__ (3)   **12.** A radio telescope does all of the following except   12. _____
   a. record sounds.
   b. change waves into patterns.
   c. tell the position of an object.
   d. take a photograph of an object.

13. __c__ (4)   **13.** The constellation shown below is   13. _____
   a. Orion.   **c.** Cygnus.
   b. Cassiopeia.   **d.** the Big Dipper.

14. __a__ (4)   **14.** You could locate the North Star by drawing an arrow from   14. _____
   a. the Big Dipper.   **c.** Polaris.
   b. the Little Dipper.   **d.** Orion.

15. __a__ (4)   **15.** In the Northern Hemisphere, the Big Dipper and Little Dipper can be seen   15. _____
   a. all year.   **c.** only in summer.
   b. only in winter.   **d.** only in the fall.

16. __c__ (4)   **16.** How many constellations are there?   16. _____
   a. less than 10   **c.** between 80 and 90
   b. about 50   **d.** over 100

17. One theory of how the universe was formed states that   17._____   17. <u>d</u> (5)
   a. galaxies came out of a black hole.
   b. planets evolved from comets.
   c. quasars exploded.
   d. a giant explosion gave rise to separate stars and planets.

18. The shape of the Milky Way is   18._____   18. <u>c</u> (5)
   a. elliptical.   c. spiral.
   b. irregular.   d. cigar-shaped.

19. Elliptical galaxies have   19._____   19. <u>a</u> (5)
   a. little dust and gas.
   b. many nebulae.
   c. arms that seem to come from the center.
   d. very few stars.

20. Nebulae are formed from   20._____   20. <u>b</u> (5)
   a. water and gases.   c. dust and water.
   b. dust and gases.   d. hydrogen and helium.

Day, Night and the Seasons

SKILL WORKSHEET

A. On the diagram label the positions of the vernal equinox, autumnal equinox, summer solstice, and winter solstice.

B. Label the areas on the orbit that represent spring, summer, winter, and fall.

C. Draw an arrow to show the direction in which the earth revolves around the sun.

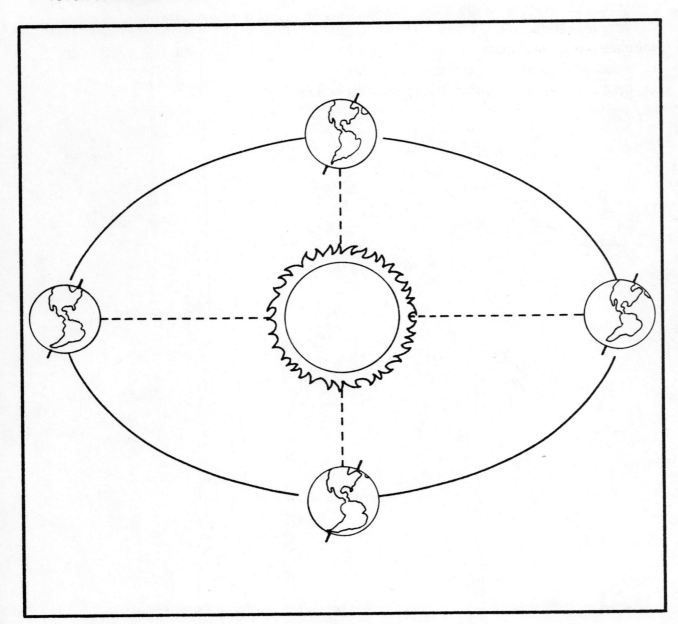

Name_____ Date _____

The Moon

A. Draw the position of the moon during a total solar eclipse. Show the shadows.

From where on earth would a solar eclipse be visible?

_____

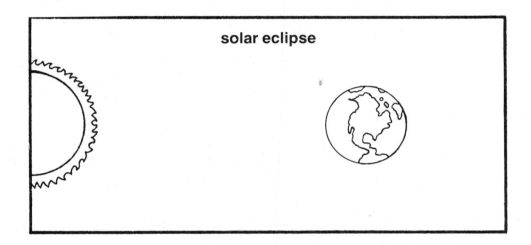

solar eclipse

B. Draw the position of the moon during a lunar eclipse. Show the shadows.

From where on earth would a lunar eclipse be visible?

_____

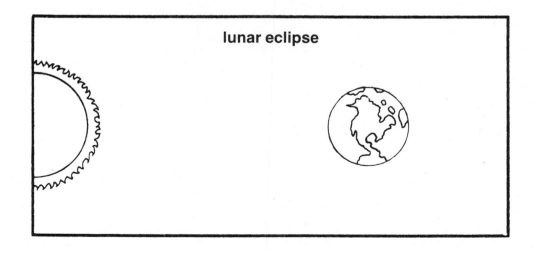

lunar eclipse

Name_____ Date _____

The Moon

At school you are learning about the earth's satellite, the moon. In this at-home activity, you will find the distance between the earth and the moon.

A. Obtain these materials: index card, string 2 m (80 in.) long, tape, metric ruler, scissors.

B. As shown in the picture below, cut a round notch in one edge of the index card. The notch should be exactly 1 cm (2.5 in.) wide.

C. On a night when there is a full moon, tape the card to a window from which you can see the moon. Then tape one end of the string to the card.

D. Look at the moon through the notch in the card. As you hold the end of the string, back up until the moon fills the notch.

E. Carefully hold the string up to your eye. Have another person measure the length of the string between the notch and your eye.

F. Multiply the length of the string by 3,500 km (2,170 mi). This will tell you the distance.

What was the length of the string? _____
What is the distance from the earth to the moon?

_____

The Sun

A. Label the parts of the sun in the picture below.

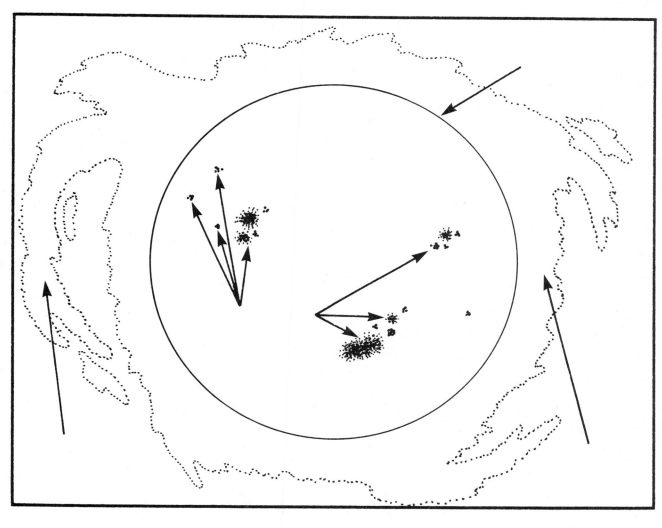

B. Fill in the missing words.

The sun is a _____ made of hot gases. Unlike

planets, stars give off their own _____. The

hot gases that make up the sun are _____ and

_____. In the sun's _____

nuclear reactions release huge amounts of energy.

Name _____ Date _____

The Solar System

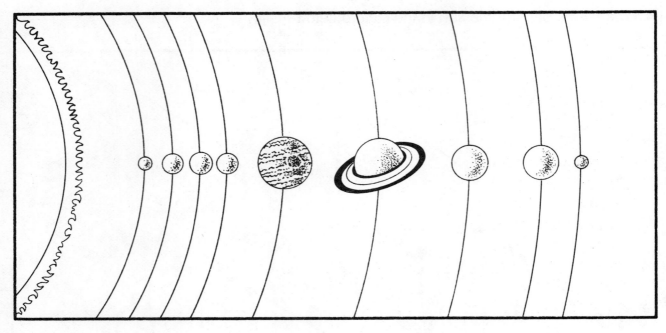

Label the planets in the solar system in the above picture. Then, choose two planets other than the earth to write about. In a brief paragraph, you should include their places in the solar system, the temperature on their surfaces, their atmospheric makeup, some prominent features of their surfaces, and their moons.

_____

_____

_____

_____

_____

_____

_____

_____

_____

Permission to reproduce ...is page is granted to users of HOLT SCIENCE 5   Holt, Rinehart and Winston, Publishers

Name _____ Date _____

The Solar System

You are learning how the planets revolve around the sun. In this activity you will observe how the speed of revolution can vary with distance.

A. Obtain these materials: cardboard tube, paper ball, strong cord.

B. Pass the cord through the cardboard tube. Make a loop in one end of the string. Attach the paper ball to the other end.

C. Use one hand to hold the tube. The ball should be hanging from the bottom. Hold the loop in your other hand.

D. Rotate the tube in a small circle so that the ball revolves. Observe its speed.

E. Stop rotating the tube and slowly pull the cord up through the tube. Observe what happens to the ball's speed.

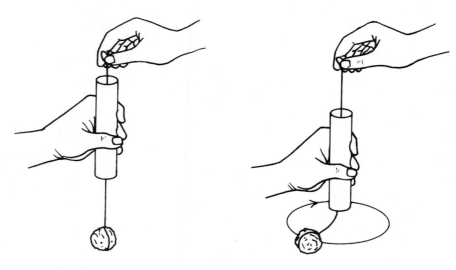

QUESTIONS

1. What happened when you pulled on the string?

   _____

2. How do you think this relates to how planets revolve around the sun?

   _____

   _____

Travel Through the Solar System

You are learning about the world's first reusable spaceship, the space shuttle. The shuttle is not totally reusable, however, because its fuel tank burns up as it reenters the atmosphere. In this activity, you will use your imagination and information from your textbook to design a totally reusable spacecraft of the future.

The Solar System

1. _ | _ | _ _ _ _ _ _
2. _ _ _ _ _ | _ | _
3. | _ | _ _ _ _ _ _
4. | _ | _ _ _ _
5.   _ _ _ | _ | _ _ _ _
6. | _ | _ _ _ _ _ _ _ _
7. | _ | _ _ _ _
8.   _ _ | _ | _ _ _ _
9.   _ _ | _ | _ _ _ _
10. _ _ _ | _ | _ _ _ _
11. _ _ _ _ | _ |

Using the clues below, complete the above puzzle with science words. The letters in the box will spell the term used for space rockets that can send information back to earth.

1. Rocky objects that orbit the sun
2. An instrument that makes distant objects appear closer and larger
3. A scientist who studies objects in space
4. Objects made of ice and rock particles that orbit the sun
5. Chunks of iron, nickel, and other materials that move through space
6. A reusable spacecraft
7. An engine that burns fuel and moves forward by pushing exhaust backward
8. A powerful rocket
9. The part of the shuttle that orbits the earth
10. A meteoroid that lands on a surface
11. The path of objects in space around another object

The Stars

1. Other than the sun, the closest star to earth is Proxima Centauri. It is 4.27 light years from earth. If it had a large solar flare today, how long would it be before we could observe it?

   _____

2. Arrange these star colors in order of increasing temperatures: blue-white, red, yellow, blue, orange, white

   _____

3. a. What is a star's magnitude? _____
   b. On what three things does a star's brightness depend?

   _____

4. Match each object listed at the left with the correct description given at the right.

1. Supergiants		**A.**	Picks up and records space sounds
2. White dwarf		**B.**	Gives off huge amounts of energy
3. Quasar		**C.**	Very large stars
4. Radio telescope		**D.**	A star about the size of earth
5. Black hole		**E.**	No light escapes here

5. Connect the dots to see an important tool in astronomy.

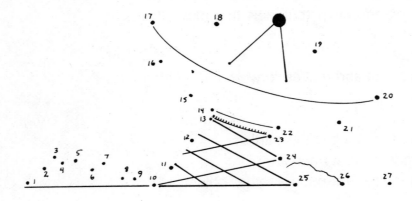

Name_____ Date_____

Constellations

You are learning about constellations. When ancient people looked at the stars they saw patterns that were familiar to them. In this activity, you will identify the constellations and use the same star patterns to create new constellations. Connect the stars to show new patterns.

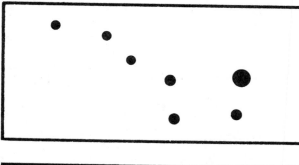

Old name _____

New name _____

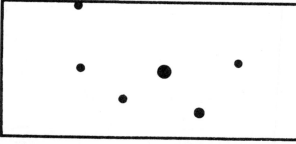

Old name _____

New name _____

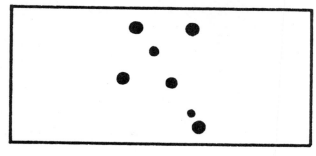

Old name _____

New name _____

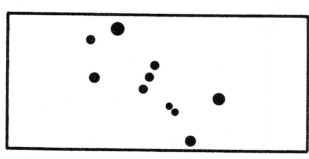

Old name _____

New name _____

The Universe

A. Match the term to the proper drawing.

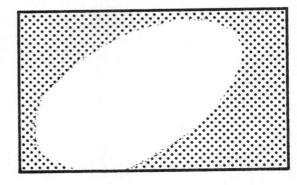

spiral galaxy

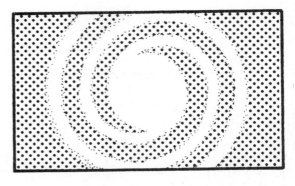

nebula

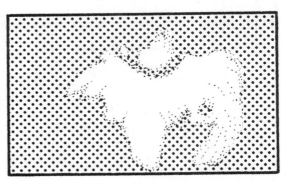

elliptical galaxy

B. Name and explain one theory on how scientists think the universe may have been formed.

_____

_____

_____

Name _____ Date _____

Day, Night and the Seasons

CLASSIFYING, SEQUENCING   SKILL WORKSHEET

A. On the diagram label the positions of the vernal equinox, autumnal equinox, summer solstice, and winter solstice.

B. Label the areas on the orbit that represent spring, summer, winter, and fall.

C. Draw an arrow to show the direction in which the earth revolves around the sun.

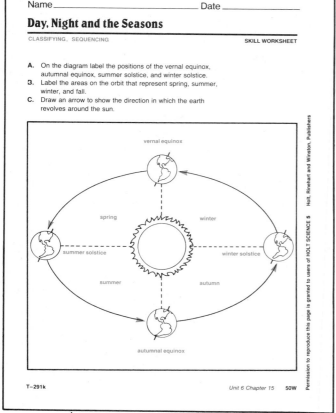

T–291k   Unit 6 Chapter 15   50W

Name _____ Date _____

Moon

CLASSIFYING, SEQUENCING, FINDING CAUSE AND EFFECT   SKILL WORKSHEET

A. Draw the position of the moon during a total solar eclipse. Show the shadows.

From where on earth would a solar eclipse be visible?
Only where the moon's shadow falls on the earth

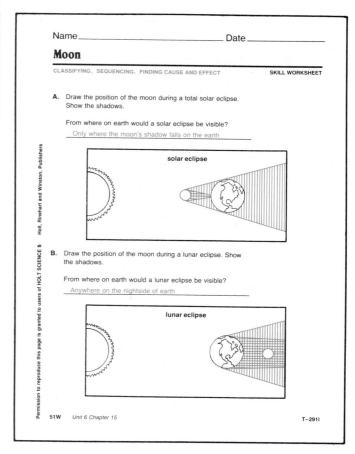

B. Draw the position of the moon during a lunar eclipse. Show the shadows.

From where on earth would a lunar eclipse be visible?
Anywhere on the nightside of earth

51W   Unit 6 Chapter 15   T–291l

Name _____ Date _____

The Moon

                                                    AT HOME WORKSHEET

At school you are learning about the earth's satellite, the moon. In this at-home activity, you will find the distance between the earth and the moon.

A. Obtain these materials: index card, string 2 m (80 in.) long, tape, metric ruler, scissors.

B. As shown in the picture below, cut a round notch in one edge of the index card. The notch should be exactly 1 cm (2.5 in.) wide.

C. On a night when there is a full moon, tape the card to a window from which you can see the moon. Then tape one end of the string to the card.

D. Look at the moon through the notch in the card. As you hold the end of the string, back up until the moon fills the notch.

E. Carefully hold the string up to your eye. Have another person measure the length of the string between the notch and your eye.

F. Multiply the length of the string by 3,500 km (2,170 mi). This will tell you the distance.

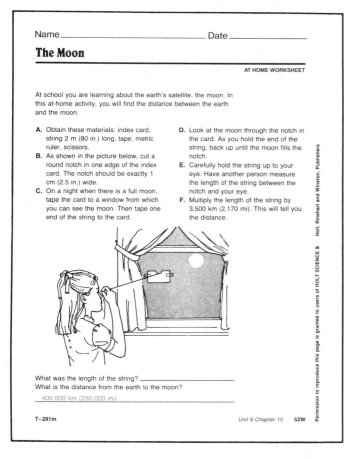

What was the length of the string? _____
What is the distance from the earth to the moon?
400,000 km (250,000 mi)

T–291m   Unit 6 Chapter 15   52W

Name _____ Date _____

The Sun

CLASSIFYING   SKILL WORKSHEET

A. Label the parts of the sun in the picture below.

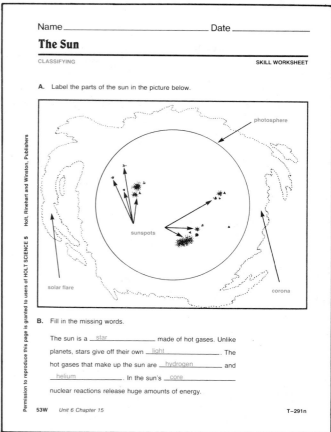

B. Fill in the missing words.

The sun is a __star__ made of hot gases. Unlike planets, stars give off their own __light__. The hot gases that make up the sun are __hydrogen__ and __helium__. In the sun's __core__ nuclear reactions release huge amounts of energy.

53W   Unit 6 Chapter 15   T–291n

Name_____ Date_____

The Solar System

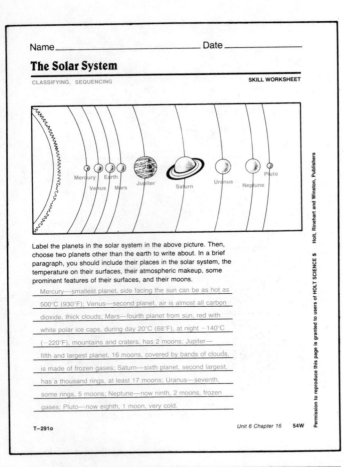

Label the planets in the solar system in the above picture. Then, choose two planets other than the earth to write about. In a brief paragraph, you should include their places in the solar system, the temperature on their surfaces, their atmospheric makeup, some prominent features of their surfaces, and their moons.

Mercury—smallest planet, side facing the sun can be as hot as

500°C (930°F); Venus—second planet, air is almost all carbon

dioxide, thick clouds; Mars—fourth planet from sun, red with

white polar ice caps, during day 20°C (68°F), at night −140°C

(−220°F), mountains and craters, has 2 moons; Jupiter—

fifth and largest planet, 16 moons, covered by bands of clouds,

is made of frozen gases; Saturn—sixth planet, second largest,

has a thousand rings, at least 17 moons; Uranus—seventh,

some rings, 5 moons; Neptune—now ninth, 2 moons, frozen

gases; Pluto—now eighth, 1 moon, very cold.

T–291o   Unit 6 Chapter 16   54W

Permission to reproduce this page is granted to users of HOLT SCIENCE 5   Holt, Rinehart and Winston, Publishers

---

Name_____ Date_____

The Solar System

You are learning how the planets revolve around the sun. In this activity you will observe how the speed of revolution can vary with distance.

A. Obtain these materials: cardboard tube, paper ball, strong cord.
B. Pass the cord through the cardboard tube. Make a loop in one end of the string. Attach the paper ball to the other end.
C. Use one hand to hold the tube. The ball should be hanging from the bottom. Hold the loop in your other hand.
D. Rotate the tube in a small circle so that the ball revolves. Observe its speed.
E. Stop rotating the tube and slowly pull the cord up through the tube. Observe what happens to the ball's speed.

QUESTIONS

1. What happened when you pulled on the string?
   The ball spun faster in a smaller circle.

2. How do you think this relates to how planets revolve around the sun?
   Planets closer to the sun will revolve at a greater speed
   than will those farther away.

55W   Unit 6 Chapter 16   T–291p

Permission to reproduce this page is granted to users of HOLT SCIENCE 5   Holt, Rinehart and Winston, Publishers

---

Name_____ Date_____

Travel Through the Solar System

You are learning about the world's first reusable spaceship, the space shuttle. The shuttle is not totally reusable, however, because its fuel tank burns up as it reenters the atmosphere. In this activity, you will use your imagination and information from your textbook to design a totally reusable spacecraft of the future.

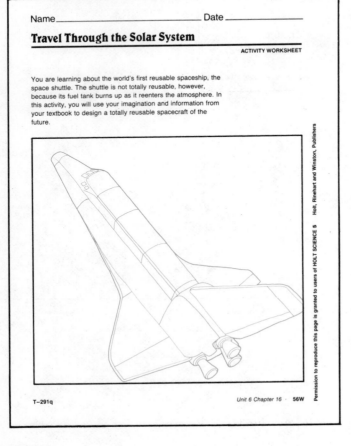

T–291q   Unit 6 Chapter 16 · 56W

Permission to reproduce this page is granted to users of HOLT SCIENCE 5   Holt, Rinehart and Winston, Publishers

---

Name_____ Date_____

The Solar System

1.   A S T E R O I D S
2.   T E L E S C O P E
3.   A S T R O N O M E R
4.   C O M E T S
5.   M E T E O R O I D S
6.   S P A C E S H U T T L E
7.   R O C K E T
8.   B O O S T E R
9.   O R B I T E R
10. M E T E O R I T E
11. O R B I T S

Using the clues below, complete the above puzzle with science words. The letters in the box will spell the term used for space rockets that can send information back to earth.

1. Rocky objects that orbit the sun
2. An instrument that makes distant objects appear closer and larger
3. A scientist who studies objects in space
4. Objects made of ice and rock particles that orbit the sun
5. Chunks of iron, nickel, and other materials that move through space
6. A reusable spacecraft
7. An engine that burns fuel and moves forward by pushing exhaust backward
8. A powerful rocket
9. The part of the shuttle that orbits the earth
10. A meteoroid that lands on a surface
11. The path of objects in space around another object

57W   Unit 6 Chapter 16   T–291r

Permission to reproduce this page is granted to users of HOLT SCIENCE 5   Holt, Rinehart and Winston, Publishers

Name_____ Date_____

The Stars

CLASSIFYING, SEQUENCING   SKILL WORKSHEET

1. Other than the sun, the closest star to earth is Proxima Centauri. It is 4.27 light years from earth. If it had a large solar flare today, how long would it be before we could observe it?

   4.27 years

2. Arrange these star colors in order of increasing temperatures: blue-white, red, yellow, blue, orange, white

   red, orange, yellow, white, blue, blue-white

3. a. What is a star's magnitude? Its brightness
   b. On what three things does a star's brightness depend?
      Its size and temperature and distance from the earth

4. Match each object listed at the left with the correct description given at the right.

   1. Supergiants   A. Picks up and records space sounds
   2. White dwarf   B. Gives off huge amounts of energy
   3. Quasar   C. Very large stars
   4. Radio telescope   D. A star about the size of earth
   5. Black hole   E. No light escapes here

5. Connect the dots to see an important tool in astronomy.

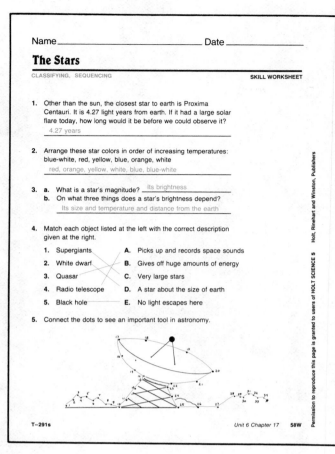

Name_____ Date_____

Constellations

ACTIVITY WORKSHEET

You are learning about constellations. When ancient people looked at the stars they saw patterns that were familiar to them. In this activity, you will identify the constellations and use the same star patterns to create new constellations. Connect the stars to show new patterns.

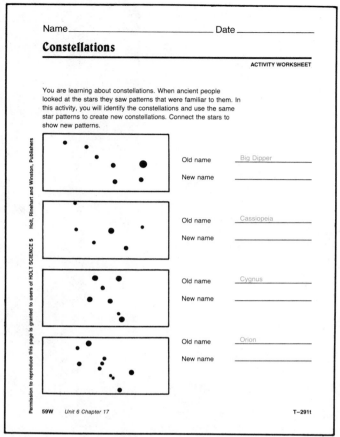

Old name Big Dipper _____
New name _____

Old name Cassiopeia _____
New name _____

Old name Cygnus _____
New name _____

Old name Orion _____
New name _____

Name_____ Date_____

The Universe

CLASSIFYING, FINDING THE MAIN IDEAS   SKILL WORKSHEET

A. Match the term to the proper drawing.

spiral galaxy

nebula

elliptical galaxy

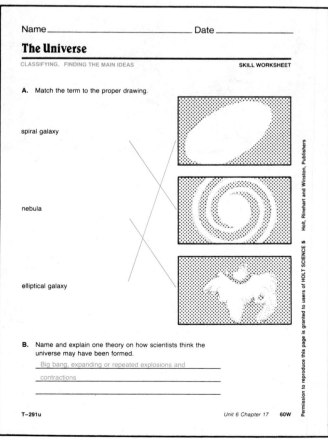

B. Name and explain one theory on how scientists think the universe may have been formed.

   Big bang, expanding or repeated explosions and

   contractions

   _____

UNIT OVERVIEW

This is a space science unit on the earth, the solar system, and the universe. The rotation of the earth on its axis causes day and night. The rotation of the earth and its revolution around the sun cause the seasons. The earth's satellite, the moon, revolves around the earth, causing the moon's phases. The sun, a star 150,000 million kilometers away, sends light energy out from its surface. This energy, caused by nuclear fusion, is necessary for life on earth.

The inner planets, Mercury, Venus, earth, and Mars, revolve around the sun in elliptical orbits. The outer planets, Jupiter, Saturn, Uranus, Neptune, and Pluto, revolve in orbits which take them farther from the sun. Jupiter, with its red spot, and Saturn, with its many rings, both have many satellites. Astronomers have learned a great deal about the planets by powerful telescopes and the space probes that have flown by or landed on planets. Meteoroids, comets, and asteroids are also found in our solar system. Travel in space has been achieved by rockets.

Stars are so far away that their distances from earth are measured in light years. Stars differ from each other in color, brightness or magnitude, and size. Quasars and black holes were discovered with the use of radio telescopes. Groups of stars form constellations; groups of billions of stars form galaxies. Billions of galaxies exist in the universe.

Exceptional Student
IEP Unit Goal

When requested by the teacher, the student will state one relationship between the following items: sun-earth-seasons, planets-solar system-sun, stars-constellations, solar system-Milky Way-galaxy.

EXPLORING THE UNIVERSE

UNIT OPENER

This is a photo of the planet Saturn taken by the Voyager 2 spacecraft in its flyby past that planet in 1980. It has been color enhanced by computers. Using the photo, ask the students the following questions as motivation: What is shown in this photograph? *The planet Saturn.* How can you tell it is Saturn? *By its many rings.* How do you think this picture was taken? *By cameras on a spacecraft sent into space to explore the planets of our solar system.* What are the rings made of? *Frozen particles.* How many are there? *About a thousand.* How is this planet different from our planet, earth? *It is much larger; it is very far from the sun; it has no life.* How is it like our planet? *Both are planets that revolve around the sun in our solar system.*

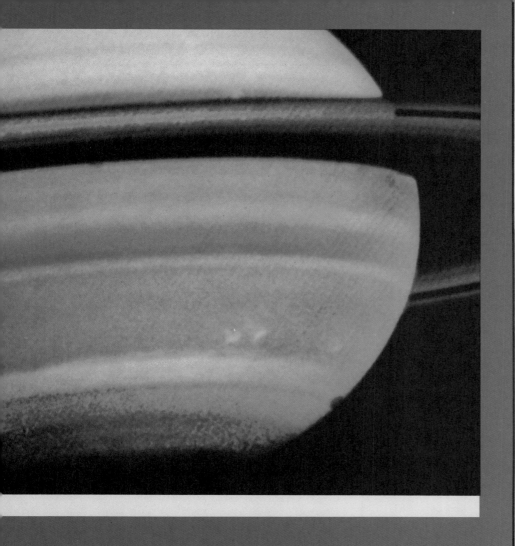

UNIT 6

LEARNING CENTER

A suggested title for the Learning Center for Unit 6 could be "Our Place in Space." Photos of the earth from space, the moon, and the other planets and their moons which are available from NASA could be used as displays. Displayed also could be photographs of the phases of the moon, eclipses, and star maps. You may wish to create a file for copies of the worksheet masters and Extensions that the students can work on independently.

The following Extensions are especially suitable for the Learning Center. The materials for these Extensions should be available in the Learning Center: comparing direct and indirect rays, p. T–296 (black construction paper, thermometer, cardboard); eclipse simulation, p. T–303 (globe, lamp, ball); measuring the diameter of the sun, p. T–306 (aluminum foil, carton, index card, meterstick, pin, scissors, tape, pencil); model solar system, p. T–321 (clay, papier mâché, paint, sewing needles, tape, string, hanger); making a spectroscope, p. T–333 (carton, construction paper, diffraction grating, tape, scissors, paper punch); twinkling stars, p. T–335 (flashlight, construction paper, paper clip, hot plate).

In addition, an index file of suggested research topics could be set up using the following Extensions: living conditions in space (p. T–300), eclipses (p. T–304), famous astronomers (p. T–316), Jupiter's moons (p. T–318), comets (p. T–324), extraterrestrial life (p. T–346).

CHAPTER 15

CHAPTER OBJECTIVES

1. Explain the effect of the earth's rotation and revolution in terms of why we have night and day and the seasons.
2. Describe the moon and explain the phases of the moon.
3. Explain how lunar and solar eclipses can occur.
4. Describe some characteristics of the sun and one way in which the sun's energy can be used.

SECTION BACKGROUND

The earth is the third planet from the sun. Two of the motions of the earth are its revolution around the sun and its rotation on its axis.

The basis for time measurements on earth is the time needed for the earth to make one complete revolution around the sun. This period of time is the year. The axis of the earth is tilted with respect to the plane of the earth's orbit. This tilt results in the northern regions being pointed toward the sun at some times of the year and away from the sun at others. This change in orientation of the earth with respect to the sun is the cause for the changes in seasons.

A complete rotation of the earth on its axis takes approximately 24 hours. This period of time is the day.

MATERIALS

chalk, flashlight, sheet of black construction paper

Exceptional Student IEP Chapter Goal

At the end of this chapter the student will explain the cause of the following: day and night, the four seasons, the phases of the moon.

THE EARTH, MOON, AND SUN

15-1.

Day, Night, and the Seasons

294

Morning already? It always happens, doesn't it? Night and day are two things we can depend on. Bob slept soundly through the night. But he was actually moving! He and all the things around him were speeding along on the earth through space. It is the movement of the earth

BASIC TEACHING PLAN

MOTIVATION

Display a number of common articles such as a toothbrush, coin, or sponge, and have the students imagine what an extraterrestrial visiting Earth might imagine that these articles are used for. Encourage the students to think of these items from the point of view of someone who has never seen an earthling and has never used the articles. Get the students started by giving an example such as "This object (a coin) is a photograph made with very advanced cameras. Notice the image of the person on the front. Earthlings can probably carry photographs of all their friends in their pockets." Continue the motivation by asking the students to make a list of some of the major characteristics of the planet (Earth) that would be observed by a visitor from outer space. For example, its shape, the type of movement it makes in space, any other objects that are its neighbors (e.g., the moon).

that causes day and night. When you finish this section, you should be able to:

☐ **A.** Explain what causes night and day.
☐ **B.** Describe how the earth moves around the sun.
☐ **C.** Explain what causes the seasons.

1 Look at the two photos in the margin. What can you tell about the time of day? The change from day to night happens during every 24-hour period. During the day the sun brightens the sky. At night the sky is dark. But in another part of the world it is light. Ancient people did not know this. They believed the sun moved across the sky each day. But it is really the earth that moves.

The sun is many times larger than the earth and very far away. Great amounts of light from the sun reach the earth. The side of the earth facing the sun receives the light. It is daytime for that part of the earth.

2 The earth is spinning. It moves at about 1,600 kilometers per hour (1,000 miles per hour). As the earth moves, new parts of it come into the sun's light. This spinning motion of the earth is called **rotation**. It takes 24 hours to complete one *rotation*. During that time, there is one day and one night.

Rotation: The spinning of an object.

295

Reinforcement
Science Skills — Recording Data, Inferring

If possible, students could gather data and make a graph showing the number of hours of daylight on the first day of each month of the year. They will be able to observe that the greatest number of hours of daylight is in June and July and the fewest in January and February. Here are some guidelines you may wish to provide:

A. Prepare a sheet of graph paper so that the first day of each month is on the vertical axis. You should have 12 dates.

B. On the horizontal axis, write the 24 hours in a day from 4:00 A.M. to 3:00 A.M.

C. Use newspapers, almanacs and, wherever possible, your own observations to record sunrise and sunset times on the first day of each month.

D. Discuss what their graphs tell them about how the number of hours of daylight changes during the year.

DEVELOPMENT

1 **Text Questions** — What can you tell about the time of day? *It is dark in the second picture.*

2 **Teaching Tips** — Display magazine photographs of dawn and dusk, seasonal changes, changes in the fur or coloration of animals, changes that occur as a seed becomes a plant, etc. The purpose of this is to establish a background for the text material dealing with daily and seasonal changes on earth.

Exceptional Student
Learning Disabled
Using two balls representing the sun and the earth, demonstrate the earth's rotation and the rising sun.

Visually Impaired
Modify this activity by having the visually impaired student have a hand on the two balls while demonstrating rotation. Describe how this causes night and day.

Application
Science Skills — Hypothesizing, Recording Data

Students could carry out an experiment to test the hypothesis that sun rays that directly strike a surface raise the temperature of that surface more than rays that strike at an angle. Here are some guidelines you may wish to suggest:

A. Get two pieces of black construction paper and place each on a separate piece of cardboard. Tape a thermometer under each one. Then place one piece of tape on the top of each sheet of paper so that it works as a hinge and also holds the paper in place.

B. Place one thermometer-cardboard set so that it is flat on the ground to receive sunlight directly.

C. Place stones under the top edge of the other thermometer so that the bottom end is touching the ground and the top end is lifted almost straight up.

D. Test the hypothesis by checking the temperature on each thermometer every three minutes. Do this five times.

E. Discuss how your results compare with your hypothesis.

Exceptional Student
Learning Disabled

To help the students understand how the earth turns on an axis, have them stick a pencil through a Styrofoam or clay ball, and then rotate the ball.

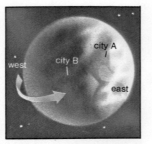

Axis: An imaginary line around which the earth spins.

Revolution: The movement of one object around another.

In what direction do you look to see the rising sun? The sun appears to rise in the east. What is really happening is that the earth rotates from west to east. Look at the diagram at left. If you are in city A, it is already morning. But in city B you might still be sleeping.

3

The earth rotates around its **axis**. The *axis* is an imaginary line. It goes from the top of the earth, through the center, to the bottom of the earth. Use a pencil to get an idea of the earth's axis. Place a pencil point on a piece of paper. The pencil should stand straight up. Now slowly rotate the pencil. Imagine a round earth spinning with the pencil at its center. Now tip the pencil slightly so it is no longer straight up and down. Rotate again. This is more like the way the earth spins. Its axis is tilted slightly. This tilt of the earth is what causes the seasons.

4

Do you dress differently in January than you do in June? The months of the year bring different weather. The earth rotates on its axis and moves through space at the same time. The earth makes a trip around the sun. This trip takes one year. Every 365¼ days the earth completes its **revolution** around the sun. During one *revolution* most places on earth have four seasons. What are the names of the seasons?

5

6

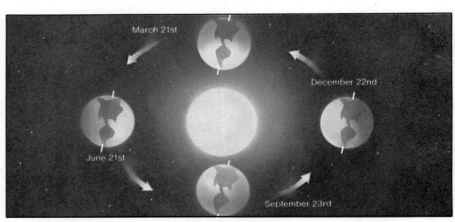

296

---

3 **Teaching Tips** — If you have access to a globe, this is a good opportunity to display it. Have a student act as the sun as you demonstrate rotation. Tilt the earth on its axis and spin it from west to east.

4 **Skill Development** — The terms "rotation" and "revolution" are easily confused by students. Reinforce their meanings by demonstrating each and asking the class to tell you whether you are showing rotation or revolution.

5 **Text Questions** — What are the names of the seasons? *Summer, winter, autumn, spring.*

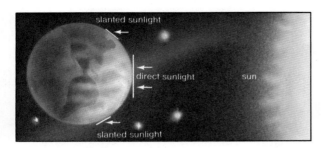

slanted sunlight

direct sunlight

sun

slanted sunlight

The first day of summer in the Northern Hemisphere is June 21. The diagram shows that on this day the axis of the earth is pointed toward the sun. This means that the Northern Hemisphere receives a great deal of the sun's energy. Sunlight hits the Northern Hemisphere directly. It gives the light and heat we think of when we think of summer. June 21 is known as the **summer solstice**.

The diagram on page 296 also shows the earth on December 22. It is on the opposite side of the sun. Notice that the earth's tilt is still the same. But the earth has moved. Now the Southern Hemisphere is facing directly into the sun. The Northern Hemisphere is pointed away from the sun. The Northern Hemisphere is receiving sunlight that is weaker. The sun's rays hit the Northern Hemisphere on a slant, not directly. December 22 is the first day of winter. It is also known as the **8** **winter solstice**.

Look at the two other positions of earth. March 21 is the first day of spring. It is also called the **vernal equinox**. September 23 is the first day of autumn. It is the **autumnal equinox**. In these seasons, the earth has moved to positions that are halfway between winter and summer. The tilt of the earth has not changed. In these seasons, neither the Northern Hemisphere nor the Southern Hemisphere receives sunlight that is direct.

The diagram above shows the difference between the slanted and direct light. You can imitate how sunlight strikes the earth by using a flashlight.

Summer solstice: The first day of summer in the Northern Hemisphere.

7

Winter solstice: The first day of winter in the Northern Hemisphere.

Vernal equinox: The first day of spring in the Northern Hemisphere.

Autumnal equinox: The first day of fall in the Northern Hemisphere.

297

EXTENSIONS

Enrichment
Activity

As a way of emphasizing the earth's revolution around the sun, students could make a flip book that illustrates this phenomenon. A flip book is a set of index cards stapled together at one end. On each card an object is drawn at a slightly different position. By flipping the cards and looking into the side of the book, simple animation is observed. Their flip books should show at least eight positions. Include the earth at summer solstice, winter solstice, vernal equinox and autumnal equinox.

6 **Skill Development** — In examining the illustrations of the solstices and equinoxes, ask students to demonstrate the position of the earth relative to the sun for each situation.

7 **Teaching Tips** — On a bulletin board, mount pictures displaying each of the four seasons. Ask students to describe on index cards the cause for the solstices and equinoxes.

8 **Teaching Tips** — Explain to the students that the earth is closer to the sun in the winter than in the summer. However, the hours the sun is above the horizon are fewer, and this accounts for the lower winter temperatures.

Application
Science Skills — Observing

You may wish to have the students observe the effect of the sun's apparent northward movement in the first half of the year and southward movement in the second half of the year. The following is a suggested activity:

A. Although the sun seems to rise and set each day, the location of the sun at sunrise and sunset seems to change during the year. To observe this change, use a large tree or building as a reference point in the east and in the west. Observe sunrise once a week for the remainder of the year. Do the same for the sunset.

B. Answer the following: What do you observe about the location of the sun at sunrise and sunset? (The sun rises and sets north of the east and west points during the first half of the year.)

Reinforcement
Research — Library

Since this is the first section of an astronomy unit, you may wish to have each student make a labeled drawing of the earth. They should include a brief description of our planet. As time goes on, they can extend their illustrations to include the other heavenly bodies covered in this unit. At the end of the unit they will then have a nice series of drawings and descriptions to use for review purposes. Encourage the students to use color in their major features of the object.

SUGGESTED WORKSHEET MASTER
p. T–291k

ACTIVITY

The spreading out of light energy

A. With a partner, obtain these materials: chalk, flashlight, 1 sheet of construction paper.

B. Hold the flashlight about 10 cm from the paper. Have your partner draw a circle around the lit area.

 1. What does the light from the flashlight represent?
 2. What does the paper represent?
 3. Predict how the lit area will look when the paper is tilted away from the light.

C. Tilt the paper away from the light. Draw a line around the lit area.

 4. What do you observe?
 5. Compare your predictions and results.

Section Review

Main Ideas: The earth rotates around its axis every 24 hours, causing day and night. The earth makes one revolution around the sun in 365¼ days. The tilt of the earth's axis and its movement around the sun cause the seasons: summer, autumn, winter and spring.

Questions: Answer in complete sentences.

1. How long does it take for earth to complete one rotation? How long for one revolution?
2. How can it be light in one city and dark in another?
3. Draw a simple diagram that shows the earth's axis.
4. What is the direction of the earth's tilt on June 21? What is this date called?
5. Weak, slanted rays describe the light that hits the Northern Hemisphere during which season?

298

ACTIVITY

Skill Development — *Predicting, Cause and Effect*

Teaching Tips — Darken the room as the students begin their work.

Answers to Questions — **1.** Sunlight.   **2.** earth.   **3.** The light will spread out.   **4.** More of the paper was lit.   **5.** We predicted that the light would spread out more with the paper tilted away. It was.

SECTION REVIEW

Answers to Questions
1. One rotation takes 24 hours. One revolution takes one year.
2. The city in darkness is located on a part of the earth that has not yet turned into the sun.
3. See the diagram on the top of page 296.
4. The tilt is pointed toward the sun; summer solstice.
5. Winter

The Moon

On July 20, 1969, these words were sent to earth: "Houston . . . the *Eagle* has landed." Those words were spoken by astronaut Neil Armstrong. He was speaking to the Mission Control Center in Houston. The *Eagle* he mentioned was not a bird. It was the first spacecraft with passengers to land on the moon's surface. Neil Armstrong and Edwin Aldrin were in the *Eagle*. Neil Armstrong was the first human to step on the moon's surface. When you finish this section, you should be able to:

☐ **A.** Describe the surface of the moon.
☐ **B.** Explain why the moon seems to change in shape.
☐ **C.** Describe what happens when the moon or earth blocks the sun's light.

The moon is the earth's closest neighbor in space. It is only 400,000 kilometers (250,000 miles) away! But the moon and earth are quite different. The earth is a **planet**. A *planet* is a solid body in space that does not give off its own light.

Planet: A solid body in space that does not give off its own light.

299

SECTION BACKGROUND

The moon, a satellite of the earth, revolves around the earth in an elliptical orbit. It rotates on its axis about once every 27 1/3 days. The moon revolves around the earth in 27 1/3 days. A person on earth observing the moon essentially sees just one side of the moon since its periods of rotation and revolution are approximately the same.

Sunlight always shines on half of the moon's surface. The changing appearance of the moon depends on its change in position. The new moon phase occurs when the side of the moon facing the earth is dark. This occurs when the moon is in the same direction from earth as the sun. The moon's revolution moves it eastward. When it reaches a position of 90 degrees from the sun, it is in its first quarter phase. When it is 180 degrees from the sun (i.e. opposite the sun), we see the full moon phase. The last quarter phase occurs when the moon has moved 270 degrees from the sun. As the moon moves from this position toward the sun, we see less and less of the lit side of the moon. Eventually, the moon returns to its position in line with the sun and we have the new moon phase once again.

The moon's surface consists of mountains, craters, and marias. Marias are smooth areas on the moon and are often called seas.

MATERIALS

lamp, orange

BASIC TEACHING PLAN

MOTIVATION

Make a set of transparencies as motivation for this section. On the first, place the sun. Overlay this transparency with one that shows the earth. Review the revolution and rotation of the earth with respect to the sun at this point. Finally, overlay a third transparency that shows the moon revolving around the earth and rotating on its axis. Tell the students that this section will deal with the characteristics of the moon and what occurs when all three heavenly bodies happen to be lined up.

Most adults remember what they were doing when the astronauts first landed on the moon. Have students conduct a survey by asking people what they remember about that occasion.

DEVELOPMENT

1 **Teaching Tips** — As the orbit of the moon is elliptical, this is an average distance.

EXTENSIONS

Enrichment
Research — Library

Astronauts who go to the moon must be prepared to meet the lunar "living" conditions. Discuss with your students the factors which must be overcome to ensure the safety of humans who go on such a journey. Include the following conditions:

1. No air and therefore no oxygen.
2. No air pressure.
3. Temperatures that range from −140°C (−220°F) to 260°C (500°F). Inform the students that our earth temperatures do not reach such a range because air and water spread out the sun's heat.
4. Sound cannot travel on the moon since there is no air.
5. The presence of immense mountains (some taller than the tallest earth mountains) and craters.
6. The pull of the moon's gravity is one-sixth of the earth's gravity.

Satellite: An object in space that revolves around a planet.

Craters: Bowl-shaped holes.

Marias: Smooth places on the moon's surface.

The moon is a **satellite** (sat-uh-lite). A *satellite* is an object in space that revolves around another object. The moon makes one complete trip around earth in 27⅓ days, or about once a month.

You can observe the moon's motion in the sky. But some people have observed the moon up close. In three years, 12 brave Americans landed on the moon. They took pictures and made maps. They brought back moon rocks. They gathered 2,000 rocks, weighing over 380 kilograms (840 pounds). Most of the rocks, like the one shown at left, were given to scientists for study.

The scientists learned that the moon once had lots of volcanoes. They sent out huge amounts of melted rock material. This material flowed outward and formed the flat parts of the moon. Between the flat parts are bowl-shaped holes. These are called **craters** (kray-terz). The picture on the left below shows a *crater*.

Scientists think the moon's craters were formed when objects traveling in space hit and dented the moon's surface. The flat, smooth places on the moon's surface are called **marias** (muh-**ree**-uhz). This means "seas" in Latin. But these seas are dry. Look at the picture on the right. It shows a *maria* on the moon that scientists named the

Sea
of
Serenity
Sea
of
Tranquility

300

---

2 **Teaching Tips** — You may want to demonstrate the motion of a satellite by whirling a rubber ball attached to a string around your head. Ask the students how long it would take the ball to make one complete path around you if it moved as fast as the moon.

3 **Teaching Tips** — One of the rocks brought back was found to be 4.6 billion years old. It is the oldest rock ever recorded on the moon or the earth.

4 **Skill Development** — Have the students locate craters and marias on the photographs shown.

Sea of Serenity (suh-**ren**-ih-tee). Another maria on the moon was named the Sea of Tranquility (tran-**kwil**-ih-tee). Some of the craters have been named after famous scientists. One of the craters is named Copernicus (kuh-**per**-nih-kus). Another is Tycho (**ty**-koh). There are also mountains on the moon's surface.

Even though the moon has mountains and "seas," it is not at all like earth. It has only its barren, rocky surface. The moon has no air around it like earth has. That is why the astronauts brought their own air supply to the moon.

Probably you have seen the moon many times. Does it always look the same to you? How does the moon change? The moon appears to change its shape. The moon, of course, does not change shape. The moon, like earth, does not produce any light of its own. That may be a little hard to believe, since the moon seems so bright on some nights. Actually, the light we see from the moon is reflected sunlight. Sunlight strikes the moon, bounces off, and comes to earth. But remember — one side of the moon always faces the sun. So when the moon moves around the earth, we can't always see the entire lighted side of the moon. We only see part of that side. As a result, the moon seems to change shape.

The pictures on the right show some of the shapes the moon seems to have. Sometimes we see only a tiny part of the lighted side of the moon. This is called a crescent moon. As the moon moves in its path around the earth, more of its lighted side can be seen. The second picture shows a first quarter moon. The moon is one quarter through its trip around the earth. When the whole lighted surface is seen, the moon is full. Then the moon seems to shrink again. It goes through its last quarter and then a crescent shape again. Then the moon disappears altogether. When the moon's entire lighted surface faces away from the earth, it is known as a new moon. These shapes of the moon are its **phases**. Have you seen each of the moon's *phases*?

new crescent

first quarter

full moon

last quarter

old crescent

7

Phases: The shapes the moon appears to be as seen from the earth.

301

EXTENSIONS

Reinforcement
Research — Library

Students could begin to supplement the illustration that they began in the Extension on p. T–298. They should prepare a labeled drawing of the moon that includes information that they have gathered during the class and during additional research that they may have done. They should label as many features on a full moon as possible.

Enrichment
Activity

Students could do some observations to answer the following question: In which direction does the moon seem to move compared to the stars in back of it? Have the students do the following:

A. Start the activity on a night when there is a new crescent moon.

B. Observe the moon at the same hour each night and notice its position compared to some object on the horizon.

C. At the end of one week report on the answer to the question. They should have observed that the moon moved toward the east.

5   Teaching Tips — You may be able to locate some brief biographical information about Copernicus and Tycho Brahe. Mention that the names for some of the craters commemorate the work of various astronomers.

6   Teaching Tips — As there is no rain nor wind on the moon, the astronauts' footprints will remain for many years to come.

7   Skill Development — Have the students *identify* the name for each view of the moon shown in the drawings along the side of the page. Ask them what the new moon looks like.

Exceptional Student
Visually Impaired

Using clay, make a small replica of the moon. Have the student feel the craters.

Enrichment
Science Skills — Observing, Recording Data

Some students could do more extensive moon observations. The results of their observations should be shared with the class as a whole. Ask this group to observe the moon on a regular basis and complete charts that show the data and diagrams revealing the following information: date, moonrise, moonset, the number of hours when the moon is visible, shape.

They should use almanacs to gather the data on days when moonrise will be too late for them to directly observe it, or when the sun is too bright for them to observe moonset.

Exceptional Student
Visually Impaired
Using cardboard, cut out the various shapes of the moon. Have the student feel the shapes. Discuss the phases of the moon. Be aware that even students with severe visual impairments may see shadows of light and dark.

ACTIVITY

The phases of the moon

A. Obtain these materials: lamp, orange.

B. Imagine that the lamp is the sun, the orange is the moon, and you are earth. Place the lamp on a table so that it is level with your eyes. You may need to place books under the lamp. Turn on the lamp. Stand about 60 cm from the lamp, facing it.

C. Hold up the orange, halfway between the lamp and your eyes.
  1. How much of its lit surface can you see?

D. Turn so that your side faces the lamp. Hold up the orange about 25 cm from your eyes.
  2. How much of its lit surface can you see?

E. Turn so that your back is facing the lamp. Hold up the orange about 25 cm from your eyes, but slightly to the left of your head.
  3. How much of its lit surface can you see?
  4. Write a summary of your results. Explain why the shape of the moon seems to change.

302

ACTIVITY

Skill Development — *Observing, Cause and Effect*

1. Teaching Tips — Darken the room as much as possible for this activity.

Answers to Questions — 1. None of the lit surface.   2. Half of the lit surface.   3. The entire lit surface.   4. The shape of the "moon" seems to change since we could not always see all of the lit surface. The amount of lit surface visible to us depends on the location of the earth and the moon as compared to the location of the sun.

8 The moon goes through all the phases each time it makes a complete trip around the earth. Do you know what phase the moon is in right now? Check a calendar to **9** see. Better still, look at the moon tonight.

The moon revolves around earth at the same time that earth revolves around the sun. Sometimes the moon passes between earth and the sun. The moon slowly blocks the sun's light. When this happens, a shadow of the moon is cast on earth. Even though it's daytime, the sky gets dark. The moon has caused a **solar eclipse** (**soh**-ler ee-**klips**). It is a *solar eclipse* because the sun is blocked out as you can see in the photograph. The total solar eclipse can only be seen from the small area on earth where the moon's shadow falls. Find that area in the diagram below. From other parts of the earth, the sun looks partially blocked out. Total solar eclipses do not happen often. A total solar eclipse won't be seen from North America until after the year 2000.

Solar eclipse: Occurs when the moon passes between the earth and the sun.

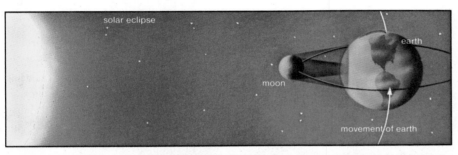

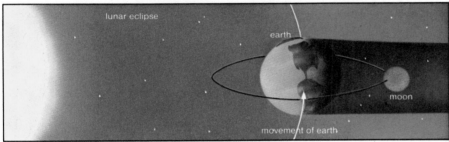

303

EXTENSIONS

Application
Activity

After researching additional information about solar and lunar eclipses, some members of your class could do the following demonstration. The group should practice their presentation prior to their doing it for the remainder of the class.

A. Obtain a globe of earth, a gooseneck or table lamp without a shade, and a ball. The lamp will represent the sun, and the ball will represent the moon. Label each.

B. Hold the ball between the lamp and the globe so that a shadow of the ball is cast on the globe. You may have to move the ball back and forth to get a sharp shadow.

C. Make sure that the class will be able to see the shadow on the globe. Explain that what has occured represents a solar eclipse.

D. To show a lunar eclipse, hold the ball about 60 cm (2 ft) from that side of the globe which is not facing the lamp. The ball will then be in the shadow of earth. Be sure that the class will be able to observe the ball in the shadow. Explain this arrangement as being a lunar eclipse.

---

8 Skill Development — Encourage the students to *observe* the shape of the moon at this time of the month. They may wish to *predict* how its shape will change over the next week. Some students with an interest in photography may wish to take some pictures to show the changes in the apparent shape of the moon.

9 Skill Development — Prior to having the students study this part of the section, you may wish to have some students make *hypotheses* about what will occur when the moon passes between the earth and the sun and when the earth passes between the moon and the sun. This part of the section explains the *effects* produced so they will be able to compare their hypotheses with what really occurs.

Lunar eclipse: Occurs when the earth passes between the moon and the sun.

Sometimes earth passes between the moon and the sun. Earth blocks the sun's light that would light up the moon. A shadow of earth is cast on the moon. The moon loses its light. It may appear to have a red color. This is a **lunar eclipse** (**loo**-ner ee-**klips**), shown above. The bottom diagram on page 303 shows the positions of the moon, earth, and sun during a *lunar eclipse*.

Section Review

Main Ideas: The moon is earth's satellite. Its surface has craters, mountains, and marias. The moon seems to change in shape. At certain times, solar and lunar eclipses can occur.

Questions: Answer in complete sentences.

1. What is a satellite? What is the earth's satellite called?
2. Name and describe two features that are found on the moon's surface.
3. Why does the moon seem to change shape?
4. Name six phases of the moon. In which phase is the moon invisible?
5. What is the difference between a solar eclipse and a lunar eclipse?

304

How would you like to fly the plane shown below? This was the first plane to fly using the energy of the sun. When you finish this section, you should be able to:

☐ **A.** Describe some characteristics of the sun.
☐ **B.** Explain one way in which the sun's energy can be used.

The sun is a **star.** *Stars* are objects in space made of hot gases. The gases are so hot that they glow, giving off light. Unlike planets, stars give off their own light. Our sun is a star that is about 150 million kilometers (93 million miles) away. The sun is spinning through space, as are the earth and the other planets.

The sun is made of the gases hydrogen (**hy**-druh-jen) and helium (**heel**-ee-um). The sun has a central **core** with layers around it. At the *core*, hydrogen takes part in a nuclear reaction. The hydrogen changes to helium. This

15-3.

The Sun

1

Core: The central part of the sun.

305

SECTION BACKGROUND

Our sun is one star in the Milky Way galaxy. Its gravitational field holds the planets and other bodies of the solar system in orbit. The mass of the sun is 99.86 percent of all the mass in the solar system. The sun is predominately composed of the gases hydrogen and helium. The sun produces energy as a result of nuclear fusion at its core. It is within this core that hydrogen gas is changed into helium. The nuclear reaction also produces enormous amounts of energy. Some of this energy reaches the sun's surface and radiates outward into space.

Through observations, astronomers have detected the following phenomena: sunspots (dark and cooler areas on the sun's surface); solar flares (bright areas in the sun's atmosphere); solar prominences (blasts of hydrogen atoms that are missing electrons); and numerous other solar features. The faint white light seen around the sun during a solar eclipse is the sun's corona.

MATERIALS

pencil, tape, cardboard 20 cm square, watch, compass, marking pen

BASIC TEACHING PLAN

MOTIVATION

Allow the students to hypothesize what they believe to be the sun's source of energy. Ask them what they think would happen if the sun were to stop shining. Students will realize that the earth would be in darkness, but they might not foresee the threat to our food supply on earth as a consequence of the inability of plants to produce food. Tell the students that they should not worry too much about the sun not shining as it will last about another 5 billion years before it uses up all of its fuel (hydrogen that undergoes fusion and releases energy).

DEVELOPMENT

1 **Teaching Tips** — You may wish to list the physical characteristics of the sun on the chalkboard as they are discussed in the text.

EXTENSIONS

Application
Science Skills — Measuring, Recording Data

Students could perform the following experiment to understand how astronomers use indirect measurements to obtain information about the sun. They will need aluminum foil, a cardboard carton, an index card, a meterstick, a pencil, a safety pin, scissors, and clear tape. They should follow these directions:

A. On one end of the box, cut out a small square, 5 cm (2 in.) from one edge.

B. Tape aluminum foil over the square hole. Open the safety pin and make a small hole in the center of the foil. Close the safety pin.

C. Tape the index card to the inside of the box at the end that is opposite the foil and pinhole.

D. Go outdoors and place the box over your head so that you are looking at the index card which will show the image of the sun. Do not look at the pinhole!

E. Next to the image of the sun on the card, draw a circle the same size as the image. Then lower the box.

F. Measure the width of the circle; measure the distance from the pinhole to the index card. Divide the distance measured by the width of the circle. Divide 150,000,000 km (93,000,000 mi) by the number you got as your answer. The final answer should be approximately 1,400,000 km (870,000 mi). This calculation is the approximate diameter of the sun.

Photosphere: The surface of the sun.

Sunspots: Dark spots on the sun.

Solar flares: Bright areas in the sun's atmosphere from which hot gases shoot out.

occurs at a temperature of about 15 million degrees centigrade. The process of changing hydrogen to helium releases huge amounts of energy. The energy is in the form of heat and light. The heat and light move outward from the core to the sun's surface.

The sun's surface is the **photosphere** (foh-toh-sfeer). **2** Above the *photosphere* are layers of gases. They form the sun's atmosphere. The sun's energy leaves the photosphere and travels outward into space. Some of the sun's energy reaches the earth and the other planets.

Look at the picture below. Do you see dark spots on the sun's surface? These dark spots are **sunspots.** *Sunspots* are places on the sun where the gases have cooled. Cool gases do not give off as much light as hot gases.

Sometimes there are bright areas in the sun's atmosphere from which hot gases shoot out into space. These bright areas are called **solar flares.** *Solar flares* seem to affect things on earth. For example, they can interfere with radio messages.

You have already learned about a solar eclipse. Look back at the picture on page 303. It shows the sun during a

306

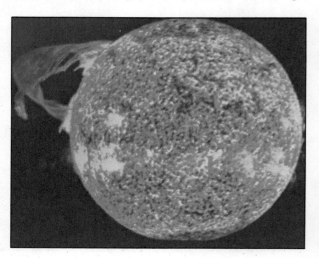

Look back at the picture on page 303.

2 Skill Development — Be sure the students understand the *sequence* in the production and release of energy in the sun: 1. Nuclear reactions at the core produce energy. 2. Energy moves upward to the photosphere. 3. Energy leaves the photosphere and travels outward into space.

3 Text Questions — Do you see dark spots on the sun's surface? Explain to the class that these sunspots are observed by using a special telescope.

4 Teaching Tips — Caution your students against looking directly at the sun to see such sunspots. Do the same for the term *solar flares*.

solar eclipse. The moon is blocking most of the sun's light. Notice the faint white light around the edges of the sun. This light is called the **corona** (kuh-**roh**-nuh). The word *corona* also means *crown*. Why do you think the light is called the corona?

Life on earth depends on the sun. Without the sun, earth would be an empty, cold place. There wouldn't be any plants or animals. The sun is earth's main source of heat and light.

Examine the photograph above. It shows a house that uses *solar energy*. The glass panels on the roof are solar panels. Inside the solar panels are pipes carrying water. The sun's light heats the water in the pipes. The pipes carry the hot water to a storage tank under the house. When hot water is needed for washing, it is carried through other pipes from the tank to the faucets. To heat the house, hot water in pipes passes by a fan that blows air on the pipes. The air is warmed by the hot water. The warm air is sent around the house through air vents.

The airplane pictured on page 305 also uses the sun's energy, but not for heat. The sun's energy is changed into electricity by solar cells like those on page 210.

5   **6**

Corona: The faint, white light seen around the sun during a solar eclipse.

307

EXTENSIONS

Enrichment
Science Skills — Measuring

Provide the students with the following information and have them make graphs or charts to show the results of their calculations. Scientists believe the sun uses 600 million tons of hydrogen per second during its internal fusion reactions. Tell this number to the students. Then ask them to compute the amount of hydrogen used in a minute, hour, day, year, one billion years, and five billion years.

5   **Skill Development** — You may wish to have the students make *diagrams* to review the *difference* between a lunar and solar eclipse. After they have done this, have them refer to the text material on the page that discusses one of the phenomena observed during a solar eclipse.

6   **Teaching Tips** — The inner part of the corona is made of thin gas, and the outer part is composed of tiny particles that reflect the light of the sun.

7   **Text Questions** — Why do you think the light is called the corona? *The faint light creates a halo or crown effect.*

Enrichment
Research — Library

You may wish to have some students engage in library research to obtain additional information about the nature of sunspots. They can use the supplementary information as part of a report to the class as a whole.

Among other things, they will find out that: the diameters of sunspots are over 1500 km across, temperatures are about 4000°C, and they sometimes last as long as several months.

Reinforcement
Research — Library

You may wish to have some students do research as background for the preparation of their own diagrams that show the following: corona, solar prominence, sunspots, solar flare, photosphere, chromosphere.

ACTIVITY

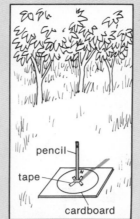

pencil
tape
cardboard

Making a sundial

A. Obtain these materials: pencil, tape, cardboard 20 cm square, watch, compass, marking pen.
B. Draw a circle 15 cm across on the cardboard. Mark one place on the circle N for north.
C. Make a hole in the center of the circle big enough for the pencil. Tape the pencil to keep it upright.
D. Bring the sundial outdoors on a sunny day. Find north with the compass. Turn the cardboard so that the N faces north. Mark the place where the shadow of the pencil points. Write the time there. Do this several times during the day.
  1. What direction is the sun when the shadow of the pencil is the shortest? the longest?
  2. Can you tell the time by the shadow the next day?

Section Review

Main Ideas: The sun is a star 150 million kilometers (93 million miles) from earth. The sun produces great amounts of energy. Some of this energy travels to earth. The sun's sunspots, solar flares, and corona can be seen from earth. Solar energy is used to heat the air and water in some homes.

Questions: Answer in complete sentences.

1. From what does the sun get its energy?
2. Make a diagram of the sun's corona. When can you see the corona?
3. What is a solar flare?
4. Why do sunspots look dark?
5. What is one way in which people can use the sun's energy?

308

ACTIVITY

Skill Development — *Observing, Cause and Effect.*

Teaching Tips — The students' sundial will be accurate for a few days, but becomes less so as the relative position of the earth changes with respect to the sun.

Answers to Questions — 1. Almost directly overhead. When the sun is furthest east or west. 2. The sundial should work the next sunny day. But as the earth moves in its orbit, the sun will rise and set in different places, making the time markings incorrect.

SECTION REVIEW

Answers to Questions
1. From the nuclear reaction of hydrogen being changed to helium
2. Drawing similar to that of page 303; during a solar eclipse.
3. Bright areas in the sun's atmosphere caused by hot gases
4. A sunspot appears as a dark spot on the sun.
5. To heat the air and water in a building

CHAPTER REVIEW

Science Words:

On a sheet of paper, write the word that fits each definition.

1. The movement of one object around another.
2. An object in space that revolves around another.
3. The first day of summer in the Northern Hemisphere.
4. The first day of autumn in the Northern Hemisphere.
5. Smooth places on the moon's surface.

Define each of these terms.

6. Crater
7. Winter solstice
8. Photosphere
9. Rotation
10. Phase

Questions: Answer in complete sentences.

1. What causes day and night?
2. In Washington, D.C., the sun has just come up. In a town that is 2,000 km to the west, has the sun come up yet? Explain your answer.
3. List the four seasons. Identify the direction in which the Northern Hemisphere is pointed for each.
4. True or false: The tilt of the earth changes with each season. Explain your answer.
5. You have just landed on the moon. Describe all the features that you see.
6. During which phase of the moon do you see the entire side of the moon that faces the sun? How often can you see this phase?
7. Sketch the sun, moon, and earth in the order they would be during a solar eclipse. What part of the sun can be seen then?
8. What are two different features that are visible on the surface of the sun?

309

EXTENSIONS

Reinforcement
Activity

Students could prepare a chart for classroom display, listing the following information about the earth, moon and the sun:
1. Size
2. Surface features
3. Relative positions and revolution time for the earth and moon
4. Atmosphere
5. Temperature
6. Eclipses

CHAPTER REVIEW

Science Words 1. rotation, **2.** satellite, **3.** summer solstice, **4.** autumnal equinox, **5.** maria, **6.** A bowl-shaped hole on the moon's surface **7.** The first day of winter in the Northern Hemisphere. **8.** The sun's surface **9.** The spinning motion of the earth **10.** The shape the moon appears to have

Answers to Questions
1. Day and night are caused by the rotation of the earth on its axis.
2. This part of the earth has not yet turned toward the sun.
3. Winter (away from the sun); spring (in a position halfway between winter and summer); summer (toward the sun); fall (in a position halfway between summer and winter)
4. False. The earth moves into a different position.
5. Craters and marias would be seen on its barren surface.
6. Full moon. Once every 27 1/3 days.
7. The moon is between the sun and the earth. The corona
8. Sunspots and solar flares

SUGGESTED TEST MASTERS
pp. T–291d,e

CHAPTER OBJECTIVES

1. Describe the solar system and some of the characteristics of the inner planets.
2. Describe the outer planets.
3. Compare the orbits of the outer planets.
4. Describe other objects in our solar system and tell where they are found.
5. Describe what a rocket is and how it is launched and returned to earth.

SECTION BACKGROUND

Our solar system consists of the sun, nine planets and their moons, asteroids, meteoroids, and comets. The four planets closest to the sun are Mercury, Venus, earth, and Mars. These inner planets are solid bodies. Mercury, the second smallest planet in the solar system, is thought to have a core that is predominately iron and an atmosphere that is mostly helium. Venus is very similar to earth with respect to its size and mass. Its atmosphere is thought to be about 97 percent carbon dioxide. Mars, the last of the inner planets, has a number of interesting features including polar caps, volcanoes, an enormous mountain system, numerous large craters, and an atmosphere that includes clouds and fog.

MATERIALS

sheets of graph paper, pencil, ruler

**Exceptional Student
IEP Chapter Goal**

At the end of this chapter, the student will name two examples from each of the following: inner planets, outer planets, objects other than planets that move in the solar system.

THE SOLAR SYSTEM

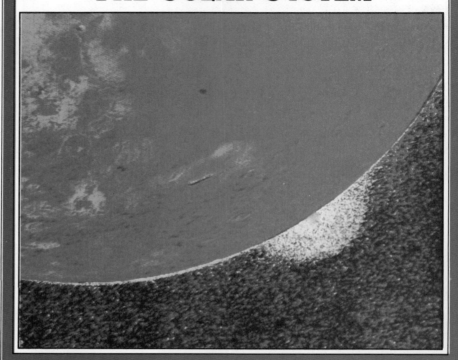

16-1.

The Inner Planets

310

Imagine a place with huge volcanoes that are constantly erupting. That's what it's like in the place that you see above. The photograph shows a moon of one of the planets in our *solar system*. When you finish this section, you should be able to:

BASIC TEACHING PLAN
MOTIVATION

Make a "human" model of the location of the inner planets. Have students represent the sun, Mercury, Venus, earth, and Mars. Tell the class that there are nine planets in our solar system and in this section they will be focusing their attention on just the four closest to the sun. Have the students who represented the planets go to the chalkboard and write the names of their planets. As you continue through this section, these specific students could come forward to record the physical characteristics of "their" planets. If you use this motivation, you will have a listing of the planets and characteristics on the chalkboard when you finish the section. This will serve as a nice way to review the material.

☐ **A.** Identify and describe the characteristics of the four inner planets.

☐ **B.** Compare two ideas about the movements of the earth and the planets.

Earth is not the only planet that revolves around the sun. Eight other planets do, too. These nine planets, their moons, and the sun are called our **solar system**. For thousands of years, people have looked at the planets of our *solar system*. Ancient people noticed that some objects in the night sky did not twinkle. These objects also seemed to wander through the night sky. They would not always appear in the same part of the sky the way stars did. These objects were named "planets," after the Greek word for *wanderer*.

Most ancient people believed that the sun, stars, and planets traveled around the earth. Almost 2,000 years ago, a man named Ptolemy (**tul**-uh-mee) wrote a book that described these ideas in great detail. This book was studied by people for hundreds of years. People agreed

Solar system: The nine planets, their moons, and the sun.

1

311

Application
Science Skills — Observing

You may wish to have some students do nighttime astronomy using binoculars. They will need to have access to at least 8-power binoculars (or a telescope). Have them attempt to locate Mercury, Venus, and Mars. The following directions will assist them:

1. Mercury: Look after sunset, close to the horizon, in the springtime. Use an almanac to find out what direction to look for it on the day that you try to find it. It will appear gray in color.
2. Venus: Use an almanac to find where it will rise and set. It will appear to be very bright and silver-colored.
3. Mars: Use an almanac to find where it will rise and set. It will appear to be reddish in color.

DEVELOPMENT

1 **Teaching Tips** — You may wish to ask two students to briefly play the parts of Ptolemy and Copernicus and explain "their" theories of planetary motion. The old reproduction may help students imagine Ptolemy's system.

Enrichment
Research

Students could write a letter to request information about the planets that has been obtained through space exploration. They could write to the Public Information Officer, Goddard Space Flight Center, Greenbelt, MD 20771. They should ask for available published information and pictures from the *Pioneer*, *Mariner*, and *Viking* space probes.

Orbit: The path of one object in space around another.

Ellipses: The shapes of the orbits of the planets.

Mercury, Venus, Earth, Mars: The four planets closest to the sun. They are also called the inner planets.

with Ptolemy's ideas. They thought all the objects in the sky moved around the earth.

In 1543, a Polish scientist, Nicolaus Copernicus, wrote a book that announced a new idea. He said that the earth and the planets moved around the sun. People were shocked at that idea. They wanted to believe that the earth was the center of everything. Galileo, an Italian scientist, agreed with Copernicus. He wrote a book that used the same ideas. Galileo got into trouble for his book. It went against the beliefs of the time. As the years passed, other scientists observed that the earth moved around the sun. Today we have instruments and spacecraft that help us explore our solar system. We now know much more about the planets.

The planets revolve around the sun in paths called **orbits** (**or**-bits). Their *orbits* are shaped like stretched-out circles, or **ellipses**. The drawing shows the planets in their orbits around the sun. Look at the four planets closest to the sun. They are **Mercury** (**mer**-kyer-ee), **Venus** (**vee**-nus), **Earth**, and **Mars** (**marz**). They are called the inner planets.

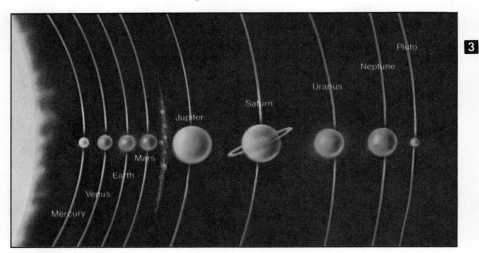

312

Exceptional Student
Visually Impaired
Learning Disabled

Using small Styrofoam or clay balls, make a miniature replica of the solar system. Let the learning disabled student rotate and revolve the planets. Glue the planets to oaktag. Allow the visually impaired student to feel their relative positions and sizes.

2 Skill Development — Some of the students may be encouraged to make *hypotheses* about why Galileo got into so much trouble over a matter that we take for granted—the idea that the sun is the center around which planets revolve. Also, some students may be encouraged to do a little research on Galileo and the rather serious problems that he caused for himself by espousing Copernicus's ideas.

3 Skill Development — Have the students try to locate the inner planets and name them. Then ask the students if they *observe* anything interesting in the diagram at a location beyond Mars. They should see a region of material that looks a bit like rubble. Indicate that later they will be learning about this region (a belt of asteroids).

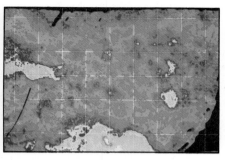

Mercury is the smallest planet. It is also the closest to the sun. The surface temperature on the side of Mercury facing the sun can be as high as 500°C (930°F). The surface temperature on the dark side can be −200°C (−330°F). Pictures taken by spacecraft sent to Mercury show a surface like that of the moon. Look at the top left picture. Mercury has craters. Scientists believe that there is no air, water, or life on Mercury. The planet has no moons.

Venus is the second planet from the sun. It is the closest planet to earth. Venus has often been called earth's twin. Both planets are about the same size. Both planets are covered with clouds. But the yellow clouds of Venus are so thick that only a gloomy light reaches the surface. The sun's light and heat are trapped in the clouds. That makes the temperature at the surface about 500°C (930°F). The air is almost all carbon dioxide. There is no water. There are erupting volcanoes. Winds roar. Lightning flashes. Venus has no moon.

The cloud cover kept scientists from knowing what Venus was like. We know more now because of the use of **space probes**. A *space probe* is a rocket in space that contains cameras and other devices. Space probes record what it's like on other planets. Some space probes fly past objects in space. The *Pioneer* space probe flew past Venus. It sent back information that helped scientists make the map of Venus you see above.

Space probe: A rocket launched into space to send information back to earth.

313

EXTENSIONS

Application
Science Skills — Observing

The planet Venus is often referred to as a morning and evening star because it is seen just above the horizon at sunrise and sunset and looks like a very bright star. Have some students observe Venus at sunrise or sunset. An almanac or daily newspaper will indicate the date and hour at which the planet is visible.

4 **Skill Development** — As the students *observe* the *photograph*, tell them that the photo of Mercury is a mosaic. It is many small pictures of parts of the planet's surface that were placed together like the parts of a puzzle to give an overall or complete picture.

5 **Teaching Tips** — The students may wonder why the surface of Venus is similar to that of Mercury, since Venus is farther from the sun. Tell the students that the thick layer of clouds around Venus insulates the planet and retains surface heat.

6 **Teaching Tips** — Radar signals from the Pioneer spacecraft have been arranged by computer graphics to produce maps such as the one pictured. Each color represents a different elevation.

EXTENSIONS

Reinforcement
Science Skills — Classifying

Have some of your students begin preparing information to use in the development of a game that can be played by the entire class. The game is to have students attempt to name a planet based on the smallest numbers of clues.

The group developing the game should prepare 20 index cards for each of the inner planets. Each card should have one fact that they have researched. The cards should be arranged from those that contain the most specific (possibly most obscure) facts to those that are more obvious.

They should save these cards and do the same for the outer planets. Then toward the end of the unit, they can see how well their classmates can classify planets when they provide the class with the information on the index cards.

Charting the inner planets

A. Obtain these materials: paper, pencil, ruler.

B. Study the chart below.

	Mercury	Venus	Earth	Mars
Distance from sun (millions of km)	58	108	150	228
Diameter (km)	4,880	12,100	12,756	6,786
Length of planet year (days)	88	225	365	687

C. Prepare three bar graphs. Each graph will compare the inner planets on a different characteristic. They are: distance from the sun, diameter, length of the year (one revolution around the sun). Prepare one graph for each characteristic.

1. Which planet has the largest diameter? Which planet has the smallest diameter?
2. Which planet is the farthest from the sun? Which planet is the closest?
3. Which planet has the longest year? Which planet has the shortest?
4. Write a summary for your graphs.

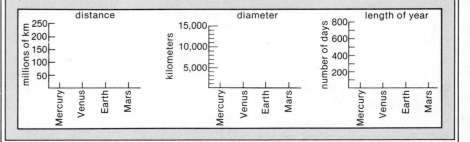

314

ACTIVITY

Skill Development — *Comparing and Contrasting, Measuring, Recording Data, Inferring*

Teaching Tips — If you happen to have graph paper available you may wish to supply it to the students for this activity.

Teaching Tips — You can extend this activity a bit by supplying the students with colored pencils and having them also make drawings to represent each of the planets.

Answers to Questions — 1. Earth, Mercury. 2. Mars, Mercury. 3. Mars, Mercury. 4. The students should relate the length of the year to the distance from the sun.

Earth is the third planet from the sun. Scientists believe earth is the only planet that has water and air that contains oxygen. Therefore, they think it is the only planet in our solar system that has life as we know it. Earth has one moon. **7**

Mars is the fourth planet from the sun. It is about half the size of earth. Mars appears to be red, except for white spots at its poles which are ice caps. You can see one in the photo below. The ice caps are made of solid carbon dioxide. There is no water on Mars. Its air is mostly carbon dioxide. Its surface is covered with mountains, craters, and volcanoes. You can see a volcano below. During the day on Mars, the temperature is about 20°C (68°F). At night, the temperature may drop to −140°C (−220°F). Why do you think it is colder on Mars than it is on earth? Mars has two moons. **8** **9**

EXTENSIONS

Enrichment
Research — Library

You may wish to have a group of students do some detective work to determine the name and locaton of the largest known volcano in the solar system. With some effort and some hints, they will find that it is Olympus Mons. It reaches a height of 25 km above the surface of Mars.

7 **Teaching Tips** — If you used the motivation suggested at the beginning of this section, you will want to remember to have students come forward to record physical characteristics under "their" planets.

8 **Text Questions** — Why do you think the temperature is colder on Mars than on earth? *Because Mars is farther from the sun, and its atmosphere does not hold the heat in.*

9 **Teaching Tips** — The most difficult part of the weather on Mars is the wind. Winds can be so intense as to create storms with winds as high as 300 mph.

The *Viking* space probe shown above landed on the cold, rocky surface of Mars. Samples of Martian soil were taken by the scooping arm of the space probe. From that soil, scientists think that there is no life on Mars.

Section Review

Main Ideas: The nine planets revolve in elliptical orbits around the sun. The four planets closest to the sun are called the inner planets.

Questions: Answer in complete sentences.

1. Compare Ptolemy's ideas about the solar system with those of Copernicus.
2. Which planet is described in each phrase below?
   a. red planet with ice caps
   b. closest planet to the sun
   c. about the same size as earth
   d. has one moon
   e. has surface temperatures of 500°C and −200°C
   f. has water and air that contains oxygen
   g. has constant cloud cover
3. What is an orbit? What shape are the orbits of the planets?
4. What help do scientists have in learning about the inner planets?

316

The Outer Planets

In October 1981, *Voyager 2* sped close to the planet *Saturn*. This spacecraft sent wonderful photographs of Saturn's famous rings back to earth. Saturn is one of the outer planets of our solar system. When you finish this section, you should be able to:

1

☐ **A.** Identify and describe the characteristics of the outer planets.
☐ **B.** Compare the orbits of the outer planets around the sun.

The outer planets are **Jupiter** (**joo**-pih-ter), **Saturn** (**sa**-tern), **Uranus** (yoo-**ray**-nus), **Neptune** (**nep**-toon), and **Pluto** (**ploo**-toh). For years, people have searched the sky for these outer planets. Two of them are bright and can be seen easily. *Jupiter* and *Saturn* are very large. They reflect a lot of light. The other planets are small. They are also very far away. To see them, scientists need powerful instruments. Scientists use **telescopes** to gather light from distant objects. *Telescopes* make distant objects appear closer and larger. Scientists who study objects in the sky are called **astronomers** (uh-**strah**-nuh-merz).

Jupiter, Saturn, Uranus, Neptune, Pluto: The outer planets.

Telescope: An instrument that makes distant objects appear closer and larger.

Astronomer: A scientist who studies objects in space.

317

SECTION BACKGROUND

Between the inner planets and the outer planets is a region of asteroids. The outer planets differ from the inner planets with respect to the gaseous nature of the outer planets. Except for Pluto, the outer planets are larger and less dense than the inner planets.

Jupiter, the largest planet of the solar system, has a particularly interesting feature known as the Great Red Spot. This appears to be a storm on its surface. The region is composed of a gaseous mass of phosphorus that reaches over ten km above surrounding clouds. Saturn has numerous rings and satellites. Uranus and Neptune are similar in diameter and their period of rotation around the sun. Pluto is the planet that is farthest from the sun. Its highly eccentric orbit took it within Neptune's orbit in 1979. Pluto will again be the planet farthest from the sun in 1999.

MATERIALS

BASIC TEACHING PLAN

MOTIVATION

Ask the students who represented the inner planets to come forward with the names of "their" planets on a piece of cardboard. Have an additional group of students represent the five outer planets. They also should have posters with planet names. You could proceed in the same manner as in the last section.

DEVELOPMENT

1 **Teaching Tips** — With the "planets" at the front of the room, walk between Mars and Jupiter and separate the inner planets from the outer planets. Bring up another student to represent the Voyager 2 spacecraft on its journey past Mars, Jupiter, Saturn, and Uranus.

EXTENSIONS

Enrichment
Science Skills — Comparing and Contrasting

Students could do research to compare the features and prices of various telescopes that are displayed in stores, catalogs of mail order vendors, or science magazines.

The students should be encouraged to make drawings of the various telescopes to accompany their analysis.

Research — Library

Students could research some of Jupiter's larger moons. They could compare and contrast the characteristics of the following:
1. Io (closest to Jupiter, solid rock, atmosphere has sulfur, sodium, and an erupting volcano)
2. Ganymede (half rock, half ice)
3. Europa (rock and ice)
4. Callisto (rock center surrounded by ice)

Io: One of Jupiter's moons.

A simple telescope was used by Galileo, an Italian *astronomer*. His telescope contained pieces of curved glass called lenses. With this telescope he observed our solar system. He observed *Jupiter*, the largest planet.

This giant planet is so big that 1,300 earths could fit into it. Jupiter is covered by bands of clouds. It also has a giant red spot. Find it in the photograph of Jupiter below. Scientists think this spot on Jupiter may be a large and long-lasting storm. The red spot is believed to be as wide as earth and four times as long. There is no water on Jupiter. It is made of frozen gases.

In 1610, when Galileo looked at Jupiter, he saw four objects near it. These were four of Jupiter's 16 moons. With modern telescopes we can see these moons. One of Jupiter's moons is **Io** (**eye**-oh). The picture in the margin below shows Io. This moon has many erupting volcanoes. One of Io's volcanoes is shown on page 310. That picture of Io was made by computers which can add bright colors to photographs that are taken in space.

318

2 **Skill Development** — You may wish to have the students do an activity at this point that will help them get a sense of the relative sizes of Jupiter and Earth. Distribute graph paper and have the students label one square as Earth. Now have them make a circle on their graph paper that includes at least 1300 Earths. If the graph paper does not have a grid sufficiently small, the students could work in groups of two or three so that they will have enough squares. Students could also represent the size of the red spot on Jupiter.

Voyager 2 sent many photographs of the planet *Saturn* **3** back to earth. Saturn is the second largest planet in our solar system. It is the next planet from the sun after Jupi- **4** ter. Saturn is covered with clouds. Its bright rings extend out into space around the planet. Saturn has about a thousand rings made of millions of frozen particles.

Saturn has at least 17 moons. The photograph below shows Saturn with some of its moons. The one in the front is Dione. This moon may look big, but it is really much smaller than Saturn. The picture in the margin shows Dione in orbit with Saturn in the background.

5

 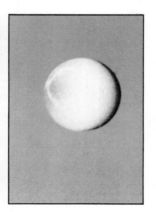

319

EXTENSIONS

Enrichment
Research — Library

Students could research some of Saturn's moons including Ti-tan (its largest), Rhea (second largest), Dione, and Tethys.

3　**Teaching Tips** — Saturn's density is so low (0.68) that it would float if it were thrown into a giant sea. Its rings extend from the planet for a distance of about 136,400 km (85,000 mi). Each of the particles moves at its own speed.

4　**Teaching Tips** — Prior to the invention of more powerful tele-scopes during the latter part of the 18th century, the sun was thought to have only six planets.

5　**Teaching Tips** — The picture above is a montage of Saturn's moons based on *Voyager I* photographs. Dione is in the foreground. Tethys and Minas are on the bottom right. Enceladas and Rhea are off to the left and Titan, actually the largest moon, is in its distant orbit on the top right.

EXTENSIONS

Enrichment
Activity

You may wish to provide the following information to a group of students and have them prepare paper circles to show the relative sizes of the planets and the sun. Their major challenge will be to study the data below and attempt to develop a scale that will enable them to create a sun that is sufficiently large so as to allow them to make the small planets visible. This activity will also provide additional practice with the metric system.

Diameter of Members of
the Solar System
(kilometers)
Sun   1,392,000
Mercury   4,880
Venus   12,100
Earth   12,756
Moon   3,476
Mars   6,786
Jupiter   142,200
Saturn   119,300
Uranus   47,100
Neptune   48,400
Pluto   2,414

You may wish to supply sheets of newspaper that can be taped together to make a sun of sufficient diameter.

The next planet from the sun is *Uranus*. It is so far away that little is known about the planet. Uranus is about half the size of Saturn. Uranus has rings like Saturn, but fewer. The planet has five moons.

Beyond Uranus are the planets *Neptune* and *Pluto*. These two planets are far from the sun. Their orbits have different shapes. In 1979, Pluto moved inside Neptune's **6** orbit. Now Pluto is the eighth planet from the sun. Neptune is the ninth. In 1999, Pluto will again move outside Neptune's orbit. Pluto will then be farther away from the sun than Neptune.

Neptune is about the same size as Uranus. Pluto is about the size of our moon. Neptune has two moons. Pluto has one rather large moon. Pluto's moon is about

7

Planet	Distance from sun in millions of km (mi)	Rotation	Revolution
Mercury	58 (36)	58 days, 18 hr	88 days
Venus	108 (67)	243 days	224.7 days
Earth	150 (93)	23 hr, 56 min	365.2 days
Mars	228 (141)	24 hr, 37 min	687 days
Jupiter	778 (482)	9 hr, 50 min	11.86 years
Saturn	1,430 (887)	16 hr, 39 min	29.46 years
Uranus	2,870 (1,780)	12 hr, 48 min	84.01 years
Neptune	4,500 (2,790)	15 hr, 48 min	164.8 years
Pluto	5,900 (3,660)	6 days, 9 hr	247.7 years

320

6   **Teaching Tips** — Neptune and Pluto cross each other's orbit twice in each revolution. Even so, the closest distance that they come to one another is 38.6 million km (24 million mi).

7   **Skill Development** — Since the orbits of Neptune and Pluto are so intertwined with one another, students are asked to *compare* their characteristics. Pluto's orbit is very long and narrow while Neptune's orbit is more regular.

one half its own size. Both Neptune and Pluto are extremely cold. Both are made of frozen gases.

When planets come close to each other, their orbits change a little. Scientists have noticed changes in the orbits of Uranus and Neptune. But Pluto is too small a planet to cause these changes. Some scientists feel a tenth planet may be beyond Neptune and Pluto.

The chart on page 320 compares the planets in different ways. The chart shows how far away from the sun each planet is. It shows how long it takes for each planet to rotate on its axis and to revolve around the sun.

Section Review

Main Ideas: Astronomers look at the planets through telescopes. Jupiter, Saturn, Uranus, Neptune, and Pluto are the outer planets. *Voyager* 2 has sent back many photographs of Jupiter and Saturn and their moons.

Questions: Answer in complete sentences.

1. Which planet is described in each phrase below?
   - **a.** will be the farthest away until 1999
   - **b.** the largest planet
   - **c.** has a thousand rings
   - **d.** about half the size of Jupiter
   - **e.** has a giant red spot

Use the chart on page 320 to answer questions 2 through 4 below.

2. Which planet rotates in about the same amount of time as earth?
3. Which planet revolves around the sun in the shortest amount of time?
4. Which planet takes the longest time to make one revolution around the sun?
5. How has observing the planets changed since Galileo's time?

EXTENSIONS

Enrichment

Activity

Students with artistic skills would enjoy creating a solar system mobile using clay models. Have them follow these directions:

A. Cover the clay models with a papier-mâché mixture.

B. When each covering has dried and hardened, paint it to resemble one of the planets. Add rings to Saturn and Uranus. This can be done by cutting the rings out of paper, placing the point of a long sewing needle through them and then into the model.

C. Tape one end of a piece of string to each model and the other end to the bottom wire of a hanger.

SECTION REVIEW

Answers to Questions

1. a. Neptune, **b.** Jupiter, **c.** Saturn, **d.** Uranus, **e.** Jupiter

2. Mars

3. Mercury

4. Pluto

5. Telescopes are more powerful and space probes such as *Voyager 2* sent back many photographs of the planets.

SUGGESTED WORKSHEET MASTERS
pp. T–291o,p

Since our solar system is dynamic, objects other than planets have been observed, labeled and examined over thousands of years. As telescopes were improved, these bodies became better understood. Asteroids, minor planets that are mainly found in orbit between Mars and Jupiter, range in size from the size of a grain of sand to 800 km (500 mi). Those that are not in the asteroid belt have irregular orbits that take them into the orbits of other planets. Asteroids that pass into the earth's orbit are called Apollo asteroids.

Traveling from beyond the orbit of Pluto and toward the sun are objects composed of frozen gases, small rocks, and dust. They are called comets and as they come closer to the sun the frozen gases become vaporized. The comet consists of a head or coma (dust and gas surrounding the frozen core) and a tail (dust and gas that are pushed away from the head). The tail of a comet always points away from the sun.

Meteoroids are bits of matter which, when they enter the earth's atmosphere at about 120 km (75 mi), become visible. As they pass through our atmosphere, they burn up and are then referred to as meteors. Meteors may be pieces of comets or asteroids or may be composed of the dust that trails a comet. The latter is referred to as a "meteorite shower" and predictions for their occurrences are listed in the newspaper. When pieces fall to the earth, they are called meteorites. The largest fell at Hoba West in Southwest Africa (Namibia) and was recorded to be 60 metric tons (66 short tons).

MATERIALS

basketball, clay, meter stick

16-3.

Asteroids, Meteors, and Comets

3

Meteoroids: Chunks of iron, nickel, and other materials that move through space.

Meteor: A burning meteoroid.

Meteorite: A meteoroid that lands on a surface.

What caused the hole in the ceiling the man below is looking at? The chunk of metal on the right crashed through the roof of someone's home! Millions of tons of this material enter the earth's atmosphere each year. When you finish this section, you should be able to:

☐ **A.** Identify three types of objects other than planets that move through our solar system.
☐ **B.** Describe each type of object and where each is found.

   Meteoroids (mee-tee-er-oydz) are chunks of iron, nickel, and other materials that move through space. Millions of tons of *meteoroids* enter the earth's atmosphere each year. Most burn up as they move through our atmosphere. The light they cause can be seen across the sky. People call them shooting stars. A shooting star is really a **meteor** (mee-tee-or). Some meteoroids actually hit the earth's surface. When the material lands, it is called a **meteorite**. Most *meteorites* that strike the surface are very small. The one shown below is about the size of a grapefruit. Now and then a large one hits the earth. Our moon is also hit by meteorites. Because the moon has no atmosphere, they do not burn up. Many more meteorites hit the surface. They form craters.

 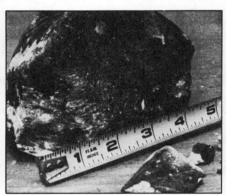

322

BASIC TEACHING PLAN

MOTIVATION

Encounters with comets, asteroids and large meteorites are rare. However, every day the earth "bumps" into approximately 100 million meteorites and billions of micro-meteorites. When added together, these particles contribute two to four million tons of matter to the earth each year.

DEVELOPMENT

1 **Teaching Tips** — If meteorites have hit the earth since it formed more than 3m (10 ft) of material have been added to its surface.
2 **Teaching Tips** — It is believed that a huge meteorite hit the moon over 800 years ago and that there is an irregularity in the moon's rotation as a result. This theory is based on an account by English monks that describes a "flaming torch" that "leapt" from a crescent moon.
3 **Skill Development** — Students learn to *classify* celestial bodies that roam through space and occasionally become visible to us.

ACTIVITY

Making a model solar system

A. Obtain the following materials: basketball, clay, meter stick.

B. The chart lists the nine planets. It also lists scale numbers to use in making a solar system model. For each planet, make a ball of clay that measures across the number shown for the model scale.

C. When all the planet models are complete, go outside to the schoolyard with the models. Have a classmate stand at one end of the yard and hold the basketball. The basketball represents the sun. Have another classmate stand 12 m from the "sun" and hold up the Mercury model.

D. Measure the distances from the "sun" for each planet shown on the chart.

　1. What planets did not fit in your schoolyard?

　2. Where would you put the asteroids?

　3. What would the path of a comet be like?

　4. Based on your model, which planet do you think we probably know the least about? Explain your answer.

Planet	Model scale	Distance scale
Mercury	1 mm	12 m
Venus	2 mm	22 m
Earth	2 mm	30 m
Mars	1 mm	46 m
Jupiter	28 mm	155 m
Saturn	26 mm	285 m
Uranus	10 mm	574 m
Neptune	9 mm	899 m
Pluto	1 mm	1,191 m

323

ACTIVITY

Skill Development — *Comparing and Contrasting, Measuring, Predicting*

Teaching Tips — The latter parts of this activity will require the students to go outside into the school yard. If this is not possible, you may wish to consider using a long corridor.

Answers to Questions — 1. This will depend on the length of the school yard. Saturn, Uranus, Neptune, and Pluto will probably be outside the school yard. 2. Between Mars and Jupiter. 3. Comets follow an orbit around the sun. They travel from beyond the outer planets towards the sun. 4. Pluto. It is very far from our planet.

Enrichment
Research — Library

One of the most famous collisions of a comet with the earth occurred on June 30, 1908, along the Tunguska River in Siberia. The blast was seen at a distance of 750 km (466 mi) and felt as far away as 80 km (50 mi). Barometers in England were affected by the explosion. Students could investigate further effects of this comet's collision and how scientists reached their conclusions about the reason for its immense effects.

Enrichment
Science Skills — Recording Data

Periodic comets are those that are trapped in smaller orbits around the sun. For this reason, they make regular and predictable appearances. Using the following list, students could prepare bar graphs showing the periods of orbit: Encke (3.30 years); Honda - Mrkos - Pajdusakova (5.22 years); Giacobini - Zinner (6.42 years); Linlay (6.90 years); Borrelly (7.02 years); Faye (7.41 years); Tuttle 1 (13.61 years); Westphal (61.73 years); Halley (76.04 years). Students could do research to find the year each of these comets was first sighted and the year when each is predicted to appear again.

Asteroids: Rocky objects that orbit the sun.

Comets: Objects that are made of ice and rock particles and orbit the sun.

If you traveled between Mars and Jupiter, you would see a strange sight. You would see thousands of rocky objects much smaller than planets. They are called **asteroids** (as-ter-oydz). About 1,600 *asteroids* have been observed and named. The largest asteroid is less than 1,000 kilometers (600 miles) long. Some scientists think that asteroids are pieces of a planet that broke apart. Others think asteroids are pieces of material that will someday form a planet. Each asteroid has its own orbit around the sun. **4**

Comets are objects that are made of ice and rock particles and orbit the sun. *Comets* travel from beyond the outer planets toward the sun. As a comet comes close to the sun, some of the ice changes into gas. The gas is pushed away from the comet. It forms a tail. The tail of a comet always streams away from the sun. Each time a comet comes near the sun, more of its ice changes to gas. It gets smaller and smaller. Comets are named for the people who discover them. The most well-known comet is Halley's comet. **5**

Section Review

Main Ideas: Meteoroids are objects that travel through the solar system. Some become meteors or meteorites. Comets made of ice and rock particles orbit around the sun. Asteroids located between Mars and Jupiter also orbit around the sun.

Questions: Answer in complete sentences.

1. What is a meteoroid? What is a meteorite?
2. Give two possible explanations for the asteroids.
3. Where are the asteroids found?
4. How can you tell where the sun is in a picture of a comet?
5. A comet goes around the sun three times. The third time it is smaller. Explain.

324

4 **Teaching Tips** — The largest asteroid, Ceres, was first sighted in the 1800s and thought to be a planet. The asteroid Icanus travels to within Mercury's orbit. The Apollo asteroids pass within the earth's orbit.
5 **Teaching Tips** — Comets whose orbits come too close to the sun can split apart causing a meteor shower. The regularly occurring Biela's comet was seen until the year 1846, when it split. In 1852, the comet reappeared as a double comet, disappeared, then caused a meteor shower in 1872.

SECTION REVIEW
Answers to Questions
1. A meteoroid is a chunk of metal that moves through space. The name given to a meteoroid when it hits the earth.
2. Asteroids may be pieces of a planet that broke apart or pieces of material that will someday form a planet.
3. Between Mars and Jupiter
4. The sun is always in the opposite direction from the comet's tail.
5. As it comes near the sun, more ice melts, making it smaller.

Does this photo of a *space shuttle* lift-off look familiar? Right now only people with special training can take trips in it. But in the future, people without special training will travel in it. They will be able to get on board, buckle up their safety belts, and blast off. Imagine yourself going on a journey that will be out of this world! When you finish this section, you should be able to:

☐ **A.** Describe what a rocket is.
☐ **B.** Describe the events that occur when a space shuttle is launched and returns to earth.

People have been interested in space travel for many years. The thought of breaking free of the earth's atmosphere and exploring the solar system is an exciting one. The dreams of space travel did not come true until this century.

SECTION BACKGROUND

Modern space exploration is made possible through the use of reaction motors, called rockets. Rockets emit hot, expanding gases rearward, which produce a reaction that moves the rocket forward. Rockets are used to place artificial satellites in orbit around the earth. Artificial satellites are used to photograph and measure features on the earth, gather data for weather forecasting, and as devices that can receive and retransmit electromagnetic waves used in radio, television, and telephone communication.

Rockets have also been used to transport humans to the moon and return them to earth. In recent years, rockets have been used to carry the space shuttle orbiter into earth orbit. Future uses for the shuttle include transporting people and equipment back and forth between the earth and a space colony.

MATERIALS

325

BASIC TEACHING PLAN

MOTIVATION

If you have retained any magazine photographs or related materials from space shuttle launchings, show each item and ask the students to describe what they observe. Ask the class how many would like to go on a trip on board the space shuttle and why they would want to make such a trip. Discuss the preparations that would have to be made. Allow the students to use their imaginations. Find out the actual sizes of space shuttle components and go outside with your class and measure off the various sizes.

EXTENSIONS

Application
Activity

Students who enjoy model building could bring in assembled spacecraft models for display to the class. Models could be compared with respect to the purposes of the spacecraft and their success in fulfilling their purposes. Data on the scale of the model displays should be included.

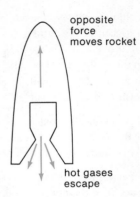

1

opposite force moves rocket

fuel tank

fuel burns

hot gases escape

Rocket: An engine that burns fuel and moves forward by pushing exhaust backward.

Travel in space presented a big problem. How could an object get away from the pull of the earth? What was needed was a special engine. It would have to produce enough force to lift a spacecraft weighing many tons. Airplane engines use oxygen. There is no oxygen in space. So a spacecraft needs an engine that works without oxygen. Finding the right kind of engine took many years. Modern scientists used a very old idea—the **rocket**.

A *rocket* is an engine that burns fuel and moves forward by pushing exhaust backward. Rockets operate by burning fuel in a tube. When the fuel burns, the hot gases produced are allowed to escape in one direction only. This causes a force to push in the opposite direction. Rockets do not need the presence of air. Any oxygen they need is in the fuel mixture that they burn. **2**

Rockets can be used to place satellites, such as the one at left, in orbit. The rocket provides the power for the satellite to get into space. Once the satellite is far enough away from earth, the rocket falls off. The satellite then circles around earth on its own. **3**

In 1957, the Soviet Union used a rocket to put the first spacecraft into orbit around earth. It was called *Sputnik I*. One year later, the United States sent a spacecraft

326

DEVELOPMENT

1 **Teaching Tips** — To demonstrate the action of a rocket engine, blow up a balloon and release it. Inform your class that the action of the gases pushing backward causes a forward reaction by the balloon. Also you could buy a small water powered rocket available at toy stores. They cost just a few dollars. These rockets come with a small pump that allows you to force water under pressure into the rocket. You can take students outside for the launch of the water rocket.

2 **Skill Development** — Newton's law of action-reaction is a basic application of *cause* and *effect*.

3 **Teaching Tips** — Students could research additional details with respect to the exploration of the moon. Information could include types of rockets used, the duration of various trips, and discoveries made and special cameras, equipment, apparel and foods taken on space explorations.

named *Explorer I* into space. These events marked the start of the space age. Since then, powerful rockets have placed heavier satellites into orbit. They have carried astronauts to the moon. Rockets have launched space probes to fly near the other planets. Powerful computers help these spacecraft to stay on course.

Large spacecraft are very expensive to build. The United States has developed a spacecraft that is powerful and can be reused. It is the **space shuttle**. The *space shuttle* is different from other spacecraft. It can do three important things. It takes off like a rocket. It can fly in orbit around the earth like a rocket. Most important of all, it can land like an airplane. The shuttle is used to place satellites in orbit. It can also repair satellites that are in orbit. Someday the shuttle will carry people to orbiting space stations. Best of all, the same shuttle will fly to space and back more than 100 times.

The drawing shows the launching of a shuttle and its return to earth. Refer to it as you read. The shuttle is made of two parts: the **booster** and the **orbiter**. The *booster* contains large rockets. The *orbiter* looks like an airplane. The orbiter is attached to the top of the rockets.

Space shuttle: A reusable spacecraft that can orbit the earth and return like an airplane.

Booster: Powerful rockets that help spacecraft reach orbit.

Orbiter: The part of the shuttle that orbits and returns to the earth.

4

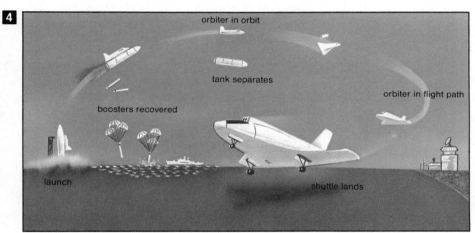

orbiter in orbit

tank separates

boosters recovered

orbiter in flight path

launch

shuttle lands

327

---

4   Skill Development — The text information and accompanying *illustration* place a heavy emphasis on the process of launching, orbiting, and landing during a space shuttle mission. You may wish to have the students use the information as the basis for preparing a *series* of diagrams that show each major step. When they finish, they should place their diagrams in scrambled order and exchange them with partners for the purpose of trying to put them back into proper *sequence*.

EXTENSIONS

Application
Science Skills — Predicting, Hypothesizing

Students could prepare a report describing the materials that they would include in a space station that would form the basis for an eventual city in orbit. As background for this, they should attempt to locate artists' conceptions of the nature of space colonies. They could make a hypothesis about the likelihood of space colonies being developed within the next 100 years. They should include a discussion of the evidence that supports their hypothesis.

At lift-off the rockets push the orbiter about 40 kilometers (25 miles). There they separate from the orbiter. The rockets fall to the ocean by parachute. They are picked up, cleaned, and used again.

The orbiter keeps flying, using its own engines. The fuel for this part of the trip comes from large tanks. The fuel tanks drop off as the fuel is used up. Then the orbiter does what its name says it will do. It enters an orbit around earth.

When its mission is over, the shuttle flies back to earth like an airplane. The orbiter lands without any engine power. Small rockets get the orbiter on a path to the landing area. The pilot carefully aims for the runway. The pilot flies to the surface of earth without power. These pilots are experts. Can you imagine landing an object weighing 68,000 kilograms (150,000 pounds) going 335 kilometers per hour (210 miles per hour)? They only get one try. There is no way of getting back into the air once they have started down.

Section Review

Main Ideas: Rockets provide the power to place satellites in orbit. The space shuttle is placed into orbit by rockets and lands like an airplane.

Questions: Answer in complete sentences.

1. What causes a rocket to move forward?
2. What makes the space shuttle different from other spacecraft?
3. What is a booster?
4. What are some uses of the space shuttle?
5. Describe the lift-off, orbiting, and landing of the space shuttle. Then answer these questions.
   a. What drops from the shuttle as it goes into orbit?
   b. What part of the shuttle goes into orbit?

SECTION REVIEW

Answers to Questions

1. The escape of hot gases backwards causes the rocket to move forward or in an opposite direction.
2. The space shuttle can land like an airplane.
3. A booster is the part of the shuttle that contains the rockets.
4. It can place satellites in orbit, repair satellites in orbit, and carry people to orbiting space stations.
5. The shuttle lifts off with the help of its booster rockets. The booster separates and parachutes down to earth for recovery. The orbiter flies on its own power and enters its orbit. When its mission is complete, the orbiter lands on earth like an airplane. a. booster rockets and fuel tanks, b. orbiter

SUGGESTED WORKSHEET MASTER
p. T–291q

CHAPTER REVIEW

Science Words: Think of a word for each blank. List the letters **a** through **r** on paper. Write the word next to each letter.

The ___a___ is made of the sun and the nine ___b___. The planets travel in ___c___ around the sun. ___d___ is the planet closest to the sun. The planet often called the earth's twin is ___e___. It is the ___f___ planet from the sun. Our own planet, earth, is the ___g___ planet from the sun. Just beyond us is ___h___ which appears red. The largest planet is ___i___ which has 16 ___j___. Beyond that planet is ___k___ with its thousand rings. The last three planets, ___l___, ___m___, and ___n___ are so far away from us that we do not know very much about them. Between the inner and outer planets are rocky objects called ___o___ that orbit around the sun. ___p___ are bright objects with tails that speed through space. We have learned much from the samples and photos sent back from the ___q___. People will get into space on the ___r___, a reusable spacecraft.

Questions: Answer in complete sentences.

1. Was Ptolemy's idea about the movement of the sun and planets correct? Explain.
2. List the names of the inner and outer planets in order, starting with the planet closest to the sun.
3. How has space travel helped astronomers learn about the solar system?
4. Compare the planets Venus and Jupiter in three ways: size, distance from sun, and number of moons.
5. What are the parts of a comet? What happens to a comet each time it goes around the sun?
6. You're at the controls of the space shuttle and are about to leave your orbit and head for home. What will you depend on to get you safely to earth?

329

EXTENSIONS

Enrichment
Research — Library

Students can write to the National Aeronautics and Space Administration, 400 Maryland Avenue, S.W., Washington, D.C. 20546, to receive additional information about the space shuttle and the *Mercury*, *Gemini*, and *Apollo* space programs.

Reinforcement
Activity

A series of review cards could be prepared to check the students' understanding of the chapter. The first card for each term or concept could include a clue about the object. Subsequent cards would build on this initial card. These cards could be prepared by the students and used for group or individual purposes. Drawings could also be used as clues.

CHAPTER REVIEW

Science Words
a. solar system   b. planets   c. orbits   d. Mercury   e. Venus
f. second   g. third   h. Mars   i. Jupiter   j. moons (satellites)
k. Saturn   l. Uranus   m. Neptune   n. Pluto   o. asteroids
p. comets   q. space probes   r. space shuttles

Answers to Questions
1. No. He thought the planets revolved around the earth.
2. Mercury, Venus, earth, Mars, Jupiter, Saturn, Uranus, Neptune, Pluto
3. Instruments have taken pictures and made maps of some planets. The *Viking* space probe landed on Mars and obtained soil samples.
4. Venus: 12,100 km diameter; 108 million km from sun; no moons. Jupiter: 143,200 km diameter; 778 million km from sun; 16 moons.
5. The part made of ice and rock particles and the tail made of gas
6. Small rockets direct the orbiter on a path to the landing area.

SUGGESTED WORKSHEET MASTER
p. T–291r

SUGGESTED TEST MASTERS
pp. T–291f,g

CHAPTER OBJECTIVES

1. Explain the ways in which stars differ from one another.
2. Explain a hypothesis that describes the formation of stars.
3. Explain what quasars and black holes are.
4. Identify five constellations and explain the reason for the apparent movement of stars.
5. Classify galaxies and explain three theories for the formation of the universe.

SECTION BACKGROUND

Stars begin as clouds of gas and dust called nebulae. The particles present in a nebula attract one another and in some cases move closer and closer together to form larger masses. As this occurs, the temperature of the nebula increases, hydrogen becomes converted to helium, energy is released into space, and a new star is created. Stars differ in size, color, and magnitude. The color of a star is related to its temperature.

Among the instruments used to study objects in space are the refracting telescope (contains a convex lens that bends the light from a distant object) and the reflecting telescope (contains a concave mirror that reflects the light from a distant object). Radio telescopes record radio waves emitted by some distant objects. A computer changes the waves into a pattern that can be studied.

MATERIALS

graph paper, colored pencils or markers

**Exceptional Student
IEP Chapter Goal**

At the end of this chapter, the student will state the relationships between stars, constellations, and galaxies.

THE STARS AND BEYOND

17-1.

The Stars

330

Do you ever look up at the stars and wonder about them? On a clear night stars may seem very close. They are actually very, very far away. It takes years for the light from even the closest stars to reach us. When you finish this section, you should be able to:

BASIC TEACHING PLAN
MOTIVATION

Ask the students what they would notice if at this very instant all the stars in the photograph stopped producing energy. Most students will say that the stars would suddenly stop twinkling and the sky would be all black. However, some students will realize that there is a delay between the moment when a star produces energy (i.e., light) and when the energy reaches earth. This disparity should provoke discussion. If no student mentions this, you should. This should set the background for the discussion of light-years that begins this section. For your information, a light year is the distance that light can travel in one year. If, for example, a star is 8.8 light years from the earth, it will take light 8.8 years to travel from the star to earth. The closest star to earth (other than the sun) is Proxima Centauri—4.27 light years away.

☐ **A.** Explain how the distance to a star from earth is measured.

☐ **B.** Describe three ways in which stars differ from each other.

☐ **C.** Describe the events that take place in the life of a star.

Imagine that you are traveling from one city to another. What units would you use to measure the distance? You would probably use kilometers or miles. However, the stars, except for the sun, are so far away that kilometers or miles are too small to use. Instead, a star's distance from earth is measured by the time it takes for the star's light to reach earth. Light travels at 300,000 kilometers per second (186,000 miles per second). The distance that light travels in one year is known as a **light-year**. This is how to figure out how many kilometers are in a *light-year*: Find the number of seconds that are in a year. Then multiply that number times 300,000 kilometers. You'll get a very large number. Do you see why light-years are used instead of kilometers?

The chart below lists the names of four stars. Next to each name is that star's distance from earth. The light leaving the star **Sirius** (**seer**-ee-us) will take 8.6 years to travel to earth. Which star listed is farthest from earth? How far away is it? Which star is closest? **Proxima Centauri** (**prox**-ih-muh sen-**tor**-ee) is the closest star to earth, other than the sun.

Star	Distance from Earth
Proxima Centauri	4.27 light-years
Sirius	8.6 light-years
Betelgeuse	520 light-years
Polaris	1,086 light-years

Stars differ from each other in three ways: color, brightness, and size.

Light-year: The distance light travels in one year.

How many seconds are in one year?
1 minute has 60 seconds
x
1 hour has 60 minutes
x
1 day has 24 hours
x
1 year has 365 days
? seconds in 1 year

331

DEVELOPMENT

1 **Text Questions** — How many seconds are in one year? *31,536,000 seconds in one year*; The number of kilometers in one light-year is *9,460,800,000,000*

2 **Text Questions** — Which star is farthest from earth? *Polaris*

3 **Skill Development** — You can now capitalize on the motivation by asking students to refer to the chart and make a *hypothesis* about how long it would take us to know that Sirius and Polaris stopped producing energy. (The hypothesis should be 8.6 years and 1,086 years respectively.

What color are the stars you see at night? You probably said white. Stars may be blue, white, yellow, orange, or red. Stars differ in color because of their different temperatures. Look at the flame shown. A hot gas is producing the flame. What colors do you see? The hottest part of the flame is at its bottom. What color is the bottom of the flame? If you said blue, you are right. The cooler part of the flame is orange. **4**

Stars are balls of hot gases. Like the flame, stars with a high temperature are blue or blue-white in color. Red stars have lower temperatures. Yellow and orange stars have medium temperatures. The chart below lists the names of some stars, their colors, and their surface temperatures. What color star is our sun? **5**

6

Star	Color	Temperature
Rigel	blue-white	12,000°C (21,600°F)
Sirius	white	10,500°C (18,900°F)
Sun	yellow	5,500°C (9,900°F)
Arcturus	orange	4,200°C (7,600°F)
Antares	red	3,000°C (5,400°F)

Magnitude: The brightness of a star as seen from earth.

Dwarfs: Small stars.

Giants: Stars that swell and become large.

Supergiants: Very large stars.

When you look at the stars at night, some stars look brighter than others. The brightness of a star is called its **magnitude** (mag-nih-tood). A star's *magnitude* depends on its size, temperature, and distance from earth. The brightest star in the night sky is Sirius, although Proxima Centauri is the closest star to earth. What star is the brightest in the daytime sky? **7**

Stars are different sizes. The smallest stars are a little larger than earth. Small stars are called **dwarfs**. Stars that swell and become large are called **giants**. And of course very large stars are called **supergiants**.

By observing many stars, some scientists have made a very interesting hypothesis. They think that stars come into being, exist for a while, and then die. Stars begin as giant clouds of dust and gas. All the parts of the giant

332

4 **Text Questions** — What colors do you see? *Blue and orange*
5 **Text Questions** — What color star is our sun? *Yellow*
6 **Skill Development** — Have the students *read* and review the *chart* and make up questions to ask one another that require an analysis of the chart. For example "I am a star that is 11,900°C. Could I be a red star?" *No.*
7 **Text Questions** — What star is brightest in the daytime sky? *Sun*

ACTIVITY

Graphing star temperature data

A. Obtain these materials: sheet of graph paper, colored pencils or markers.

B. Prepare a bar graph that shows the temperature of stars and the colors of their light. Use the chart for the information.

Star color	Temperature
Red	4,000°C
Yellow	6,000°C
White	9,000°C
Blue	20,000°C

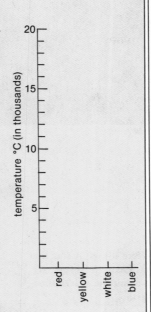

C. Along the left side of your graph, show the temperature. Along the bottom line, show the color of the light from the star. Use the graph shown as a guide. Color the bar so it is the color of the light from stars at that temperature.

D. Use the chart of stars shown on page 332 to answer the following.

1. Where would each of the following stars be in your graph? Rigel, Sirius, Sun, Arcturus, Antares.

2. Place a black dot to show them. Label each.

cloud pull on all the other parts. The particles of matter move closer and closer together. As this happens, the temperature of the cloud rises. For many stars, the temperature reaches about 10 million degrees. The cloud begins to glow. It keeps shrinking in size. Inside it, nuclear reactions take place. Energy is released into space. Some of the energy reaches us on earth. We see the light glowing from the star.

333

ACTIVITY

Skill Development — *Recording Data, Inferring*

Teaching Tips — You may wish to select some students to do this activity on transparency film, using marking pens. This group can then display the results of their work as part of the post-activity discussion. Students can do research to identify other stars that have different temperatures and colors. This group can add these stars to their graphs.

Answers to Questions — 1. Rigel—between blue and white; Sirius—toward top of yellow; Arcturus—slightly above red; Antares—red.

EXTENSIONS

Application
Activity

Students could build and use spectroscopes. They will need a toothpaste carton, a sheet of black construction paper, a 1 × 2 cm (1/2 × 1 in) piece of diffraction grating, tape, scissors, and a paper punch. The diffraction grating is available in rolls from Edmund Scientific Company, 300 Edscorp Building, Barrington, NJ 08007. The students should follow these directions:

A. Cover the toothpaste carton with the construction paper.

B. Cut a slit about 1.5 mm (1/16 in.) wide in the middle of the flap at one end of the carton.

C. Punch a hole in the center of the other end of the carton.

D. Place the diffraction grating over the hole so that the long dimension of the grating is parallel to the slit at the other end of the box.

E. Point the slit at a light bulb, and look through the hole over which you taped the diffraction grating. The spectrum emitted by the light bulb can be viewed. Caution the students not to attempt to view the sun through the spectroscope.

Exceptional Student
Visually Impaired

Depending on the degree of impairment, the student may not be able to include colors on the graph. To modify this activity, have the student use yarn to make a three-dimensional bar graph.

T–333

Application
Activity

You may be able to expand your students' interest in astronomy if you can locate an amateur astronomy club or astronomer in your community. Check with high school earth/space science teachers for leads in this area.

If you can locate an amateur astronomer invite him or her to class to speak to the students. Encourage the person to bring astronomical instruments used for observing distant objects.

Prior to the visit, have students prepare a list of questions to ask their guest.

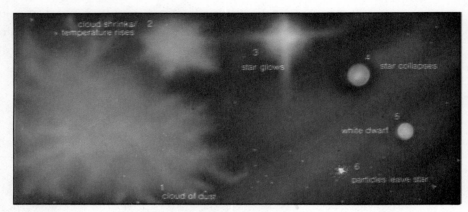

White dwarf: A star that has begun to shrink. It is about the size of the earth.

Quasar: An object about the size of a star that gives off huge amounts of energy.

334

8 The energy of a star comes from the reactions that change hydrogen to helium. Our sun produces energy in the same way. As long as there are hydrogen and high **9** temperatures, the star releases energy. When the hydrogen is all used up, great changes take place.

One thing that happens is that the inside of the star collapses. The star shrinks in size. It becomes a special kind of dwarf star called a **white dwarf**. A *white dwarf* is about the size of the earth. The white dwarf's energy moves outward into space. The magnitude of the dwarf star gets less and less. It gets dimmer and dimmer. The star is dying. As the star dies, gas and other materials leave it. It takes hundreds of millions of years for a star to be born and die as a white dwarf. The matter and energy that were part of the white dwarf go into space. Someday the matter from the old star may come into contact with matter from other stars. The particles will be drawn together slowly. The process will begin. The remains of old stars become the raw material for new stars.

Have you ever heard of **quasars** (**kway**-zarz)? They are objects about the size of stars that move very rapidly. They give out huge amounts of energy. One *quasar* may give out as much energy as hundreds of millions of stars. Quasars are billions of light-years away.

DEVELOPMENT

8 **Teaching Tips** — Stars produce their energy by nuclear fusion. Essentially the nuclei of hydrogen atoms combine to form a helium nucleus. The helium nucleus that is formed contains less matter than the hydrogen nuclei that combined to form it. Some of the matter that seems to have disappeared was changed into energy that flows to the star's surface. The light that we see is part of that energy. The amount of energy that is produced is calculated using Einstein's famous equation, $E = mc^2$, where "m" is the mass that is converted to energy and "c" is the speed of light. The superscript "2" indicates that the speed of light is squared (multiplied by itself) in the calculation. It is possible to see that large amounts of energy are liberated. In the case of the sun, if only one percent of its hydrogen mass is converted into helium, it would shine at its present rate for another billion years.

9 **Teaching Tips** — If you do get into a discussion of nuclear fusion, you may wish to tell your students that the sun converts about 600,000,000 tons of hydrogen into energy each second.

Quasars were first discovered in 1961. Scientists 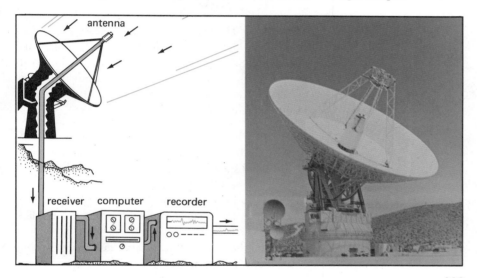 noticed that large amounts of energy were coming from a certain place in the sky. The only way to explain that energy was that it was a new object. They named it a quasar. The energy from quasars was discovered not by looking, but by listening. Quasars give out radio waves. Radio waves can be picked up with a **radio telescope**.

A *radio telescope* is shaped like a soup bowl. In its center is an antenna. The antenna is pointed toward the sky. The radio telescope records sounds made by such objects as quasars. The radio waves travel through space. They are picked up by the antenna. The antenna passes the waves to a receiver. The receiver changes the waves into a pattern. The pattern is drawn on a roll of paper in the recorder. The pattern tells astronomers the position of the object. One of the largest radio telescopes is at Arecibo, Puerto Rico. It is shown in the photograph.

There is another object in space that is even stranger than a quasar. It is known as a **black hole**. Scientists think that when some giant stars collapse, all their star material

Radio telescope: A telescope that picks up and records sounds from space.

Black hole: An area in space from which no light escapes.

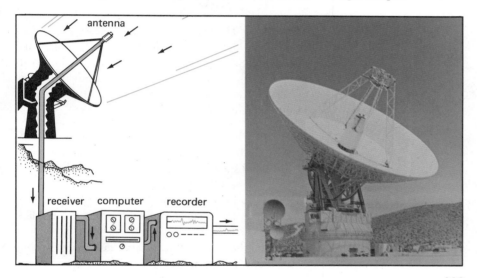

antenna

receiver   computer   recorder

335

🔟 **Skill Development** — Students learn the *sequencing* involved in the birth and death of stars. It would probably be a good idea to have students write down the *vocabulary terms* "quasar" and "black hole" and their definitions at this point. Also, more advanced students should be strongly encouraged to do some of their own library research to develop further understanding of each of these astronomical phenomena.

1️⃣1️⃣ **Teaching Tips** — If you have a world map available in the classroom, ask a student to locate Arecibo, Puerto Rico. Tell the students that the Arecibo telescope is not on top of a building or pedestal, but, rather, in a natural land formation (a bowl) that is slightly below ground level.

EXTENSIONS

Enrichment
Research — Library

It is known that 97 percent of the mass of a star consists of hydrogen and helium. The remaining three percent of the mass includes elements such as argon, carbon, chlorine, iron, magnesium, neon, nitrogen, oxygen, silicon, and sulfur. The ages of stars can be determined by the percentage of lighter mass elements (hydrogen and helium) that they contain. A younger star (Population I star) contains more of the heavier elements while an older star (Population II star) mainly consists of hydrogen and helium. Students could research various stars to determine their categories.

is forced into a space less than 3 kilometers (about 2 miles) across. This area has so much matter that it pulls anything nearby into it. A *black hole* can even pull in light. This means that a black hole cannot be seen. Scientists think black holes exist because there are areas of space where star material seems to disappear. This discovery was made in 1971. The black hole was named Cygnus (**sig-nus**) X-1. A spacecraft discovered X rays coming from the place where matter was disappearing. X rays are thought to be given off when matter is pulled into a black hole.

The idea of a black hole is very exciting. Some scientists think that black holes may be like strange bridges. They may connect one part of space with another. If this is so, then anything that is sucked into a black hole may reappear someplace else. Maybe the "time travel" or "space warps" that you may have seen in science fiction movies are like black holes.

Section Review

Main Ideas: The distance to a star is measured in light-years. Stars differ from each other in size, color, and magnitude. Some stars seem to go through a definite pattern of birth, existence, and death. There are some objects, such as quasars and black holes, that we do not know very much about.

Questions: Answer in complete sentences.

1. Why are light-years and not kilometers used to measure the distance to a star?
2. How do stars differ in size and color?
3. What is a radio telescope?
4. Describe the characteristics of quasars and black holes.
5. Explain the steps that some stars go through as they are born, exist, and die.

336

SUGGESTED WORKSHEET MASTER
p. T–291s

SECTION REVIEW

Answers to Questions

1. They are used because of the great distances of stars from our planet.
2. Small stars are called dwarfs. Stars that swell and become large are called giants. Very large stars are supergiants. Stars can be red, yellow, white or blue in color depending on their temperatures.
3. A radio telescope picks up radio waves from distant objects in space and changes them into a pattern that astronomers can read.
4. A quasar is an object the size of a star that gives out large amounts of energy. A black hole is an area of space that light cannot escape from.
5. Stars are formed when the particles in giant clouds of gas and dust in the universe attract and pull closer together. When this happens, the temperature rises and the cloud starts to glow. Energy is produced and released into space. When its hydrogen fuel is used up, the star shrinks in size becoming a white dwarf. The matter and energy that formed the star leave and may combine to form a new star.

Have you ever done follow-the-dot puzzles? If you have, then you will like learning about the patterns that people see in the night sky. For years people have imagined that the twinkling dots in the sky were the outlines of real objects. When you finish this section, you should be able to:

☐ **A.** Identify five groups of star patterns.
☐ **B.** Explain the cause for the apparent movement of stars.

Ancient people thought that the skies were a magical place. They thought that the stars formed part of the outlines of kings and queens. They saw magical beasts and even giant objects.

People saw what they were familiar with. Hunters saw animals. Other people saw famous heroes from stories. Beliefs about the star patterns were passed down from one group of people to the next. Groups of stars that form patterns in the sky are called **constellations** (kahn-steh-lay-shunz). There are 88 *constellations*. The patterns

Constellations: Groups of stars that form patterns in the sky.

337

SECTION BACKGROUND

Over the many thousands of years during which people have observed the heavens, human imagination has tended to group stars into patterns, or constellations. In recent times, astronomers have divided the sky into 88 areas. Each of these areas has been given a name based on a pattern of stars found within it.

The constellations seem to move across the night sky as the earth rotates. The constellations seen from earth also change with the seasons because the earth is in different places in space at different times of the year.

Polaris, the star situated almost above earth's North Pole, is the only star that does not seem to change in position. The constellations close to Polaris, such as the Big Dipper, remain above the horizon each night, while other constellations appear to rise and set.

MATERIALS

black construction paper, clear tape, flashlight, safety pin, scissors, shoe box, tracing paper

BASIC TEACHING PLAN

MOTIVATION

Prior to teaching this section (and without the students' knowledge), create a totally random pattern of dots on the chalkboard. Try to make at least 100 large dots. Cover the pattern with sheets of newsprint. When you begin this section, uncover your dots and ask the students if they can find any patterns within it. After they have indicated they have done this, tell them that you made the dots at random. This will serve as a good background for the explanation of the constellations that follows in the text.

EXTENSIONS

Reinforcement
Activity

The stars that make up the pattern of a constellation are at different distances from us. However, the pattern as seen from the earth appears to be on one plane. Using buttons, long pins, and a sponge covered with black paper, students could secure the buttons onto the sponge so that the buttons form a pattern when viewed overhead. By having students vary the length of the pins protruding from the sponge, the pattern of buttons will be random when viewed from the side.

Enrichment
Research — Library

Send some students to the library with instructions to find the myths from which the following names are borrowed: Cassiopeia, Cepheus, Andromeda, Perseus, and Cetus.

The students should report their findings to the class and include diagrams of the constellations for the class to observe.

Orion: A constellation that looks like a hunter.

Cassiopeia: A constellation.

Cygnus: A constellation that looks like a swan.

---

appear to look like animals, people, or objects. It takes a little imagination to see some of them.

Look at the three drawings of the sky shown below.

1 Look at the star patterns. The first pattern shows the constellation **Orion** (oh-**ry**-un). People think *Orion* looks like a hunter. The three stars across the center are supposed to be his belt. The small stars below his belt are his sword. The two stars above Orion's belt are his shoulders. The two stars at the bottom are the hunter's legs. The star at Orion's left shoulder is a red star. It is named Betelgeuse (**bet**-ul-jooz). The star at his right leg is a blue **2** **3** star. It is named Rigel (**ry**-jel). Which star is hotter, Betelgeuse or Rigel?

Another constellation is **Cassiopeia** (kas-ee-oh-**pay**-ah). People think the pattern forms the crown of the queen *Cassiopeia*. Other people see her chair. Look at the drawing of the queen. Do you see her crown?

The third drawing shows **Cygnus** (**sig**-nus). People think *Cygnus* looks like a swan. Do you? There is a very bright star in Cygnus called **Deneb** (**den**-eb). *Deneb* is a **4** white star. Is it hotter or cooler than Rigel?

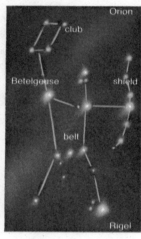

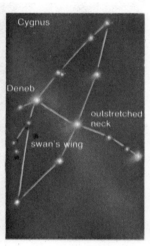

338

DEVELOPMENT

1 **Skill Development** — This section places a great deal of emphasis on *reading illustrations*. Be sure that the students focus their attention on the illustrations as the constellations are discussed. You may wish to emphasize the skill even further by providing additional photographs from reference books that show constellations.

2 **Text Questions** — Which star is hotter, Betelgeuse or Rigel? *Rigel*

3 **Skill Development** — Here is a good opportunity to see if the students have retained the *main ideas* of the previous section. Ask: How do you know Rigel is hotter than Betelgeuse? *Rigel is a blue star and Betelgeuse is a red star. Blue stars are hotter than red stars.*

4 **Text Questions** — Is it hotter or cooler than Rigel? *Deneb is a white star and is therefore cooler than the blue star Rigel.*

The constellations are not seen in the exact same place in the sky all night. They seem to move across the sky. The constellations seem to move because earth is rotating on its axis.

5

The constellations seen from earth in the winter are different from those seen in the summer. This occurs because earth is in different places in space at different times of the year. However, there are two constellations that can be seen all year in the Northern Hemisphere. They are the **Big Dipper** and **Little Dipper**. No matter where earth is, the North Pole is pointed toward these two constellations.

6

The *Big Dipper* and *Little Dipper* look like spoons or ladles. Look at the drawing below. The two stars at the end of the dipper of the Big Dipper are called *pointer stars*. An arrow drawn from these two stars will point to the last star of the handle of the Little Dipper. That star in the Little Dipper is called **Polaris** (poh-lar-is). *Polaris* is the North Star. Polaris is a star that does not seem to move. It is always above earth's North Pole. People use the North Star to tell their direction.

Big Dipper, Little Dipper: Constellations that are seen all year in the Northern Hemisphere.

7

Polaris: The North Star. A star always above earth's North Pole.

339

---

5 **Skill Development** — As the students work through this portion of the section, check their understanding of the earth's rotation and their ability to *make inferences* based on these facts. Ask: What is the direction of earth's rotation? *West to east.* Since the constellations seem to rise and set just as the sun does, in what direction do the constellations move? *East to west*

6 **Teaching Tips** — You may wish to tell the students that the Big Dipper and Little Dipper are called *circumpolar* constellations. This means that their apparent movement is around the north pole of the earth.

7 **Teaching Tips** — If your students are going to observe the stars, they should do so on a clear night when the moon is not in a visible phase, stand at a place where they will receive no glare from street or car lights, and use a flashlight to follow star maps. It is a good idea to cover the lamp of the flashlight with a piece of colored cellophane.

T–339

EXTENSIONS

Enrichment
Activity

Here is a challenge you may wish to pose to some of your students. Ask them to do research to find the answer to this riddle.

"I am a star. The Vikings called me the Iodestar, Navajos call me the Star That Does Not Move, some people call me the Pole Star. Who Am I?"

With a little effort, the student will find that the star is Polaris.

Application
Research — Library

Have students research the following nautical instruments to discover their importance to navigation at sea and exploration of the earth: cross-staff, magnetic compass, sextant, chronometer.

ACTIVITY

Making a constellation projector

A. Obtain these materials: black construction paper, clear tape, flashlight, safety pin, scissor, shoe box, tracing paper.
B. Cut out a square at one end of the shoe box. At the other end, cut out a circle so that the head of the flashlight fits into the hole.
C. Cut pieces of black paper and tracing paper that are slightly larger than the square opening.
D. On each sheet of tracing paper, trace one of the three groups of dots shown below.
E. Place each sheet of tracing paper over a piece of black paper.
F. Make a hole through each dot with an open safety pin so that the hole is made through the black paper, too.
G. Face that end of the box about 25 cm from a wall.
H. Darken the room. Turn on the flashlight.

1. What do you see on the wall?
2. What constellation is projected with the first star pattern?
3. What constellation is projected with the second?
4. What constellation is projected with the third?

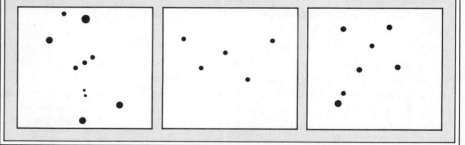

340

ACTIVITY

Skill Development — *Following Directions, Reading Illustrations, Classifying*

Teaching Tips — Remember to darken the room once students have prepared the apparatus. You may wish to have additional constellation diagrams available for those students who move rapidly through the activity to use as enrichment.

Answers to Questions — 1. A pattern formed by the white dots. 2. Orion. 3. Cassiopeia. 4. Cygnus

Section Review

Main Ideas: There are 88 constellations. People think the constellations look like people, animals, or objects. Orion, Cassiopeia, Cygnus, the Big Dipper, and the Little Dipper are constellations.

Questions: Answer in complete sentences.

1. What do we call stars that form patterns in the sky?
2. Why do constellations seem to move across the sky?
3. What is the main idea shown in the first drawing of this section?
4. Why do we see different constellations at different times of the year?
5. Name and describe the objects, people, or animals shown in the star patterns on the right.

People in Science

Susan Jocelyn Burnell

This young Irish scientist has made an important discovery in astronomy. While a student at Cambridge University in England, she studied the radio waves coming to earth from outer space. She used a giant antenna that received radio waves and sent the waves to a computer. The computer changed the waves into printed charts. Susan Burnell studied the charts for changes in the radio waves. One day she noticed some very suspicious wiggly lines on the charts. Radio waves were coming from deep space. Soon she noticed more of these waves. What Susan Burnell discovered were objects that scientists now call **neutron** (**nyoo-trahn**) stars. *Neutron* stars have the same weight as the sun but are only about the size of a city. They have a very strong magnetic field and spin quite rapidly.

341

SECTION REVIEW

Answers to Questions
1. Constellation
2. Because the earth rotates
3. People used to think that the stars formed patterns that stood for real people, kings, queens, gods, and goddesses.
4. Because the earth is in different places in space at different times of the year
5. Cassiopeia—the queen, Cygnus—the swan, the Big Dipper—shaped like a large spoon

SUGGESTED WORKSHEET MASTER
p. T–291t

SECTION BACKGROUND

The universe consists of more than 100 billion discrete groups of stars known as galaxies. Each galaxy contains billions of stars. Galaxies are classified with respect to their general appearance. There are irregular, elliptical, and spiral galaxies. Our galaxy, the Milky Way, is a spiral galaxy. Spiral galaxies have "arms" that rotate around a dense center.

The Milky Way is about 100,000 light-years across. The edges of the Milky Way are much thinner than its center. Our solar system is 30,000 light years from the center of the Milky Way. The thickness of the Milky Way in the region of our solar system is about 2,000 light years.

MATERIALS

graph paper, pencil

17-3.
The Universe

Galaxy: A group of billions of stars.

Have you seen any science fiction movies lately? You may have seen pictures of gigantic space platforms. On them people live and work. Plants are able to grow. The people wear normal clothing because there is oxygen there. Wouldn't it be fun to ride on one? You are on one! It is called earth and it is whizzing through space. When you finish this section, you should be able to:

☐ **A.** Describe the group of over 100 billion stars that includes our solar system.
☐ **B.** Classify three types of *galaxies* by their shapes.
☐ **C.** Explain three theories about how everything in space was formed.

As you travel on the space platform earth, you can see many stars and some planets. You are looking at part of a **galaxy** (gal-ux-ee).

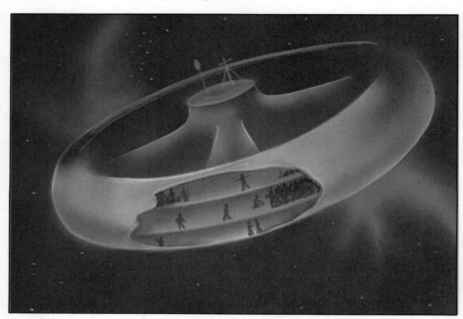

342

BASIC TEACHING PLAN
MOTIVATION

Make a series of color transparencies that you can lay over one another to take the students on an imaginary ride through space. This will help them see the relationship between the planet earth and the solar system, the solar system and our galaxy, and our galaxy and other galaxies. On the first transparency, show earth. On the second, show earth and the solar system. On the next, show the solar system as a dot in the Milky Way galaxy (use the illustrations of the spiral Milky Way in this section as a reference.) On the next, show the universe as a place that has possibly 100 billion galaxies.

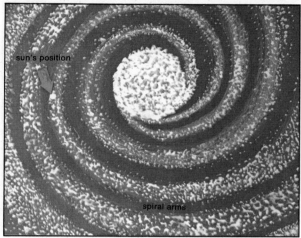

sun's position

spiral arms

A *galaxy* is a group of billions of stars. The earth is in the **Milky Way** Galaxy. The *Milky Way* contains about 100 billion stars, including our sun. Look at the drawings above. From the side, the Milky Way is shaped like a huge disc with a bulge at its center. From above, it appears to have arms that spiral around the center. That is why the Milky Way is called a spiral galaxy. The distance from one edge of the Milky Way to the other is about 100,000 light-years. Our solar system is about 30,000 light-years from the center of the Milky Way. Look at the drawings again. The arrows point to the position of the sun in the solar system.

You are moving around the center of the Milky Way at 1,000,000 kilometers per hour (620,000 miles per hour). At that speed it would take you about one second to travel from Los Angeles to San Diego.

Milky Way: Our galaxy.

343

DEVELOPMENT

1 **Skill Development** — If you carried out the suggested motivation, the students should be able to easily relate the text material to the *illustrations* at the top of the page. Be sure that the students understand that the top illustration is a side view of the Milky Way galaxy. The bottom illustration is a view from above (or below).

EXTENSIONS

Enrichment
Research — Library

You may wish to have some students do research to prepare a group of index cards in which each card contains a diagram that shows the general pattern of a galaxy. They should put the name of the galaxy on the card as well.

After this group has done this, they can see if they can classify the cards according to general shape: irregular, spiral, elliptical

Andromeda Galaxy: A spiral galaxy close to our galaxy.

Nebulae: Clouds of dust and gas.

The Milky Way is not the only galaxy. By using radio telescopes, scientists have discovered millions of galaxies. Sixteen of these galaxies are within 3 million light-years of ours. One of the closest is called the **Andromeda** (an-**drah**-mih-duh) **Galaxy**. From earth this galaxy is seen in the same area of the sky as a constellation also named Andromeda. However, the galaxy is millions of light-years farther away from earth than the constellation. The *Andromeda Galaxy* is also a spiral galaxy. How is a spiral galaxy shaped?

The Milky Way contains dust and gases. Sometimes the dust and gases form clouds. The clouds are called **nebulae** (**neb**-yoo-lay). Look at the two pictures above. The first picture is of the Orion *nebula*. The second is the Horsehead nebula. Do you see a horse's head?

There are other types of galaxies that are not spiral.

344

2 **Teaching Tip** — Here is a good opportunity for you to assess whether the students have indeed understood the concept of light-year developed previously in the unit. The text indicates that sixteen galaxies are within 3 million light-years of the Milky Way. Ask the students how they would *calculate* how far away those galaxies are in kilometers or miles. They should multiply the light-years by the number of seconds in a year and then multiply that figure by the distance that light travels in a second (300,000 km or 186,000 mi). Don't have the students actually make the calculation unless you have someone who insists on doing it. The point is to see if students understand how they would go about finding the distance in kilometers or miles.

3 **Text Questions** — How is a spiral galaxy shaped? *It is shaped like a huge disc with a bulge at its center and arms that spiral around the center.*

4 **Text Questions** — Do you see a horse's head? *Most students will be able to visualize the horse's head.*

Some galaxies have the shape of a circle that has been stretched out. They are called **elliptical** (ee-**lip**-tih-kul) **galaxies.** *Elliptical galaxies* have little dust and gas. Within them are trillions of stars. Another type is called an irregular galaxy. They got this name because they have no definite shape. Within irregular galaxies are clouds of gas, dust, and stars.

Elliptical galaxy: A galaxy that has the shape of a stretched-out circle.

Galaxies have different shapes. Now scientists think galaxies group together, forming even larger structures that are cigar-shaped or flattened like pancakes.

All of the galaxies and the space they exist in are called the **universe** (**yoo**-nih-vers). How was the *universe* formed? Scientists have many theories. A theory is a possible explanation for what is observed. When people use theories, it means that they cannot prove that something is true.

Universe: All the galaxies and the space they exist in.

ACTIVITY

Making a model of the Milky Way

A. Obtain these materials: sheet of graph paper, pencil, ruler.
B. Use the following information to prepare a scale drawing of the Milky Way Galaxy. It is 100,000 light-years across. The center of the galaxy is 30,000 light-years from our solar system. Its thickness near earth is 3,000 light-years. Its thickness at the center is 10,000 light-years.
C. Label your scale drawing to show the following information. The galaxy is rotating. The speed of our solar system around the galaxy is 240 kilometers per second. It will take 230 million years for our solar system to make one revolution around the Milky Way Galaxy.

345

EXTENSIONS

Application
Science Skills — Measuring and Recording Data

You may wish to have a group of students be responsible for doing research to locate a star map that shows the location of stars in the heavens for your geographic area at this time of the year. When the students have located such a map, have them redraw the major elements of the map on a bulletin board for class reference.

By using maps such as these, astronomers are able to make full use of the other tools of astronomy. Some of the members of the class may select parts of the map to focus on as part of evening observations of the sky.

ACTIVITY

Skill Development — *Measuring and Recording Data*

Teaching Tips — Some students will need to be instructed as to the meaning of a scale drawing and may need some assistance getting started. You may wish to convert this activity into a cooperative class project by using one wall of the room as the surface on which to prepare a large scale drawing of the Milky Way galaxy. If you do this, you will need to first cover the wall with shelf paper or blank newsprint paper. You should be able to involve each student at one or another phase of the drawing.

Exceptional Student
Visually Impaired
This activity may not be appropriate for the visually impaired student.

EXTENSIONS

Application
Research — Library

The purpose of this extension is to help students undertand that *astrology* is not a scientific term. Have your students use an unabridged dictionary to find the derivation of the words *astronomy* and *astrology*. Have them research the difference between astronomy and astrology and write a report about the difference. The reports can be used in a classroom discussion.

The students should be made aware that astronomy is a science based upon the collection and interpretation of evidence. Astrology is the practice of relating the positions of the planets to the imagined destinies of people. There is no scientific evidence that the positions of the planets in any way influence aspects of behavior, personality, or circumstance.

Enrichment
Research — Library

Movies, books, and magazines often discuss the possibility of life existing elsewhere in the universe. The search for extraterrestrial life raises many questions about how people will react if life is found somewhere else, or if extraterrestrials visit the earth. It also raises questions about whether the search for life elsewhere should receive funds, when there are human problems on earth that need attention.

You can capitalize on this interest by having some students do research to find out how scientists search for the presence of life in other places, and then compare both sides of the debate. Have the students do the following as they carry out the Extension:

1. List techniques being used to search for signs of extraterrestrial life.
2. Compare both sides of the debate on whether we should spend money to solve problems on earth or spend money to explore the universe.

5 Here is one theory. Over 10 billion years ago, everything in the universe was packed together. Suddenly there was a giant explosion. Everything went flying outward. The galaxies, stars, and planets were formed.

Another theory states that galaxies are always moving out of the universe. New galaxies are always forming to take their places.

A third theory states that the universe explodes, comes together, and explodes again. This is believed to happen about every 80 billion years. There are still other theories about how the universe was formed.

Section Review

Main Ideas: The Milky Way and the Andromeda galaxies are spiral galaxies. Galaxies may also be irregular or elliptical. There are many theories about how the universe was formed.

Questions: Answer in complete sentences.

1. What name is given to the group of 100 billion stars that includes our solar system?
2. Describe the three types of galaxies.
3. Describe three theories about how the universe was formed.
4. What is the main idea shown in the drawings that show the location of the sun in the Milky Way?
5. A nebula contains many galaxies. Is this statement true or false? Explain your answer.

346

5 **Teaching Tips** — The "Big Bang Theory," received considerable support by the discovery in 1965 of weak radiation in all regions of space that is presumed to be a "left over" of the Big Bang.

SECTION REVIEW
Answers to Questions
1. Milky Way galaxy
2. Elliptical, irregular, and spiral
3. One scientific theory states that the universe formed all at once during a gigantic explosion. Another says that galaxies are moving out of the universe and new galaxies are formed to take their place. Another theory holds that the universe explodes, comes together, and explodes again, and again.
4. The main idea is that the sun is only one of many billions of stars in the Milky Way galaxy. The sun is in one of the spiral arms of the galaxy.
5. False. A galaxy may contain many nebulae.

CHAPTER REVIEW

Science Words: Match the terms in column A with the definitions in column B.

Column A	Column B
1. Quasar	A. The brightness of a star as seen from the earth
2. Constellation	B. A place from which no light escapes
3. Polaris	C. An object the size of a star that gives off as much energy as hundreds of millions of stars
4. Galaxy	D. The closest galaxy to ours
5. Light-year	E. A cloud of dust and gas
6. Elliptical	F. A galaxy that is the shape of a stretched-out circle
7. Nebula	G. A group of billions of stars
8. Andromeda Galaxy	H. A pattern of stars in the sky
9. Magnitude	I. A star that is always above the North Pole
10. Black hole	J. The distance light travels in a year

Questions: Answer in complete sentences.

1. Compare three types of galaxies.
2. Describe the galaxy that our solar system is in.
3. Explain what is meant by the term *light-year*. Why don't astronomers use kilometers instead of light-years?
4. A person looking at stars through a telescope notices that some of them appear to have different colors. Give an explanation for these colors.
5. If a person said that our sun is made of recycled material (material that is used again), what might he or she mean?
6. Does a radio telescope use light? Explain.

347

CHAPTER REVIEW

Science Words — 1. C, 2. H, 3. I, 4. G, 5. J, 6. F, 7. E, 8. D, 9. A, 10. B

Answers to Questions

1. A spiral galaxy is shaped like a disc with a bulge at its center. An elliptical galaxy has the shape of flattened circle. An irregular galaxy has no definite shape.
2. Our galaxy, the Milky Way, is a spiral galaxy that contains about 100 billion stars. The distance from one edge to the other is about 100,000 light-years.
3. A light-year is the distance that light travels in one year. The kilometer measure would be an enormous number.
4. Stars differ in colors because of their temperature variations.
5. Stars like the sun were formed from the remains of old stars.
6. No. A radio telescope picks up radio waves from space.

SUGGESTED WORKSHEET MASTER
p. T–291u

EXTENSIONS

Enrichment
Activity

Students could add a wide straw to the top of their astrolabe to ensure better accuracy in locating a distant object. If students use the astrolabe, they should observe the sky on a very clear night. They could locate north by sighting Polaris. After finding the two stars at the end of the Big Dipper's bowl, their eyes should follow an imaginary line that extends beyond the open end of the Dipper for a distance of about five times the distance between the two end stars. This star is Polaris. Students could then locate the other directions. The measure in degrees (north is 0 or 360°) of the direction of a star is called its azimuth, and the measure in degrees of its distance above the horizon is its altitude. Students could attempt to take both measures using their astrolabes.

Building and using an astrolabe

A. Obtain these materials: small weight such as a washer or nut, piece of cardboard (25 cm square), tape, protractor, pencil.

B. Place a degree mark at the lower left-hand corner of the cardboard. Place a 90° mark at the upper right-hand corner. Using the string as a guide, draw a curved line from the lower left-hand corner to the upper right-hand corner. Make additional marks at 10° intervals from 0° to 90° using the protractor.

C. Tie the weight to the string. Tape the free end to the upper left corner. You have made an **astrolabe** (**as**-troh-layb). This is used to locate objects in the sky. You sight objects along the top edge of the cardboard. When you use the *astrolabe* to sight an object at the horizon, the string should cross the 0° mark.

D. Prepare a chart to record the number of degrees that objects are above the horizon. Sight the following: tops of trees, chimneys, moon, brightest star. CAUTION: DO NOT SIGHT THE SUN. YOU COULD DAMAGE YOUR EYES. Record your data.

  1. What is the astrolabe reading for an object straight ahead?
  2. What is the astrolabe reading for an object directly above you?
  3. What is the astrolabe reading for an object halfway between the horizon and the position directly above you?

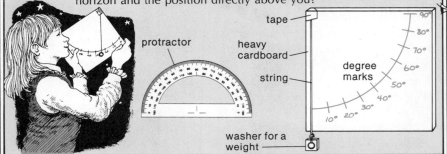

348

Skill Development — *Observing, Following Directions, Measuring*

Teaching Tips — Students should work in teams so that one person can do the observations and the others record the results. The astrolabe should be held to the eye at the 90° mark.

Answers to Questions — 1. 0°, 2. 90°, 3. 45°

SUGGESTED TEST MASTERS
pp. T–291h,i,j

T–348

CAREERS

Astronaut ▶

An **astronaut** has an exciting job. Most *astronauts* are good jet pilots who take special training. They ride on special airplanes to experience the weightlessness of space. They learn how to use radar, computers, and even space-age clothing and food containers. Astronauts have to be in topnotch physical condition. Their job requires them to work very hard for a long time.

◀ Lens maker

A **lens maker** grinds clear pieces of glass into various shapes. Many telescopes contain lenses that have been carefully ground. The *lens maker* has to have a good eye for detail. The glass that is used cannot have any marks or scratches. Lens makers also have to be very patient and able to handle delicate objects. Lens makers usually learn their trade by working with an experienced lens maker for many years.

349

Application
Research — Library

The career of mission specialist is a new and exciting prospect for the future. These positions are opening up for professionals and technicians who would go on space shuttle missions to do experiments in their specific areas of expertise. Information could be obtained by writing to NASA (address is listed below). An aeronautical technician would work with engineers and scientists on the design and production of space vehicles.

Teaching Tips — Information about the career of an astronaut can be obtained by writing to the National Aeronautics and Space Administration, 400 Maryland Avenue S.W., Washington, D.C. 20546. More information about the requirements for the career of lens maker can be acquired by contacting the International Union of Electrical, Radio and Machine Workers, 1126 16th Street N.W., Washington, D.C. 20036.

GLOSSARY/INDEX

In this Glossary/Index, the definitions
are printed in italics.

Breaker: *a wave in which the crest has tumbled forward,* 33, 36

Carbon dioxide (kar-bon die-ox-side): *a gas found in the air,* 241, 242; carried by blood, 273, 274; on Mars, 315; on Venus, 313

Cardiac muscle (kar-dee-ak): *a type of muscle that the heart is made of,* 156

Cartilage (kar-tuh-lij): *a soft substance that is found where some bones meet,* 145–146, 149; *a firm but bendable material that forms the skeleton,* 274

Cassiopeia (kas-ee-oh-**pay**-ah): *a constellation,* 338, 341

Cell(s) (selz): *tiny living parts of the body,* 115; *tiny living parts of which all organisms are made,* 226–229; and spores, 248; and viruses, 230–231; food carried to, 115; of animals, 242, 256; of bones, 140; of muscles, 156–157, 158; of plants, 232; of plants compared to animals, 229; of sponges, 255; of vertebrates, 273; oxygen carried to, 115, 226, 227, 229; red blood, 228, 273; reproduction of, 115, 227; types of, 115–117

Cell membrane (mem-brayn): *outside covering of a cell,* 115, 226, 229

Cell wall: *a stiff protective layer around plant cells,* 229

Centipede (sen-tuh-peed): *an arthropod with many body segments and one pair of legs on most segments,* 269–270

Central processing unit (CPU): *the "brain" of a computer,* 213, 216

Characteristic (kar-ik-ter-is-tik): *something that helps set one thing apart from another,* 223, 225

Charge(s) (char-jez): *the electrical property of matter,* 165–168; positive and negative, 165–168, 170

Chip: *a small electric circuit,* 211–212, 216

Chlorophyll (klor-uh-fil): *green material in plants' cells that helps them make their own food,* 228–229, 232, 235, 236, 237, 240–242, 246

Circuit (ser-kut): *the path through which current electricity flows,* 170; closed, 170; design of, 219; four parts of, 170; kinds of, 170, 173, 177; open, 170; parallel, 177–181; series, 173–176

Circuit breaker: *a safety device for circuits that opens a switch to break a circuit,* 179, 181

Classification (klas-ih-fih-**kay**-shun): *a way of sorting things into groups according to ways they are alike and ways they are different,* 222–225; of animals, 290; of bacteria, 234; of birds, 283; of plants, 290; of reptiles, 283

Closed circuit, 170

Cold-blooded animals: *vertebrates whose body temperature stays the same as the temperature of the surroundings,* 274, 275, 278, 281

Comets: *objects that are made of ice and rock particles and orbit the sun,* 324

Computer: *a device that stores and handles information,* 212–216, 341; used in space travel, 313, 315, 327; uses of, 214–216

Computer program: *a series of directions for a computer to follow,* 214

Conclusion: *a final statement based on observations,* 3

Conductors (kun-**duk**-terz): *materials that allow current to flow through them easily,* 169–172, 180

Conservation (kahn-ser-**vay**-shun): *careful use of a natural resource,* 207–208, 210, 291

Constellations (kahn-steh-**lay**-shunz): *groups of stars that form patterns in the sky,* 337–341

Continental shelf (kahn-tih-**nen**-tul): *part of the ocean bottom near land,* 11, 14, 18, 19

Continental slope: *part of the ocean bottom where the continental shelf plunges downward sharply,* 11, 14

Copepods (koh-peh-podz): *tiny shrimplike animals,* 49, 54

Copernicus, Nicolaus (ko-**purr**-nih-kus): *a Polish scientist who in 1543 wrote that the earth moved around the sun,* 312

Core: *the central part of the sun,* 305–306

Corona (kuh-**roh**-nuh): *the faint, white light seen around the sun during a solar eclipse,* 307, 308

Cranium (kray-nee-um): *group of skull bones that surround the brain,* 142

Craters (kray-terz): *bowl-shaped holes,* 300, 304, 315, 322

Crest: *the highest point of a wave,* 32, 33, 36

Current(s): *water that moves in a certain direction,* 26–30, 65; caused by sun, 29, 30; caused by temperature, 64; caused by wind, 27–28; deep, 29–30

Current electricity: *the flow of negative charges, or electrons,* 170

Cycads (sy-kadz): *the earliest plants that reproduced by seeds,* 249–250

Frequency: *the number of vibrations made in one second,* 92–93, 96

Fuel (fyoo-el): *anything that can be burned to produce heat,* 205, 207; used in rockets, 326, 328

Fungi (fun-jy): *plantlike protists that cannot make their own food,* 236–237

Fuse: *a safety device for circuits with a piece of wire that melts to break the circuit,* 179, 181

Galaxy (gal-ux-ee): *a group of billions of stars,* 342–346; spiral, 343, 344, 346

Galileo: *Italian astronomer who wrote book using Copernicus' ideas,* 312, 318

Galvanometer (gal-vuh-**nahm**-uh-ter): *an instrument that can measure a weak electric current,* 193, 195

Gas(es), *a form of matter,* 207; above the sun's surface, 306; as medium for sound, 88, 90; made from a liquid, 16; of stars, 332

Generator (jen-uh-ray-ter): *a machine in which current electricity is produced with magnetism,* 194–196, 203–206

Genetics (juh-**neh**-tiks): *study of how characteristics are passed along from one generation to the next,* 252

Giants: *stars that swell and become large,* 332

Gills: *structures in some water-dwelling animals that pick up oxygen from the water,* 274, 275, 276

Gymnosperms (**jim**-nuh-spermz): *seed-bearing plants that form seeds on cones exposed directly to the air,* 250

Hearing, 123–127. *See also* Sound.

Heart, four-chambered compared to three-chambered, 280; heard by stethoscope, 88; made of muscles, 116, 154, 156; of amphibians, 276–277, 279–280; of fish, 273–274; of reptiles, 278

Heat, and ocean currents, 29, 30; and pollution of rivers, 209; energy, 199–200

Helium (heel-ee-um), 305–306, 334

Herb: *a plant without a woody stem,* 245

Hinge joint: *a kind of joint where the bones can move back and forth or up and down,* 146

Hollow-bodied animal: *a simple invertebrate with one body opening that is surrounded by tentacles,* 256, 258

Hydroelectric plant (hy-droh-ih-lek-trik): *a power plant at which falling water is the energy source,* 205

Hydrogen (hy-druh-gen), 305–306, 334

Hypothesis: *a scientific guess,* 3

Input: *the information that goes into a computer,* 213, 216

Insects, 267–269, 270, 273, 276; eaten by centipedes, 270; eaten by lizards, 280

Insulators (in-suh-lay-terz): *materials that do not allow current to flow through them,* 171, 172

Intensity: *the loudness or softness of a sound,* 91–92, 94, 95, 96

Invertebrates (in-ver-tuh-brayts): *animals without backbones,* 254–270; compared to vertebrates, 273; spiny-skinned, 262–263

Investigate: *to study carefully,* 2

Involuntary muscles (in-vahl-un-teh-ree): *muscles, such as the heart, that cannot be controlled,* 154

Io: *one of Jupiter's moons,* 318

Iris (eye-rus): *the colored part of the eye,* 129, 132

Jawbone: *a bone that is part of the head,* 143

Joint: *the place where two bones meet,* 146; immovable, 148, 149; kinds of, 146–148, 149

Jupiter (joo-pih-ter): *the fifth planet from the sun in the solar system,* 317, 318, 321, 324

Kelp: *the largest kind of seaweed,* 235

Kilowatt-hour: *a unit used to measure electricity use,* 201, 202

Leaf: *the plant structure that usually makes food,* 243, 246; eaten by caterpillars, 268; of ferns, 248

Lens (lenz): *the part of the eye that changes light into a pattern,* 129–130, 132

Ligaments (lig-uh-ments): *strong bands of material that hold bones in place at joints,* 147, 149

Light, traveling through the eye, 129–130, 131, 132

Light energy, from the sun, 209–210, 228, 295, 297, 298; speed of, 81, 90; travels, 79–82

Light-year: *the distance light travels in one year,* 331

Lines of force: *lines around a magnet that show where the magnetic force is found,* 185–187, 189

Liquid(s), as sound media, 90; changed into a gas, 16

Little Dipper: *a constellation that is seen all year in the Northern Hemisphere,* 339, 341

Lunar eclipse (loo-ner ee-klips): *occurs when the earth passes between the moon and the sun,* 304

Lungs, of amphibians, 275; of reptiles, 279

Magnets: *objects that pick up or attract iron, nickel, and cobalt,* 184; and speakers, 106; and electricity, 188–196, 205; poles, 184, 194

Magnetic field: *the space around a magnet in which there is a magnetic force,* 185, 189

Magnetic force, 185–187, 189

Magnitude (mag-nih-tood): *the brightness of a star as seen from earth,* 332

Mammals: *vertebrates that have hair and feed milk from their bodies to their young,* 284; groups of, 288; in the sea, 286; meat-eating, 285, 286; most intelligent, 287; plant-eating, 286, 287; pouched, 285, 288

Marias (muh-ree-uhz): *smooth places on the moon's surface,* 300–301, 304

Marine biologist, 62, 65

Marrow (mar-roh): *a soft substance in the hollow of some bones,* 144

Mars (marz): *a planet in the solar system,* 312, 315–316, 324

Mechanical energy (muh-kan-ih-kul): *the energy of motion,* 200

Media: *more than one medium,* 87–90

Medium: *matter through which sound can travel,* 87–90

Membrane (mem-braine): *the thin skinlike covering of a cell,* 115, 226, 229; and viruses, 231

Mercury (mer-kyer-ee): *the planet in the solar system closest to the sun,* 312–313

Metamorphosis (met-uh-mor-fuh-sis): *a series of major changes in the structure of an animal as it develops from its early stages to become an adult,* 268, 276

Meteor (mee-tee-or): *a burning meteoroid,* 322, 324

Meteorite: *a meteoroid that lands on a surface,* 322, 324

Meteoroids (mee-tee-er-oydz): *chunks of iron, nickel, and other materials that move through space,* 322, 324

Microscope, 223, 226, 229

Mid-ocean ridge: *mountain chain on the ocean floor,* 11, 14

Milky Way: *our galaxy,* 343, 344, 345, 346

Millipede (mil-uh-peed): *an arthropod with many body segments and two pairs of legs on most segments,* 270

Minerals, in ocean water, 15–19; make up bones, 140; used by plants, 243

Mollusk (mahl-usk): *an invertebrate with a soft body, usually protected by a shell,* 259; three kinds of, 259–261, 263

Molten (mol-ten): *melted by heat,* 21, 23, 24

Moon(s), 299–304; and tides, 38, 40, 41; changing appearance of, 301; compared to the earth, 301; hit by meteorites, 322; light from, 301; motion of, 300; of Neptune, 320; of Saturn, 319; of Uranus, 320; of Jupiter, 318; phases of, 301, 302, 303; volcanoes on, 300

Morse, Samuel: *first person to send a message using the telegraph,* 103

Mosses: *small plants without real roots, stems, or leaves,* 247–248

Muscle cells, exercise important to, 157; requiring energy, 157, 158; three types of, 156–157, 158

Muscles, 150–158; attached to exoskeleton, 264; functions of, 150; types of, 151, 153, 154, 155–158

Muscular system: *all the muscles of the body,* 150

Musical instruments, 73, 75–78

Natural gas: *a fossil fuel in gas form,* 46

Natural resource: *something useful found in nature,* 207, 210

Neap (neep) **tides:** *low tides that are not very low; high tides that are not very high,* 40–41

Nearsightedness: *difficulty in seeing far-away objects,* 130

Nebulae (neb-yoo-lay): *clouds of dust and gas,* 344

Negative terminal: *part of the dry cell that has extra electrons,* 176

Neptune (nep-toon): *a planet in the solar system,* 317, 320–321

Nerve cell(s): *cell that carries information,* 115, 134; and hearing, 127; and sight, 129

Nervous (nerv-us) **system:** *the system that controls all other systems in the body,* 116, 117; of land-living animals, 277; sense of taste as part of, 120, 122

Nose, 116–117, 118

Nuclear reaction (nyoo-klee-er ree-ak-shun): *a reaction that occurs when tiny particles of matter are split apart*, 206; waste product of, 208–209, 210

Nucleus (nyoo-klee-us): *the part of the cell that controls its activities*, 115, 156, 227, 230

Observe: *to watch closely*, 2

Ocean, and fossil fuels, 46; farming, 45; forms of life in, 49–51; movements of, 26–41; pollution of, 52–56; resources in, 43–48; salt removed from, 47–48; three areas of, 49; water of, 15–19. *See also* Current(s), Tides, Waves.

Ocean bottom, 10–14; changes in, 14

Ocean floor: *part of the ocean bottom that lies at the bottom of the continental slope*, 11, 14; changes in, 20–24; exploration of, 57–62; layers of sediments on, 60–61, 62

Olfactory nerve (ol-fak-tore-ee): *nerve that carries smell messages to the brain*, 117, 120

Optic nerve (op-tik): *the nerve that carries sight messages to the brain*, 12

Orbit: *the path of one object in space around another*, 312, 316; of outer planets, 317, 320–321

Orbiter: *the part of the shuttle that orbits and returns to the earth*, 327–328

Organ: *group of tissues that works together*, 116, 117

Organism: *a living thing*, 225; eaten by sponges, 255; grown from cells, 248; one-celled, 232

Orion (oh-ry-un): *a constellation that looks like a hunter*, 338, 341, 344

Outer ear: *the part of the ear that gathers sound vibrations*, 126, 127

Output: *the information that comes out of a computer*, 213, 215, 216

Oxygen, absent in space, 326; carried to cells by blood, 115, 157, 228, 276; needed by animals, 242; needed by cells, 226, 227, 229, 273; on earth, 315; picked up by gills, 274, 275; released by plants, 241, 242; supplied by four-chambered heart, 280

Parallel circuit: *a circuit with more than one path through which charges can flow*, 177–181; compared to series circuit, 178

Paramecium (par-uh-mee-see-um): *an animal-like protist shaped like a slipper*, 232

Pelvis (pel-vis): *the hipbones and backbone*, 144

Percussion instrument (per-kush-shun): *an instrument that produces a musical sound when hit*, 77–78

Pesticides (pes-tih-sidz): *chemicals sprayed on crops*, 53–56

Petroleum (peh-troh-lee-um): *a fossil fuel in liquid form*, 46

Phases (fay-zes): *the shapes the moon appears to be as seen from the earth*, 301

Phonograph, 104–105, 106, 107, 108

Photosphere (foh-toh-sfeer): *the surface of the sun*, 306

Photosynthesis (foh-toh-sin-thuh-sis): *the process by which plants use light energy to make food*, 240, 246

Pitch: *the highness or lowness of a sound*, 92–93, 94, 95, 96

Pivot joint: *a kind of joint where the bones can move around and back*, 147

Planet(s): *a solid body in space that does not give off its own light*, 299; four closest to the sun, 312–316; in the solar system, 310–328; outer, 317–321

Plankton (plank-tun): *tiny plants and animals on the ocean surface*, 49, 54

Plants, cells of, 226, 228–229, 232; classification of, 239–242, 290; needed by animals, 242; ocean, 49–51; release oxygen, 241, 242; structures of, 243–246; sunlight essential to, 307; types of, 240, 247–252; use chlorophyll, 240–242

Pluto (ploo-toh): *a planet in the solar system*, 317, 320–321

Polaris (poh-lar-is): *the North Star, always above earth's North Pole*, 331, 339

Poles: *the ends of a magnet*, 184, 186, 187, 194

Pollution (poh-loo-shun): *the adding of harmful materials to the environment*, 52, 208–210; noise, 100–101; of ocean, 52–56; prevention of, 53

Population: *a group of the same kind of plant or animal living in the same place*, 1

Positive terminal: *part of the dry cell that has a shortage of electrons*, 176

Primates: *the most intelligent mammals*, 287, 288

Protists: *a group of living things that are not animals or plants, but have some characteristics of each*, 232, 233, 234; eaten by mollusks, 260; plantlike, 235–237

Ptolemy (tul-uh-mee): *ancient Greek astronomer*, 311–312

Pupil (pyoo-pul): *the opening in the center of your iris*, 129, 132

PHOTO CREDITS

ART CREDITS

HELPING THE EXCEPTIONAL STUDENT

P.L. 94-142: Education For All Handicapped Children Act: Federal Law P.L. 94-142 states that all handicapped children are entitled to a free appropriate public education with services designed to meet each child's individual needs. The law requires all students with handicapping conditions to be identified, tested, and evaluated by the appropriate agencies or school services. The school service, in agreement with the student and his or her parents, selects the most appropriate least restrictive educational environment.

Mainstreaming: The least restrictive environment for many exceptional students may be total or partial integration into the mainstream classes. Some children, however, need to be in self-contained special education classes during the entire day. The goal is to mainstream each child into as many regular classes as possible.

Individualized Education Planning (IEP): Any child who has been classified by state or local agencies as handicapped must have an Individualized Educational Plan. An IEP is an individualized written statement which projects the student's achievements of particular goals within a specific time frame. Contributors to the IEP include the parents, the teacher, and a representative of the local educational agency. The IEP is updated when appropriate.

Using the Exceptional Student Suggestions and IEP goals: Suggestions for the Exceptional Student are included in the Teacher's Edition to aid the classroom teacher who has a handicapped child in the class. A teacher of the special education class can utilize the suggestions when adapting the curriculum for the specific population of that class. All suggestions are not appropriate for all children. An activity will often need to be varied depending on the degree of impairment.

The IEP goals are to aid the teacher in focusing in on specific objectives of each chapter and/or unit. These goals may be used on the IEP.

STRATEGIES	ORTHOPEDIC AND OTHER HEALTH IMPAIRMENTS	VISUAL IMPAIRMENT	HEARING IMPAIRMENT	SPEECH IMPAIRMENT	SPECIFIC LEARNING DISABILITY	MILD MENTAL RETARDA-TION	EMOTIONAL DISTURBANCE
CLASSROOM MANAGEMENT	Restricted movement / Special furniture	Front-row seating / Assign "buddy" for assignments	Front- or second-row seating / Face child when speaking	No adjustment necessary	Structured daily procedures / Concepts presented by varied methods (Visual, tactile, auditory) / Environment with minimal distraction	Structured daily procedures	Structured daily procedures / Calm atmosphere, low in tension / Positive verbal reinforcement
TEXT BOOK MANAGEMENT	No adjustment necessary	Text read orally to student / Use of magnifying glass / †Use of Braille reader / °°Taped texts	No adjustment necessary	No adjustment necessary	°°Taped text / Text read to student / Modify content as needed	Modify content as needed	No adjustment necessary
ADDITIONAL INSTRUCTIONAL MATERIAL	No adjustment necessary	Use concrete materials	°Captioned films for the deaf	No adjustment necessary	Use of concrete materials	Use of concrete materials	Motivating materials
ACHIEVEMENT MONITORING/ TESTING MODIFICATIONS	Answers to exams recorded on tape / Exam administered orally	Exam administered orally or on tape / Exam sheet enlarged / †Exam transcribed into Braille	Committee assignments or oral reports	Committee assignments for reports	Committee assignments for oral reports / Written exams rephrased when necessary / Oral exam administered when necessary / Answers recorded in any manner appropriate / Time limit extended	Time limit extended / Written exam rephrased when necessary	Time limit extended

†Local Braillists will transcribe books. Check with your local church or synagogue.

°Films can be borrowed from the distribution center nearest your school and shown in any classroom where there is one hearing-impaired student. Write: Department of Education.

°°Cassettes available at the Library of Congress, Washington, D.C.

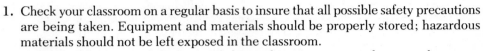

SAFETY IN THE

The Activities in *Holt Science* have been designed with safety in mind. Nonetheless, wherever children work with materials of any sort, the potential for unsafe practices exists. The following suggestions are offered with the intent of reducing that potential.[1]

SAFETY CHECKLIST

1. Check your classroom on a regular basis to insure that all possible safety precautions are being taken. Equipment and materials should be properly stored; hazardous materials should not be left exposed in the classroom.
2. Be extra cautious when dealing with fire and instruct your students to take appropriate precautions.
3. At the start of each science Activity, instruct students regarding potential hazards and the precautions to be taken.
4. The group size of students working on an experiment should be limited to a number that can safely perform the experiment without causing confusion and accidents.
5. Students should be instructed never to taste or touch substances in the science classroom without first obtaining specific instructions from the teacher.
6. All accidents or injuries—no matter how small—should be reported to you immediately.
7. Students should be instructed that it is unsafe to touch the face, mouth, eyes, and other parts of the body while they are working with plants, animals, or chemical substances until they have washed their hands and cleaned their nails.

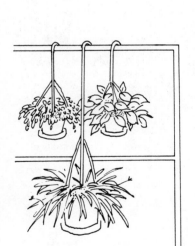

HANDLING OF ANIMALS AND PLANTS

1. Do not allow students to bring live or diseased wild animals, such as snapping turtles, snakes, insects, or arachnids (spiders, ticks, mites), into the classroom.
2. Provide proper living quarters for animals. They must be kept clean and free from contamination in a securely closed cage. Provisions for their care during weekends and holidays must be made.
3. Discourage students from bringing personal pets to school. If they are brought into the room, they should be handled only by their owners and provisions should be made for their care during the day by providing fresh water and a place to rest.
4. Caution students never to tease animals, or to insert their fingers or objects through wire mesh cages. Report animal bites and scratches immediately to the school's medical authority. Provide basic first aid.

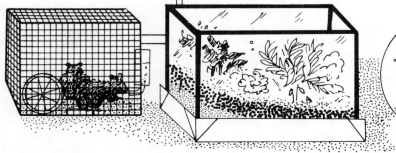

SCIENCE CLASSROOM

5. Rats, rabbits, hamsters, and mice are best picked up by the scruff of the neck, with a hand placed under the body for support. If the young are to be handled, the mother should be removed to another cage. By nature she will be fiercely protective.

6. Use heavy gloves for handling animals and have students wash their hands before and after they handle animals.

7. Prior to allowing animals to be brought into the classroom, check school district procedures to determine if there are any local regulations to be observed. Personnel at the local humane society or zoo are often very cooperative in assisting teachers to create a wholesome animal environment in the classroom.

8. Students should be instructed never to place any part of a plant in their mouth. (Note: Teachers may want to emphasize the distinction between edible plants, fruits and vegetables, and nonedible plants.)

9. Students should never allow any sap or fruit to set into their skin.

10. Students should never inhale or expose their skin or eyes to the smoke of any burning plant.

11. Do not allow students to pick any unknown wildflowers, seeds, berries, or cultivated plants.

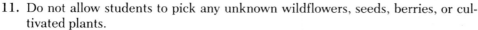

ELECTRICITY

1. Students should be taught safety precautions when using electricity.

2. At the start of any unit on electricity, students should be told not to experiment with the electric current of home circuits.

3. Connecting cords should be short, in good condition, and plugged in at the nearest outlet; electrical extensions should not be used.

4. Tap water is a conductor of electricity. Students' hands should be dry when touching electrical cords, switches, or appliances.

5. Instruct students never to grasp any electrical device which has just been used. Most electrical devices remain hot after use and serious burns may result.

6. Students should never short circuit (connect the terminals) dry cells or storage batteries. High temperature will develop in the connecting wire and can cause serious burns.

7. In removing an electrical plug from its socket, pull the plug, not the electric cord.

8. The following items should be used with caution: heating element for a fish tank, small motors, soldering irons, hot plates, and electrical fans.

[1]The information above is taken from *Safety in the Elementary Science Classroom* prepared by the National Science Teachers' Association Subcommittee on Safety. The complete publication may be ordered from NSTA, 1742 Connecticut Ave. NW, Washington, DC 20009.

LOW LIGHT

BRIGHT LIGHT

POTTING SOIL

PLANT FERTILIZER

PLANTS

Children like to care for plants and watch them grow and change. Hardy plants, such as snake plants, coleus, philodendron, English ivy, geranium, Swedish ivy, cacti, spider plants, and grape ivy are the most likely to thrive in the classroom. Although there are many good books about plant care available, following these general rules will keep your plants healthy:

Pots and Potting: Most plants grow well in plastic or clay pots. Whichever you choose, it is important that the pot has drainage holes in the bottom. Some pots come with their own catch saucer, which collects the drained water. If yours does not, place a small saucer or aluminum pie plate under the pot. As the plant grows, check it periodically to see if it needs repotting. Remove the plant by tapping the inverted pot while holding your fingers on either side of the plant stem. If the roots have grown to the edges of the pot and form a thick mass, then the plant should be repotted. A good general rule is to repot the plant in a container with a diameter about 2½ centimeters (1 inch) larger than the container the plant was in. Thoroughly wash the new pot with soap and water before repotting and always use fresh potting soil. Take care not to damage the roots when repotting. Do not leave the roots exposed to the air for too long, since they will dry out. After repotting, water the plant thoroughly.

Watering: Do not overwater! This is a common mistake that often kills plants. Water the plant only when the soil feels dry (usually once or twice a week), and water thoroughly (until water comes out the drainage hole). Plants need different amounts of water, depending on the season, light conditions, temperature, and humidity. As a general rule, the higher the temperature and light intensity, and the lower the humidity, the more water the plant will need. In winter, the light intensity is lower, and plants do not grow as much or need as much water.

Temperature: Plants should be placed in an area where the temperature remains constant, with neither excessive heat nor drafts. Plants should not be placed near heating or cooling units, or too close to windows in winter.

Lighting: Green plants will not survive without light. Some plants (e.g., philodendra, snake plants, grape ivy) will survive in low light conditions. Others (coleus, geranium, Swedish ivy, spider plants) need direct sunlight. We suggest you check a reference source to find out the light requirements for specific plants.

Soil: Different plants have different soil requirements. Usually, however, any good potting soil (easily obtainable at a five-and-dime or garden supply store) is appropriate. Do not use soil dug up from outside. It is much too heavy for a potted plant and may contain weed seeds and disease organisms.

Cleansing and Checking: Gently wash the leaves of smooth-leaved plants once a week to remove the dust and dirt that clog the plant's pores. Check the leaves for insects and diseases. Isolate any infected plants from other plants. During times of rapid growth, plants may need fertilizer. Obtain some plant fertilizer and carefully follow the instructions on the package. Some plants, like Swedish ivy and avocado, need to be pruned so that the stems do not get long and stringy. Start new plants with the cuttings.

Terrariums can be made and can serve as a temporary home for small salamanders, frogs, and toads. Put a thin layer of charcoal fragments at the bottom. Then add one-half inch of sand and two inches of rich forest soil. Dig up small, compact woodland

AND ANIMALS

plants such as moss, ferns, and wintergreen. Dig up a lot of soil with the roots so that they will be disturbed as little as possible when transplanted into the terrarium. Imbed a water dish so that the edge is level with the soil surface. Water the plants and cover the terrarium.

ANIMALS

Animals in the classroom require more care than plants. However, they provide a continual source of motivation for all kinds of learning. Keeping animals in the classroom helps youngsters develop enthusiasm, respect, and love for all forms of life. Before bringing an animal into the classroom, be sure that you are fully prepared. Obtain a handbook on the care and feeding of the animal and determine the animal's needs. Have food, water, and other supplies ready beforehand.

The students should share the responsibility for the care of the animals. Teach them how to properly handle them. They will be enthusiastic and should be cautioned not to handle them too much or too harshly. Animals should be handled gently, and never hurriedly or nervously. Here are some general rules for animal care:

1. The animal should have enough space to move around and be comfortable.
2. Create a habitat as nearly like the animal's natural habitat as possible.
3. Provide a place to hide from sight.
4. The animal should have proper food, clean water, and fresh air.
5. The cage should be clean and free from odor at all times.
6. The animal should be provided with adequate food, water, and heat over the weekends and during vacations.
7. Unless accustomed to captive life, the animal should not be kept for a long time.

Mammals: Hamsters, white rats, white mice, and guinea pigs can be kept in 2-foot cages. Gerbils should be kept in 10-gallon aquariums with a generous layer of sand for burrowing. Metal cages should be washed with soap and rinsed in laundry bleach solution once per week. There should be a debris-catching metal tray with sawdust in it at the bottom of the cage. Remove water, food, and soiled bedding daily. Heavy glass ashtrays work well for food, and water bottles work best for water. Keep a nest box in the cage where the animal can retreat for rest and escape drafts. Rats and mice need an exercise wheel.

Amphibians and Reptiles: Tadpole eggs can be collected in the spring. Keep them in covered glass containers to reduce evaporation. They should be kept relatively cool, and should be exposed to some sunlight. After hatching, make sure there is scum in the water for the tadpoles to feed on. Most frog eggs hatch in three months. Small amphibians can be kept in moist woodland terrariums. Keep a shallow dish of water in the terrarium so that they can soak their skins. This should be cleaned and refilled daily. They can be induced to eat by dangling insects, worms, or hamburger before them. Some reptiles, such as small snakes and chameleons, can be kept in the classroom if the right conditions are provided. A cage can be constructed from an aquarium. The optimum temperature for most reptiles is 80°F. They should not be exposed to temperatures below 65°F. Provide a shady place, such as a broken pot, as well as bark, branches, rocks, and a heavy, shallow dish of water.

Fish: As a rule of thumb, provide one gallon of water per fish. Goldfish and guppies are hardy and easy to care for. You will need fish food, aquarium plants (to provide oxygen), snails (to clean debris), and washed sand. Tropical fish need a heater and thermostat. Pond, stream, or rain water is best. If you use tap water, let it stand for three days so that chlorine can evaporate from it. Do not put the tank near radiators.

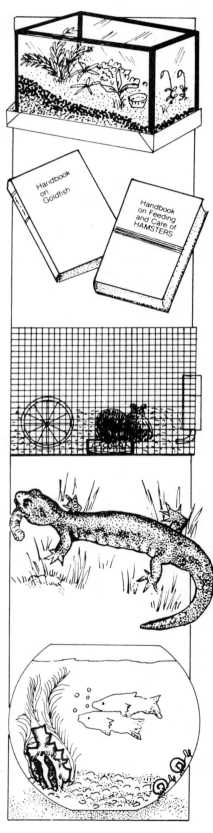

MATERIALS LIST

MATERIAL	AMOUNT	PAGE
aluminum foil		T-171
aquarium	1	T-13, T-260, T-275
basketball	1	T-323
batteries (D)	2	T-218
batteries, dry cell (1.5 volt)	3	T-171, T-175, T-192
beakers, large and small	2	T-64
beans, lima	2	T-241
blindfold	1	T-121, T-125
board (15 cm x 60 cm)	1	T-110
books	2	T-152
bottles	6	T-94
bowls, small plastic	2	T-17
button, plastic	1	T-171
cardboard (20 -cm square)	1 piece	T-308
cardboard (25-cm square)	1 piece	T-348
chalk	1 piece	T-298
clay		T-323
comb, plastic	1	T-167
compass	1	T-195, T-308
containers	2	T-17
cotton		T-54
cover slips	several	T-233
cups, paper	2	T-121
door key	1	T-171
drinking straws	4	T-76
eyedropper	1	T-233
fish , aquarium	several	T-275
flashlight	1	T-298, T-340
flashlight bulbs	2	T-218
flower, long-stemmed white	1	T-244
food coloring (various colors)		T-64, T-244
glass	1	T-244
gravel		T-13
guitar strings	3	T-110
iron filings		T-185
jar	1	T-233
lamp	1	T-233, T-302
lens, hand	1	T-244, T-260, T-269
light bulbs with sockets	3	T-171, T-175
magnet, bar	1	T-185, T-195
masses	1 set	T-110
mealworm culture	1	T-269
metal screw eyes	3	T-110
meter stick	1	T-89, T-323
microscope	1	T-233
milk container	1	T-34
mirror	1	T-131
motor oil		T-54
nail, iron	1	T-192
newspaper articles	several	T-208
orange	1	T-302
pan	1	T-54
paper	several sheets	T-54, T-107, T-121, T-125, T-131, T-158, T-167, T-171, T-201, T-224, T-275, T-290
paper clips	several	T-136, T-192

MATERIAL	AMOUNT	PAGE
paper, black construction	4 sheets	T-298, T-340
paper, drawing	2 sheets	T-233, T-269
paper, graph	4 sheets	T-39, T-118, T-333, T-345
paper, poster	1 sheet	T-208
paper, tracing	4 sheets	T-282, T-340
paper, white	1 sheet	T-160
pebbles		T-13, T-34
pen, dark marking	1	T-160 , T-308
pencils	several	T-118, T-121, T-125, T-131, T-158, T-171, T-201, T-224, T-233, T-260, T-269, T-275, T-282, T-290, T-308, T-314, T-345
pencil, grease	1	T-94
pencils, colored or marker	several	T-333
pens, marking	several	T-208
perfume		T-118
phonograph	1	T-107
plastic (15-cm square)	1 sheet	T-185
potholder	1	T-64
pots	2	T-241
protractor	1	T-348
record, 33-RPM	1	T-107
reference book	1	T-290
roll, cardboard	1	T-195
rubber bands	2	T-171, T-218
rulers	1	T-13, T-136, T-314
ruler, plastic	1	T-69
ruler or wooden stick	1	T-94
safety pin	1	T-340
salt	30	T-17
sand		T-34
scissors	1	T-76, T-107, T-244, T-340
screwdriver	1	T-171, T-175, T-192
shoe box	1	T-340
slides, glass	several	T-233
snails, pond	several	T-260
sockets	2	T-218
soil		T-241
spoon	1	T-54
switch	1	T-180, T-192
tape		T-107, T-308, T-348
tape, clear		T-340
toothpicks	10	T-121
tray (30 cm x 40 cm)	1	T-34
washer or nut	1	T-348
watch	1	T-89, T-308
water		T-13, T-17, T-34, T-54, T-76, T-94, T-121, T-244
water, hot		T-64
water, ice		T-64
water, pond		T-233
watering can	1	T-241
wire	assorted lengths	T-171, T-192, T-195
wire, bell	60 cm	T-218
wood, blocks of	2	T-34
wood molding (15-cm long)	2	T-110
wood shavings		T-167
wool cloth (15-cm square)	1 piece	T-167

A/V EQUIPMENT AND SUPPLIERS

FILM/FILMSTRIP SUPPLIERS

ABC Wide World of Learning
1330 Avenue of the Americas
New York, NY 10019

Aevac
1500 Park Avenue
South Plainfield, NJ 07080

Agency for Instructional Television
Box A
Bloomington, IN 47042

Alfred Higgins Productions, Inc.
9100 Sunset Boulevard
Los Angeles, CA 90069

Audio Visual Narrative Arts, Inc.
Box 9
Pleasantville, NY 10570

Barr Films
P.O. Box 5667
3490 East Foothill Boulevard
Pasadena, CA 91107

Bullfrog Films
Oley, PA 19547

Captioned Films for the Deaf
814 Thayer Avenue
Silver Spring, MD 20900

Centron Educational Films
1621 West 9th Street
Lawrence, KS 66044

Churchill Films
662 North Robertson Boulevard
Los Angeles, CA 90060

Coronet Films
65 East South Water Street
Chicago, IL 60601

CRM/McGraw-Hill
110 15th Street
Del Mar, CA 92104

Educational Activity
Box 392
Freeport, NY 11520

Educational Dimensions Group
Box 126
Stamford, CT 06904

Educational Images
P.O. Box 367
Lyon Falls, NY 13368

Encyclopaedia Britannica
  Educational Corp.
425 North Michigan Avenue
Chicago, IL 60611

Focus Media, Inc.
16 South Oaks Boulevard
Plainview, NY 11803

Green Mountain Post Films
P.O. Box 229
Turner Falls, MA 01376

Guidance Associates
Communications Park, P.O. Box 3000
Mt. Kisco, NY 10549

Human Relations Media
175 Tompkins Avenue
Pleasantville, NY 10570

Indiana University Films
Audio-Visual Center
Bloomington, IN 47401

International Film Bureau, Inc.
332 South Michigan Avenue
Chicago, IL 60604

National Geographic Society,
  Educational Services
17th and M Streets, NW
Washington, DC 20036

Phoenix/BFA Films
468 Park Avenue South
New York, NY 10016

Random House
201 East 50th Street
New York, NY 10022

Shell Film Library
1433 Sadlier
Circle West Drive
Indianapolis, IN

Society for Visual Education, Inc.
1345 West Diversey Parkway
Chicago, IL 60614

Sterling Educational Films
241 East 34th Street
New York, NY 10016

Stuart Finley, Inc.
3428 Mansfield Road
Falls Church, VA 20041

Time-Life Films
100 Eisenhower Drive
Paramus, NJ 07652

United Learning
6633 West Howard
Nibo, IL 60648

Universal Education and Visual Arts
100 Universal City Plaza
Universal City, CA 91608

Walt Disney Educational Media Co.
500 South Buena Vista Street
Burbank, CA 91521

Wombat Productions, Inc.
Little Lake, Glendale Road
P.O. Box 70
Ossining, NY 10562

SOFTWARE PRODUCERS

Atari Program Exchange
155 Moffett Park
Box 427
Sunnyvale, CA 94086

Creative Computing Software
Dept. T52
One Park Avenue
Room 458
New York, NY 10016

Educational Activities Inc.
P.O. Box 392
Freeport, NY 11520

Med System Software
66 Church Street
Ellenville, NY 12428

Micro Power and Light
12820 Hillcrest Road #224
Dallas, TX 75230

National Coordinating Center for
  Curriculum Development
SUNY of Stonybrook
Stonybrook, NY 11794
Attn: Professor Braun

Project Sereal Software
c/o Dresdan Associates
P.O. Box 426
Dresden, ME 04342

Right On Programs
P.O. Box 977
Huntington, NY 11743

T.I.E.S.
1925 West Country Road B2
St. Paul, MN 55113

SOURCES OF EQUIPMENT AND SUPPLIES

American Science and Engineering,
  Inc.
20 Oberland Street
Boston, MA 02215

Carolina Biological Supply Co.
2700 York Road
Burlington, NC 27215

Central Scientific Co.
2600 South Kostner Avenue
Chicago, IL 60623

Edmund Scientific Co.
101 East Gloucester Pike
Barrington, NJ 08007

Fisher Scientific
Educational Materials Division
1259 North Wood Street
Chicago, IL 60622

Sargent-Welch Scientific Co.
1300 Lindere Avenue
Skokie, IL 60076

Science Kit, Inc.
777 East Park Drive
Tonawanda, NY 14150

Selective Educational Equipment
  (SEE), Inc.
3 Bridge Street
Newton, MA 02195

Ward's Natural Science
  Establishment, Inc.
300 Ridge Road East
Rochester, NY 14683